THE WINES OF BI
A Guide to the Vineyards and Wines of
England, Wales, Ireland and the Channel Isles

Stephen Skelton has been involved with growing vines and making wine since 1975. After two years in Germany – working at Schloss Schönborn in the Rheingau and studying at the Geisenheim wine college – he returned to England in 1977 to plant vineyards at Tenterden in Kent. Since then he has been looking after vineyards and making English wines both at Tenterden and as a consultant to other vineyards. From 1988 to 1991 he was winemaker and general manager at Lamberhurst Vineyards, then the UK's largest wine producer. He has been writing and lecturing about wine since 1986 and in 1989 published his first book *The Vineyards of England*. He was director of the English Vineyards Association from 1982 to 1995 and of the United Kingdom Vineyards Association (UKVA) from 1995, of which he has been Chairman since 1999. He has been Secretary of the Circle of Wine Writers since 1991 and is currently taking a BSc in Multimedia Technology and Design at Brunel University.

FABER BOOKS ON WINE

Series Editor: Julian Jeffs

THE WINES
OF BRITAIN AND
IRELAND

A Guide to the Vineyards and Wines
of England, Wales, Ireland and
the Channel Isles

STEPHEN SKELTON

faber and faber
LONDON·NEW YORK

First published in 2001
by Faber and Faber Limited
3 Queen Square London WC1N 3AU
Published in the United States by Faber and Faber Inc.,
An affiliate of Farrar, Straus and Giroux, New York

Typeset by Steven Gardiner Ltd, Cambridge
Printed in England by Clays Ltd, St Ives plc

A CIP record for this book
is available from the British Library

ISBN 0-571-20045-1

2 4 6 8 10 9 7 5 3 1

This book is dedicated to my friends and colleagues, past and present, who strive to produce good wines in Britain and Ireland and to the memory of the late John Leroy without whose help and support I would not have been able to turn my dreams into reality.

Contents

━━━━━━

Introduction   ix

1 Viticulture in the British Isles before the Revival
  – pre-Roman to 1939   1

2 The Revival, 1939–1951   27

3 Commercial Viticulture, 1951–2001   66

4 English Vineyards Association and the United Kingdom
  Vineyards Association   87

5 The Ministry of Agriculture, Fisheries and Food   92

6 Viticulture and Vinification   104

7 Vine Varieties   118

8 Vine Variety Descriptions A–Z   148

9 Vineyards by Region   185
    East Anglia: Cambridgeshire, Norfolk, Suffolk,
      Hertfordshire, Essex   185
    South East: Surrey, Kent, West Sussex, East Sussex   229
    South: Wiltshire, Hampshire, Isle of Wight, Dorset,
      Channel Isles   326
    South West: Herefordshire, Worcestershire,
      Gloucestershire, South Gloucestershire, Bristol,
      Somerset, Devon, Cornwall, Isles of Scilly, South
      Wales, Republic of Ireland   362

CONTENTS

Central: Lancashire, Yorkshire, Lincolnshire,
    Nottinghamshire, Leicestershire, Rutland,
    Staffordshire, Shropshire, Northamptonshire,
    Oxfordshire, Buckinghamshire, Bedfordshire,
    Berkshire, London   437

Appendices
    I UKVA English & Welsh Wine of the Year
        Competition   485
    II International Wine and Spirit Competition Trophy   493
    III Vineyard websites   495
    IV Rootstocks   497
Glossary   499
Bibliography   511
List of Vineyards   514
Index   517

Introduction

The level of production of wine in Britain, Ireland and the Channel Isles is minute. For every one bottle of wine made from grapes grown in our vineyards, there are over 18,000 bottles of wine from other countries and it is therefore hardly surprising that English and Welsh wines, to say nothing of wines from Ireland and the Channel Islands, are sometimes hard to track down. This book is both an introduction to the subject – its past and recent history, present-day viticultural and winemaking practices, including the major vine varieties being grown today – as well as a guide to some 263 vineyards and wineries. As with any book of this nature, there are some omissions. It has not been possible to track down every vineyard and indeed, some vineyards, even though their details were known to me, specifically asked to be left out for privacy reasons. It does, however, contain details of all the major estates both in terms of size and importance and of wine quality.

English wine has been dear to my heart for over twenty-five years. My career in wine started in 1974 with a conviction that it was possible to produce good wines in this climate. It had been done in the past – there was a history of viticulture in these islands stretching back to before the Roman invasion – and others around me in Kent were doing it again; why shouldn't I have a go? Of course, the lure of owning a vineyard and of having a bottle of wine with one's name on it is seductive and hides the sheer hard work it takes to plant and look after a vineyard, to say nothing of the heartache over the years.

To pretend that growing grapes and making wine in our climate is easy would be crazy. Many are the times over the past twenty-two vintages when I have wished for a slightly better climate, one more naturally suited to growing a species which has its origins in the

Middle East. However, my answer to those who have constantly asked me 'why England?' is always the same; ripening the grapes is not actually the problem and in all the time I have made wine in the UK I have never had grapes so unripe that I could not make them into palatable wine. My career in wine has been as fulfilling and rewarding as I had ever hoped and I have enjoyed the 'big fish, little pond' reputation that surrounds English winegrowers wherever they go.

In the introduction to the first book I wrote on this subject – *The Vineyards of England*, published in 1989 – I wrote: 'the future of the industry is unpredictable' and 'who knows what developments lie ahead'. I also wrote about the few producers who had started to move away from the German style of wines then being produced and were experimenting with oak-ageing and bottle-fermented sparkling wines. Today, that move has accelerated into a rush. Leaders of the industry are producing still wines with a distinctly new world slant and sparkling wines that are as good (yes, really) as those from Champagne. In addition, there are red wines of genuine interest and sweet wines of an extremely high standard.

These changes have been brought about by the need, in the face of today's competitive wine environment, to sink or swim; there are no half-measures. The UK has a very sophisticated retail wine market and one which does not accept poor quality, over-priced products. If English and Welsh wines are to stand on the shelves alongside those from the rest of the world they have to be of the right quality and available at the right price. It is a testament to today's growers and winemakers that every major supermarket chain and every major high street wine merchant (at least in their branches in the southern half of the country) stock at least one home-grown wine.

Although I do not believe that global warming is having much practical effect upon growing grapes in these islands (if it were, surely we would be enjoying earlier harvests and higher natural sugar levels?), growers do seem to be able to ripen grapes more fully, and wine quality rises year on year. This is probably due to a better understanding of the correct way to trellis and prune vines and a greater degree of control over diseases. It is also certainly due to more experienced winemakers and better equipped wineries. Stainless steel tanks were only just appearing in UK wineries in the late 1980s, whereas today they are everywhere and many wineries can control the temperatures at fermentation time. I also believe that modern yeast strains have played their part in improving wine quality.

The one really bright star on the horizon is that of bottle-fermented sparkling wines. Whilst I have never been a fan of the classic Champagne varieties for the UK, I have to admit that the few specialist producers who have had the courage (and the wallets) to invest heavily in all aspects of the job have pulled off some remarkable coups and proved – at least to themselves and to some of the nation's wine writers – that we really can make sparkling wines of high quality The only (only!) task now facing these producers is to convince the public that these wines are worth paying the right price. Everyone in the industry wishes them good luck.

So what of the future? Most of the early pioneers are no longer alive and sadly many of their vineyards have been grubbed up. Although the number of growers in England and Wales has fallen between 1989 and 1999 from 442 (owning vineyards of one tenth of a hectare or over) to around 370 – a fall of 16 per cent – the productive area of vines has risen from 652 hectares (ha) to 835 ha, a rise of 28 per cent! Clearly this shows that there is some consolidation in the industry as the smaller 'hobby' growers get out and the larger, more commercial growers find their feet. This can only be welcomed by those both within and without the industry. Many of these small growers had neither the resources for, nor really the interest in, the production of good wine and their vineyards were often planted on poor sites and with the wrong varieties. Sad though I am to see any vineyard fail, it has to be said that some did the general reputation of our wines no good at all. The next decade will undoubtedly see this consolidation continue. The bigger wineries will get bigger and small producers, unless they can successfully sell their wines direct to the public over the farm gate, will find life increasingly more difficult. The internet may well become a valuable way of selling wine and sites like my own (www.englishwine.com) will help spread the word about the subject.

The greatest challenge facing the industry today is that of persuading more buyers, both trade and retail, to buy our wines. The best of our wines are now genuinely world class and deserve a place on the nation's tables. The recent MAFF grant given to the

United Kingdom Vineyards Association (UKVA) and English Wine Producers (EWP) to aid the marketing of English wine (the Welsh have their own scheme) has given the industry a one-off chance to try and inform the public of its wines. The development of the 'English Wine Marque' is a significant step in the right direction.

I

Viticulture in the British Isles before the Revival – pre-Roman to 1939

─────────

PRE-ROMAN BRITAIN

Whether or not vines were grown, grapes harvested and wine made in Britain before the arrival of the Romans is open to debate. There are no reliable records pointing one way or the other. The native Celts, heavy drinkers though they were, seem to have preferred beer and mead which they could make from local indigenous ingredients. The Belgae, who had established themselves in the east and south of Britain prior to the Roman invasion, did have a liking for wine, and wine amphorae, dating from before the Roman conquest, have been discovered on sites in southern England. Edward Hyams in his book *Dionysus – A Social History of the Wine Vine* shows a fine picture of a 4 ft high Roman amphora, together with a silver wine cup, both recovered from the British tombs of Belgic chieftains of the first century BC. Their strong trading links with France and Italy allowed them to import wine relatively easily and it would therefore seem unlikely that they had any need to establish vineyards in this country.

ROMAN BRITAIN

On the subject of winegrowing in the British Isles, most books say with absolute certainty 'that the Romans introduced the vine' to these shores, and then usually go on to give the impression that swathes of vines covered most of the slopes in southern England. The evidence that supports this assertion is, however, less easy to find. Dr Tim Unwin, in his scholarly book *Wine and the Vine – An Historical Geography of Viticulture and the Wine Trade* writes that 'the northern limit of viticulture in the Roman era is widely considered to have been just north of Paris' and that 'much of the evidence adduced in support of the cultivation of vines in Roman Britain has been shown . . . to be of dubious validity'. Moreover, Tacitus, writing at the end of the first century AD, declared that our climate was 'objectionable', and not at all suitable for growing vines, which could suggest that someone had at least tried to establish vines, even if they had been unsuccessful. Hyams says that vines were introduced by the Romans 'more by way of an ornamental re-creation of the Mediterranean atmosphere, than for the grapes they yielded'. There is therefore considerable uncertainty about the scope and scale of Roman viticulture.

What does not appear to be in doubt is the Romans' liking for wine – whether home grown or imported. After Claudius's army invaded Britain in AD 43, wine drinking became more commonplace and whenever Roman villas, houses and garrisons have been excavated, archaeologists have nearly always found remains of wine amphorae and drinking cups. In addition, grape pips and stems of bunches are occasionally found, although whether these are from imported or home-grown fruit, it is not possible to say. According to the Roman writer Suetonius, in AD 90 the Emperor Domitian issued an edict forbidding native inhabitants of countries conquered by the Romans to plant vines on their own lands. Of course, this edict – about whose accuracy Hugh Barty-King in his book *A Tradition of English Wine* has expressed some doubts – did not specifically relate to Britain and therefore neither proves, nor disproves, the existence of vineyards in these islands.

However, recent archaeological investigations in Northampton-shire have uncovered evidence that suggests that vineyards *were* established on something more than just a trial scale during the Roman occupation. Ian Meadows, an archaeologist with Northamptonshire County Council, has proved beyond doubt that grapes were grown in Roman Britain. At a 35 ha Romano-British site at Wollaston in the Nene valley (near Wellingborough), initial surveys revealed the presence of parallel trenches covering what appeared to be a substantial area of ground. These trenches, measuring 0.85 m wide by 0.30 m deep and spaced 5 m apart, were excavated to see what they might have been used for. Early theories about irrigation channels or deep cultivation beds were discounted when what appeared to be regular holes along the trenches were uncovered. The formation of deposits within these holes suggested that each hole had contained both a post and the roots of a plant, suggesting that a crop had been grown up some form of trelliswork. These holes, each measuring about 0.15 m in diameter and the same distance in depth, were spaced at more or less regular intervals of 1.5 m – the sort of spacing within the row one would adopt for vines. A Roman writer called Columella, writing in the first century AD, described growing vines in just such a manner, calling it 'pastinatio'.

Soil samples were taken from across the 11 ha site containing the trenches. Simple washing and sieving failed to reveal any plant matter that might give a clue as to what species of plant had been grown in the trenches and therefore Dr Tony Brown from Exeter University, an expert in this type of investigative work, was asked to inspect the samples and see what conclusions he came to. To his surprise, in two samples, he discovered large deposits of grape vine pollen. This, he suggested, had become washed down the stem of the vines and survived in the soil which had surrounded the roots. In addition, the soil samples revealed that few other plants such as grasses – whose pollen is very persistent – weeds or other agricultural crops, had been grown on the site at the time. This absence of other pollens would indicate that if there were grasses and weeds they were kept short by mowing so that they did not flower (and produce pollen) or that the soil was kept bare – a common practice on the continent both then and now – as a way of improving the microclimate in the vineyard.

Since this initial site was excavated, further sites in this area have been looked at, one of between 4 and 5 ha and several smaller ones. As at Wollaston, the same pattern of trenches and post holes has been discovered, as well as the conclusive grapevine pollen. In addition, a very recent dig has discovered what appears to be the base of a Roman amphora but made from British clay from either the Nene valley or St Albans and dating from AD 200–300. If this can be confirmed as being a *wine* amphora (they were used for a wide range of other liquids) this is indeed further proof that the Romans and their native subjects did grow vines in at least a few locations on something more than a very limited scale. Of course, growing grapes and making wine are two different occupations and the discovery of artefacts associated with winemaking would further strengthen the claims that the Romans introduced vinegrowing *and* winemaking to our islands.

In AD 277 (some references say AD 280), the Emperor Probus repealed Domitian's earlier edict. This may have provided the impetus needed for Britons to start growing vines and supplying both their rulers and perhaps some of the very early Christians with home-produced wines.

AFTER THE ROMANS

When the Romans began to leave at the end of the fourth century, Christianity, which had been made the official religion in the empire by Constantine in AD 312, became more widespread and wine drinking, playing as it did an important part in Christian ceremonies, became more accepted. Whether this was of local or imported wine, it is hard to say. If there were vineyards, then they were undoubtedly attached to religious institutions such as monasteries. As the Romans finally left, the country was plunged into what we call the Dark Ages and invasions by the Jutes, the Angles and the Saxons destroyed much of the limited civilisation that the Romans had established during their 300 years of occupation. These warring tribes neither had the time nor the inclination to settle and set up vineyards and whatever vineyards there had been undoubtedly became neglected. The early Christians, fleeing from these tribal disturbances, retreated to the corners of these islands, mainly to Wales and Cornwall, taking with them their skills as winegrowers. Whether they set up vineyards is not recorded. Apart from any other reason, many of these early Christian settlements (such as Lindisfarne and Iona) were in areas not suitable, either then or now, for vines.

When St Augustine landed in 596, sent to Britain by Pope Gregory to convert the early Celtic Christians to a Roman way of Christian worship, he probably brought wine with him and obtained further supplies from traders from the continent. As many of the communities he founded and encouraged were in Scotland and the north of England, it is unlikely that vineyards were contemplated, let alone planted. However, as Christianity spread south and east into climatically more favourable areas, old skills were revived and there is some evidence that vineyards were established. However, given that growing conditions on the continent were more suitable for commercial viticulture and that wine travelled, why would anyone want to establish a vineyard with all its attendant costs unless they were perhaps members of an enclosed religious order? The fact is that trade with mainland Europe was increasing and it is well recorded that wine played an important part in that trade, thus lessening the need for the home-grown product.

The Venerable Bede in his *History of the English Church and People*, completed in 731, writes that 'vines are cultivated in various localities' (which Hyams renders as 'it [Britain] also produces wines in some places' which is slightly more positive than the former statement). Whichever translation is more accurate, Bede's words seem to have been taken by many as proof positive that vineyards flourished all over these islands. However, Dr Unwin notes that there is doubt about its accuracy and Bede's later assertion that Ireland had 'no lack of vines' was challenged by a twelfth-century writer, Giraldus Cambrensis, who stated that Bede was wrong and that Ireland 'has not, and never had, vines.' In any event, the Vikings, who raped and pillaged their way around much of the country during this period, destroyed many monasteries. Once again, skills such as vinegrowing and winemaking – had they existed – would have been lost.

King Alfred, the Anglo-Saxon ruler of Wessex from 871 to 899, who defeated the Danes at Edington in Wiltshire and saved the country from becoming ruled by Scandinavians, helped re-establish the Christian religion, and in doing so, undoubtedly encouraged the revival of viticulture. It is often stated that he approved a law giving owners of vineyards compensation in the event of damage by trespassers and this is often taken as proof that vineyards were once again being cultivated. Dr Unwin questions this and states that in fact this reference to vineyards occurs in the preamble to Alfred's laws where he is quoting from the Bible (Exodus XXII) and that there is *no* mention of vineyards in his own new laws. However, whether or not winegrowing was a feature of ninth-century Britain, there is far less doubt that by the tenth century, vineyards did exist and wine was made.

In 956 King Eadwig (sometimes called Edwy), Alfred's great grandson, granted Dunstan, the Abbot of St Mary's Abbey,

Glastonbury, a vineyard at Panborough in Somerset, and although the original document is lost, it survives in a fourteenth-century copy in the Bodleian Library. Panborough, which has south-facing slopes, is only four miles from Glastonbury where the Benedictine monastery was re-established in AD 940. Somerset then, as now, appears to have been somewhat of a centre of winegrowing and several vineyards were recorded including one at Watchet, overlooking the Bristol Channel, which King Edgar (the Peaceful) granted to Abingdon Abbey in 962 (Hooke, 1990).

THE NORMAN CONQUEST

By the time William the Conqueror set foot on British soil in 1066 and defeated King Harold at Hastings, monastic viticulture was at a fairly low ebb. Seward, in his *Monks and Wine* says that 'there were probably no more than 850 monks in the whole of England' at the time of the Norman invasion (out of a population of 3 million), so it is unlikely that monastic vineyards were widespread. However, not only did William bring with him French soldiers and courtiers for whom wine was a daily requirement, he also brought French Abbots and their monks who were experienced in winegrowing. The year 1066 marked the start of an era of viticultural activity that would not be matched until the current revival which began some 900 years later.

The Domesday Surveys conducted between 1080 and 1086 which covered an area south of a line between the Wash and Bristol and as far west as Somerset and Dorset, show vineyards in forty-two definite locations, with references to vines and wines another three. Ten of the vineyards had been recently planted, suggesting that the Normans were instrumental in supporting viticulture in their newly conquered country. The vineyards recorded (and there may well have been vineyards which went unrecorded or in areas of the country not surveyed) were in two main regions: around London and up into Essex and Suffolk, and in the western counties of Somerset and Dorset. Apart from three in Kent at Leeds Castle, Chart Sutton (near Maidstone) and at Chislet near Canterbury and one at Staines in Surrey, none were recorded in the southern counties of Kent, Surrey, East and West Sussex or Hampshire, the home of a large number of today's vineyards. Was

6

this to do with land ownership, with land use, or for some other reason?

It is also interesting to note that only twelve of the Domesday vineyards were attached to monasteries. The majority belonged to nobles and were undoubtedly cultivated to provide them with wine for their dining tables and altars, rather than with wine for commercial sale. On almost all the manors where Domesday vineyards were recorded, there were higher than average numbers of both slaves and plough teams, and Unwin suggests that these indicate that vineyards were situated on 'large and prosperous manors'. Even King William himself was recorded as owning one at North Curry in Somerset which had been owned by Harold and was, at 7 acres, the largest vineyard recorded in the Domesday Book of 1086. In a few instances the size of vineyards is given in acres, whereas it is mostly given in *arpents* – a measure of area about whose exact size there is uncertainty, but believed to be slightly less than one acre. In one instance the Domesday Book records a yield of a vineyard at Rayleigh in Essex. Here, 6 *arpents* (about 2 ha) yielded 20 *modii*, each *modius* being a measure of liquid volume that Barty-King gives as equal to 36 gallons or 164 litres. This gives a yield of about 16 hl/ha which compares not unfavourably with the current UK average yield (1989–1999) of 22.67 hl/ha and with pre-*phylloxera* vineyards in France of the 1860s of 20 hl/ha. Another vineyard listed is at Leeds Castle in Kent which William the Conqueror gave to his half-brother Bishop Odo of Bayeux. This was sized at 2 *arpents* and was given together with 8 acres of meadow. Whether today's vineyard at Leeds Castle, planted almost 900 years later, occupies exactly the same site is not known, but the direct connection with the past cannot be denied.

The conquest of the country by the Normans led to a large influx of different religious orders. The pre-conquest Benedictine monks were soon joined by Cistercians, Carthusians and Augustinians, all of whom needed wine for their religious observances and the number of vineyards known to be in existence expanded to new levels. There were two main areas of monastic viticulture: the southern coastal areas of Kent, east and west Sussex and Hampshire; and Somerset, Gloucestershire and Hereford and Worcester. In Gloucestershire over 20 vineyards are known to have been cultivated in the 1200s, all of them attached to monasteries. William of Malmesbury claimed that the county was 'more thickly planted with vineyards than any other part of England'. The Archbishop of Canterbury had vineyards at Teynham and Northfleet in Kent, both near the north coast, on which he spent considerable sums of money. His accounts of 1235 show that the expenses were somewhat greater than the income – another reminder that England was then, and is still today, on the margins of successful commercial viticulture. Many sources point out that the climate improved for a period of 300 years starting from about the time of the Norman invasion and citing this as the reason why so many vineyards were planted. However, not everyone found this to be the case.

In 1230 the Abbot of Glastonbury – Michael of Amesbury – who had a summer palace at Pilton, had a vineyard planted on a sloping site and in 1235 appointed William the Goldsmith to manage it and make the wine. Although the Abbot liked Pilton – he had a new house built there in about 1240 – his vineyard was relatively short-lived and after 30 years the vines were taken out and the hillside converted into a park for game. It is recorded that the summers between 1220 and 1260 were particularly poor and several other vineyards in the country at that time were grubbed up. (What makes this tale doubly interesting is that Pilton Manor was the site of one of the first major commercial vineyards to be planted in the twentieth century. Nigel Godden started planting in 1966 and at one time there were almost 8 ha of vines planted. The wines produced were amongst the best in the country, winning the Gore-Browne Trophy three times – 1975, 1976 and 1992. Today, after a change of ownership and change of direction, the vineyard has almost disappeared and is down to less than 0.60 ha. Only a little wine is now produced.) By 1270, there were some 14,000 monks in the country, out of a total population of less than 3 million. Many of the monks, especially the Benedictine and Cistercian orders, lived in enclosed communities, dependent on what they could grow and make to survive, and vineyards would have been a necessity rather than a luxury. Vineyards were also cultivated by the nobles of the period, and many mansions and castles had vineyards attached. The many references to vineyards in the records of the day show that they were far from rare.

Of course, what wines were like during this era, no one can tell. The wine would have been made in wooden casks and kept in them until consumed. Glass was in use by the nobility for serving wine in and drinking wine from, but bottles and corks were not in use for storing wine in the way we do today. The process of sweetening the juice before fermentation to increase the final alcoholic content was understood and the wines of that period would probably have been high in alcohol as a result. This would have aided their keeping properties and made them more palatable. They would also quite possibly have been sweetened after fermentation with honey and perhaps flavoured with herbs and spices as well. Wines were often made using raisins, either in conjunction with fresh grapes or, when they were not available, on their own. This enabled a 'wine' to be made at any time of the year. The idea that wine is only made 'from the freshly fermented juice of fresh grapes' (the modern definition of wine) is relatively recent. Winemakers in the Middle Ages (and indeed until more modern times) thought nothing of 'improving' wine by adding whatever they felt was required. Apart from water to increase volume, the 'marc' (the residue left over after the pressing of white grapes or the fermentation of reds) could be soaked in water to extract some flavour and, with enough sugar added, could be turned into something that vaguely resembled wine. Sometimes pine resin was added to wine, a practice the Romans learnt from the Greeks and which of course is still practised today in the making of retsina. The resin both helped preserve the wine and cover up any off-flavours that might have developed. Grapes were looked upon in those times as just one of the ingredients that went into making wine and without today's rules and regulations, almost anything could be added to help improve the wine or aid its keeping qualities.

The wines made at this time were probably all consumed during the cooler weather of the winter and spring following the harvest, and in any event well before the weather warmed up which would have caused the wine to oxidise, spoil and turn to vinegar. The principle of conserving wine with sulphur dioxide had not been discovered and wines kept for any length of time, unless they were high in alcohol or sugar – both of which can act as preservatives – would have deteriorated badly. Imported wines, of which there appeared to be no shortage, also suffered from the same problems and 'sour' wine (that is wine affected by acetic bacteria) appears to have been a constant complaint. At least home-produced wine did not have to travel far and probably suffered less than imported wines from oxidation, thus partially explaining its apparent popularity.

THE MIDDLE AGES TO THE GREAT WAR

The story of vinegrowing and winemaking during this long 600-year period is one of change and gradual decline. Why viticulture did not really become a viable alternative to other crops, as it did in other countries where monastic viticulture was common, is open to debate, but commercial and practical considerations have to be important.

Whilst vineyards were tended by monks and friars, by serfs and slaves, who in truth had little option but to do what their masters required of them, the question of whether making wine was an economical activity was probably of little importance. However, when workers required reward for their hire, the question of whether it was more economical to drink home-grown or imported wine became important. Before the Black Death arrived, the religious orders had prospered, reliant on a pliable and available workforce. However, finding their manpower depleted by the plague, they took to leasing their land, rather than working it themselves, and their new tenants, dependent on short-term cash crops to pay the rent, did not want to grow vines, which then, as now, can only be grown on a long-term basis. The last vineyard owned by the Archbishop of Canterbury was given up in 1350, the year the plague arrived in Kent. By 1370, the number of monks and friars had dropped to 8,000 compared with a high point of 14,000 a century earlier (Seward, 1979). Although the Dissolution of the Monasteries in 1536, which came about after the break-up of Henry VIII's marriage to Anne Boleyn in 1533, is often cited as the single event that destroyed winegrowing and winemaking in England, it would appear that by this time many monasteries had given up viticulture from either lack of manpower, indolence or a combination of both. After the split with Rome and the seizing of Church properties by the King, fewer vineyards remained to be cultivated. The new barons and earls who had been handed these religious assets, like their monastic predecessors, wanted rents in cash, not in kind, and there was no place for viticulture.

Climate change can also be introduced as a possible reason for the decline in vineyard numbers. It is known from a wide number of sources that the northern European climate slowly warmed from about 550 BC until the middle of the thirteenth century. This meant that in the period between 1100 and 1300 summers were warmer with average temperatures about 1–1.5°C higher than today, but with colder winters. It is argued that this equates to today's climate on the Mosel or in Champagne and Chablis, all marginal but successful modern winegrowing regions. After the mid-1300s, it is said that the British climate generally became wetter, with cooler summers and milder winters, leading to less ripe grapes and more fungal disease, both of which would have been disincentives to profitable winemaking. Wine had been coming into the country from Bordeaux since Henry II (who had married Eleanor of Aquitaine in 1152) became King of England. As more and more wine (and other goods) came into the country from overseas, both transport conditions and speeds improved and the transport of wine became cheaper. Also, as techniques of preserving wine for long journeys improved, imported wines arrived in better condition. Thus, poorer quality, lower alcohol (and mainly white) home produced wine stood little chance against the competition. The British love of 'claret', the light red wines of Bordeaux, stems from this day. England signed trading treaties with Portugal as early as 1353 and whenever we were at war with France, we were at peace with Portugal which helped secure a supply of good wine (Fielden, 1989). According to Seward, 3 million gallons came into the country from Bordeaux in 1448–49 which on a per capita basis is higher than today's consumption from the same region!

Other factors also played their part in viticulture's problems. The Black Death, which lasted from 1348 until the 1370s, not only cut the population dramatically, but forced changes in agriculture which had far-reaching social and demographic effects. Our fields, until then tended on the feudal strip system, became divided into larger fenced and hedged enclosures. Livestock – in particular sheep – required far less manpower than arable crops, and they became commonplace. The resultant drop in the production of grain was compensated for by a rise in imports from the mainland of Europe, where growing conditions were generally better and supplies could be obtained more easily. This led to an increase in trade of many other goods from overseas, including wine.

During the almost 400 years between the Dissolution of the Monasteries and the First World War, viticulture became very much an occupation for the enthusiast, the eccentric and the adventurous, rather than for the farmer seeking income from his land, and although there may have been vineyards cultivated for profit, the best known were cultivated more for pleasure. The reasons why growing grapes for the production of wine declined in this period are the same reasons why viticulture at the end of the twentieth century remains an uncertain way of making a living: climate and competition. The weather during this later period was, as far as one can tell, broadly similar to the weather we 'enjoy' today. Growers faced the same hazards that we now face (although hopefully not all in the same year) – spring frosts, poor weather at flowering, wet summers that bring on mould and rot (although *oidium tuckerii* – powdery mildew – was unknown in Europe until it was discovered in Mr Tucker's greenhouse in Margate in 1847) and cool autumns that fail to ripen grapes sufficiently. Remember also that growers then had neither today's modern varieties nor clones of varieties which have been developed both to fruit and ripen in cooler climates and to resist disease. They also did not have the armoury of modern fungicides to prevent disease, without which commercial viticulture would not be possible today.

Home-produced wines also faced, as they do today, considerable competition from imported wines. From the mid-1300s, the trade in wine from overseas became more and more sophisticated and England (and for that matter Scotland and Ireland) were substantial importers of wine from all over the world. In 1363, Sir Henry Picard, a member of the 'Mistery of Vintners' (the forerunner of the Worshipful Company of Vintners which was incorporated in 1437) gave a celebrated banquet for the Kings of England, Scotland, France, Denmark and Cyprus (which is why today the London address of the Vintner's Hall is Five Kings House) and secured for his members the exclusive right to buy and sell wine from Gascony, a region which then supplied much of our wine requirements. Great Britain became renowned for its expertise in selecting, importing, bottling and cellaring wine and much of the finest wine came into ports like London, Bristol and Leith. Indeed, wines such as claret, port, madeira, sherry, hock and moselle were, if not invented, then refined, nurtured and made more famous by their association with Britain. The taste of winedrinkers of the day was for red wines, for sweet wines and for fortified wines – wines which today's UK winegrowers have difficulty producing regularly and which certainly winegrowers centuries ago would have found even more difficult to produce, given the vine varieties and technology available, as well as the prevailing climate.

With these disadvantages, it is perhaps not surprising that commercial viticulture suffered and vineyard owners, unless they were prepared to support their efforts out of funds from other sources, found more profitable uses for their land. However, despite these problems, vineyards *were* planted and wines *were* made. There are many references to vineyards throughout the literature of the era and Hugh Barty-King's book *A Tradition of English Wine* is the most complete history of viticulture in the British Isles yet to have been published. Space in this book does not allow more than the mention of a few that are of special interest.

James I, who ruled England from 1603–1625, had vineyards at Oatlands Park in Surrey, together with a 'Vine Garden' at St James's Palace, although it is not recorded whether they cropped well (or at all) or whether the grapes were for the table or for winemaking. In 1610, Robert Cecil, the first Earl of Salisbury, asked the great botanist John Tradescant to go to Flanders to search for some suitable vines for his estate. The next year, 1611, 20,000 vines (at '8 crowns the thousand') were sent from France with more following in later years. Lord Salisbury's vineyard at Hatfield House, planted on the banks of the river Lee, was well known throughout the seventeenth century. The great diarist Samuel Pepys visited Hatfield House on 22 July 1661 and commented that he 'walked all alone to the Vineyard which is now a very beautiful place again' (as if it had perhaps been neglected previously). He visited it again in 1667. In between 1661 and 1667, Pepys visited another famous vineyard which was owned by 'Colonell Blunt' [sic] near Blackheath. Pepys writes in his diary that he saw some 'brave plantations' (meaning some rare plants) and went on to say that he saw 'a vineyard, the first I ever did see'! He had obviously forgotten about his earlier visit to Hatfield House.

Blunt's vineyard was obviously famous (and rare?) enough for several writers of the day to visit and comment upon it. John Evelyn, the writer and diarist, visited Blunt's house and gardens a few years before Pepys in 1655 and wrote that he had 'drunk of the wine of his [Blunt's] vineyard which was good for little'! Sir Thomas Hamner (a well connected Welsh Royalist and gardening authority) also visited it (in 1656). In 1659 Hamner wrote in his *Garden Book* – one of the first and most important books on gardening in English – that the vineyard was 'betwixt one and two acres' and was on a hill 'which lyes full facing on the south'. Hamner describes the system of growing in full and comments that 'The Colonell sayth hee uses no dung or compost to this barren earth of his vineyard, which is very strange'. Evidently, 'the Colonell' had discovered what modern growers know only too well: vines in our climate benefit from a lack of nitrogenous fertiliser! Hamner makes no comments on the produce of the vineyard, so perhaps by then Blunt had stopped offering it to visitors, however grand. Samuel Hartlib, also writing in 1659, said 'I dare say it's probable that vineyards have formerly flourished in England, and we are to blame that so little is attempted to revive them again' (Barty-King, 1977).

In 1666, John Rose, 'Gard'ner to his Majesty [Charles II] at His Royal Garden in St James's', wrote a treatise (a bare 35 small pages long) on the cultivation of vines in this country called *The English Vineyard Vindicated* which was published bound together (as if it did not really warrant being separately published on its own) with a translation by John Evelyn of *The French Gardiner* [sic] – an important work in its time. In his opening 'Epistle Dedicatory' Rose states: 'I know your Majesty can have no great opinion of our English Wines as hitherto they have been order'd' and goes on to say that he hopes that by his instructions and recommendations 'that precious Liquor may haply once again recover its just estimation'. In the preface, written by 'Philocepos' (John Evelyn) it is stated that he (Evelyn) discussed with Mr Rose 'the Cause of the neglect of Vineyards of late in England' and questioned why they had declined when one considered 'how frequently they were heretofore planted in this Country of ours'. In his treatise, Rose discusses the question of site selection, vine varieties, pruning and training (with illustrations) and care of the vines up to the harvest. He ends by advertising that he has 'plentiful a stock of sets and plants' for sale and that readers 'may receive them of me at very reasonable rates'! (John Rose is also reputed to have grown the first pineapple in England which he presented to the King).

In 1670, one Will Hughes a 'servant to the Right Honourable Edward, Lord Viscount Conway and Kilulta' wrote a book entitled *The Compleat Vineyard: or An Excellent Way for the Planting of Vines According to the French and German Manner and Long Practised in England*. In the introduction he states 'that there have been plenty of vineyards in England heretofore; and it is very well known that there are now in Kent, and other places of this Nation, such Vineyards and Wall-vines as produce great store of excellent good wine'. In his book he gives explicit instructions on all aspects of growing vines: site selection and preparation, choice of varieties – 'the lesser and greater white Muscadine, the red Muscadine, the Frantinick, the Parsley-grape (more for show and rarity than profit) and the Rhenishwine vine' – how to stake and grow them, when to pick ('when they are ripe by their sweet and pleasant taste') and finally how to make the most of them in the winery. Despite these exhortations, viticulture did not seem to be taken up as a profitable or worthwhile use for land and the decline continued.

However, between 1720 and 1732, the young MP for Haslemere, James Oglethorpe, who lived in some splendour at Westbrook Place, Godalming, Surrey, had a 400-yard wall built in his garden and constructed two broad south facing terraces on which he planted vines. His wine, which he served at the many soirées and political gatherings that were held there, became well known, as did the French snails which he apparently bred on the vine leaves. His vineyard and press-house appeared to survive for many years. When Oglethorpe died and his estate was put up for sale in 1785, part of the property was described as 'a Vineyard of considerable extent'. However, 38 years later (1823) when the estate was again sold, no mention was made of a vineyard.

In 1727, a 'Gentleman', known only by his initials 'S.J.', published a relatively large handbook (192 pages) on growing vines (as well as a wide variety of other fruits) called *The Vineyard* in which he said: 'Tis not above a century or two of years since the planting of the Peach, the Nectrine, the Apricot, the Cherry and the Hop, were treated in as ridiculous a manner, as the Vine-yards at present are, in this Country' and went on to demonstrate in careful detail how vines would grow and fruit in our climate. He continued that 'the Want of Wine in England is not owing to the Unkindness of our Soil, or the Want of a benign Climate, but to the Inexperience of our Natives'. How experienced 'S.J.' was is open to conjecture as he also advocated the growing of almonds and olives, fruits which even the most optimistic of growers would find difficult to grow today in the open air.

One of the most famous vineyards of this era was that at Painshill Place, Cobham, Surrey (the Painshill junction on the A3 is named after it) which was planted by the Honourable Charles Hamilton in 1740. Hamilton was an extraordinary character, as so many in this saga seemed to be. In 1738 he took a long lease on the 300 acre property and started to construct one of the most fabulous gardens of its time. He landscaped it and filled it with follies including a ruined abbey, a Roman temple, a Turkish tent, a fantastic shell-filled grotto, a hermitage (complete with hermit) and some Roman steps. The garden also featured a vineyard. Planted on a steep 45° slope, it overlooked a magnificent lake. (The lake was constructed so that it was 12 ft above the level of the nearby river Mole – to stop it becoming flooded – and was kept at exactly the same level, summer and winter by being constantly topped up by a 28 ft water wheel which brought water up from the adjacent river.)

Hamilton planted 'two sorts of Burgundy grapes, the Auvernat, which is the most delicate, but the tenderest, and the Miller grape, commonly called the black cluster, which is more hardy'. He employed a Huguenot refugee, David Geneste, to tend his vines and make his wine. In Sir Edward Barry's book *Observations on the Wines of the Ancients*, published in 1775, Barry quotes from an essay written by Hamilton. In it he says that his wine 'had a finer flavour than the best Champaign [sic] I ever tasted' and that 'I am convinced that much good Wine might be made in many parts of the south of England.' Hamilton also issued a warning which many of today's growers know to their cost is still true. He says 'such is the prejudice against any thing of English growth, I generally found it most prudent not to declare where it grew, till they [his guests] had passed their verdict upon it.'

Painshill's vineyard survived many years until Hamilton fell on hard times and in 1773 sold it to Benjamin Bond Hopkins. Hopkins kept the park and vineyard as it had been in Hamilton's time (although he tore down Hamilton's 'modest' residence and built a far grander one) and had a picture painted of the vineyard, the lake and the 'Ruined Abbey' by George Barrett and Sawrey Gilpin. This, and another painting of the vineyard by an unknown artist, remain the only known pictures of an eighteenth-century English vineyard. How long the vineyard lasted no one is sure. Hopkins died in 1794 and the estate remained untended until 1804 when it was bought by the Earl of Carhampton. He had no time for vineyards, saying that they were 'fine for eccentric romantics' (Barty-King, 1977) and one must assume that whatever remains were still there were removed. What makes this vineyard doubly interesting is that in 1989 the vineyard site was restored and vines replanted. Since 1980 the estate has been in the hands of the Painshill Park Trust, a charity dedicated to the restoration of the park in all its glory. As part of this restoration, I was asked to advise on the replanting of the vineyard and in the winter of 1988 the task of clearing the original site, by then covered with 200-year-old Scot's pine trees, was started with the help of men and machinery loaned by Sir Robert McAlpine and Sons. After the site was cleared and stabilized, the first vines, Chardonnay and Pinot noir – varieties which were as near to the original as possible – were planted, as well as Seyval blanc (in order to guarantee a harvest). Today, the 0.73 ha vineyard is back in production and attempting to recreate a wine in the style of Hamilton's 'best Champaign'!

In 1747, Philip Miller, writing in his *Gardener's Dictionary* (the first edition of which was published in 1731) said that 'there have of late years been but very few vineyards in England though they were formerly very common' and that 'at this day very few Persons will believe it [wine production] possible to be effected'. (Barty-King surmises that the 'Dusty Miller', a synonym for Pinot Meunier, was named after Philip Miller. I find this less than probable and prefer the idea that the name derives from the floury look that the leaves of this vine have. In my edition, the sixth published in 1771, Miller calls it 'the Black Cluster or Munier [sic] Grape, as it is called by the French, from the hoary down of the leaves'.) Miller's *Gardener's Dictionary* became a standard work on all things horticultural and went to nine editions, the last being published in 1835 with the inscription 'Ebenus Cretica' – no more published (Gabler 1985). The sixth edition, although it has a large section on wine and winemaking (not only from grapes), has more on growing table grapes than on wine grapes under the entry for 'Vitis'.

In 1786, Francis Xavier Vispré, who had had a small vineyard in Wimbledon (and was later to have another one in Chelsea) and who had given a talk at the Society of Arts two years earlier on the subject of establishing vineyards, wrote a small handbook on the subject which gained some popularity – even notoriety. This was possibly because he challenged a Mr Le Brocq over a system of growing vines that he (Vispré) had been using for some years and which Le Brocq had patented. Vispré writes (with little modesty) that he was 'sufficiently satisfied with the prospect of being the restorer of Vineyards in this country' and was obviously peeved that Le Brocq had stolen both his thunder and apparently his methods.

The Duke of Norfolk had a vineyard at Arundel Castle which

shows up on maps of the estate dated 1772 and 1804 (Barty-King, 1977). H. M. Tod, a writer and vineyard owner, wrote in his *Vine-Growing in England* (1911) that in 1763 'sixty pipes of burgundy' were made 'not as equal to the best of Beaune, but better than ordinary'. Quite how long this vineyard was kept going no one appears to be able to say; even the Duke of Norfolk's archives give no clues.

It was in the latter half of the eighteenth century that the cultivation of table grapes became widespread and one of the most important books on British viticulture (British because Ireland, Scotland and Wales had their share of table grapes as well) came to be written. *Speechley on the Vine* as it is known amongst afficionados – *A Treatise on the Culture of the Vine, Exhibiting New and Advantageous Methods of Propagating, Cultivating, and Training that Plant so as to Render it Abundantly Fruitful. Together with New Hints on the Formation of Vineyards in England* by William Speechley, Gardener to the Duke of Portland – to give it is full title, was written in 1789 and privately published in 1790 by the author for a list of subscribers whose names appear in the front. They comprise a glorious roll-call of the good and the great of the late eighteenth century. In the year that their compatriots in France were suffering a little pruning by the guillotine, Dukes and Earls, Marquises and Viscounts (and their gardeners) were subscribing to this book on the mysteries of the vine. Speechley's greatest triumph as a gardener seems to have been a bunch of grapes that he produced at Welbeck (the Duke of Portland's mansion) in 1781. The bunch, from a vine of the 'Syrian' variety, weighed 19½ lbs, had a diameter of 19 in, a length of 21¾ in and was presented by the Duke to the Marquis of Rockingham. Four 'labourers' carried it 'suspended on a staff, in pairs, by turns' to Wentworth House, Rockingham's home.

The use of glass as a means of cultivating what we might today call 'exotics' came about quite slowly, although it was known about from about the middle of the sixteenth century (at the same time as glass was used for house windows). The first 'greenhouses' were just simple cloches, free standing or leaning against walls. Sheets of glass were at first small and very expensive and the technique of making larger sheets of glass which could then be placed into frames and used to build 'houses' was not learnt until towards the end of the 1500s when French glassmakers settled in Britain. Once secure structures, walled and roofed with glass, could be built which would keep out the elements and could be heated if necessary with stoves or heating pipes, the production of table grapes became commonplace. The literature on growing table grapes in green-houses in this country published between 1600 and the early 1900s is prodigious. Almost every large house, mansion and palace had its 'vinery' (as well as in many cases a separate greenhouse for growing pineapples, figs, peaches, nectarines and even oranges) and there was tremendous interest in growing vines.

On the subject of vines out of doors for the production of wine, Speechley is not so certain. In the preface to his book he writes that 'of all the numerous sorts of fruits indulgent nature produces for the use of man, that of the grape must be esteemed her noblest gift'. He then writes that the vine's 'most important and most transcendant [sic] article' is wine, but continues that 'from the situation of this island, and from the nature of the Vine, it may seem doubtful whether wine can be made in this country to any considerable advantage'. In the back of the book is a chapter 'On Vineyards' which is largely taken up with the account of Hamilton's Painshill vineyard that Barry reproduced in his 1775 book. Speechley says that 'It has much been disputed of late whether the various places in the different counties of England, which still retain the name of Vineyards, were plantations for the purpose of making wine'. He refrains from entering into the debate as he has 'not the least pretension to antiquarian knowledge' but goes on to say that since the climate in Germany allows for profitable viticulture and many of the places that produce good wines there are on the same latitude as the southern counties of England (vineyards in Germany at this period were planted further north than the Ahr region which is today their most northerly growing area), there is no reason why 'where the situation and soil are proper' vines will not prosper in Britain.

Speechley cited several other commentators of the day on out-door viticulture – Vispré, Bradley, Switzer and Barry – and ends by saying 'from the foregoing accounts it is evident that good wine may be made in this country, in a propitious season'. He ends by saying about the disappearance of vineyards that 'Antiquaries are silent as to the reasons of their being rooted up and neglected.' One cannot help but get the impression from this articulate and seasoned gardener that he felt that outdoor vineyards for wine production were fairly speculative. Speechley, who lived until 1819 (having been born in 1733), went on to write two more editions of his book, the last at 363 pages over half as long again as the first edition and containing much more information about growing 'the Ananas or Pine-Apple' – a fruit then all the rage.

Despite all this writing and proselytizing about outdoor vineyards, they did not really become widespread or commercially successful. Painshill's died out at the end of the 1800s and although there were others, the story was much the same. After the initial enthusiasm of the owners (mainly gentlemen of property and considerable income), the uncertainty of the climate and the variability of the crops in terms of both quality and quantity took their toll and the vineyards were abandoned. Tastes and fashions in wines also changed. Sweet, heavy, fortified wines from 'the colonies' (Australia and South Africa) were popular and home-grown wines could never match these. During the shortages of wine from the mainland of Europe in the latter part of the nineteenth century due to the damage done to vineyards by *phylloxera*, British companies, as did firms on the continent, started to make wines from both raisins and grape concentrate and the 'British Wine' industry was born. (These so-called 'wines' – under EU law they are not 'wines' as defined, nor for that matter are they very British – achieved a significant share of the bottom end of the market. This was partly because the raw ingredients were cheap, but also because these wines bore a preferential rate of excise duty. Until the excise duty on these wines was aligned with that of 'proper' wines, British Wines, especially fortified examples, were one of the cheapest ways of buying alcohol).

The last great experiment into commercial viticulture – that is before the start of the modern revival – was that of Lord Bute's at Castell Coch – to give it its Welsh name – although it is often called Castle Coch (sometimes also called in literature of the time Castle Cock). The third Marquis of Bute, John Patrick Crichton-Stuart, was a landowner and industrialist who had the wherewithal to indulge his visions and fantasies. His father, sometimes called 'the creator of modern Cardiff' had died in 1848, leaving him not only vast properties all over the country, but also the ruins of Castell Coch, a few miles outside Cardiff. In 1871, the 24-year-old Marquis, who was intrigued by the Middle Ages, commissioned the architect William Burges to restore the castle to its medieval glory.

In 1873 he summoned his head gardener in Scotland, Mr Andrew Pettigrew, and told him of his plan to complete his vision of the past at Castell Coch by surrounding it with a vineyard. He sent Pettigrew to Castell Coch to survey the site and report back.

Not one to do anything by half, the enthusiastic Marquess then dispatched Pettigrew to France to see how vines should be grown. Pettigrew appears to have been well looked after especially by a Champagne grower called Jacquesson who arranged for him to travel to Bordeaux in the company of one of his clerks, Scottish by birth but a fluent French speaker, who showed Pettigrew the 1873 *vendange* at Châteaux Latour, Lafite and Margaux. Following his visit, vines were ordered and in the spring of 1875 they were delivered, the varieties chosen being Gamay noir and Millie Blanche (also sometimes called the 'Miel Blanc'). According to a report by Pettigrew in the Royal Horticultural Society's (RHS) Journal of 1895, only enough vines were procured to cover one eighth of the 3 acres selected to be planted, so Pettigrew took cuttings and had soon propagated enough to cover the full area. The land chosen was the southern slope below the castle, just four miles from the Bristol Channel. It had previously been cleaned of weeds by taking a crop of potatoes and had then been trenched to help with the drainage. The vines were planted on a 3 ft × 3 ft square system, low trained to the ground on a 4 ft high trellis, in the manner suggested by Miller in his *Gardener's Dictionary*. (Millie Blanche did not prove to be a successful variety and it was eventually replaced with Gamay.)

The years between 1875 and 1877 were good ones – warm and dry – and the vines were able to establish themselves well, while disease, especially *Oidium tuckerii*, was kept to a minimum. In 1877, the first small crop was harvested and made into wine at a winery established in Cardiff Castle. The grapes were crushed and 'a little water and 3 lbs of cane sugar to every gallon' was added and the wine allowed to ferment for twenty days. In that first vintage only 240 bottles were made. Despite *Punch* magazine's assertion that if ever a bottle of wine was produced it would take 'four men to drink it – the victim, two to hold the victim and one to pour it down his throat', the wine was well received and likened to a 'still champagne' (as was the wine from Painshill).

Lord Bute was pleased with the success of the original vineyard and asked Pettigrew to look for further sites on his estate. Over the next 35 years, the original site below Castell Coch was expanded and a further two sites were planted; one was at nearby Swanbridge, between Penarth and Barry, where in 1886 11 acres were established; the third, a smaller one, was planted at St Quentins near Cowbridge overlooking the Bristol Channel but was abandoned as it was much too windswept. These two later sites were planted with Gamay noir cuttings from the Castell Coch site.

Throughout the life of Bute's vineyards there were tremendous variations in cropping levels. In 1879, poor flowering weather caused all the flowers to drop off and no crop was taken at all, Pettigrew reporting that a total of 44.4 in of rain fell on 196 days in the year. Likewise, cold weather caused total crop losses in 1880, 1882, 1883 and 1886. However, 1,500 bottles were made in both 1884 and 1885 and in 1887 3,600 bottles were made, the largest ever crop from the Castle site. Between 1878 and 1892 only white wines were made, but in 1893 the harvest was huge and a 'good red wine' was made. In total, from all the vineyards, 'twenty three hogsheads' were made, yielding a total of 1000 cases of a dozen bottles each (a yield of about 2.25 tonnes/acre or 39 hl/ha). It was calculated that at 60 shillings the dozen (£3) the potential income from the 1893 harvest alone was sufficient to repay all the expenses of the vineyards to date. It was also reported that in 1893 'not a particle of sugar was used'. However, as the usual winemaking practice was to leave the wine in barrel for three years and four in bottle before it was sold, there was no instant income.

Contemporary accounts vary as to the quality of the wine. At an RHS meeting in September 1894, at which Pettigrew (a Fellow of the RHS) gave a talk, samples of the wines were available. Mr Lance, a fellow Fellow and a chemist to boot, said that 'the samples of wine on the table were most excellent as a British production; not only full of alcoholic strength, but containing an agreeable amount of natural acid tartrate, as well as aroma, being far in advance of Grape wines generally manufactured in this country'. However, another member of the audience, Mr W. Roupell, said that 'experiments should be conducted with a view to producing a wine with a character of hock not sherry' indicating that the some of the wines shown at the talk were both high in alcohol and quite sweet (dry sherry being a relatively modern invention). Pettigrew said that the standard winemaking practice was to bring the must up to '30° proof [approx 15 per cent alcohol] before putting it in the barrel'. Tod, writing in 1911, says that he was 'a regular visitor to the vineyards' and had drunk several vintages. He had the 1881 in the Angel Hotel, Cardiff (a Bute-owned establishment) and likened it (again) to a 'still champagne'. Tod says that there was 'a want of definiteness of style and character' in the wines and that they 'remind one of a mixture of incompatible sorts'.

Tod continued to keep in contact with Pettigrew and in 1905 Tod was sent some Noir Hâtif de Saumur which he planted in his own vineyard at Wisley. This vineyard, for which Tod had great plans, seems to have disappeared into the ether and it is unclear whether it ever produced any wine. Tod claimed the (fairly dubious) distinction of having been the person who introduced the French-American hybrid 'Brandt' (often incorrectly spelt as 'Brant') into the country in 1886 which, being resistant to *Oidium* – then causing very bad damage to vines – he felt was the ideal vine for England. Tod supplied cuttings of both Brandt and Gamay – presumably obtained from Castell Coch – to a Mr James Wingfield who lived 'in Middlesex, in a town on the Thames' and who grew vines outside without shelter up until at least 1943. Wingfield moved from the un-named Thames-side town and, as reported in the *RHS Journal* of December 1943, ended up 'in Kent' where he successfully grew Brandt outside, but only used the grapes for the table or to produce 'some very good jelly'. He did not make wine with them.

Pettigrew continued to look after the vines for Lord Bute and despite a run of dreadful years, continued to be optimistic. The wines were sold locally and the 1881 was sold 'at the usual price of 60/- per dozen' and some even higher. A price of 115 shillings a dozen (£5.75) was achieved at auction when the contents of a local doctor's cellar was sold! The wines were also promoted by the London firm of Hatch, Mansfield & Co. as 'Canary Brand, Welsh Wines' with the 1887 vintage available in four different styles, at '44/- the dozen, carriage paid to any railway station in Great Britain'. Interestingly, the styles of wine described mainly appear to be sweet; the 1887 wines are described as 'Full Golden, Rather Sweet', Dark Golden Medium Sweet', 'A Luscious, Golden Wine' and 'Light Golden, Mellow'. Considering that Gamay would be considered an impossible variety to ripen today and knowing the usual natural sugar levels of suitable varieties of grapes grown in South Wales today, it is not surprising that considerable amounts of sugar had to be added to the juice before fermentation. Whatever these tasted like, it is fairly certain that they can have borne little relation to the light fruity wines that are produced in South Wales today.

The third Marquis of Bute died in 1900 and was succeeded by his 19-year-old son, who was equally enthusiastic. Pettigrew was himself succeeded by his own son (also called Andrew) who continued his father's work. Poor vintages, however, coupled with bad attacks of *Oidium*, put the whole venture at risk. Even so, Tod visited the vineyard in 1905 and notes that he found 63,000 vines in fruit which at 3 ft × 3 ft meant there were some 13 acres cropping. The summer of 1911 was apparently good and wines were made, but even so (according to Barty-King), 3.5 lb of sugar to every gallon was required (which by my calculations would have raised the potential alcohol to 20 per cent above its natural level. This would have indeed given a very sweet, high alcohol wine!)

The 1911 vintage appears to have been the last successful one. The Great War brought many shortages, and sugar, which then as now, was required to bring the alcohol up to acceptable levels, could not be spared. No wine was made during the war and the vines were eventually grubbed up in 1920. Pettigrew junior, speaking to the Cardiff Naturalist's Society in 1926, long after the vineyards previously under his and his father's care had been grubbed up, was fairly clear as to why the vineyard had not survived: '. . . here [in Glamorgan] viticulture holds out no promise of success. There is obviously something wrong with the climate when even in the most favourable of seasons it has been found necessary to resort to the artificial addition of sugar or (as in some cases) of alcohol'. He also said that in only seven of the forty-five years did the grapes fully ripen.

The Bute vineyards at Castell Coch and Swanbridge were the last vineyards of anything approaching a commercial size to be planted in Great Britain expressly for the production of wine before the modern revival began in the 1950s. Between 1911 and 1951 (when the first 'modern' vineyard was planted at Hambledon) there were two world wars and the economic upheaval of the depression of the 1930s. It is perhaps not surprising that planting vineyards and making wine did not occur on a commercial scale during this forty-year period. The cultivation of table grapes, on the other hand, was another matter. Archibald Barron, Superintendent of the RHS Gardens at Chiswick, wrote the standard work on table grape production *Vines and Vine Culture* in 1883. This book, which ran to five editions, the last being updated by his widow in 1912, gives a fascinating glimpse into the late Victorian and Edwardian era where even people of modest means had servants and those with larger incomes could afford teams of gardeners to grow every conceivable product. Without the transport systems and refrigeration that we accept today as standard, the only way then to have fresh fruit and vegetables on the table on a regular basis was to grow them yourself. Barron goes into every conceivable detail on growing table grapes, ending up with a list of over 100 varieties, including speciality varieties – producing the largest bunch, for early forcing, for late keeping, for pot culture and so on. He shows how, using a selection of varieties, it was possible to produce grapes for the table all year round. Black Hamburg, then as now, one of the standard greenhouse varieties, if forced into growth in November, would have ripe fruit by April. For late grapes, a variety such as Gros Colman (or Colmar) could be left hanging on the vine until March or April or, if a proper 'grape house' was available, the bunches could be cut after Christmas and inserted into bottles filled with water on a special angled rack that left the bunches hanging freely. Barron also mentions 'famous vines'. The largest in the country was at Manresa Lodge in Roehampton where a single Black Hamburg filled a vinery which was 424 ft long. The most productive vine was at Cumberland Lodge, Windsor Park where another Black Hamburg in a greenhouse measuring 138 ft × 20 ft, produced, in 1879, 2,500 lb of fruit. The largest single bunch then recorded was one from a Trebbiano, which Mr Curror of Eskbank exhibited in Edinburgh in 1875 which weighed 26 lb 4 oz (approximately 12 kg)!

In a short chapter in the 1892 edition on *Commercial Grape Culture* Barron writes about the 'extraordinary increase in the cultivation of Grapes for sale or market purposes' over the past few years. He says that the popularity of grapes is due to the public's sudden demand for tomatoes which were then becoming a very popular product. Growers were able to erect glass houses, plant them with vines and during the first four or five years while the vine was making wood and not producing fruit, crop the house with tomatoes. Once the vines were established and fruiting, tomato growing would stop. Barron says that the centres of table grape production were the Channel Islands, Hertfordshire, Worthing,

Finchley and at Galashiels in Scotland. One grower, Rochfords at Cheshunt (Hertfordshire) had over 50 acres of glass in total, with half of it devoted to vines and expected to send between 300 and 400 tons of grapes annually to Covent Garden. At two shillings a pound, this equated to a return of £3,360 an acre – worth over £175,000 at today's values! Sadly, many of these enterprises ended in the First World War when both manpower and fuel became short and expensive, although a few growers in Worthing did keep going until the 1930s.

Anyone looking back over the almost two thousand years from the Roman occupation to the end of the Bute vineyards, would have to say that outdoor viticulture for the production of grapes had been tried and had not proved itself commercially viable in these islands. The historical evidence is of brave attempts – some would even say foolhardy attempts – at establishing vineyards, only to have them ultimately fail. Whatever successes growers did have at growing and ripening grapes, the quality of the wine was never good enough to sustain the vineyard longer than the enthusiasm of the man (and in all this history I can find no record of a female vigneron) who initially planted and supported it.

The revival, if that is what it is, had to wait for the arrival of some brave – again, some would call them foolhardy – pioneers who wanted to disprove the theory then abroad that wine could not be made from grapes grown outside in our climate. A combination of new varieties, more suitable growing techniques, better disease control and an acceptance by the public of the style of wines that those varieties produced, were the key elements in that revival.

2

The Revival, 1939–1951

RAY BROCK AND THE OXTED VITICULTURAL
RESEARCH STATION, EDWARD HYAMS AND
GEORGE ORDISH

To say that vinegrowing in the British Isles totally disappeared after the Marquis of Bute's enterprise in South Wales ended would be incorrect. Yes, it would appear that the growing of vines for commercial wine production ceased, but this did not stop there being a lively interest in the growing of grapes for both home-made wines and for the table. No doubt because of the state of the economy after the First World War and during the recession of the late 1920s and 1930s, many more people had vegetable gardens, allotments and smallholdings in which they raised a wide variety of fruit – vines included – than they do today. In addition, there was a very wide use of glass cloches to protect tender plants and two manufacturers – Horticultural Utilities Ltd of Liverpool and Chase Protected Cultivation Ltd of Shepperton – did much to promote the cultivation of vines under glass, both before and after the Second World War. There were also growers in several places – Worthing in West Sussex and in the Channel Islands – to name but two, who still grew dessert varieties such as Black Hamburg, Muscat of Alexandria and Gros Colmar under glass and who sent the fruit carefully packed in baskets up to Covent Garden for sale.

A small booklet called *Growing Grapes in the Open* by Roland Lee, published in 1939, throws some interesting light on the situation before the experimental vineyards at Oxted were planted by Ray Barrington Brock (of whom more later). In this booklet, Lee states that 'the urge to cultivate the grapevine was handed down by my forebears' and said that he came from a long line of vinegrowers, claiming that 'as long ago as 1249 an ancestor, one Robert Dacre, was Keeper of Vineyards by Letters Patent'. He also stated that 'the first vineyard owned by the Lee's was established by James Lee in about 1720 . . . at Hammersmith' although his business logo states 'First Established in 1770'! Barty-King (1977) throws some light on the Lee family and says that they co-owned the famous 'Vineyard Nursery' which was started in about 1745 on the site of what had been a vineyard (and which is today the site of Olympia) and which was operated by the Lees and their descendants until the 1890s. J. C. Loudon's *Encyclopaedia of Gardening* of 1834 says that there was a vineyard on the site, owned by Lee and Kennedy and that 'a considerable quantity of burgundy wine was made year by year'.

It is obvious from both the text and the photographs in Lee's booklet that he was serious when it came to growing vines out of doors. At Oxton (near Birkenhead) in Cheshire, he had a 2.5 acre vineyard (said on the back of the booklet to be 'the only Outdoor Vineyard Nursery in Great Britain') of 12,500 grafted vines of three to four years old of the varieties Alicante and Black Campanella (the latter being a black variety which he claimed as his own crossing), together with a vine nursery containing over 90,000 young grafted vines ready for lifting and sale. Apart from Alicante and Black Campanella, Lee recommended two other black varieties, Black Hamburg and Reine Olga; and three whites, Roland's Muscatel (another exclusive variety), Royal Muscadine (also known as Chasselas Doré) and Queen of Vineyards. On the inside back cover of the booklet Lee quotes many articles from newspapers and magazines (*Daily Mail, The Times, Daily Herald, Ideal Home, Popular Gardening* and several more) all of which take the same line: that they were surprised, but pleased, that someone was showing that table grapes (and nowhere in the booklet are wine varieties mentioned) could be successfully grown outside and ripened without glass of one form or another. Lee's booklet also contains a report of a radio broadcast (BBC National 2 pm Sunday 23 October 1938) by a Mr Middleton (C. H. Middleton – a popular radio broadcaster of the time) and a Mr F. Jordan on 'Outdoor Vines, Peaches and suitable Fruits for Walls'. The booklet said that the twenty-minute talk 'has done much to popularise outdoor Vines'. It is interesting to note that the *Listener* (a

BBC magazine which printed transcripts and reviews of radio programmes) made no mention of vines for winemaking.

What happened to Roland Lee and his vineyards remains something of a mystery. In 1939 his company appears to have been taken over by Cheshire Vineyards Ltd, who also claimed 'the only Outdoor Vineyard Nursery in Great Britain' (presumably the same one). It is known from a letter dated 1949, sent to Ray Barrington Brock by the well-known vine nursery owned by the Teleki family in Austria, that they sent 'important quantities of grafted vines to Liverpool' in 1939 and Cheshire Vineyards may well have been the destination. (Unfortunately, all Teleki's records were 'destroyed through bombing' so they could not be certain where the vines had actually been sent.)

After 1939, the trail more or less goes cold. Edward Hyams (another early pioneer whose story is told below) in the preface to his book *The Grape Vine in England* published in 1949 apologises for not including a reference to 'the Cheshire vineyard of hardy hybrids which was established successfully before the late war', but gives no further details. Brock mentions neither Lee nor his proprietary varieties, even though Lee's booklet was in his possession. Both Hyams and Brock mention Horticultural Utilities Ltd of Rigby Street, Liverpool, who in catalogues from 1951 claimed that at Formby they had 'The Principal Vine Nursery of England'. Since Birkenhead and Formby are but twelve miles apart (as the crow flies) one has to assume that by that time, Lee's vineyard had, if not totally disappeared, significantly diminished. Horticultural Utilities published two small pamphlets *Vines under glass and in the open* (*ca.* 1951) and *Successful growing of grape vines* (*ca.* 1954) both written by S. E. Lytle. In the 1951 booklet, virtually all the varieties offered are for table grape production, whereas by 1954, both *viniferas* and hybrids (including Seyve Villard 5/276) are offered, reflecting the early trials being carried out by Brock at Oxted.

Raymond Bush, a noted writer in the 1930s and 1940s on matters both agricultural and horticultural, has a few pages on 'Grapes out of doors' in his book *Fruit Growing Outdoors* – first published in 1935, with subsequent editions in 1942 and 1946. He states that 'Excellent wine has been made from English grapes in the past, and there is no reason why it should not be made today if we cared to grow the grapes.' His varietal selection, however, leaves much to be desired. The 1935 edition gives Black Hamburg and Royal Muscadine as the only two varieties worth considering. In the 1946 edition, Bush quotes James Wingfield (the grower who had obtained cuttings of the Castell Coch vines from H. M. Tod) who said that the best reds are 'Brandt, Gamay Frew [sic] and Black Hamburg' and the best whites 'Royal Muscadine and Muscatel'. With hindsight one can now say that the level of knowledge of what grape varieties might be grown to full ripeness and successfully turned into palatable wine, was pretty low. If English and Welsh viticulturalists were ever to succeed, they were, in the mid-1940s, badly in need of a Moses to lead them to the promised vineyard. In fact, three people appeared who, in their own individual ways, brought about the start of the revival which led to the planting, in 1951, of the first commercial vineyard of modern times at Hambledon in Hampshire. The three were Ray Barrington Brock, Edward Hyams and George Ordish.

Ray Barrington Brock

Ray Barrington Brock must be considered as one of the founding fathers – if not *the* founding father – of the revival in wine production in the British Isles. At the start of the Second World War he was in a reserved occupation, managing director of a firm of scientific instrument makers, and wished to move away from Croydon where he and his wife lived and which at the time was being heavily bombed. In 1941, he moved to a new house which he had built called 'Summerfield' at Rockfield Road, Oxted, Surrey, situated at an altitude of 400–450 ft on the South Downs, overlooking the Weald. With considerable enthusiasm and dedication, and aged only 34, he took to gardening and, as recorded in his meticulously kept garden notebooks, planned and set out a substantial garden, including a large area devoted to fruit trees of all types. In March 1943, on one wall of the house, he planted the first of what was to be many vines – a Brandt which came from Hilliers of Winchester. He noted when it arrived that it was 'very badly pruned'!

Among his fruit collection were several peach trees which, he recorded, even at that altitude ripened their fruit well. The received horticultural wisdom of the time was that peaches needed at least a south-facing wall, if not a proper peach house, to ripen them. Brock started to consider what other 'exotic' fruits he might grow and his thoughts turned to grapes. In the preface to his book, *Report No. 1 – Outdoor Grapes in Cool Climates* (1949) he writes that 'it is now difficult to remember just why we originally decided to start a Vineyard, although we are now very frequently asked this question. We think that primarily we were so interested to discover the ease with which Peaches could be ripened on bush trees out-of-doors, despite all the old gardening literature on the subject, that we felt equally sceptical about the comments on Grapes.'

Brock was an avid user of cloches to advance the maturity of a wide range of different fruits and vegetables and maybe one of the cloche manufacturers had also sparked his enthusiasm. As can be seen from the Roland Lee booklet, there seems to have been considerable press interest in the subject before (and possibly during) the war and perhaps Brock saw grapes as just the challenge he needed. Maybe he had also heard the radio talk between Middleton and Jordan? Whatever it was that really started him down this road, he was determined from the outset to undertake the task in a thoroughly professional manner. Brock had managed to obtain François de Castella's *Handbook on Viticulture for Victoria*, written in 1891 and published by the (Australian) Royal Commission on Vegetable Products, which contained some interesting observations on growing vines in cool regions. This book, which Brock considered to be 'a masterpiece of compression and lucidity' and gave 'an extremely clear résumé of methods in use in Europe', convinced him that close planting was the key to achieving full ripeness and did much to determine the layout of the vineyards at Oxted. In 1946 Brock was amazed to discover that de Castella was still very much alive and well and living in Ivanhoe-East near Melbourne aged 80. He was only 24 when he wrote the handbook. De Castella conducted a correspondence with Brock about the Research Station and recommended planting 'the Pinots, Riesling, Gamay and Chasselas' and planting them 'very close, so that each will be quite small'. The correspondence went on for a few years.

The Oxted vineyard, initially called the 'Beebrock Vineyard', was conceived with great care and a 'grand plan' was drawn up. There would be a number of trial plots with vines planted in accordance with their assumed ripening period (First Epoch, Second Epoch etc) and as many varieties as possible would be tried. The accent would be on table grape varieties, although some wine grape varieties were to be included. The standard spacing was 2 ft between the rows and 2 ft 6 in between the vines (impossibly close by today's standards) although some plots were laid out with twin rows 18 in apart with a 2 ft 6 in gangway between the pairs. The lower half of each vine, where the grapes could be expected to appear, would be protected with glass cloches although one plot was to be devoted to closely spaced table grapes without cloche protection. The rows would all run north–south and the borders would be planted with bush peaches and pyramid apples and pears.

The vineyard was located on two separate plots. A small part was in Brock's existing garden and this he prepared in July 1945. The larger part was established on an additional acre of land that adjoined his garden and which his accounts for 1944/5 show he purchased for £980. Brock noted in his garden diary that he 'Spent two whole days (four in all) clearing Vineyard site. Managed to burn everything and got up a lot of Brambles.' On 28 November 1945, Ernie Walker, a man he had taken on to help with the work (and who had been offered the job while still a serving soldier 'building Bailey bridges in Germany'), ploughed the land.

The scientist in Brock could not be suppressed, and a long, low wall was built to conduct an experiment into whether different wall surfaces would advance maturity. The wall was constructed in the following sections:

- plain brick, left dark red
- plain brick, whitewashed
- plain brick, blackened
- breeze block, whitewashed
- breeze block, blackened
- sheet metal, whitewashed
- sheet metal, blackened.

Two Black Hamburg vines were planted in each section (raised from cuttings from the Royal Horticultural Society). This experiment was unfortunately a failure. In his PhD thesis of 1951 Brock states that 'this grape [Black Hamburg] appears to be one of the most unsuccessful for outdoor cultivation of all those which have been tested . . . and it has completely ruined this experiment'.

The major task facing Brock in 1945 was that of locating and obtaining different grape varieties to plant. The effort and diligence – as well as time and money – which he put into this task was formidable. With the benefit of hindsight one can safely say that the real achievement of the 'Oxted Viticultural Research Station' (as he soon began to call it) was the assembling and trialling of some 600 different grape varieties over the 25 years of the station's life. Brock mounted what can only be described as a campaign to collect as many different grape varieties as he could. He already had a few vines on various walls around the house and garden and cuttings were taken (his garden notebook records that he bought a new pair of 'Rolcut' secateurs at a cost of 11/6d for the purpose). He was a member of the Royal Horticultural Society and was invited to serve on their Fruit Group Committee in 1946. Through their magazine he asked members to send hardwood cuttings to Wisley, which, when they had been assembled, were sent to Oxted. They were heeled in and, on 25 March 1946, the first were planted out. Brock, assisted by Walker and another gardener called Poynter, did all the work and Brock noted 'home for 1½ days to plant Vineyard. Weather perfect and up to 56°F in shade. Frost at night.' Initially, the varieties selected were all standard greenhouse table grape varieties: Black Hamburg, Muscat Hamburg, Ascot Citronelle, White Frontignon, together with another eight varieties, were set out in rows. He also obtained rooted cuttings from Mr Lytle of Horticultural Utilities. These were, however, but the beginning. By 1947, Brock had 1,400 vines of 29 varieties and by 1950 this had expanded to over 7,000 vines of 60 different varieties.

Brock knew that to find the most suitable varieties, he would have to search far and wide. He therefore set about writing to as many overseas sources as possible and, starting in 1946, he wrote to all the colleges, universities and viticultural research stations in the major winegrowing countries of Europe (including Hungary) as well as to Russia and various parts of the United States. He visited Switzerland in 1946 (and again in 1947) and made good contact with Mr Leyvraz at the Swiss Federal Vine Testing Station at Caudoz-sur-Pully. For several years they sent him (free of charge) cuttings of a large number of varieties from their collection including the two which would, in future years, become the backbone of the early English and Welsh wine industry: Müller-Thurgau (then called Riesling Sylvaner) and Seyve Villard 5/276 (Seyval blanc). Others included Chasselas doré 1921, Perle de Czaba, Pirovano 14 (Bellino × Madeleine Angevine), Seibel 13/053, all of which Brock trialled and thought highly of. Perle de Czaba and

Seibel 13/053 (now renamed 'Cascade') are still to be found in UK vineyards, albeit in tiny amounts. The relationship with Mr Leyraz at Pully continued until at least 1956 and the 'trade' in vines became a two-way affair with Brock offering interesting vines that he had obtained from Germany and Russia back to the Swiss. Leyraz did refuse the offer of Wrotham Pinot plants, saying that the 'Swiss did not like this variety'.

Import licences were obtained from the Ministry of Agriculture and Fisheries (MAFF) and in the spring of 1947, the first vines arrived and were inspected by 'Mr Rhodes' the local MAFF plant health inspector and pronounced 'healthy'. The Director of the French vine research station in Colmar, Alsace, offered 50 each of Riesling, Portugieser Blau, Chasselas Rosé and Madeleine Royale and these were gladly accepted. Contact with Herr Kessler, Director of the Swiss research station at Wädenswil in Thurgau (which in the 1890s had been where Dr Müller had carried out development work on his eponymous crossing) was made and both valuable advice and varieties were obtained. In 1947 he received a copy of a letter originally sent to East Malling Research Station by a Mr Ed Graville of Junction City, Oregon, who suggested that 'the genuine American grape' (by which he meant *vitis labrusca* varieties) ought to be grown in Great Britain. Graville wrote that they made 'grand juices, jams and jellies' which would 'add something to the average diet of the Britisher'. Brock wrote back saying that he already grew one – Brandt – and that the flavour was 'considered a little foxy, but not impossibly so for British palates'. A correspondence ensued and yet more varieties arrived.

In 1949 Brock received a letter (complete with a purple censor's stamp) from Andor Teleki, Director of the Österreichischen Rebschulen Teleki (renamed Pépinières Teleki SA in the 1950s) in Vienna. (The family were responsible for the rootstocks 5BB and 5C, had huge mother-vine nurseries in Austria, Hungary and Israel and were major suppliers of vines for both wine and table grapes). Teleki said that he had read articles in both the *Bulletin International du Vin* and the *Swiss Wine Journal* about the Oxted Viticultural Research Station and was intrigued to know more. He pointed out that his firm had supplied vines to nurseries 'in Liverpool and Kent' before the war and that he knew of a vineyard near Dartford in Kent which had been planted with his vines. Teleki made several suggestions for varieties that Brock ought to try and put him in touch with a good friend who was the Director of the Luxembourg Experimental Vineyard at Remich. Brock and Teleki corresponded for some while and Teleki suggested a visit to Austria in September 1951.

In 1950 Brock made contact with the *Selskabet Til Vinavlens Fremme I Norden* (translated on their headed notepaper as 'The society for the promotion of Vine-Grapes in Scandinavia') based at Hillerød in Denmark. This unlikely sounding organisation put him in touch with growers in Denmark, Sweden and Finland, who in turn passed on varieties obtained from Russia, Hungary and East Germany. He was in correspondence with a grower in Sweden – Nils Endlandsson – who sent him cuttings of a variety called 'Schmidtmann' that had been growing in Sweden since it was sent from Germany in 1860 and which he hoped would do well in English conditions. Endlandsson, who knew other growers in both Denmark and Finland (where it was reported – but not really believed – that a 'good Burgundy had been made from American varieties') also had contact with Hyams, and together the three of them seemed to have operated a vine-swopping service.

Requests for varieties were sent to the University of California, the University of Florida's Watermelon and Grape Investigations Laboratory, Cornell University's New York State Agricultural Experiment Station in Geneva (New York), Professor Duruz at the Oregon State College and the research station at Summerland in British Columbia. Although quarantine regulations made importations of vines difficult from some of these, a few varieties were obtained and eventually planted out at Oxted. Trade with some of these again was a two-way affair, with vines going back to Oregon and Florida in later years.

Surprising as it may seem from today's perspective, there was once a small, but vocal body of opinion in some parts of wine-growing Europe (especially the less climatically favoured parts) that supported the use of hybrids for both wine and table grape production. In France there was an organisation called the *Fédération Nationale d'Etudes de la Défense des Hybrides et Métis* (FENAVINO), founded in 1948 in Poitiers, to promote '*les cépage Français issus de l'hybridation & metissage*' (French grape varieties produced by hybridisation and cross breeding). The growers of non-*vinifera* varieties had a real fight on their hands and were up against the combined forces of the chemical and rootstock industries who did not want to see pest and disease resistant varieties grown, as well as those *vignerons* in the classic areas who saw their livelihoods under pressure from hybrid growers whose costs of production were lower than theirs. Brock subscribed to the magazine of FENAVINO, *La Viticulture Nouvelle*, which was described in an editorial as 'a medium of battle and friendship'! It contained all the latest information and advice for those wishing to grow and make wine without having to resort to grafted vines or to fungicides and pesticides.

Through this magazine Brock was put in contact with nursery-men such as Bertille and Joannès Seyve, Jean Tissier-Ravat, Seibel, Couderc and Landot, all of whom offered advice and vines. He corresponded with other vine-growing members of FENAVINO in the Pas-de-Calais and Finistère in France and in Belgium and Holland, searching for information, advice and varieties. The magazine's editor, Gerard Marot, later contributed a chapter on 'Hybrid Vines and the New Viticulture' in the book edited by Edward Hyams (*The Vineyards in England* 1953) which did so much to promote the revival of interest in viticulture in the UK.

Brock also had close contact with growers in other marginal parts of Europe including Belgium where he got to know Georges Mariman who had a small vineyard at Boitsfort outside Brussels. Here the best varieties were Oberlin 595, Maréchal Foch, Triomphe d'Alsace, Seibel 13/053 and Seyve-Villard 5/276 – all hardy hybrids. There appear to have been quite a number of small vineyards in the north-east of France, Belgium and Holland mostly planted just after the war, although a few were much older. Most of these growers seemed to be adherents of *La Viticulture Nouvelle* and mainly grew French-American hybrids, with a sprinkling of American crosses, although Riesling Sylvaner was starting to make its mark.

Belgium has a history of viticulture at least as old as Great Britain's and the earliest recorded vineyard – at Dinant – dates from 854 AD. The Prince-Bishops of Liège owned vineyards situated along the rivers Ourthe and Meuse, and at Huy, where they had their main summer residence, vineyards that were producing wine throughout the period 900–1200 AD. Belgium's viticultural history is in many respects similar to that of Great Britain with vineyards being mainly owned and supported by Royalty and the Church and records show that vines were grown and wines were made until the end of the 1900s; the vintages of 1836, 1875 and 1882 were noted for their quality and abundance. The varieties grown for wine production were the Gros and Petit Morillon noir (both clones of Pinot noir), Chasselas blanc and Chasselas-de-Bar-sur-Aube. With the advent of better communications, Belgium became a centre of hot-house grape production with large areas of Black Hamburg – or Hammelshoden as it was known locally – and Foster's White Seedling being grown for the table. The Comte de Flandres, brother of King Leopold II, was a major glasshouse owner (von Basserman-Jordan, 1955).

Mariman wrote several articles for the French magazine *Arbres et Fruits* and the Belgian magazine *Courier Horticole* on the subject of '*La viticulture septentrionale*' (cool-climate viticulture). Two articles in the French magazine of April and May 1948, which Brock obtained, gave the history of vinegrowing in Belgium and north-eastern France (around Lille) and discussed in some detail the varieties that were best suited for a cooler climate. Brock sent Mariman the first tentative results of his Oxted experiments and an article on these appeared in the *Courier Horticole* of May 1950 (it also mentioned Hyams who likewise corresponded with Mariman). In a letter to Brock dated November 1951, Mariman thanked Brock for sending him a copy of his PhD thesis and gave him copious information about the situation in the Belgian and Dutch vineyards, including the one at the Vilvorde Horticultural School near Brussels. He enclosed data covering the 51 varieties grown in the experimental vineyard at the School and gave him the names of 19 varieties that Brock was not growing at Oxted, saying that he must try them and that 'success is nearly certain' with these varieties! (Of the 19 recommended, only Maréchal Foch, Léon Millot and Triomphe remain in fairly minor use in the UK today). He also gave Brock the names of some useful contacts in France and Italy – nurserymen and vine breeders – and it is known that Brock obtained stock from them. Mariman seems to have been something of a guru for cool climate winegrowers and it would be interesting to know how much influence he had over Brock's (and Hyams') choice of varieties. Mariman invited Brock to see the vineyards of the Vilvorde Horticultural School, which had substantial variety trials, together with a number of other vineyards in the area. Whether Brock went or not is not recorded, although Brock was a seasoned traveller.

Some of the most interesting and fruitful contacts Brock made

were with the German vine-breeding stations at Geilweilerhof and
Alzey. Geilweilerhof, which was (and is still) at Siebeldingen near
Landau in the Pfalz, was established at the end of the war by staff
from the Kaiser Wilhelm Institut near Berlin. This research station
had been 'liberated' by the Russian Army in 1944/5 and many of the
varieties available immediately after the war had been developed
there. Geilweilerhof was at that time run by Professor Husfeld (who
remained there until 1970) and also employed Peter Morio, a well
known vine breeder, who developed Bacchus, Optima and Morio-
Muskat. Apart from breeding new *vinifera* crosses, the station also
concentrated on disease resistant hybrids using Seyve Villard
12/375 (Villard blanc) as a crossing partner and was therefore a
source of great interest to Brock. Geilweilerhof is today state – as
opposed to *Land* – owned and concentrates entirely on producing
disease-resistant clones and crosses. It is responsible for Orion,
Phoenix and Regent, all today in use in UK vineyards. In 1949,
Hyams had been in touch with Husfeld and in 1950 was sent
three new crosses: Madeleine Angevine × Gutedal No. 3 28/28,
Madeleine Angevine × Sylvaner F2 31/16/52 and Madeleine
Angevine × Sylvaner No. 3 28/51. Hyams had then sent two
cuttings of each to Brock to put in his collection at Oxted. In 1955,
Brock sent a report on these three varieties to Husfeld which set out
how each had fared and ended by saying that only the Madeleine
Angevine × Sylvaner No. 3 28/51 was really worth continuing with
and the other two crosses had been abandoned. Brock kept in
touch with Husfeld, sending him reports from time to time and so
fascinated was Husfeld by the apparent success of the Madeleine
Angevine × Sylvaner No. 3 28/51, and finding that his own
institute had abandoned it some years previously, that in 1961 he
asked Brock to send him back cuttings so he could evaluate them.
This Brock naturally agreed to do and six cuttings were sent the
next March. (Husfeld and Morio developed several Madeleine
Angevine × Sylvaner F2 crossings including Forta and Noblessa
which are still in the Geilweilerhof research vineyard). Brock also
made some suggestions about varieties he thought Husfeld should
be using as crossing partners (Gamay Hâtif des Vosges and Précoce
de Malingre) and suggested various combinations that he thought
might be interesting. Again, Husfeld asked Brock to send him the
special clonal selections of Gamay Hâtif des Vosges that he had at
Oxted, as the ones at Geilweilerhof did not show any real promise.

Brock's Alzey connection was even more fruitful. This research station in the Rheinland-Pfalz had its origins in the Hessiche Rebenzuchtstation which had been located at Pfeddersheim near Worms and whose Director was Georg Scheu. It was moved to Alzey before the 1939–45 war and there Scheu was responsible for developing, through clonal selection, many of the varieties he had raised at Pfedersheim, as well as breeding new varieties. The roll-call of his crossings is impressive: Scheurebe (1916), Huxelrebe, Kanzler and Septimer (all 1927), Faberrebe, Siegerrebe and Regner (all 1929), and Würzer (1932). He was also responsible for doing much of the clonal selection work on Müller-Thurgau after it had been released by the Swiss in the 1920s and was principally responsible for introducing it into the Rheinland-Pfalz where it became the dominant variety – very widely planted during the post-war reconstruction and replanting of vineyards in this region. He was very interested in breeding aromatic varieties and all of his show good fruit characters. He used Gewürztraminer in many of his crossings as well as table grape varieties such as Madeleine Angevine, Courtillier musqué, Chasselas and Luglienca bianca. He smoked a pipe and was always to be seen in his trial plots, pipe in one hand, grape in the other. It is said that he knew when he had a grape worth persevering with when he could detect the fruit flavour through the taste of the tobacco!

In 1957, Brock was sent hardwood cuttings from Alzey of three named varieties – Müller-Thurgau, Siegerrebe and Scheurebe – and two unnamed varieties known only by their breeding titles 'Sämling [seedling] 7672' and 'Sämling 23469'. These five varieties were rooted and set out in the vineyard. By 1960, Brock was able to report the following:

Müller-Thurgau: appears to be identical to Riesling Sylvaner received from the Swiss [it was] and giving excellent flavour and bouquet;

Siegerrebe: exceptionally early and the grapes have a strong bouquet;

Scheurebe: giving big crops, but appears to be very late ripening. Even in 1959 [which was a very hot year] it only ripened after the late varieties;

Seedling 7672 Giving large crops which ripen with Riesling Sylvaner. Considered to be a promising variety;

Seedling 23469: has not produced any flowers and cannot be recommended at all.

To start with, the parentage of the two seedlings was unknown, but a letter to Dr Zimmerman (who later became Director of the station) produced the information that Seedling 7672 was a freely pollinated seedling of Madeleine Angevine and that Seedling 23469 was Lübeck × Triomph. (Interestingly Siegerrebe, which at one time was credited with being a Madeleine Angevine × Gewürztraminer crossing, was unmasked by Heinz Scheu – Georg's son – as also being a freely pollinated Madeleine Angevine seedling.) The naming of Seedling 23469 never became an issue as it performed badly and Brock soon abandoned it. However, as Seedling 7672 was showing promise, Brock started calling it Madeleine Angevine 7672 for the sake of convenience. Unfortunately, as vineyards started to be planted with this variety and wine was made, the '7672' was left off labels and it soon became referred to simply as 'Madeleine Angevine'.

When the UK joined the Common Market in 1973 and the UK had to register varieties with the Commission, this was the name used. Why this was allowed is a mystery as Madeleine Angevine is a perfectly well-known table grape variety (a crossing of Précoce de Malingre and Madeleine Royale carried out in Angers in 1860) which only has female flowers and needs to be grown alongside a pollinator. Confusion was bound to arise. When vineyard owners started ordering 'Madeleine Angevine' vines directly from nurseries in France and Germany, that was exactly what they received – the table grape, rather than Seedling 7672. This led to growers being less than satisfied with what they thought was Brock's selection and in part gave rise to its reputation as being a poor flowering variety. Brock's 'Seedling 7672', of which a few vineyards survive today, is a variety that definitely shows promise and should be more widely planted.

As information about the work Brock was doing at Oxted spread, so did his circle of contacts. In June 1961, he heard from Professor Nelson Shaulis, Professor of Pomology (and inventor of the Geneva Double Curtain – GDC – training system) at Cornell University, Geneva, New York, who said that he would be coming to the UK in September and wished to visit Oxted. Shaulis paid a visit and in a letter sent in November that year, thanked Brock for his hospitality, saying that 'the noon meal was very delightful, especially the ginger beer shandy'! Shaulis also said that he was just concluding the harvest at Geneva and yields had been between three and nine tons per acre! What Brock must have made of Shaulis's views on trellising is not recorded, but it would be interesting to know. Brock's standard planting distances for wine grapes were by that time 3 ft between the rows and 4 ft between the vines – 3,620 per acre – with vines Guyot trained low to the ground. The standard GDC is based on 12 ft × 8 ft spacings – 454 vines per acre – and is a high-wire cordon system. Brock remained convinced throughout the life of the Oxted Station that close planting encouraged root competition and that vines close to the ground ripened their fruit better as they absorbed heat from the soil.

Brock also had correspondence with Pierre Galet, long-term Director of the Montpellier School of Viticulture and author of several massive works on vine varieties and the science of ampelography (vine identification). In a letter dated May 1961, Galet thanked Brock for his Report No. 3 and hoped that he would get in touch if he needed help, partly because he was always interested in other people's researches into vines, but also because 'je suis anglais par la famille de ma mère' (I am English on my mother's side) – what better reason?

Brock also had quite extensive contacts with a variety of Russian institutions and, as ever, vines were both received and sent. In 1961, Brock was sent some cuttings by a Mr G. G. Yearsley of Grantham who had received some new varieties from a friend at the Moscow Botanical Gardens. One of these was Saperavi Servenyi which was a crossing of Précoce de Malingre and a wild vitis Amurensis carried out in the 'Michurin Central Genetic Laboratory' in 1936. Yearsley thought highly of it, mainly because it was very early, which it would need to have been to ripen in Grantham! Brock, however, never thought much of it. It is interesting to note, however, that this was the variety used by Professor Helmut Becker at Geisenheim Research Station in Germany for crossing with St Laurent to produce Rondo (Gm 6494/5), one of the best red varieties grown in the UK today.

In 1965, Brock received a letter from a Mr Ibrahim Aitov, a 75-year-old scientist who worked at the Caucasian Research Station at Rostov-on-the-Don. He had been sent an extract from Brock's Report No. 4 which gave details of two Amurensis crosses which were on trial at Oxted and of which Brock thought quite highly. They had come to Oxted via Yearsley and were rather crudely known as 'Early Violet' (a Saperavi Servenyi × Muscat Hamburg) and 'Early Ripening' (of unknown parentage). Brock, not knowing anything about their parentage at the time he received them, had taken it upon himself to rename them and had called them 'Gagarin Blue' and 'Terseshkova' (in honour of the first astronauts). In a reply to Aitov he sent copies of Reports Nos 3 and 4 and asked for more details about the vines that he had and asked him to send some wine from these two varieties (which Aitov had offered to do). In due course the wine arrived and Brock, in reply, sent them 'two secateurs and eight pencils' (both probably being in short supply in Russia at the time and therefore highly prized). Aitov wrote that he had given one pair of secateurs and four pencils to his Director, Yakov Potapenko, who was 'very grateful' for the gift and asked Brock to send two more pairs of the 'Lion' brand secateurs 'one of them required by the Institute for their collection'. Aitov said that Potapenko had been to Moscow to try and get an export permit to send cuttings to the UK (and Canada) but without success as the registration of the varieties had not yet been completed. He added: 'if you should arrive in the USSR in the autumn you could take the cuttings yourself'! Whether Brock took up this offer is not known.

In 1965, Brock conducted a correspondence with a Professeur Henri Brécot who had recently retired after 40 years working with vines, 30 of them at the Centre for Viticultural Research at the School of Agriculture in La Mothe-Achard, a town near the coast between Nantes and La Rochelle. Brécot had been President of FENAVINO in the Vendée and had, in his time at the School, been a great proponent of disease-resistant hybrids. Brécot, who was now a brother at St Gabriel's College in Putney, had written an article for *La Viticulture Nouvelle* on grapegrowing in England and needed it proof-read by Brock. Brécot also arranged for cuttings of Seibel 11701, Joannès Seyve 24.651 and Castel 19.637 to be sent to Oxted from the School, as well as some wines from the Vendée region. Brock was very pleased that Brécot had made contact, took him out to lunch on several occasions and took delight in showing him the vines at Oxted.

A grower in New Zealand, E. D. Forester, who grew vines at Rotorua (centre of the North Island), visited Oxted in 1965 (Brock was unfortunately away at the time and Forester had to make do with Ernie Walker) and on returning home, write to Brock suggesting that the only vines that would thrive in our climate were American hybrids. Despite Brock's scepticism that these would be any good, Forester sent him cuttings of Iona, Gaillard Gerrard 157 and Pontac. As these never appeared in any of Brock's recommendations, one has to assume that they were not a success. He corresponded with Forester and exchanged winemaking tips. Brock was especially interested in learning how to retain a small amount of residual sugar in his wines without them re-fermenting: he obviously had not learnt the secret of sterile filtration and bottling.

As a result of this worldwide search for suitable varieties, the scope and nature of the Viticulture Research Station changed and expanded. Once the initial plantings of mainly table grape varieties started cropping and ripeness levels and cultural suitabilities were assessed, it soon became obvious that the size of the vineyards (and the cost of running them) would expand beyond all reason and as early as the winter of 1948, culling of less suitable varieties started. A common problem with many of the first vines which came via the RHS appeal was that they were in fact the same varieties, masquerading under different (and often incorrect) names, and Brock quickly had to become skilled in ampelography in order to distinguish the different varieties. He admitted that this task remained one of the hardest. He was also constantly being offered from overseas sources varieties 'sure to succeed', which ultimately, after years of trialling, proved worthless in our climate. As late as 1970, Brock laments in his vine price list 'twenty-seven new French hybrids recommended recently by some of the French Research Stations have all proved hopeless after five years of testing'.

Much of the early work concentrated on growing vines – mainly table grape varieties – under cloches. Chase Protected Cultivation Ltd of Shepperton, a company that specialised in glass cloches, did much to help and encourage the work and undoubtedly helped spread the news that vines could be grown in Great Britain. The company ran a club for its customers known as the Chase Guild and through its publication, *Chase News*, helped promote both viticulture and of course, the company's cloches. At the first of the Station's Open Days in 1948, 140 members of the Chase Guild arrived eager to learn more about the subject. Mr J. L. H. Chase, the company's owner, was personally very interested in the work at

Oxted and gave much helpful advice, as well as practical assistance in the shape of redesigned cloches, more suited to grape cultivation, which were supplied free of charge. The standard cloche used at Oxted was the Tomato Cloche made of three pieces of glass; two 24 in × 24 in pieces for the walls and a single 24 in × 12 in piece for the roof. Chase made a modification to the spring wire clip that held the glass together so that the abundant shoots and foliage of the vines could continue to grow upwards, outside the cloche, just leaving the fruit protected beneath.

Until 1954, the work at Oxted concentrated on table grapes. Although a few wine grape varieties had been planted in the first years, it was not until 1950 that it was decided that this might in the long term prove a more interesting and successful avenue to go down. There were a number of reasons why this change took place. The knowledge that table grapes could be successfully grown in an open vineyard, but under cloches, was perhaps not too surprising. The cultivation of table grapes in greenhouses – which is after all essentially what a cloche is – was a pursuit that the British had long excelled at. Indeed, it is surprising how many of the standard table grape varieties used both in greenhouses and outside throughout the world today have British origins.

Brock first picked grapes from the Brandt on the house wall in November 1946: 'gathered the vintage' he noted 'about 50 grapes!!!' The next year he was more successful. In October 1947 he exhibited 'five bunches of Brandt (small but good)' at the RHS Fruit Show on the 11 October 1947. The first harvest from the 1946 planted vines in the trial plots did not come until 1948 and owing to tremendous problems with diseases – powdery and downy mildew and *botrytis* – as well as birds and rabbits, yields were small and the grapes were either eaten, sold or given away. The situation in 1949 was different. More timely use of Bordeaux mixture to control downy mildew and sulphur dusting against powdery mildew, together with better bird control (using both netting and a new shotgun – a Webley and Scott .410 – bought from the Army and Navy Stores in December 1948 for £14) meant that on 9 October 1949 Brock picked about 100 lb of grapes. These were taken over to Hyams's cottage at Molash in Kent and together with others from Hyams's own vineyard, were crushed, pressed and eventually fermented, using a yeast culture – Johannisberg 43 – sent to Hyams by the Wädenswill Research Station in Switzerland.

(Hyams had offered his winemaking skills to Brock as he had already been making home-made wines for some years.) However, when Brock arrived with his grapes, the press was not ready and much of the juice was lost! When Brock tasted the Shottenden Rosé (as they called the wine) shortly after it had finished fermenting, he commented 'flavour very poor and yeasty'. After some of it had been bottled and kept for almost a year, it was tasted again and the comments were no more favourable: 'distinctly sedimented, yeasty and decidedly off flavour. Rejected as of no promise. Used both bottles for Fire Water.' It would appear that Hyams' prowess as a winemaker did not impress Brock very much!

Brock harvested the remainder of his 1949 grapes a week later and had a go at turning it into wine himself at Oxted. He seems to have all kinds of problems with the wine which was fermented on the skins as many of the grapes were red. He also used the same Johannisberg 43 yeast which was so active that the fermentation was finished before Brock thought it had even started. He tried heating it twice to get it to start, but merely destroyed what character it originally had. He wrote that he 'left the skins in contact with the wine for far too long'. The wine was over acidic and some calcium carbonate was added to reduce the acidity. This helped soften the wine, but it still tasted harsh and tannic (due Brock thought to the heating he had given it) and the end results were not spectacular. Some was bottled, but the remainder used for a trial into vinegar production (which appears to have been as unsuccessful as the winemaking) or for distillation.

In 1950, Brock seems to have got himself better organized for winemaking and the results were more promising. He also sent grapes over to Hyams and this year the wine was described as 'definitely a good normal light wine. One of the best with real character.' Brock's remarks, made in his fermentations book, are heavily underlined and one can almost sense the relief that at last something drinkable had come from his years of hard work – to say nothing of the expense. Brock seems to have had the services of a Mr Rivollier who acted as his winetaster and came by from time to time to pass judgement on various wines. Perhaps he had good reason, but some of his comments seem very harsh! Over the next three years, Brock seems to have had his fair share of problems in the winery. Much wine seems to have been destroyed because of oxidation or films of mould and fungus forming on top of the wines, or so terrible to taste, usually far too acidic, that distillation was the only course. In 1954 the new winery was under construction and no wine was made at all. By the 1955 harvest, the new winery was complete and Brock at last started to make some batches of trial wines that could be bottled and put away to see how they matured.

With a total lack of winemaking experience, it is perhaps not surprising that Brock's early efforts were less than perfect. Whether he was helped or hindered by Hyams's involvement – who can say – the wines produced by Hyams seem to have been no better than those Brock made himself. Hyams' section on winemaking in his 1949 book, *The Grape Vine in England* is fairly rudimentary and it is obvious from his instructions that winemaking was not his first discipline! In the 1953 book *Vineyards in England* which Hyams edited, the winemaking chapter was written by Dr Alfred Pollard of the Cider Department at Long Ashton Research Station – then part of Bristol University (where in 1965 a half acre of vines was established). This chapter gives far more technical (and accurate) information than in Hyams' own 1949 book and whilst today some of the instructions look very old-fashioned, no doubt at the time they were current industry practice. Bottling 'light' wines (as opposed to fortified wines) with residual sugar was obviously something that winemakers of the day had not fully mastered and the art of sterile bottling using very fine filters to remove yeasts (developed in about 1947 by the Seitz Filter company in Germany) had obviously not been heard of in the UK. This meant that wines that were bottled with residual sugar either had to be so heavily dosed with free sulphur as to render them objectionable or were subject to chance re-fermentation which inevitably led to spoilage or explosion (or both). One of the most useful tools in the English or Welsh winemaker's locker today is the ability to soften fresh, fruity wines which have what one might call a 'crisp' (i.e. high) acidity with a few grammes per litre of residual sugar. This can only really be achieved through sterile bottling. Brock also made bottle-fermented sparkling wines, a few bottles of which survived until the 1980s.

To improve his winemaking skills, Brock made contact with various institutions and organisations. Dr Pollard (Long Ashton) and his colleague Fred Beech, were keen to help and offered advice and yeast cultures. (Beech continued to help both Brock and others in the industry for many years and as late as 1980 was running seminars for English and Welsh winemakers.) Another organization that helped out with yeasts was the Brewing Industry Research Foundation who maintained the National Yeast Collection. He received yeasts from various other sources, including Beecham's Food and Drink Division Ltd. In the first few years he sent batches of grapes to the Moussec company which was part of the 'British Wine' industry (i.e. wine made from imported grape concentrates) and they made several trial batches. He also received yeasts from them with which he made starter cultures. There was no doubt that his enterprise created a lot of goodwill and people were intrigued to see how English and Welsh viticulture was developing.

Distillation was something that Brock was particularly keen on. It was a subject that fascinated him and, as Managing Director of Townson and Mercer, an important scientific instrument maker, he had access to simple laboratory distillation equipment. It was also a way of turning relatively small quantities of not very good quality (usually quite acidic) wine made from the wide variety of grapes grown, into something that might be of interest. On 25 October 1949 Brock wrote to the Customs and Excise in Croydon requesting permission to keep and use an experimental laboratory still. On 23 March he received a letter granting him an 'indulgence for experimental brandy distillation'. In September of the same year Customs and Excise wrote to him, asking when the experiments would begin and reminding him that he needed to take out a still licence at a cost of 10s for a full year or 7s 6d if taken out after 11 October. Brock wrote at once and sent a cheque for 10s requesting a licence for a full year. As ever, he took the subject seriously and made enquiries wherever he could about the best methods and techniques, including Professor Creuss at the University of California. Each year (apart from 1954 when no wine was produced because the new winery was under construction) distillation of what Brock called 'Fire Water' or 'Grappa' took place. The quantities were necessarily small and once he had refined his techniques, the quality was good. He sent samples of the 1952 distillations to his friends in Switzerland where they were adjudged to be 'equal to best Italian and superior to Swiss normal'. Brock's last distillations were in 1960, after which he appeared to lose interest in brandy production, although he kept a distillation licence and record book until 1973.

Throughout the 27 years of its existence, the only income that Brock derived from his activities with vines was through sales of books and vine cuttings and the occasional lecture and writing fee. No entry fees were charged for the annual 'Open Days'. In reality the income amounted to far less than the outgoings. The first sales were of books following the publication in 1949 of a small book he had written, *Report No. 1 – Outdoor Grapes in Cold Climates*. He had this privately printed and paid Tonbridge Printers £73.19.6 to print 2,000 copies with a cover price of 6s each – an income of some £600 if all were sold at the full price. Three subsequent publications followed (*Report No. 2 – More Outdoor Grapes* 1950, *Report No. 3 – Progress with Vines and Wines* 1961 and *Report No. 4 – Starting a Vineyard* 1964) all privately financed by Brock. These masterly booklets contained a mass of information to anyone contemplating planting a vineyard and are, in many respects, still relevant, although his varietal recommendations leave something to be desired. In his first book he gave a fairly unexciting list of varieties for open air (as opposed to cloched) wine production and suggested several varieties: Blue Portuguese, Chasselas 1921, Gamay Hâtif des Vosges, Golden Chasselas, Madeleine Royale and Meslier Précoce. These were early days in his researches. He adds that Riesling Sylvaner (Müller-Thurgau) had just been imported and 'may be possible over here' but needed another vintage to assess it. The next year – 1950 – when the second report was published, Madeleine Royale and Gamay Hâtif des Vosges took pride of place for wine grapes, with a suggestion that Seyve-Villard 5/276 and Seibel 13/053 might be suitable. He added though that 'there is far too much partisanship among the sponsors of these various varieties' to believe anything they told him and he was waiting until he had 'tried them under our own conditions' before recommending them. The propaganda war between the pro and anti hybrid forces was then raging in France.

Brock did contemplate writing a much longer book on the whole subject to be called *Vine Growing and Wine Making* and wrote a 50,000 word draft of the winemaking section. A synopsis of the book was sent to Edward Hyams in January 1961, asking for his advice on the best way to publish it. Hyams replied in February saying that he thought that a joint venture with a publisher such as Faber & Faber (who had published two of Hyams's viticulture books) or Collingridge, well known for publishing books on gardening and horticulture, would be best, with Brock, who reckoned he could sell 3,000 copies himself, putting up £1,000 to fund printing and publication. In the end, the venture came to nought.

The Oxted Open Days became something of an institution and they were the ideal opportunity for him to demonstrate what he was achieving, sell books, take orders for vines and engender enthusiasm for his cause. He encouraged people to bring samples of leaves and grapes for him to identify and very often found that varieties sold with one name, turned out to be something completely different. The first Open Day was on 23 October 1948, when about 150 people turned up, most of them members of the Chase Guild. The 1949 Open Day was held on 8 October when 200 people arrived and Brock and his wife entertained Chase Protected Cultivation Ltd staff to tea. Brock records that he 'sold some grapes and 29 books and the television cameras took pictures'. It would be fascinating to know where that camera footage is now! By 1950 the number of Open Days had expanded to three per season; one for RHS members (150 arrived including large parties from East Malling and Wye College), one for Chase Guild members and a third for general members of the public. 1951 saw four Open Days, but perhaps by then some of the novelty had worn off, as, on the first day, there were no visitors at all (it also rained hard all day), and the subsequent ones were poorly attended. Despite this setback, Brock continued to open the vineyard to the public on two to three days a year and although numbers never reached those achieved in the first three years, a regular thirty to forty people would turn up on each occasion and the Open Days continued until at least 1971, by which time most of the vines had been grubbed up.

Income from vine sales started in 1950 following the establishment of a nursery bed the previous year and continued throughout the life of the Station. Many of the varieties that Brock received from his contacts were unique and he was in reality the only source of varieties such as Madeleine × Angevine 7672, Madeleine Angevine × Sylvaner No. 3 28/51 and Seibel 13/053, all of which in the early years were much sought after. He only ever sold barewood cuttings for prospective vineyard owners to root themselves or one-year-old rooted cuttings for immediate planting. Many of the earliest vineyards to be planted (Beaulieu, Horam Manor, Elmham Park, Felsted and Yearlstone) obtained vines from

Oxted. However, as the new commercially orientated vineyards needed larger quantities than Brock could reasonably supply, and additionally most wanted them grafted on to *phylloxera* resistant rootstock, vines were imported directly from French and German nurseries. (Looking through the sales lists for the early years, the names of a few of Brock's customers give something of the flavour of the time: Lt Col. A. J. Odling-Smee, Lady Stubb, Hon. T. Brand, Dr G. Loxton – a very regular customer – and Col. Sir E. le Breton.) The first year that any income was earned was 1948/49 when £52 was gathered in; the next year a much more acceptable £416 was taken and in subsequent years (at least until 1960) an average of £300 a year was taken. In current terms, this is equivalent to around £10,500 a year in income.

The costs, however, of establishing and running the Research Station were considerable. Apart from the purchase of the extra land Brock erected a 'store' as it is called in his accounts (at a cost of £95.10.0), which was subsequently 'scrapped' and replaced in September 1954 with a purpose-built winery containing a small laboratory, a room for his still, and a refrigerated underground cellar. This cost a total of £770 – around £28,000 at current prices. Apart from land and buildings, the Station required a considerable amount of plant and equipment to operate it. Tractors, rotovators, mowers and a myriad of hand tools had to be bought for the growing side of the business and the winery – although not lavishly equipped since it was never the intention to produce wine for sale – had the usual small crusher, press and fermentation equipment. Throughout the life of the enterprise, Brock continued to support it from his other income (he remained in full-time employment throughout the life of the Station). He established it as a separate venture which had its own accounts and initially was able to offset losses against his other income. In 1960 a struggle started with the Inspector of Taxes who, realizing that it would never make a profit, decided to end this arrangement, although allowing him to offset depreciation on plant and equipment already bought until such time as it was down to a nil balance. Brock battled against this decision but, as is the way of these things, eventually lost. It was at that stage that the separate accounting ended and although a 'Research Station' bank account was maintained, no detailed account books were kept after this time. In *Report No. 3* (1961) Brock wrote that until he lost his battle with the Inland Revenue, 'the total loss on the vineyard was the sort of amount which . . . could reasonably be spent on my hobby'.

Brock employed Ernie Walker on a full-time basis, paying him £3.10.0 a week to start with (in 1946) plus a bonus of a week's pay at Christmas. Walker's pay rose to £8.5.0 in 1960. He also employed additional help when and as required. The accounts books also show that Brock paid himself a weekly wage out of the enterprise, amounting to half Walker's earnings and in addition, charged considerable travelling expenses (undoubtedly fact and vine-finding trips to France and Switzerland were included) as well as entertaining expenses, quite a large annual sum for 'sample wines', various gardening publications and memberships to clubs and societies. At one stage the Inspector wished to know whether the purchase of a Bond Minicar (for £368.15.10) was necessary for the running of the Research Station and Brock convinced him that it was, estimating that he did 7000 miles a year in it on behalf of the business! The accounts would also suggest that some of Brock's other living expenses were probably met out of the Research Station, so perhaps after 15 years of continuous losses and mounting expenses, the Inspector's view that Brock had had a good run for his money was understandable.

In the early years, Brock had looked for support from various organisations. On 27 September 1951, he wrote to Sir William Slater at the Agricultural Research Council asking for financial assistance. They replied on the 5 December saying that 'until such time as there is evidence of the economic possibilities of the grape crop' they could not support him. They also added that 'With France prepared to sell us more wine than we can buy, it is clear that the market would be highly competitive, and this country must start with an ecological handicap in raising the crop.' Ray found this response something of an affront to his five or six years of work and said that unless the work was carried out, it would never be possible to prove one way or the other whether growing grapes was viable or not. Brock felt it was very much a 'heads you lose, tails I win' situation. In February 1952, he applied to The Royal Society for a grant, but D. C. Martin, the Assistant Secretary, wrote saying that Sir Edward Salisbury, a Fellow of the society, had commented that 'the work is essentially of an applied nature and I doubt if the demonstration that vines can be grown successfully in England is of great practical importance' and he was again turned down.

In 1951 he completed and submitted to his old university – London – a thesis entitled 'Some Aspects of Viticulture in Southern England'. This thesis, which is over 100 pages long and crammed with very detailed scientific data about his experiments up to and including 1950, is unique and alone could serve as the *raison d'etre* for the establishment and operation of the Research Station. In the back is a long list of acknowledgments to various people who had helped him (Messrs Chase, Leyvraz, Hyams, Kessler, Duruz) the last one being to 'Mr E. G. Walker, the vinearon [sic] concerned with all the real work. His willingness to try anything and report on it carefully has been invaluable, apart from the very real hard work required to cope with the day to day work'. Sadly, it would appear that his thesis never gained him the Doctorate of Philosophy that he hoped it might, but he was awarded the 'Jones-Bateman Cup' – awarded triennially for original research into fruit culture – by the Royal Horticultural Society and this magnificent silver award was presented to him at the RHS Annual General Meeting on 22 February 1954.

Once it became known that England had its own living vine expert, Brock was called upon to write articles by a wide number of publishers. Apart from *Pomona Britannica*, Brock wrote the entry on 'Vine-Growing Outdoors in England' in the *RHS Dictionary* in 1951, the entry on vines in the *Oxford Junior Encyclopaedia* in 1961, articles for the *RHS Journal*, *The Smallholder*, *Gardening Illustrated*, *The Grower*, *Country Life* and *The Field*. He also made several radio broadcasts.

Brock also liked to involve the wine trade in what he was doing and used to lecture on viticulture to those preparing for their Diploma and Master of Wine exams. In August 1960 he put on the Station's first official trade wine tasting and invited a number of tasters including 16 Masters of Wine. Guests included Harry Waugh, Sir Guy Fison, Michael Druitt, John Patrick, Denis Williams, John Vaughan-Hughes, Dr A. Pollard, Colin Fenton and a Mr Morgan-Grenville They were presented with 17 different wines – all served blind – and asked for their comments. Like the curate's egg, the general response seems to have been that they were good in parts. Some they appeared genuinely to like; two samples of Riesling Sylvaner (Müller-Thurgau) and one of Seyval blanc came top, with a Précoce de Malingre and a Madeleine Angevine × Sylvaner No. 3 28/51 in second place. Brock reported that the last wine had been a bit lacking in natural acidity and had been blended with one of the higher acid varieties – of which he had an ample supply. Denis Williams of Sichel's even wrote asking whether he could buy a bottle of the Riesling Sylvaner to show to his boss, Walter Sichel, who eventually planted a small vineyard in Hertfordshire, from which came a bottle of wine that I was offered when I went for a job interview at Sichel's Mainz headquarters in 1975!

The worst of the bunch at the 1960 tasting were a Tissier-Ravat 578, a Baco No. 1 (which gave 'a very hard red wine with most excessive acidity') and a Brandt. This last variety, which had been introduced into the country by Tod in the early 1900s and featured on almost everybody's lists as one of *the* varieties for our climate, was summed up by Brock thus: 'Brandt usually gives drinkable but uninteresting wine . . . which we normally class as drinkable but poor. In 1959 it was barely drinkable'. These last three poor performers were soon taken off his 'recommended' list. Sparkling wines were also on offer at this Master of Wine tasting and three varieties – Riesling Sylvaner (Müller-Thurgau), Seyval blanc and Chasselas – showed promise. Brock told the assembled company that he had now demonstrated over a five-year period that vines would crop at a rate of '500 gallons per acre' (equivalent to around 3½ tonnes/acre or 55 hl/ha) which would be an acceptable commercial yield today. The guests all wrote effusive thank you letters, commenting on the excellence of the lunch that Mrs Brock had prepared, with slightly more guarded comments about the wines they had tasted. Brock did not mind this trade criticism, saying that it was the purpose of the Station to test varieties and it was just as important to eliminate poor performers, as it was to find good ones.

One of the major cultivation problems that Brock had to contend with was disease. *Oidium tuckerii* or powdery mildew was well known as a major problem on both indoor and outdoor vines and was one of the factors that resulted in poor yields at the Castell Coch vineyards. He first noticed the disease on his vines in June 1947 and set about using the standard remedy, dusting sulphur. This appeared to work well, although it took considerable time to dust the cloched vines, which were the majority in the early years. Brock soon discovered that once signs of powdery mildew appear, it is almost too late to start dusting and the treatment must start well before the mildew shows itself on the vines. This is as true today as it was then and although growers in the UK now use wettable or liquid sulphur which can be sprayed on, the key element in control is timing. Powdery mildew continued to be a problem throughout the life of the vineyard and susceptibility to it was one of the major reasons why a vine might be written off as unsuitable for growing in our climate. It was also certainly one of the reasons why resistant hybrid varieties such as Seyval blanc, Seibel 13/053 and Léon Millot became popular with Brock and therefore with growers in general.

Downy mildew was something that had not been seen much in Great Britain as vines grown indoors, in dry conditions, seldom suffer from it. However, outdoor vines are a different matter and it soon took up residence in the Oxted vineyards. At first, Brock was unsure whether it was downy mildew and had to call in an official, Joan Moore, from MAFF's Plant Pathology Department at Harpenden. She paid Brock a visit in November 1948 and confirmed that the outbreak was downy mildew, saying that it was 'the ninth in the country, the last one was from Yalding in Kent in 1947' (probably on George Ordish's vines). Whilst she was there, Moore also had a look at some aphids found on the vines (Brock was very concerned about *phylloxera* but was relieved to find that they were just common aphids). Brock resorted to Bordeaux mixture which, before the invention of modern fungicides, was the usual treatment for downy mildew. As ever, the scientist in Brock took over and he was forever inventing new combinations of copper sulphate and slaked lime – the major ingredients of Bordeaux mixture – to get them to work more effectively. He consulted ICI's Jealott's Hill Research Station on the matter and they suggested using copper oxychloride which was then starting to replace Bordeaux mixture on potatoes for the control of blight (a similar disease).

Botrytis on the other hand, was another matter and before the discovery of Benlate and the even newer fungicides, there was no real chemical control of it. Good hygiene, plenty of light and air and loose bunches are the greatest aid to avoiding the destructive rotting that occurs, but with the grapes under cloches, outdoors and in close proximity to the soil, Brock had his work cut out to keep a healthy crop. Time after time in his vineyard diaries and notebooks he reported tremendous losses from *botrytis* and was often forced to pick early in order to save the crop. Today's winegrowers can have no idea what life must have been like before modern fungicides made the control of this disease relatively painless. Lack of a decent anti-*botrytis* chemical must surely rank as one of the major reasons why viticulture before the mid-1960s was such a risky and unrewarding venture.

Phylloxera was an ever-present threat that Brock did his best to counter and it never surfaced at Oxted, despite the importation of thousands of rooted vines, both grafted and un-grafted, as well as barewood cuttings. An outbreak would probably have closed the Research Station as MAFF would have had no option but to demand the destruction of all non-grafted vines, which was most of them. *Phylloxera* was not unknown in Great Britain and there had been 17 distinct outbreaks in the British Isles (one was in Wicklow in 1867) since the original first sighting in a Hammersmith greenhouse in 1863. Brock established a selection of rootstock varieties (bought from Lepage et Cie, Angers in 1950) 'so that grafting can commence if *phylloxera* is found'.

The first sighting of *phylloxera* in a modern vineyard was at Major-General Sir Guy Salisbury-Jones' at Hambledon in 1955 (four years after it was planted). Brock heard about this from an indiscrete MAFF official – the location of outbreaks was meant to be confidential – who had been called in to Hambledon to deal with the outbreak. It was then, as now, a notifiable pest that must be reported. Brock had heard that *phylloxera* had surfaced in vines imported by a commercial nursery and he wrote to the Horticultural Trades Association asking them to remind their members of the dangers. They responded that as long as the vines were accompanied by a phytosanitary certificate from the relevant authorities, MAFF officials had no option but to let the plants into the country. Brock replied by saying that as all vines on the Continent were on resistant grafted stock, the presence of *phylloxera* eggs on rooted vines was very common and a phytosanitary certificate certainly did not mean that they were free of eggs. Brock was fairly incensed about Sir Guy Salisbury-Jones' attitude to the *phylloxera* outbreak in his vineyard, saying that he was adopting an 'I'm all right Jack' attitude to the problem as all the Hambledon vines were on resistant grafted stock and therefore, in theory, not in danger. Mr Rhodes, the local MAFF plant health inspector, continued to inspect the Oxted vineyard from time to time to check that no *phylloxera* had been imported.

It almost seems impossible to believe that Brock had any other interests during the hey-day of the Research Station, so all consuming does it seem to have been. However, nothing could be further from the truth. He was Managing Director of Townson and Mercer – a well known firm of scientific instrument makers and suppliers founded in 1798, with offices in Croydon and factories in Croydon, Ponders End and Slough – from 1938 until the end of 1960. The firm made and sold scientific instruments and equipment, reagents and chemicals, and equipped laboratories. In 1957 Brock became President of the Scientific Instrument Makers Association and was Master of the Worshipful Company of Scientific Instrument Makers in 1969/70. After he left his old company, he took up a number of other pursuits, owning a colour printing works and a Renault dealership and an interest in a computer dealership at a time when computers were still in their infancy.

He became a director of Chase Organics Ltd and was involved with marketing a seaweed concentrate (SM3) that had been developed for them, as well as a new selective insecticide based on Polybutylene which used the seaweed concentrate as a base and stuck the insects to the plant. He also promoted 'Scaraweb', a rayon filament material that could be spread over fruit tress and bushes to keep birds off – bullfinches especially – which do much damage to the buds of apple and pear trees in the winter and which he had heard about from Switzerland where it was invented. He held demonstration trials at Oxted to which he invited officials from various MAFF Experimental Husbandry Stations and even at one stage tried to sell it to the Russian vine testing station with which he was in touch.

Brock also had some serious hobbies. In 1948 he drove an HRG sports car, with a streamlined body designed and built by himself, to Spa in Belgium and raced it in the 24-hour race, coming third in class and then drove the car back to Oxted after the race. (On 7 July he noted in his garden diary 'all spare time spent preparing for motor race'). In 1949, he repeated the exercise and came second. He also raced at Goodwood, holding the up-to 2 litre class in 1948, took part in Swiss hill climbs, firstly in a Healey, with a body largely built by himself and then a works Jowett Javelin. Success with the Javelin prompted him to design and build a complete rear-engined coupé, capable of 100 mph and 50 mpg, using a Javelin engine. He also commented on races at Brooklands, Crystal Palace and

Donnington. During the war, he had been a Chief Air Raid Warden for the City of London, a job for which he was awarded the MBE and made a Freeman of the City. At the age of 50 he tried the Cresta run and for a short time was brakeman in the British bobsleigh team, giving up after a nasty crash in which he broke several ribs. He was also interested in yachting and boating, designing and building a steam launch, the *Silencia*. In the last decade of his life he helped recommission the Cannstadt Daimler for the National Motor Museum at Beaulieu, restored several other classic cars, and at his death had almost completed building a small steam cycle car.

Ray Brock's work on vines must be seen as really quite remarkable. That he should decide to establish a private research station to study a crop that did not have a natural home in our climate is quite a feat in itself; that he should do so with such effort, energy and diligence for little or no personal gain, apart from the satisfaction of seeing it done properly, is another matter. In retrospect the site he chose might have been better if nearer to sea level and less exposed, which would have resulted in riper grapes and better wine. He always countered this by saying that he felt comfortable in recommending a variety that had performed well at Oxted, knowing that it would therefore ripen in almost any site in the south of the country. The legacy of the Oxted Viticultural Research Station is to be seen in today's English and Welsh wine industry. Whilst minute by the standards of other (more climatologically blessed) countries, it owes its existence in great part to his work. He lived to see an industry producing an average of two and a half million bottles of wine a year and an industry that was slowly gaining recognition. He died on 14 February 1999, aged 91.

Edward Hyams

Edward Hyams, who first appears in the Oxted story at the harvest in 1949, shares with Brock the honour of being one of the fathers of the viticultural revival. Although his winegrowing and wine-making activities were never on the same scale as Brock's, through his writing and speaking he did much to publicise the subject and make the public aware that the revival was under way. Hyams was a prolific author, journalist and broadcaster whose interest in vines and specifically in vine-growing in Great Britain, was stimulated by reading a book which mentioned the historical evidence of British vineyards. Although born a Cockney, he had been partially educated in France, spoke French fluently and claimed to have studied viticulture there, although to what extent was never made clear. In any event, he felt a natural affinity to the subject.

In 1938 Hyams and his wife had bought a small house – Nut Tree Cottage – and three acres of rough garden in Molash, a village between Faversham and Ashford in the eastern part of Kent. At the beginning of the war, as Hyams was away in the forces and his wife was in the Land Army on a farm elsewhere, the cottage lay empty. At first, it was commandeered for evacuees, but later let to a local farmer who was a less than perfect tenant. By the end of the war, the cottage lay empty and almost derelict. It had been broken into and the contents stolen or vandalised.

In March 1946, Hyams was demobbed from the Royal Navy and he and his wife returned to Kent. Hyams, then 36, and his wife decided that 'the values by which they had lived before the war were morally, intellectually and spiritually unprofitable' and 'they therefore decided to dispense with any more income than could be earned by work that was congenial, therefore liberating'. In this spirit of self-sufficiency, they started to clear the land and establish a vegetable and fruit garden which contained, amongst other things, their own small tobacco plantation! Before the war, Hyams and his wife had talked about planting some vines and as soon as this became a practical possibility, he set about contacting likely sources for suitable varieties.

From the outset, the intention was to plant both table grapes as well as varieties to turn into wine and Hyams estimated that he needed 'a litre per head per day' to keep him and his wife happy. He made contact with some of the same institutions and nurseries that Brock was in touch with and ended up with some of the same varieties. For the table he had Pirovano No. 7 (Primus), Muscat de St Vallier, Landot's Oeillade de Conzieu and Muscadoule (all fairly obscure first epoch varieties); for wine production he obtained Seyve-Villard 5/276 (Seyval blanc) directly from the Seyve-Villard nurseries in St Vallier on the Rhône as well as Baco No. 1, Tissier-Ravat 578 (Téré Doré), Seibel 5279, Gamay Hâtif des Vosges and Riesling. These were planted in 1947 and 1948. Hyams made contact with Brock in 1948 and visited the Research Station on 5 September of that year. After his visit he wrote to Brock asking for various varieties, including Riesling Sylvaner (Müller-Thurgau) which had been sent to Oxted in 1947 from Switzerland. Brock replied saying that 'there is not likely to be any big demand for this variety yet' and offered him 'plenty of cuttings' as a present. These were sent the next year.

In 1950, Hyams received cuttings of three new varieties from Professor Dr B. Husfeld who ran the Geilweilerhof research institute at Siebeldingen bei Landau-Pfalz in Germany. These were Madeleine Angevine × Gutedal No. 3 28/28, Madeleine Angevine × Sylvaner F2 31/16/52 and Madeleine Angevine × Sylvaner No. 3 28/51. Two cuttings of each of these were passed on to Brock who put them into his collection. Although the first two of these proved less than satisfactory and were abandoned in 1958/59, the Madeleine Angevine × Sylvaner No. 3 28/51 proved to be very effective and at one stage Brock rated it as one of his best. Brock shortened the name to Madeleine Sylvaner 28/51 and it is still on the list of Authorised varieties for the UK as Madeleine Sylvaner. Like Brock, Hyams was in contact with Georges Mariman who provided valuable advice and contact addresses. Hyams also corresponded with the grower in Sweden – Nils Endlandsson – who was in touch with Brock. They also swapped varieties and through Endlandsson, Hyams obtained information about growers in Denmark, Finland and Russia and he was able to make contact with them.

Hyams also went searching for old varieties already growing in Britain and through an appeal in one of his many articles, discovered a vine growing on a cottage wall at Wrotham in Kent. In appearance it resembled Pinot Meunier and was therefore named Wrotham Pinot. Cuttings were taken and propagated at Oxted. When compared with supplies of Pinot Meunier from France, Brock recorded that Wrotham Pinot had a higher natural sugar content and ripened two weeks earlier. Despite the fact that today all plantings of Pinot Meunier stem from French nurseries, the name Wrotham Pinot is still the official name for this variety in the lists of allowable varieties. It is doubtful whether any cuttings from Hyams or Oxted of this variety still survive in British vineyards. Hyams kept in close contact with Brock and offered his advice and suggestions (whether asked for or not!) and was always coming up with new varieties to try and new treatments for vines to counter disease. In an undated letter to Brock, Hyams says that he has been in touch with Vidal and Laffont (two well known French nurserymen) and has received a recipe for a better way of producing Bordeaux mixture to control downy mildew. It involves steeping '125 grammes of copper tacks in one litre of concentrated nitric acid and one litre of water' and keeping the resulting 'nitrate bouillie in quart beer bottles with screw tops'. This can then be diluted and sprayed on the vines as required. Hyams says that he intends to try this for two seasons and report the experiments in the RHS *Journal* and the *Gardener's Chronicle*.

Hyams and his wife left Kent in 1960 and moved to Ashburton in Devon, taking with him 1500 unrooted cuttings which he proceeded to root in the kitchen garden. The next year he planted another small vineyard, the history of which is recorded in *An Englishman's Garden* published in 1967. Despite Hyams' experience with vines, the vineyard was not a success and after only a few years he reduced it in size and really only kept a few hardy hybrids for old times' sake and for decoration. He blamed the much wetter growing conditions of Devon (compared with East Kent) which led to too much lush growth, disease and poor fruit set.

Hyams greatest contribution to the advancement of viticulture was undoubtedly the massive amount of publicity he created through his writing and broadcasting. C. J. Greenwood at his publishers, The Bodley Head, suggested quite early on that he write a book on vineyards and in 1949 *The Grape Vine in England*, with a foreword by Vita Sackville-West, was published. This book marked a milestone in the early years of the revival. It was, and remains to this day, a scholarly work on the subject and contains chapters on the history of the grapevine in England, the work of Brock at Oxted and the cultivation of the vine and winemaking. Given that viticulture was at a very undeveloped stage at the time, it shows that Hyams had a genuine interest and regard for the subject. His recommendations to plant Riesling, Seyve Villard 5/276 and Seibel 5/279 for white wine and Gamay Hâtif des Vosges and Baco No. 1 for red, whilst strange from today's perspective, then definitely 'showed promise'.

In 1947 Hyams had read a book by Richard Church on Kent and noted what Church had to say about the possibility of a revival of viticulture in the county. In August 1949, Hyams wrote to Church to let him know what he was up to at Molash and that a book on the subject was about to be published. Church then mentioned both Hyams's vineyard and the book in his weekly article for *The*

Spectator on 2 September 1949. This alerted first the local and then the national press to Hyams' experiments. The flurry of press interest resulted in requests from general members of the public for information, advice and even cuttings, and Hyams realised that there was a wider audience to be reached on the revival of winegrowing. Church then suggested to *Country Life* that they commission Hyams to write an article, which he did, further to fan the flames of interest.

On 3 August 1950, Hyams gave a talk on the Third Programme on 'Vineyards in England' which engendered yet another round of publicity. The *Daily Mirror* of 17 August 1950 had an article entitled 'A bottle of Maidstone '49' which praised the work of both Brock and Hyams. The article ended by saying 'Perhaps ten years hence you'll be raising a glass of sparkling Canterbury in honour of the men who made an English wine industry possible'. In retrospect, these can be seen as quite prophetic words. Hyams had also been very generous in recognising the part played by Brock in the whole story and had ended his radio talk with a dedication, saying: 'If it were the practice to dedicate radio talks, I should have dedicated this one to Brock, because any man who spends so much of his leisure time, his energy and money, not to speak of intelligence, on reintroducing a fruit plant, and that plant the source of wine, deserves all the honour one can give him.'

Hyams' interest in vines and wine stayed with him throughout his life. In 1952 he wrote *Grapes Under Cloches* which drew heavily (Brock said 'rather too heavily!') on Brock's two published works – *Outdoor Grapes in Cool Climates* (1949) and *More Outdoor Grapes* (1950). Hyams dedicated his book to Brock, thanking him for his 'extraordinary generosity' in making his research available and calling him a 'notable vinearoon' – a term Hyams liked to use to mean *viticulteur* or *vigneron*. (He discovered the word in a letter written by Lord Delaware in 1616 from New York to his company in London discussing the possibility of viticulture in America.) In 1953 Hyams edited *Vineyards in England* – a masterly work which consisted of 20 chapters, many written by different specialists (although Hyams himself wrote six of them and Brock, two) covering every conceivable aspect of grape production in the British Isles. It included chapters on the history of viticulture, several on varieties, including one on new French hybrids, soils and manures, climates, cloche and greenhouse cultivation, pests and diseases and winemaking. The book stands today as one of the most important for anyone contemplating growing vines in England or Wales and despite being over 45 years old, much of it, apart from the choice of varieties, remains relevant.

Hyams was also, together with Allan Jackson of Wye College, editor of Longman's *Pomona Britannica* and in 1956 he asked Brock to write the chapter on vines. In 1959 he wrote *Vin – the Wine Country of France* which was, at the time, when books on wine are not as plentiful as they are today, considered a major work on the subject. Perhaps not surprisingly (in a book on classic French wines) he makes no mention of his experiences of growing and making wine, although he does touch upon the then thorny question of hybrids. *La Viticulture Nouvelle* was being attacked from all sides and coming under pressure from the joint forces of the chemical industry, the vine-grafting fraternity and the established *appellations* who feared that these high-cropping varieties that could be grown without fungicides would threaten their markets.

Hyams' last book on a purely vine or wine related subject was *Dionysus – A Social History of the Wine Vine* published in 1965 which charted the history of the grape vine as a plant used by man from as early as 8000 BC up to the present day. Naturally, English and Welsh viticulture features, but only really in passing. Indeed by then, Hyams appears to have become less convinced that it was a viable venture and said that although there were a few vineyards in the UK, they were not really economic. He wrote: 'only by selling their wine at a price which has nothing to do with ordinary economic laws can they be made financially viable'.

Hyams was an extremely prolific writer and kept up a tremendous output of both fiction and non-fiction: books, articles in journals, magazines and newspapers. He wrote a weekly column in *The Illustrated London News* – in its day one of the most widely read magazines, especially by those interested in gardening and the countryside. In 1975, two years before he died, he wrote a well researched article about the viability of viticulture in Great Britain, at the end of which he wrote that 'the undertaking should be profitable if you can produce 2,000 bottles of wine per acre and very profitable at 3,000 bottles' and that 'there is no doubt that English vineyards in the right places can produce fine white wines, and that such wine should be the object of English viticulture'. By then of course the revival – for which he was in no small part responsible for instigating – was well under way.

George Ordish

George Ordish had two careers. He was by training an entomologist and economist who spent most of his life working for organisations such as the United Nations and the British and Commonwealth Office. He worked on horticultural problems in Europe, Latin America and Africa and took a keen interest in the 'great' pests and diseases – those that caused the greatest damage both environmentally and economically. He was also a writer, one who specialized in writing about pests and diseases.

One of his first jobs was as an entomologist working in the Champagne region. On returning to his native Kent he was struck by the similarity in the climates and by the differences in the landscape – where the Champenoise had vineyards and vines, Kent had none. Why was this? He did some local research and discovered that England had a history of viticulture, but for a number of reasons, vines had ceased to be an economic crop. He therefore resolved to see whether he could get grapes to flourish and ripen and, in 1938, planted a few vines in his garden and on the walls of his cottage at Yalding on the Medway, near Maidstone.

The varieties he planted were those that were then considered to be the best for outdoor cultivation for wine production. The reds were Gamay Hatif des Vosges, Baco No. 1 and Brandt; the whites, Madeleine Royale and Meslier Précoce. He also discovered a vine growing on the wall of an old house nearby and cuttings were taken. The first harvest from these vines, a small one, was in 1940. At that time, Ordish worked for an ICI subsidiary, Plant Protection Ltd, which had a nearby factory making, amongst other products, a rat poison that contained a substance extracted from a product called Italian Squill. In the factory was an old wooden screw press which had previously been used in the extraction process, but now lay idle and unused. He therefore took it home, renovated it and put it into service for his first harvest.

Ordish was always a small-scale winemaker and none was ever made for sale. However, he was by all accounts an accomplished winemaker and he soon saw that good wines could be made from English grown, outdoor fruit. His trial vineyard had proved that grapes would ripen in our climate and these trials prompted his first book on the subject, *Wine Growing in England*, published by Rupert Hart-Davis, which appeared in 1953. (It appeared as No. 3 in their *The Countryman's Library* series – Nos 1 and 2 were *Keeping Pigs* and *Law and the Countryman* which says something about viticulture in the early 1950s.) This book, which came out in the same year as Hyams' second book on the subject, drew on many of the same sources. Ordish had been in contact with Ray Brock and had visited Oxted on more than one occasion. How useful his book was to fledgling winegrowers is open to question. By this time, Brock had already dismissed varieties such as Brandt and Baco No. 1 for wine production and had already started cropping Riesling Sylvaner and Seyval blanc, which he had been growing since 1947. On the subject of diseases, which was after all one of his specialist subjects, Ordish is very inaccurate. Whilst he admits the possibility of getting both powdery and downy mildew, on *botrytis* he states: 'other fungus diseases such as Grey Mould (or Noble Fungus) can attack the grapes, but are very unlikely to occur in an open vineyard in England'! Although some of his varieties were resistant hybrids, it is barely possible to grow *viniferas* of any kind without encountering *botrytis* problems and one has to question how much actual experience he had at that time.

One aspect of *Wine Growing in England* of interest is the last chapter entitled 'Commercial Production in Britain'. In it, Ordish sets out the costs and returns from an acre of grapes. He estimates that the capital outlay on planting an acre would be £255, the cost of winemaking equipment (suitable he says for a vineyard of five acres) another £215 and the annual running costs of one acre of vines £189.10.0. Based on a 'modest' crop of 2 tons per acre, he estimates the returns from selling 2,100 bottles at an average of 4/- a bottle would be £420 less excise duty at 1/9 per bottle. The net return would therefore be £46.15.0 which he says represents a return of 10 per cent 'which is not very much in view of the risks involved in starting a new industry' (and especially as he has not included either the land or buildings or the cost of winemaking and selling). However, he does point out that the winery equipment will serve a much larger tonnage and that 2 tons is really quite low.

For all its inaccuracies, Ordish's book was yet another medium of publicity for the revival of winegrowing in Great Britain and helped spread the word. It certainly helped add to the number of people in the country who looked on outdoor grape growing as a possibility, rather than as an historical anomaly. Ordish went on to write two further books concerning viticulture, *The Great Wine Blight* (a study of the causes, effects and cure for *phylloxera*) in 1972 and *Vineyards in England and Wales* in 1977. This last, dedicated 'to the memory of Edward Hyams', was a much better researched and informative handbook on the subject (he did at least admit that *botrytis* was a serious problem) and was well received. By then, of course, the revival was well under way with 385 members of the English Vineyards Association who farmed over 500 acres of vines.

Ordish wrote a number of books on a wide variety of agricultural and horticultural topics, as well as on Central and South America (he co-wrote *The Last of the Incas* with Edward Hyams in 1962) and after he retired, wrote and lectured on winegrowing in England and Wales. Ordish updated his book on *phylloxera* in 1987 and died in 1990.

Between them, Ray Brock, Edward Hyams and George Ordish had questioned why it was that outdoor viticulture in the British Isles had all but died out and had, to a certain extent, shown how it might be revived. Although they had not discovered all the answers, they had, through a combination of practical demonstration, scientific research and publicity, generated sufficient enthusiasm for those with the inclination to start planting vineyards. The first modern vineyard, Hambledon in Hampshire, planted in 1951, was the tangible evidence that the revival was underway.

3

Commercial Viticulture, 1951–2001

THE EARLY VINEYARDS 1951–1965

Hambledon

The planting of a vineyard in the winter of 1951 at Hambledon in Hampshire by Major-General Sir Guy Salisbury-Jones GCVO, CMG, MC, DL (to give him his full title) marked a turning point in the history of winegrowing in Great Britain. This was the first vineyard to be planted specifically to produce wine for sale since Andrew Pettigrew planted the Marquis of Bute's at Castell Coch in 1875. Furthermore, it was planted with a variety – Seyval blanc – that stood a good chance of both withstanding mildews and *botrytis* and of ripening its fruit, problems which up to now had so troubled previous vineyard owners that all had eventually given up the battle

It has often been recounted that Guy Salisbury-Jones acquired his love of wine during the Great War. Finding himself sharing a trench with some French soldiers, he was invited to share their wine ration and his love of both France and its wines started then and stayed with him throughout his life. He was the first Englishman to train at the famous French Military Academy at St Cyr and was taught military history there by Charles de Gaulle. As an acknowledged francophile, it was perhaps only natural that Salisbury-Jones's dreams included owning his own vineyard. He and his wife, Hilda, had retired to Mill Down in the Hampshire village of Hambledon and, looking at the south-facing field where once his daughter's pony had grazed, the thought came to him that perhaps it would be a good place to have a vineyard. The idea that vines could flourish in the UK had at that time been receiving some publicity, generated by two people, Ray Brock and Edward Hyams.

Salisbury-Jones admitted that it was the writings of these two that really inspired him to carry on and plant his vineyard. He had visited Brock at Oxted and Seyval blanc had been recommended in Brock's first two Reports as a variety worth considering.

Salisbury-Jones had been invited by a friend to a dinner given by the Confrérie des Chevaliers du Tastevin at the former Cistercian monastery of Clos-Vougeot in Burgundy. It seemed the ideal opportunity to take his idea one stage further and he decided to take his gardener, Mr Blackman, with him. The dinner was obviously a great success and as a result, Salisbury-Jones returned to England having ordered some 4000 vines 'whilst under the influence of Burgundian hospitality'. His choice of Seyve Villard 5/276 (Seyval Blanc) was an interesting one and one wonders why he made it. Perhaps his host was a member of FENAVINO or subscribed to *La Viticulture Nouvelle*? Who knows? In any event, the vines were ordered with the knowledge that both Brock and Hyams had already singled the variety out as capable of producing fair wine in our climate and perhaps also his contacts in Burgundy were from the old school, who remembered when much of France depended on hybrids for a decent crop in the days before modern fungicides had been developed to combat *Oidium*.

The vines were planted in the winter of 1951 and covered a little over an acre. They were grafted on to the rootstocks 41B and 161.49 (which are very rarely used today, but deserve more attention) that Salisbury-Jones said were required 'because the chalky soil at Hambledon resembled that of Champagne and those were the rootstocks used there'. The vines were trained in a very Burgundian way, with narrow 4 ft rows and trelliswork at the same height. The vines grew well and produced their first crop in 1954. The wine – history does not record what it tasted like – was the first commercial vintage to be made in Great Britain since the 1911 Castell Coch vintage. The fact that wine *was* now being produced and was on sale caused much publicity and Salisbury-Jones was besieged by the press and media anxious for a story. The fact that he was an imposing figure, with a colourful and honourable past, a name to conjure with and the presence to hold an audience, meant that he was much in demand. 'Hambledon' soon became synonymous with 'English Wine' and Brock's dream, ten years after he started his trials vineyard at Oxted, had become a reality.

A simple winery had been installed at Hambledon and Salisbury-Jones persuaded some French friends to help with the first few vintages. He described their results as 'encouraging'! Anton Massel then persuaded Salisbury-Jones to invest in a new winery and more suitable equipment (at an overall cost of £6,000) and took over the vinification. Further plantings over the next few years included varieties such as Chardonnay, Pinot Meunier and Pinot Noir, although these were never very successful. The site at Hambeldon is almost 100 m above sea level and fairly exposed. In the vineyard, Salisbury-Jones had the help of Bill Carcary who started work there in1966 and continued to manage the vineyards and make the wines until the late 1980s. In their day, the Hambledon wines under Salisbury-Jones' ownership were widely known and were sold from many outlets. It was one of the first vineyards to export wine to the United States. After Salisbury-Jones' death, the house and vineyards were sold to John Patterson and the vineyards were expanded and facilities upgraded. In 1987, 7.5 acres of vines were planted and a new winery, bottling hall and temperature-controlled bottle store were built. However today, following Patterson's death and the sale of the estate, only about three acres of Seyval blanc and Pinot Meunier remain and grapes are not always harvested.

Salisbury-Jones was founder President of the English Vineyards Association and remained at its head until 1981, when he relinquished this position and was appointed Honorary Life Patron. His time spent in the Diplomatic Corps was put to good use during his Presidency, and he worked diligently at securing such things as the grower's duty-free allowance, as well as pleading often against the absurdity of a lower rate of duty on 'British Made-Wines' which was then the case. Salisbury-Jones died on 8 February 1985 at the age of 88. In many ways Salisbury-Jones was the typical English winegrower of his time and many retired servicemen followed his example and planted vines. He was a magnificent spokesman for the industry (if one could have called it that in the early days) and certainly awoke the public to English wine.

Horam Manor

The second of the early vineyards was Jack Ward's at Horam in East Sussex. No history of the revival of viticulture in the British Isles would be complete without recognising the part played by Ward, his vineyards, and the company he co-founded, the Merrydown Wine Company. In 1946 Ward and his friend, Ian Howie, decided to form a business making cider and fruit wines from local Sussex produce and bought a site in the middle of Horam on which had once stood a large house – Horam Manor – and established a winery there. Ward, who had graduated from Trinity College, Cambridge with a degree in English, had become interested in wine while studying his first love, music, at the Frankfurt Conservatorium. In the early 1950s, he became interested in the revival of viticulture and in what Ray Brock, whom he visited, was doing at Oxted. In 1953 he planted six vines, obtained from Oxted, in the grounds of the winery: two each of Riesling Sylvaner (Müller-Thurgau), Madeleine Royale and Gamay Hâtif des Vosges.

No sooner had these trial vines been planted than a property known as 'The Grange', a house with several acres of garden attached, came up for sale across the road from the winery site and was bought by the company to provide accommodation for some of its employees. Ward promptly claimed the gardens and in 1954 planted a two-acre vineyard. This was at a time when Hambledon was the only other vineyard in the country, planted three years earlier in 1951 and yet to produce its first harvest. The varieties that Ward chose do not seem to be recorded, although one of them was certainly Müller-Thurgau, as a wine from this variety from the Grange vineyard was served to Prince Philip at a dinner held at The Vintners Hall in London. In 1962, however, with the vineyard only just reaching maturity, the company decided that the offer they had received from a local builder to develop the gardens and vineyard was too tempting and it was sold and the fledgling vineyard grubbed out.

Ward had perhaps foreseen this and had already thought about where else he might establish a vineyard. The company owned, in addition to the Horam Manor site, a property a mile up the road behind a row of houses known as Kingston Villas. This had been the site of an old brickworks and the heavy clay soil, although suitable for making bricks, could not be considered ideal for vines. Unperturbed by this, Ward planted 800 grafted vines in the spring of 1963, but the heavy soil conditions were too much for them and not a single one survived. He reckoned that they had all been planted too deeply and had been killed by waterlogging. Not to be put off easily, Ward planted further vines, this time using some rooted cuttings that had been raised on the site, as well as others that had been grafted by Merrydown as an experiment. However, the latter were not a success and home-grafting was soon abandoned. At the Brickyard, as the vineyard came to be known, the vines slowly established themselves, not helped by the extreme winter frosts of 1967 which cut a lot of the vines back down to the ground.

The main business of Merrydown, the making of cider, perry and fruit wines, produced a by-product in the form of vast heaps of apple pomace, fruit skins, pulp and pips left over from the pressing process. Not knowing quite what to do with it, they experimented with feeding it to pigs but soon realised that even pigs could only eat so much of the stuff and looked for other outlets. They had the idea of using it as a compost and soil conditioner and contacted a recently opened broiler-chicken producer at nearby Buxted who was only too happy to supply chicken manure for nothing. This, when mixed and turned with the press waste and then thoroughly composted, was bagged and marketed as 'Pompost'. Initially it was a great success and although eventually forced off the market by an entirely unfounded salmonella scare, it was not before large quantities of it had been spread about the Brickyard vineyard. This greatly improved the clay soil and by 1969 1.5 acres had been planted. Ward was constantly trying to improve the soil at the Brickyard by growing 'green manure' crops in the rows and I well remember seeing most of the vineyard down to sunflowers which, at the end of the summer, were cut down and then rotovated into the soil. The Brickyard vineyard was eventually expanded by cutting down a three-acre coppice that adjoined it and grubbing up all the tree roots that remained. A proper land drainage system was installed before it was planted with vines.

In addition to the Brickyard, Ward had found a spare patch of ground at the Horam Manor site and in 1968 planted almost three-quarters of an acre of vines. That year saw the first harvest from the Brickyard site, reported as '12 cwt of grapes, which yielded 100 gallons of wine'. The next year was marginally better and a yield of '106 gallons' was recorded, together with the juice from some Baco Noir vines on a wall at the Manor. 1970 was a real bumper year, and some 4.5 tons were picked from both vineyards. In 1971 another five varieties were planted at Horam Manor: Reichensteiner, Ortega, Faberrebe, Kerner and Augusta Luise, the last an early table grape. The harvest that year was '1 ton 6.5 cwt from the Horam vineyard and 1 ton 3.5 cwt from the Brickyard'. Some plastic tunnels were put up at the Brickyard and the crops under these helped improve the harvests. Somebody who shared the same enthusiasm as Ward for the vines was Reg Parsons who had been gardener at The Grange, the site of the first vineyard. Together, he and Ward managed both the Brickyard and the Horam Manor vineyards.

In 1979, Ward retired as Managing Director of Merrydown and his successor, Richard Purdey, was forced by commercial considerations to take a hard look at the future of the vineyard and (grape) winemaking operations. Reluctantly it was decided that both the vineyard and the Merrydown Co-operative Scheme would have to go and the company could no longer continue to subsidise it. The 1980 vintage had not been large and the vineyard would have to be sold.

Luckily, Ward happened to share a railway compartment back from an English Vineyards Association Board meeting with Kenneth McAlpine, owner of Lamberhurst Vineyards (who very rarely travelled by train). Ward explained the predicament that the vineyard was in and by the time they got to the end of the train journey, it was decided that the vineyard would be bought by McAlpine and become an outpost of the Lamberhurst operation. Reg Parsons had also been facing an uncertain future and although well past retirement age, he was asked to continue to help look after the vineyard. The vineyard at Horam Manor was needed for the expansion of storage tanks and bottling facilities and this was grubbed out. Reg continued to live in a cottage overlooking the vineyard until he died in 1988.

Under Lamberhurst's management, the Brickyard vineyard was almost entirely replanted with new grafted stock. The original vines were planted on a 5 ft row width, far too narrow for the tractors and implements used by Lamberhurst, and the new vines were planted with 7 ft wide rows and 4 ft between the vines. Varieties planted were Kerner, Müller-Thurgau, Reichensteiner and Schönburger. During one stage of the replanting it was realised that parts of the soil consisted almost entirely of broken bricks, probably the waste heap from the brick kilns and the vines had to be pick-axed into their new homes. Despite this, they seem to grow fairly happily and full production was resumed in 1986. The vineyard remained in McAlpine's ownership until October 1994 when it was bought by Jon Woronschak, the flying winemaker based at Valley Vineyards.

The establishment of the Merrydown Co-operative Scheme in 1969 was another important milestone in English viticulture. Ward had seen a growing number of small vineyards with owners who, having managed to grow a good crop of grapes, had problems turning them into commercially acceptable wine; their vineyards were either far too small to warrant the equipment needed or they lacked the expertise required to make wine – very often it was both. Ward's ambition was to see the revival of English winegrowing well established and anything that he or his company could do to help would be done. It is interesting to read in one of the first contracts issued by Merrydown, the reason given for the scheme 'Because it considers that the enterprise [that of growing grapes in the United Kingdom] presents a unique challenge to the British people and is therefore worthy of such support as we are able to give.'

The scheme was essentially one of contract winemaking whereby grapes would be individually processed for their owners and returned to them as finished wine. The difference between this and other contract winemakers was that the service could either be paid for in the normal way or a proportion of the wine made would be retained to cover all costs. The proportion of a grower's wine retained varied, depending on a number of factors, but to start with it was 70 per cent for the grower and 30 per cent for the co-op. As the years went by and the true costs of running and administering this scheme became apparent, the amount retained rose to 44 per cent. The scheme was run as a co-operative non-profit making enterprise and the charges were consequently very reasonable. The wine retained by the scheme was blended and sold under the 'Anderida' label, either through the Merrydown shop or through their trade sales division. A Merrydown wine list from 1974 shows that the 1971 Anderida was selling for £1.26 a bottle, whilst the Brede Riesling Sylvaner, which the year before had won the first Gore-Browne Trophy, was selling for £1.83!

In 1976, Christopher Lindlar, who had recently returned from some practical winemaking experience in Germany, joined Greg Williams in the winery just before the harvest and together they handled the largest crop ever pressed at Horam – over 180 tons – which severely strained the facilities. In 1977, the whole of the

English Wine interests of Merrydown were put into a new company 'Merrydown Vineyards Limited'. Over the ten years that it was in existence, the Merrydown Co-operative Scheme made wines for almost all the vineyards then cropping. At a time when good equipment and technical knowledge were both in short supply, it had certainly enabled many vineyards to get a properly made and presented commercial product on the shelf. It also had Royal patronage. In *Merrydown, Forty Vintage Years* by Graeme Wright, it is recalled that Princess Margaret once sent some grapes that had been grown on a wall at Kensington Palace to be made into wine, although only enough for 6 bottles! In one sense the scheme was a victim of its own success. As vineyards sending grapes to Horam became bigger and as the vines became more mature, their owners gained in confidence and started to set up their own wineries, leaving only the smaller, newer vineyards to use the scheme. Eventually it became obvious that the costs of running the scheme were too high and it was wound up in 1980. Lindlar and Williams decided that the time had come to find a new home and in August 1980 they both moved to Biddenden Vineyards, Lindlar to become a contract winemaker on his own account and Williams to concentrate on vine sales. Most of the old Merrydown customers moved with Lindlar to Biddenden. Lindlar later left Biddenden to set up his own winery, High Weald Wines. Williams continued to sell vines for a number of years until he was tragically killed in an accident in 1988.

Apart from putting the services of Merrydown at the disposal of English winegrowers through the co-operative scheme, Ward was also very involved with the English Vineyards Association. He was its Chairman from its first Annual General Meeting on 18 January 1967 until April 1981. During his time as Chairman, Customs and Excise were persuaded to grant growers their 'Domestic Use Allowance', an annual duty-free award of up to 1100 litres of wine; the Wye College experimental vineyard was planted and produced some good data for growers; and the EVA Certification Trade Mark or 'Seal of Quality' as it became to be known, was eventually agreed to by the Board of Trade and put into operation. He remained as a Director until 1983 but continued to attend Board Meetings until 1985. He was awarded the OBE in the 1979 New Year's Honours List for 'Services to English Wine' and was presented with his award by the Queen at Buckingham Palace on 27 March (and missed – for the first and last time – an EVA Board meeting). After the presentation he was given a celebration lunch at the Farmers Club by the whole Board together with Sir Guy and Hilda Salisbury-Jones. Ward also wrote the *The Complete Book of Vine Growing in the British Isles* (1984, Faber & Faber) and although now out of print, it remains the only book on viticulture written specifically for this climate.

Jack Ward died on 10 August 1986. He was responsible in no small way for the development of the industry at a time when few believed it had a future. He was a kind, sensitive man, who gave time to anyone who wanted to speak to him about growing vines or making wine and must be judged as one of the founding fathers of English wine.

Beaulieu

The third vineyard to be planted in modern times was that of the Gore-Browne's at Beaulieu. In 1956 Lieutenant-Colonel Robert and Mrs Margaret Gore-Browne, who had recently returned to Great Britain from overseas, went to view a house adjacent to the Beaulieu Estate (the Montagus were old family friends) called 'The Vineyards'. Despite initial reluctance from the Colonel, but no doubt encouraged by the success of the nearby vineyard at Hambledon (planted by a fellow soldier) they decided to try and establish a vineyard there and in the autumn of 1957 (or perhaps the spring of 1958 – reports differ) planted four rows of Müller-Thurgau and Seyval Blanc as well as a few Gamay Noir Hâtif des Vosges, Précoce de Malingre and Madeleine Sylvaner No. 3 28/51, all of which they bought from Brock at Oxted (Brock's account books show a sale to the Gore-Brownes on 24 December 1957 of £112 worth of vines). The vineyard was gradually expanded with more of the same, plus some Wrotham Pinot. By 1960 they had almost five acres. Their first vintage, in 1961, was a rosé and was apparently well received. They also experimented with Baco No. 1, Brandt, Pirovano 14, and Cascade – this despite the fact that Mrs Gore-Browne had heard that 'it was prohibited by the Common Market as it is said to have an injurious effect upon the liver', a common scare story put out by the anti-hybrid growers in France. By 1967 they had decided to eliminate the experimental varieties – no doubt due to poor performance.

Winemaking in those early days was, from all accounts, a fairly hit and miss affair. Both Salisbury-Jones and Gore-Browne, as well as others in years to come, were helped by Anton Massel, a young German who had come across to work for the Seitz Filter company in the UK in 1956. In 1961 Massel opened his own laboratory at Water Lane in London which he moved to Ockley, a village to the south of Dorking in Surrey, in 1969. It still trades as 'Corkwise Ltd', although Massel sold his interest in it in 1987. Before the first vintage at Hambledon (the 1954), Salisbury-Jones had built himself a small winery and equipped it cheaply with simple equipment – the first two vintages were made in what one might certainly call 'primitive conditions' and this showed in the results. When Massel appeared on the scene and offered his services, the first thing he did was persuade Salisbury-Jones to invest £6,000 in better equipment including a small Willmes air-bladder press – the first of many to enter the country. This press is still in use. It was first sold to Sir Reresby Sitwell Bt. at Renishaw Hall near Sheffield and subsequently to a grower in the south of the country. Massel also persuaded Salisbury-Jones that the vineyard needed to be at least three acres in size for it to be viable and to make use of the equipment that now sat in the winery; in fact Salisbury-Jones enlarged the vineyard to four and a half acres. The Gore-Brownes likewise built themselves a winery and used Massel as their consultant. Being already involved with fermentation of cider and fruit wines Merrydown had their own winemaking equipment – albeit on a rather larger scale than they needed for their small vineyard – and did not need the services of a consultant.

What these early wines were like is open to question – very few tasting notes survive. People who do remember them, recall wines of quite high acidity, lean in structure and lacking fruit. The early growers battled to control disease, powdery mildew and *botrytis* being the worst, and undoubtedly picked too early in order to get to the grapes before the birds or the rot. The wines were usually made in a fairly natural dry style, with little or no residual sugar and left to soften with age. Hambledon thought nothing of offering wines five or more years old and almost prided itself on its wine's long cellaring potential – the idea of bottling wines with a little residual sweetness to temper the acidity was something of an anathema to the early pioneers and this practice, now widespread, had to wait a few years.

The establishment of these three vineyards between the winter of 1951 and the spring of 1958, and the appearance of English Wine on sale, was proof positive that viticulture in the British Isles had been revived. Whilst it would be an exaggeration to say that the industry then took off, there is no doubt that the number of both actual and potential vineyard owners suddenly expanded and small trial plots of vines appeared in all kinds of unlikely places. The real expansion of vineyards from which commercial quantities of wine for sale could be made started in the early to mid-1960s. People such as Trevor and Joy Bates at Nettlestead outside Maidstone, Norman Cowderoy at Rock Lodge, near Uckfield in West Sussex, Robin Don at Elmham Park in Norfolk, Nigel Godden at Pilton Manor in Somerset, Messrs Gibbons and Poulter at Cranmore on the Isle of Wight, the Montagus at Beaulieu, Gillian Pearkes in Devon, Major Rook at Stragglethorpe Hall near Lincoln, Pam Smith at Flexerne, East Sussex, and Philip Tyson-Woodcock at Brede, near Rye in East Sussex, all planted vineyards. Wales too became the home of several vineyards: Lewis Mathias at Lamphey Court, George Jones at Pembrey, plus several others belonging to or with advice from Margaret Gore-Browne (who was Welsh by birth).

This spread of vineyards geographically, coupled with a diversity of owners, sites, training and pruning systems and above all, of grape varieties, meant that at last, valuable experience was being gained across the whole country. Thus, potential winegrowers were better able to judge what varieties and what training systems were actually working, how vines should be managed and, but by no means least, how grapes could be turned into palatable wine.

THE SECOND WAVE 1966–1975

Once wines from the early vineyards started to be produced in saleable quantities and could be bought, tasted and assessed by the wine trade and consumers alike, the publicity surrounding English and Welsh wine really started to gather momentum. It soon became clear that making wine in the UK, even with its 'marginal' climate, was no longer the joke it had long been considered and that grapes could be considered as a commercial crop.

The real expansion of the vineyard area and the establishment of both sizeable vineyards and wineries started in earnest in the late 1960s and it was an era of rapid growth. One of the features of English and Welsh viticulture is the diversity of background of those who plant vineyards. In other countries where new vineyards are being planted, one would expect to see existing landowners – most usually those with land in the vicinity of established vineyards – planting up, together with a smaller number of entrants with no experience of growing at all, but with serious funds, usually made in a completely unrelated industry. In the UK, those planting vineyards came from a much wider cross-section of the community: a sprinkling of retired service people, a few farmers and landowners looking for alternative, hopefully more profitable, crops, some 'lifestyle' smallholders (generally underfunded) keen to be part of the 'good life' brigade, as well as those with a few acres attached to their houses in the country who liked the idea of having their names on a wine label. Only one thing really seems to have united them – an almost complete lack of experience in growing vines (and in many cases of growing anything) or of making wine! In some cases but by no means all, this lack of experience showed in the quality of both the vineyards they planted and managed and of the wines they produced.

In the late 1960s a new crop of vineyards appeared: T. P. Baillie-Grohman at Hascombe, Surrey, Ken Barlow at Adgestone, Isle of Wight, Richard and Joyce Barnes at Biddenden, Kent, Graham and Irene Barrett at Felsted in Essex, Walter Cardy at Pangbourne in Berkshire, the Crossland-Hinchcliffe's at Castlehouse in East Susex, Jack Edgerly at Kelsale in Suffolk, Ian Grant at Knowle Hill in Kent, Bill Greenwood at New Hall, Purleigh in Essex, Anton Massel at Ockley in Surrey, Gruff Reece at Gamlinglay, Bedfordshire, and Bernard Theobald at Westbury, Berkshire. These new ventures were in many cases quite substantial and their owners, several of whom were mildly, and in some cases wildly, eccentric, helped do two things: spread the word that establishing commercial vineyards was possible in the British Isles; and reinforce the idea that to do so, in this climate, was something rather unusual and novel.

The next five years (the first half of the 1970s) saw yet another frenzy of planting: Sam Alper at Chilford Hall, Cambridgeshire, Basil Ambrose at Cavendish Manor, Suffolk, Bob Blayney at La Mare on Jersey, R. M. O. Capper at Stocks in Worcester, David Carr

Taylor at Westfield near Hastings in East Sussex, Peter Cook at Pulham in Norfolk, J. R. M. Donald at Tytherley in Wiltshire, Colin and Sue Gillespie at Wootton in Somerset, Peter Hall at Breaky Bottom, Lewes, East Sussex, Kenneth McAlpine at Lamberhurst in Kent, Mary Macrae at Highwaymans near Bury St Edmunds, Ian and Eleanor Berwick at Bruisyard in Suffolk, Alan McKechnie at Three Choirs at Newent in Gloucestershire, Andrew and Ian Paget at Chilsdown in West Sussex, Chris Stuart at Ashton Manor in Wiltshire and Bob Westphal at Penshurst in Kent. The above is by no means a comprehensive list of all those who planted vineyards and apart from these more substantial plantings, scores of other growers were experimenting with small vineyards across the whole of the south of the UK.

The fabled summer of 1976, according to legend the hottest and driest on record, gave further impetus to vine growing. In fact, although some vineyards did pick large crops, others were badly damaged by mid-April frosts and almost all vineyards suffered badly from *botrytis* as it started raining at the end of August. The next two months, September and October, the main ripening and harvesting period, were very wet. This, however, did not stop the general public believing that at last the Almighty had smiled on the country's winegrowers, further fuelling the interest in English and Welsh wines and with it, the planting of more and more vineyards.

VINEYARDS ESTABLISHED AFTER 1976

The two decades between 1976 and 1995 saw a large number of vineyards planted, including some very sizeable ones. Growers such as Mark Lambert at Barkham Manor, Piltdown, East Sussex, Jon Leighton at Valley Vineyards, Reading, Berkshire, Stuart and Sandy Moss at Nyetimber, Pulborough, West Sussex, William Ross at Barnsgate Manor, Uckfield, East Sussex, the Quirk family at Chiddingstone, Edenbridge, Kent, the Sax family at Battle, East Sussex, Andrew Vining at Wellow, Romsey, Hampshire, Adrian White at Denbies, Dorking, Surrey, all planted vineyards in excess of twenty acres in size, the largest (Denbies) growing to 258 acres. In 1977 I also started growing vines in Tenterden in Kent. In addition, existing vineyards such as those at Adgestone, Carr Taylor, Chilford, Highwaymans, Lamberhurst, New Hall and

Three Choirs all increased in size as the market for their wines expanded.

Plantings in recent years have not been quite so frenzied and the rate of new plantings has certainly declined. Several factors are responsible. A rumoured vine planting ban in 1990/91 persuaded many growers that if they were going to plant it had better be soon and between 1992 and 1994 an abnormally large number of vines were planted. This sudden surge of planting resulted in larger national yields (the 1996 UK harvest of 3,542,933 bottles was the largest to date) and increased the supply of wine at a time when demand was lessening and competition from overseas growing. The UK has one of the most sophisticated wine markets in the world and wines have to represent very good value for money if they are to succeed. The retail market is dominated by a small number of large chains of wine merchants and supermarket groups whose massive purchasing power allows them to squeeze keener and keener prices out of producers. Growers in marginal areas whose production costs are relatively high and yields relatively low (such as the UK), are therefore at a very definite disadvantage. High levels of excise duty, levelled at a flat rate rather than on the value of the wine, also create further pressure in the UK market as certain 'price points' have to be met and wines have to be correctly priced in order for them to move off the shelf. The creation of the European Union's Single Market, which meant that consumers could travel to the continent and import more or less unlimited quantities of wines at virtually nil rates of excise duty, also put pressure on English vineyards and wineries. Many of these are situated in the counties bordering the channel where access to the ferries is easiest. Taken together, these factors have had the effect of making potential growers think twice before investing in vineyards.

Of course, not all vineyards planted since 1951 in England and Wales have survived – to expect them to do so would be unrealistic. Some vineyards were planted with the wrong varieties and on the wrong sites, and the problems of getting grapes to ripen under these circumstances were just too great. Others have fallen by the wayside for reasons such as retirement, divorce and death. Quite a few vineyards, started by entrepreneurs in the boom years of the mid-1980s, were subsequently grubbed up when their other interests came under pressure or failed. Whilst many would like to believe it, not all vineyards that fail do so because the vineyard itself is in trouble. Other quite normal factors are often to blame. However, the desire to sink substantial sums of money into vineyards and wineries in the UK, where wine production has climatic and marketing problems that other countries do not share, has been quite remarkable. The profitability of growing grapes and making wine in the UK has always been open to debate and very many vineyards (mainly the smaller ones) have only survived because of a very high proportion of farm-gate sales at full retail prices, coupled with the ability of the owner to support the enterprise out of his or her own pocket in lean times. However, once a vineyard's production becomes too large to sell most of it over the farm gate and the wine has to be sold through the normal wholesale and retail distribution channels that exist in the UK, the problems of marketing begin.

Before the first Hambledon vintage of 1954, no market for English and Welsh wines existed. To start with – probably up until the early 1970s – overall volumes were very small, English and Welsh wines were still a novelty and most growers could sell all they produced with little problem. However, as the number of vineyards expanded, so the amount of wine available for sale increased. A combination of relatively high prices, reflecting the difficulty of growing grapes in the UK and the scarcity of the product, and some wines of dubious quality, reflecting the inexperience of some growers and winemakers, made the wine trade in the UK somewhat wary and they found English and Welsh difficult to market. This led to some vineyards experiencing real problems with selling their wines at anything approaching a price that was required to fund their enterprises and they subsequently gave up the struggle. Many of these, it has to be said with the benefit of hindsight, completely misread their ability to market the volume of wine they were able to produce. The UK wine market is a harsh place and English and Welsh wines have had to battle hard (and continue to battle hard) to maintain their place on the shelves against the endless stream of competing products.

One way out of the sales problem has been for vineyards to take the decision to sell some or all of their grapes to other, mainly larger concerns, whose marketing skills and abilities left them short of wines made from their own, home-grown grapes. In 1993, a new entrant to the market, Chapel Down Wines, now the largest producer of English wines and based at Tenterden Vineyard, was created. This company buys almost all its grapes from other vineyards. It has over 200 acres under contract and has undoubtedly kept some vineyards in production which would otherwise have been grubbed. Some owners have leased their vineyards to other wine producers, thus reducing the overall number of players in the market.

To say that vineyard planting since the mid-1970s has followed a pattern of any recognisable sort would be brave, mainly because until 1989 accurate data did not exist! The Ministry of Agriculture, Fisheries and Food conducted a voluntary survey in 1975 which revealed a total of 196 ha (484 acres) of vines, but this was undoubtedly on the low side. By the time MAFF undertook their second survey in 1984, the figure had risen to 431 ha (1,065 acres), but again, this was low. The third survey in 1985 came up with 488 ha (1,205 acres) and finally the fourth survey, in 1987, revealed a total of 546 ha (1,349 acres) which triggered the need for a statutory (compulsory) survey so that a Vineyard Register could be compiled. This is required by the EU in all Member States with 500 ha or more of vines.

Two years later, in 1989, when the first statutory vineyard census was undertaken, a much truer figure of 876 ha (2,164 acres) was recorded which showed that previous surveys had greatly under-estimated the extent of vineyard plantings in the UK. The high point of planting was reached in 1993 when 1,065 ha (2,631 acres) was reached. Since then, the total area has declined, with the latest (1999) figures showing 872 ha (2,154 acres). In all cases, these figures refer to planted, not productive areas. The separately recorded figure for area in production has risen from the first accurate figure in 1989 of 652 ha (1,610 acres) to the latest (1999) total of 835 ha (2,062 acres), a rise of 28 per cent. Apart from a slight decline in 1994 and 1995, the area in production rose steadily from 1989 until 1998 (see Table 7 on p. 144). The decline in productive hectares in 1999 must be seen as a result of the difficult trading conditions some vineyards are now finding. The decline in non-productive hectares and the overall number of individual vineyards since 1989 is a sign of the growing maturity of the UK winegrowing industry. Vineyards which for whatever reason could not produce sufficient quality and/or quantity of wine to make the enterprise viable have been grubbed out, leaving those capable of producing commercially acceptable wines.

VINEYARDS OF THE FUTURE

Although the history of planting vineyards in the UK would tend to suggest otherwise, ultimately it is the market for English and Welsh wines that will decide whether or not there should be a wine industry here in the future. There is no doubt that over the last 20 years, the market into which most of our wines are sold (very little English and Welsh wine is exported) has become more competitive, with better and better wines being imported at cheaper and cheaper prices. The range and standard of wines available to the average consumer has never been better than it is today. English and Welsh wines, if they are to find a market amongst these imported wines, have to be available at the right price and of the right quality. In 1980, excise duty and VAT were approximately half today's levels, while retail prices, at least as far as farm-gate prices went, were very similar. Today, excise duty and VAT on still wine (at £1.16 a bottle and 17½ per cent respectively) now absorb 44 per cent of a £3.99 bottle of wine, 38 per cent of a £4.99 bottle of wine. Given that more and more wine is sold in supermarkets and large off-licence chains, who naturally need a margin to cover their costs and make a profit, returns to UK growers at such prices (£3.99–£4.99) are to say the least, not huge. For some there is undoubtedly no margin over costs at all.

The net return from a tonne of grapes when wine is sold at £3.99 a bottle, taking all taxes, retailers margin and average production costs, including packaging and distribution, into account, amounts to £405 per tonne. At £4.99 per bottle, the return rises to £1,102 per tonne. With average yields from a well-run vineyard, planted with the right varieties, probably between 3 and 4 tonnes per acre, the income from an acre of grapes with wine sold at £3.99 per bottle directly through a retailer, amounts to between £1,215 and £1,620 per acre; with wine sold at £4.99 per bottle the return rises to between £3,306 and £4,408 per acre. Out of this has to be paid all the growing costs, together with the return on the investments in both the vineyards and winery, the overheads in running the business, interest on loans as well as profit. One thing is certain from these figures: a grower who sells the bulk of his or her wine through a retailer at prices based on a shelf price of £3.99 per bottle needs to achieve consistent yields of over 3 tonnes per acre just to stand still. In order to make a return on the investment, retail prices need to be nearer £4.99 per bottle and yields nearer 4 tonnes per acre. How realistic these prices and yields are is another matter.

Of course many growers, especially but not only the smaller ones, manage to make ends meet and survive by selling a high proportion of their wines directly to the public at full retail prices. This is usually achieved by having an on-farm off-licence and attending county shows and consumer fairs. Although this method of selling requires a level of commitment to the public that some find wearing, it does at least help the vineyard survive.

The alternative to poor returns through a combination of low yields and low prices is to produce 'added value' wines which achieve higher prices. The last twenty years has seen English and Welsh winegrowers making increasing amounts of bottle-fermented sparkling wines, oak-aged wines, red wines and sweet dessert wines, all of which sell at higher prices than the usual still wines. The costs of growing grapes for these 'speciality' wines is in most cases little different from 'standard' wines, and apart from perhaps sparkling wines, where costs of production and excise duty rates are much higher, and oak-aged red and white wines where the costs of barrels have to be taken into account, the costs of production and packaging are more or less the same. The attractions therefore are obvious and undoubtedly these added-value wines will become the norm rather than the exception.

Production of bottle-fermented sparkling wines is likely to be one of the major growth areas in UK wineries over the next two decades. In the mid-1980s both Carr Taylor and Lamberhurst vineyards started full-scale production of these wines and proved that our 'native' grape varieties could be used for producing good examples of this type of wine. Since then, a large number of vineyards have annually made batches of sparkling wines, mainly using the services of another winery to do the post-fermentation operations which require expensive specialist equipment, and today over forty vineyards have them on their lists. The largest producer in the UK is Chapel Down Wines who make their non-vintage 'Epoch Brut' from a blend of Müller-Thurgau, Reichensteiner and Seyval blanc, and are achieving good market penetration. More recently, vineyards such as Nyetimber and RidgeView Estate, both in West Sussex, have been planted solely with Champagne varieties – Chardonnay, Pinot noir and Pinot Meunier – for the production of what might be termed 'classic' bottle-fermented sparkling wines. The quality of the wines to date has been very good, proving that it is possible to ripen these varieties sufficiently for this purpose. How easy it will be to obtain satisfactory crops of these varieties at the correct levels of sugar and acidity on all sites it is perhaps too early to tell, but undoubtedly the success of these two individual vineyards will tempt other growers to attempt to emulate what they have achieved. It must be borne in mind, however, that with excise duty at £1.65 per bottle and production costs double those of still wines, a bottle of sparkling wine needs to sell at a price at least £2.50 higher than its still equivalent just to cover the additional expenses.

Oak-aged wines, once confined to the better wines from Burgundy and other traditional areas, are now commonplace in all price brackets and appear to have found favour with the average UK consumer. Winemakers in the UK have been making oak-aged wines since the mid-1980s, using not only oak barrels, the traditional, but costly method of imparting oak flavour to wine, but also by using oak staves and oak chips in the fermentation and storage tanks. There are now separate sections in the national and most regional competitions for this style of wine. In the general marketplace, red wines have been increasing their market share at the expense of whites – partly because of the increase in wine drinking at meal times and of the general maturity and sophistication of winedrinkers, but also because the perceived health benefits of modest wine drinking are greater for red than white wines. The amount of red wine produced in the UK is small (1994/98 average 8 per cent of total production) and the quality of some that is produced leaves a lot to be desired. However, some winemakers do now consistently manage to produce very acceptable results and there is a much greater understanding of which varieties perform well (Rondo, Dornfelder and Pinot noir are the current favourites) and how to extract colour. Oak is also used quite widely in the maturation of red wines. The production of sweet dessert wines, of which again there is an increasing number, is another remarkable aspect of the UK wine industry. The first seemed to have been produced more by accident than design when rampant *botrytis* infected varieties such as Huxelrebe, Ortega and Optima which led to classic *pourriture noble* as found in Sauternes or in German vineyards, rather than the damaging *pourriture gris* more commonly experienced in the UK. These early experiments, which on occasion produced wines of very high natural sugar levels and of superb quality, persuaded growers and winemakers that we could produce this style of wine on a regular basis. Today, wines labelled as 'dessert', 'noble' and '*botrytis*' are to be found on the wine lists of many vineyards and the quality of the best is excellent. As growers and winemakers gain more experience in their production and as consumers come to appreciate them, this style of wine will undoubtedly appear more often.

The last 20 years has seen a marked change in wine styles and types sold in the UK. In the late 1960s and 1970s, when English wines started making an impact on consumers, the biggest selling wines in the UK were Liebfraumilch and other German styles. Whilst there is no doubt that price played a great part in their popularity, these wines did find favour with a large sector of the wine-buying public who liked their easy, unpretentious style. In many respects the better English wines were similar – light and fruity, with a little residual sugar and not too heavy in alcohol – and they met with the approval of many consumers. In the 1980s, the tastes of UK winedrinkers started to change. Consumers seemed to want drier wines, perhaps because wine was appearing more and more at meal times, perhaps because palates were becoming more sophisticated. Wines from Australia started making a big impact on consumers and gradually the liking for German-style wines reduced so that today's largest selling brands in the UK are the Australian Jacob's Creek range and Gallo's Californian wines. English and Welsh wines have reflected these changes in the market, and today very few growers bottle in tall German-style Hock and Mosel bottles, preferring to use the non-country specific Burgundy (in brown or green) and Bordeaux (in green or clear) bottles. Many growers also refrain from using the Germanic sounding varietal names such as Müller-Thurgau, Reichensteiner, Huxelrebe etc. and will now give their wines more descriptive names (Stanlake Park, Downland Dry) believing (correctly in my view) that Germanic varietal names are both confusing and off-putting to the consumer. Those using varieties such as Bacchus, Ortega and Pinot noir, names which appear to be more acceptable to consumers, continue to do so.

As in almost all other walks of life, the only unchanging element in the wine business is change itself. If UK winegrowers are to survive and prosper, they must make wines that respond to the demands of their customers and reflect what it is that the market actually wants. In order to increase returns, cheaper ways of growing vines will have to be found and adopted and ways have to be found of increasing average yields. Whether this will be by adopting better trellising and training techniques and through improved vineyard management or whether it will be by planting rootstocks, varieties and clones of varieties more suited to our climate and to the types of wine demanded by consumers, only time will tell. The trend to produce 'added-value' wines – bottle-fermented and red in particular – that offer better returns will continue as growers strive to make their enterprises profitable. The reduction in both the number of vineyards and the area of vines in production will in all probability continue as some growers face the inevitable consequences of poorly performing vineyards, old age and changes in fortune. Those who are managing to run their vineyards economically and who are producing wines that fit the market in terms of both style and price will benefit from the reduction in the number of different English and Welsh wines on retail shelves.

4

English Vineyards Association and the United Kingdom Vineyards Association

By the mid-1960s there were enough vineyards in the country for a growers' association to be formed and discussions were held with the Ministry of Agriculture, Fisheries and Food (MAFF) to determine how this could best be done. It was decided to form an association under the auspices of the Agricultural Central Co-operative Association Ltd and in October 1965 a meeting was held at Beaulieu to elect a Steering Committee and to choose a name for the new association. It was agreed that it would be called 'The British Viticultural Association'. This, however, was rejected by the Board of Trade but an alternative, the 'English Vineyards Association' (EVA), was accepted. Wales was not included in the name as a 'Welsh Vine Growers Association' had been formed in September 1965. The Steering Committee held its first meeting on 15 November 1966. The first Annual General Meeting was subsequently held on 18 January 1967 at which the following were elected: President, Sir Guy Salisbury-Jones; Vice-President, Lady Montagu of Beaulieu; Chairman, Jack Ward; Vice-Chairman, P. Tyson-Woodcock; Secretary, Irene Barrett; and Director, Robin Don. In addition to the elected officers, there were eight full members and twelve associates.

The growth of interest in winegrowing in the country over the next few years was quite remarkable. By the end of 1968, although the number of full members – those owning at least half an acre of vines – had only risen to fifteen, the number of associate members had shot up to over 100. This was the start of the era of much larger, more commercially orientated vineyards and over the next five years, a number of major vineyards were planted. These, together with a large number of smaller vineyards, really caused the public, especially the wine buying and vineyard visiting public, to take an interest in the country's vineyards and their wines. By the end of 1972, the EVA had 330 members and associates, farming 200 acres of vines, with an additional 100 acres ready to be planted in the spring of 1973.

In the early years, the EVA was run very much on a shoestring and the amount it could do to help winegrowers was necessarily limited. Members' events included annual tastings, visits to overseas shows, and symposia on winegrowing. It also published an annual newsletter which continued until 1978 when *The Grape Press*, a bi-monthly publication, replaced it. The EVA also recognized that it had a duty to members of the public who were interested in buying English and Welsh wines. It therefore did what it could to promote them as well as answer the many inquiries it received on the subject. The Association also felt it had a duty, if not actually physically to help growers improve their wines, then to do what it could to recognise those wines that were good. In 1978, after six years of negotiations with the authorities, the EVA received permission to introduce a Certification Trade Mark, known as the the EVA Seal of Quality which gave wines, after they had been analysed and been before a tasting panel and approved on both counts, a recognised seal of approval that could be affixed to bottles. This scheme ran until 1995 when the official EU approved Quality Wine Scheme was introduced. In 1974, the EVA established the English Wine of the Year competition and Margaret Gore-Browne donated a magnificent silver bowl in memory of her husband Robert which was to be presented for the best wine in the competition. Since then, as the number and styles of wines entered has increased, several other trophies have been donated and today the Gore-Browne Trophy has been joined by the Jack Ward Memorial Salver and the President's, the Wine Guild of the United Kingdom, the Vintner's and the Maggie McNie trophies. The competition has, by showing growers and winemakers what their peers have been making, greatly helped to improve wine quality. Another function of the EVA was the need to represent the interests of growers and winemakers with the various authorities who regulate and control the industry. Since its founding, the EVA has held regular meetings with MAFF, HM Customs and Excise and the Wine Standards Board (WSB).

By 1978, for legal reasons, substantial changes to the status of the EVA were needed and in February 1979 it was incorporated as a company limited by guarantee, rather than one registered under the Industrial and Provident Societies Act. The finances of the Association were always balanced fairly finely, and during the early 1970s subscription income rarely covered expenses. In 1976, in addition to an annual subscription, a levy on each acre of vines in production was introduced and this greatly helped matters. In 1980, the management of the association also required changes when Irene Barrett, who had been unpaid Secretary since its inception, retired. Her place was taken by Kenneth McAlpine, owner of Lamberhurst Vineyards, which at that time was by far the largest wine producer in the UK. McAlpine also became Treasurer. In April 1981, Sir Guy Salisbury-Jones decided to retire from his position as President of the EVA and his place was taken by Lord Montagu of Beaulieu. Jack Ward also stood down from his position as Chairman of the Board of the EVA, a post he had held since 1967 and his place was taken by Colin Gillespie of Wootton Vineyards.

As more and more vineyards were planted and production levies started to produce solid income, the finances of the EVA improved, and at the AGM in April 1985 the membership felt that the Association was sufficiently strong to consider appointing its first full-time employee. In October 1985, Commander Geoffrey Bond RN (rtd) was appointed to the post of Chief Executive and for the next ten years he ran the EVA from an office in his house in London, dealing with a multitude of enquiries from all and sundry, handling press inquiries, talking to groups and associations and generally being 'Mr English Wine' whenever required. The EVA also appointed Anthony Steen, MP for South Hams in Devon, as its official (paid) parliamentary advisor, and for six years Steen made sure that the industry's concerns were heard in Westminster.

During the 1980s, the EVA prospered, with new vineyards being planted all over the south of the country, some good harvests and a buoyant membership list. A combination of subscription income and production levies allowed the association's reserves to build to a considerable size. As a result of this optimism in the industry, the regional associations also became strong and started, to a certain extent, to take over some of the functions of the EVA, considered to be the central body and therefore more concerned with national issues. Some members of the regional associations saw no need to belong to the EVA as they felt that they were getting all the benefits locally. From about 1990, the membership of the EVA began to fall and with it its income, while its work continued to grow. More was spent on publicity, the duties of its staff did not contract and negotiations with the authorities grew as changes to the EU Wine Regime threatened to harm growers. By 1992/93 it had become clear that the situation could not continue indefinitely and changes to the Association's structure had to be made.

The next eighteen months were taken up with the long and at times difficult process of changing the entire structure of the EVA. After considerable discussion and debate with both its own members and those of the six regional associations, a situation was reached where it was generally agreed that a new company, the United Kingdom Vineyards Association (UKVA) would be formed. The UKVA's members would be those who were members of its affiliated associations and its board of directors would be drawn exclusively from those. The UKVA would have no independent means of raising revenue from its members and all funding would come from the affiliated regional associations. On paper this seemed a workable solution and a further twelve months were taken up with the practicalities of drawing up and approving the Memorandum and Articles of Association. By the mid-summer of 1996, everything was in place for a handover of control and assets from the EVA to the UKVA. In the event, only five of the six eligible regional associations decided to become affiliated. The Thames and Chilterns Vineyards Association (T&CVA), which had been party to the negotiations and deliberations right up to the last, decided that they did not wish to be affiliated. They had reservations about the decisions taken by the majority of the EVA Board and decided that these were not the best way forward for the association. They therefore felt that they could not support the Board's decisions and decided to remain independent. It was a pity that unanimity could not have been maintained to the end, but the remainder felt, in the event, that five out of six was actually not too bad a result. The first meeting of the UKVA was held on 15 July 1996.

The functions of the UKVA remained much the same as those of the EVA. Organising meetings for members – the annual conference and the Vintners' Symposium – publishing the *Grape Press*, running the annual Wine of the Year Competition and the House of Lords prizegiving, operating the Quality and Regional Wine Schemes, liaising with members of the public, wine trade and media who wanted information about English and Welsh wine, arranging tastings of one sort or another, organising council meetings,

meetings with MAFF, Customs and Excise, Wine Standards Board, plus the hundred and one other things that a national association is asked to do. The fact that the regional associations were now both responsible for the running and financing of the association, meant that some of the work previously carried out by the central organisation could be left to the regions. In 1998, the UKVA formed a UK Winegrowers Committee under the auspices of the Wine and Spirits Association of Great Britain, thus giving it a more powerful voice when looking after the interests of its members. Today, the UKVA is lean but fit and in co-operation with the committees of the five affiliated regional associations, is looking after the interests of both its members and promoting, as far as its finances allow, English and Welsh wines. Its most recent success was, in conjunction with English Wine Producers (a group of the larger producers), to secure a grant of over £30,000 from MAFF for the promotion of an English wine quality mark, together with setting up an industry web-site, training of tasters to take part in the Quality and Regional wine schemes and training in viticulture and winemaking.

In December 2000, the T&CVA agreed to affiliate to the UKVA so that from 1 February 2001, the UKVA now represents the interests of all English and Welsh winegrowers.

Chairmen of the EVA

Jack Ward OBE	1967–1981
Colin Gillespie	1981–1987
Anthony Goddard	1987–1990
Ian Berwick	1990–1993
Robin Don	1993–1995
Ian Berwick	1995–1999
Stephen Skelton	1999–

The UKVA can be contacted at: Church Road, Bruisyard, Saxmundham, Suffolk IP17 2EF
Telephone: 01728 63808
Fax: 0870 136 3708
e-mail: 106236.463@compuserve.com

5

The Ministry of Agriculture, Fisheries and Food

WINE GROWING AND OFFICIALDOM

In the early days of the viticultural revival, the Ministry of Agriculture, Fisheries and Food (MAFF) took an active interest in the subject, and for twenty years there was an official National Vines Advisor who could be called upon to advise growers through the Agricultural Development and Advisory Service (ADAS). The first person to occupy this position was Tony Heath, a soft-fruit advisor based at the Efford Experimental Husbandry Station (EHS) at Lymington near Southampton. Although principally a strawberry specialist, he took a great personal interest in vines and was responsible for writing two MAFF publications on the subject: *Outdoor Grape Production* in 1978 and *Grapes for Wine* in 1980. Both these books were very well written and apart from some misinformation about what varieties we were actually allowed to plant (the books stated that any variety not on the Recommended or Authorised lists may be regarded as 'under test in the UK' and used for commercial wine production) contained much useful information for growers. After Heath retired, his position was taken in turn by Joanna Wood, Sheila Baxter and Jerry Garner, all of whom gave advice to growers on matters viticultural. Efford EHS had its own vineyard, planted in 1975, which undertook variety and trellising trials, as well as trials on vine nutrition, fungicides and weed control. It published several useful reports, hosted 'Open Days' and while it lasted, provided some useful information. In 1986 MAFF decided that running the vineyard was an expense it could do without and it was grubbed. One serious flaw in MAFF's approach to helping those growing grapes in the UK – given that these were solely wine varieties on which growers were being advised – was that it was adamant that its job finished at harvest time and winemaking matters were totally outside its remit. Many felt that it would have been more helpful if MAFF's advice could have covered all aspects of wine production. In recent years, with the privatisation of ADAS, the position of National Vines Advisor has lain dormant, and advice, certainly free advice, on viticulture is no longer available.

Relations with MAFF, as the authority governing the production of wine both before the UK joined the European Union and since 1973 after we joined, have always been important for UK grape growers and winemakers. To begin with, the English Vineyards Association (EVA) was invited by MAFF to meetings to discuss matters that affected the industry, such as grape varieties, winery practices, labelling legislation, pesticide registrations and a wide range of other topics. These meetings, which became known as the English and Welsh Wine Liaison Committee, were purely advisory and deliberations and decisions carried no official weight. When the 1985 voluntary MAFF survey showed that the area under vines in the UK had risen to 488 ha, two things became self-evident. The voluntary nature of the survey meant that the area was almost certainly under-reported and therefore probably over 500 ha, and a far wider range of varieties was being grown than those allowed under the regulations. These fears were confirmed two years later when the next survey revealed that the area under vines had risen to 546 ha. Action had to be taken.

VINE VARIETIES

Under Community regulations, each member state with 500 ha of vines or more has to have not only an official Vineyard Register but also a committee whose task it is to monitor and manage the lists of grape varieties being grown and make proposals to the Commission for changes. Therefore, at the next Liaison Committee meeting, it was agreed that a Vine Varieties Classification Committee (VVCC) would be established whose task it would be to look at the existing lists of varieties permitted to be grown in the UK and suggest changes. This committee was made up of industry representatives from around the country, together with representatives from the National Farmer's Union (NFU), ADAS, and the Welsh Office Agricultural Department (WOAD).

In 1973 the list of 'recommended' varieties (those which were then considered to be the most successful) consisted of just three; Müller-Thurgau, Auxerrois and Wrotham Pinot. This was a rather curious list because Auxerrois was barely grown in the UK and Wrotham Pinot was the name given to a variety found by Edward Hyams growing on a cottage wall in Wrotham, Kent and had no official status. This selection had ultimately been made by MAFF, although the EVA had been consulted. However, although the industry had never been very happy with it, for practical purposes its contents made no difference to anyone's choice of varieties to plant since until the 500 ha limit was reached, neither MAFF nor the WSB appeared to be concerned.

At its first meeting, held on 3 July 1989, the VVCC came up with a proposal to reorganise the lists of varieties and in July 1990 the 'recommended' list for the UK was officially changed so that it consisted of the six most widely grown and successful varieties; Huxelrebe, Madeleine × Angevine 7672, Müller-Thurgau, Reichensteiner, Schönburger and Seyval blanc, dropping Auxerrois and Wrotham Pinot to 'authorised' status. (In 1998, following further submissions, Bacchus was added to the 'recommended' list.) Likewise, the list of 'authorised' varieties was substantially altered to reflect the then current plantings. Since the first meeting, the VVCC has been instrumental in completely reorganising the lists of permitted varieties, removing all those of little practical use and introducing those actually used and showing promise. The practical result of this is that growers may use these varieties to make wine for sale and in addition use the names of these varieties on their labels. (Wines made from unofficial varieties have to be labelled as 'UK Table Wine' and may not bear a varietal name nor a vintage date.)

QUALITY WINE SCHEME

Reaching the 500 ha limit in 1987 caused the WSB to start the process of drawing up a Vineyard Register – a national list of all vineyards containing exact plot locations and sizes, together with both variety and rootstock names. The following year (1989)

MAFF conducted a statutory survey of all vineyards over one-tenth of a hectare (100 ares) then known to exist. Given that it was not – and is still not – obligatory to register the ownership of a vineyard unless it is producing grapes or wine for sale, this survey was bound to be a little bit hit and miss. However, comprehensive or not, the survey showed a remarkable increase in the area under vines. The total of 546 ha with 382 ha in production in 1988 jumped by over 60 per cent to 876 ha with 652 ha in production. More interesting were the yield figures. From a declared production of 4,110 hl – equivalent to 548,000 75 cl bottles – in 1988, the 1989 figure had shot to 21,447 hl or 2,859,600 75 cl bottles – a 520 per cent increase! Although this was partly due to better weather in 1989 and therefore a larger yield, it was obvious that pre-1989 surveys were only picking up the smaller, less productive vineyards and those with larger yields had, for whatever reason, declined to send in their returns.

The reason for concern over the high yield figure, both within the industry and with UK officialdom, was the existence of an EU-wide vine planting ban which applied in all member states whose annual production was in excess of 25,000 hl of wine. (This limit had originally been set at 5,000 hl and a planting ban had been mooted in 1979 to take effect in 1980/1, but the EVA had successfully petitioned MAFF at the time and the limit was raised to 25,000 hl. In 1993, when a 26,428 hl yield was announced for the 1992 harvest, MAFF successfully appealed to the Commission to take a five-year average yield figure, rather than one single year. This was accepted and is the current position. The latest five-year average yield – 1995/1999 – is 14,104 hl.)

The only official way around the planting ban was to either buy planting rights from a grower who was permanently giving up growing vines (the usual way for growers in the remainder of the EU to expand their vineyard holdings) or to apply to the authorities for permission. In this latter case, growers who wished to plant new vineyards could only do so for the production of quality wines which could be shown to be in demand by the market. The discovery that the UK had what was probably nearer 1000 ha of vines than 500 ha and in good years was capable of producing well over 25 hl/ha meant that we were in serious danger of breaching the 25,000 hl barrier which would, according to the strict interpretation of the regulations, precipitate a planting ban in the

UK. Given we had no Quality Wine Scheme (QWS), a crop in excess of this figure would have ended all new vine planting in the UK.

In early 1990, as soon as the results of the 1989 vineyard survey were known, MAFF decided that the answer to this possible problem was to set up a Quality Wine Scheme Committee (QWSC) whose task it would be to draw up a full 'Quality Wine Produced in a Specified Region' (QWpsr) scheme to give English and Welsh wines full *appellation contrôlée* status. The membership of the committee was largely based on that of the VVCC and set to work as soon as it could. Over the next eighteen months, the committee met on an almost monthly basis in an attempt to hammer out a scheme that would satisfy the demands of a diverse number of interested parties. The scheme had to conform to existing EU regulations and ultimately be approved by the Commission; it had to be practical with regard to the conditions governing wine production in England and Wales and to be one that growers found both acceptable and affordable; above all it had to be a scheme that, as far as was possible, guaranteed to the wine trade, the wine press and the wine-buying public, that a wine that had passed through the scheme was of genuine 'quality' status – whatever that word meant!

To satisfy the EU regulations was in one sense the easiest, in another the hardest. The regulations had been drawn up with a fairly broad brush so that they could cope with the myriad of different production conditions across the climatic and cultural spread of Europe. They had also been drawn up with one eye on the preservation of each region's 'traditional' practices. The fact that the UK had played no part in drawing up the regulations, and in any event was a relative newcomer to winegrowing and winemaking, meant that our tally of 'traditional' practices was fairly small. The one big impediment to getting a scheme that satisfied both the regulations and the majority of growers was the thorny problem of hybrids (vines with some non-*vitis vinifera* genetic material in them), which under EU regulations, were excluded from all QWpsr schemes. For many growers in the UK this was a difficult pill to swallow. Apart from Seyval blanc, which at the time was, and still is today, the third most widely planted variety, there were a number of older hybrid varieties (Cascade, Léon Millot, Maréchal Foch and Triomphe) together with some newer ones (Orion, Phoenix, Regent and Rondo) which growers found useful. Hybrids covered over 15 per cent of the total UK vine area and produced approximately

25 per cent of the UK's wine – a higher percentage than their area because of their higher than average yield. These varieties, apart from the fact that they existed in grower's vineyards and in most cases were useful and disease resistant, were all capable of being made into good wines. A majority on the committee thought that the UK should have a scheme that would promote, protect and guarantee English and Welsh wines solely on an objective, scientific basis, and to introduce a scheme that discriminated against one class of vines solely on the basis of their 'race' was flawed and would, if not bring the scheme into disrepute, at least lower its attraction to growers wishing to enter their wines. Wines containing even the slightest trace of wine made from hybrids would be excluded, so for many wineries, most of their wines would be ineligible. The EVA representatives on the committee urged that the scheme should be drawn up so that it 'recognized our national circumstances'.

The arguments over whether hybrids could or could not, should or should not be included in the QWS went on for many meetings. Representations were made to the Commission and their ruling was that they could not, and furthermore the basic regulations could only be altered by a qualified majority of the Council of Ministers. MAFF pointed out quite forcefully that this was a highly unlikely occurrence. Knowing that a 25,000 hl yield could be just around the corner and that a Brussels-imposed vine planting ban would not reflect well upon them and would not help relations with the general farming community ('MAFF introduces vine-planting ban' was not the headline anyone wanted to see), MAFF decided that a scheme should go ahead without the inclusion of hybrids. Once the basic framework of the scheme had been drawn up, a number of options and alternatives were still open and a 'consultation exercise' was carried out amongst interested parties – growers, wine producers, EVA members and associates, academic institutions, consumer and promotional organisations, central and local government departments, the press and wine writers, and the wine trade. In March 1991, a consultation document was sent out to 942 addresses (including those of 420 registered growers). Of these, 183 were returned which MAFF considered a very good response. Analysis of the survey showed that a large majority (90.44 per cent) of respondents felt that hybrids ought to be allowed in the scheme and that without them, the scheme would have less validity. Only 7 per cent of respondents wanted a scheme that excluded hybrids. Despite this overwhelming response in favour of hybrids, MAFF insisted that the scheme go ahead without them.

In many other respects, the QWS was fairly straightforward to design. Apart from the issue of varieties, there was less contention over such subjects as minimum natural alcohols, the geographical areas covered, whether wines could be made in one area from grapes grown in another, whether irrigation should be allowed (it was not) and what the yield restrictions should be. As to what should actually constitute a 'quality wine', the committee relied heavily on the existing EVA 'Seal of Quality' regulations. With only a few amendments and adjustments to the analytical requirements, it was able to lift almost entirely the 'Seal' regulations and place them in the scheme. Wines would be subject to a fairly stringent analysis which looked at not only the simple physical aspects such as the alcohol, acid, sulphur dioxide, iron and copper contents, but also the wine's sterility status (bacteria and yeasts) and its stability with regard to both proteins and tartrate. It had been found with the operation of the 'Seal' that the sterility and stability requirements had been valuable in weeding out those winemakers whose winemaking and bottling practices were not really up to standard; whilst they might have been able to produce wines of fine quality on the day of the tasting, they did not keep in the hands of the wine merchant or final customer. The wines would be tasted by a panel of between five and seven members, at least two of whom would be Masters of Wine, and would follow the 'Seal' twenty-point tasting schedule that had proved simple and workable. The minimum natural alcoholic strength of wines eligible for quality wines status, i.e. their potential alcohol level at harvest and before enrichment (chaptalisation) was set at 6½ per cent. A derogation existed that allowed member states to reduce this to 6 per cent and was applied for but was not granted until December 1991, too late for it to apply to wines from the 1991 vintage.

By the early summer of 1991, a basic scheme had been drawn up and was almost ready to be submitted to the Commission for its comments. The issue of hybrids remained unsettled, with a majority on the committee unwilling to see a scheme introduced which discriminated against these varieties. This majority suggested that the scheme be held in abeyance until such time as a planting ban was threatened. MAFF however, thought otherwise. Fearing the arrival of a greater than 25,000 hl crop, they were determined to press ahead with its introduction for the 1991 harvest. In an attempt to placate the pro-hybrid lobby, the then junior Agriculture Minister, David Curry, went to Brussels and on 30 May 1991 returned waving a piece of paper (in what some of us thought was a rather Neville Chamberlain 'Peace in our Time' sort of way) which promised that 'the Commission will study the possibility of including inter-specific [hybrid] varieties in the list of varieties deemed suitable for the production of quality wine produced in a specified region'. (In May 2000, after almost ten years of waiting and many questions to the Commission, it was agreed that this study will be carried out and must be completed by 31 December 2003. The only problem facing the Commission now is to find a suitably impartial organisation to undertake the study and come up with an answer which offends nobody!)

The last hurdle to be overcome before the scheme could be submitted to the Commission was that of the geographical delineation and naming of the 'specified regions' of production. Various suggestions as to how the UK might be split up into separate quality wine production regions had already been made. An obvious solution was to create regions largely based upon the existing regional vineyards association areas – East Anglia, the South East, Wessex, the South West etc – but this was quickly found to be unacceptable, once the rules on the naming of quality wine regions had been fully digested. Under the rules contained in Council Regulations 823/87 (as amended by Reg. 2043/89) grapes grown in one region could only be made into a quality wine in the same region or in an 'administrative region' (taken to mean a county) that was in 'immediate proximity' (taken to mean having a common border) to the one where the grapes were grown, so grapes from Essex for example could not have been made into quality wine in Gloucestershire had these two counties been in non-adjacent quality wine regions. The only derogation to these rules was if the practice was both 'traditional' and had taken place 'continuously since before 1973 and . . . met other specified conditions'. Since the first two restrictions could not be met by any winery in the UK, no one bothered to inquire what the 'other specified conditions were! As a trade in grapes between vineyards and wineries across the UK existed, it was felt that the 'multiple region' approach would not work and that a 'two region' approach (where one region was contiguous with another) would be best. Another problem which a multiple region system would have exacerbated was that juice used for sweetening quality wines (often called süss-reserve) had to originate from the same region in which the grapes were grown and two larger regions would make for more flexibility than several smaller ones. The option favoured by the industry members of the committee was to split the UK into two adjacent regions – England and Wales – which would have resulted in two descriptors; 'English Quality Wine psr' and 'Welsh Quality Wine psr'. Given these two regions, Welsh grapes could be taken to wineries in English counties bordering Wales, which was an important consideration given the location of the Three Choirs Winery in Gloucestershire which made wines under contract for several smaller Welsh growers.

The question of what to call table wines also had to be addressed, given that the Wine Standards Board (WSB) – responsible for policing labelling in the UK – felt that 'English Quality Wine psr' and 'English Table Wine' would not have been acceptable to the Commission. One solution, which had the approval of the industry members of the QWC, was to call them all 'United Kingdom Table Wines'. This solution was accepted by the committee and a final draft of the 'Pilot Quality Wine Scheme' (as it was initially known) was sent out to all growers in August 1991 so that wines from the 1991 vintage would be able to be considered for Quality Wine status. The WSB stated that they felt that the scheme was being hurriedly introduced and that they were really not ready to handle the additional work as the Vineyard Register was not fully completed.

Feedback from the industry soon showed that it was less than keen on re-naming its table wines by the proposed descriptor 'United Kingdom Table Wines', especially those with wines which, because they were made wholly or partly from hybrids, were not eligible for inclusion in the QWS. Once the Wine Standards Board had pointed out that certain information on labels – the name of the grape variety being the main one – could only appear on wines where the geographical descriptor covered an area smaller than the member state, this solution was effectively dead. The industry members of the committee urged MAFF to reconsider the idea to have both 'English Quality Wine' and 'English Table Wine' or some other variant which incorporated the words 'England' or 'English' (and their Welsh/Wales equivalents), but it was felt that the

Commission would not accept this. After considerable discussion and several committee meetings, and with the 1991 harvest already completed, a typical bureaucratic solution was arrived at. Two regions would be created, one called 'Northern Counties' (Durham, Humberside, South Yorkshire and West Yorkshire) which contained almost no vineyards and one called 'Southern Counties' which contained almost all existing vineyards. In addition, vines for quality wine production had to be situated below 220 metres above sea level, a height chosen with some care, as it was known that no vineyards were planted above this height, yet it further defined the geographical limits of the region.

However bizarre it seemed, this solution did allow grapes and juice to be shipped around the wine producing counties, got round the problem of re-naming table wines and satisfied MAFF and the Commission. Despite general industry opposition, letters to the Minister and a leader in *Decanter Magazine*, in January 1992 this solution was steam-rollered through committee. With the 1991 wines already made and eligible for Quality Wine status, a decision had to be made quickly and the committee was advised that this was the best stop-gap solution. Industry members of the committee felt that MAFF should have been more forceful in interpreting the regulations to suit the UK's geographical and climatic circumstances, especially as MAFF was prepared to base regions on nothing other than what was in reality administrative convenience. The fact that the regulations stipulated that a quality wine region had to describe 'a wine-growing area . . . which produces wines with particular quality characteristics' did not seem to bother anyone too much. With the best will in the world, wines from 'Southern Counties' (i.e. virtually the whole of the UK's vineyard area) could hardly be said to show any 'particular quality characteristics' that would distinguish them from those of the 'Northern Counties' especially as so few wines from this area existed!

At the same January meeting, the use of two alternative wine 'descriptors' was accepted and it was agreed that wines could be labelled 'Quality Wine' or 'Designated Origin'. Originally it had been hoped, at least by most industry committee members, that a single descriptor – that of 'Designated Origin' (similar to that used in *all* other EU member states apart from Germany) would have been acceptable to MAFF. The thinking behind this was that growers whose wines were ineligible to be entered for the scheme –

mainly because they were made in whole or in part from non-*vinifera* grapes – would be at a disadvantage by the appearance of the word 'Quality' on some wines, but not on theirs, even though they might be of equal – or even better – quality. However, MAFF officials announced that the Minister 'could not ban the term 'Quality Wine produced in a specified region' and risked prosecution if he did so. Again, the fact that most wine-producing member states *had* interpreted the regulations to suit their own purposes and had effectively banned the use of this alternative term counted for nothing – another example of UK officials playing by the rules to the disadvantage of its own citizens!

The completed scheme was quickly agreed by the Commission, the necessary Statutory Instruments were drawn up and issued, and the Pilot Quality Wine Scheme was incorporated into UK legislation. The English Vineyards Association had been appointed to be the 'recognised industry body' which was responsible for handling applications to the scheme and sending wines to be analysed and tasted. The first tasting was held on 18 May 1992 at which ten wines, which had already been analysed and had cleared the analytical requirements, were tasted. All passed and, after the producer's winemaking records had been inspected, were given quality wine status.

Over the years since the original 'pilot' scheme was incorporated into UK legislation, several changes have been made. Some sort of sense prevailed in the naming of the regions and various proposals were looked at. Eventually, after considerable argument in committee about what other member states were allowed to do (i.e. get away with) MAFF accepted that the terms 'English Vineyards' and 'Welsh Vineyards' could be used as the names of the quality wine 'specified regions'. These regions covered all English and Welsh counties that contained vineyards, so long as those vineyards were no more than 220 metres above sea level. These terms were felt to be sufficiently different from 'English Table Wine' and 'Welsh Table Wine' not to incur the displeasure of the Commission. In 1996, when a 'Regional Wine Scheme' (equivalent to the French 'Vin de Pays' category) was introduced to give some sort of quality status to wines made from non-*vinifera* varieties, the terms 'English Counties' and 'Welsh Counties' were adopted, covering exactly the same geographical areas as the quality wine regions, but being sufficiently different as vines growing over 220 metres above sea level were accepted, despite the fact that no vines were being grown – or indeed would be likely to ripen – at this altitude. Thus, in the naming of the three categories of wine allowed to be produced in the UK – Table Wine, Regional Wine and Quality Wine – the three descriptors and the regions they covered are, whilst in fact the same, on paper sufficiently different to satisfy the *amour-propre* of both Ministers and officials, as well as offering lip service to the regulations!

6

Viticulture and Vinification

This is not intended to be a handbook for grape growers or winemakers, but some mention of the systems of growing vines and comment on the methods of making wines that are used in the UK is necessary if the wines are to be fully understood and appreciated. For the specialist there is a large number of excellent books on both topics from around the world and several are listed in the bibliography at the end of this book.

SITE SELECTION

Poor site selection has probably been one of the major reasons why many English and Welsh vineyards have failed to last the course. The desire to own a vineyard and to have one's name on the label has led growers in the past to plant vineyards on really hopeless sites: windswept or frost-prone with soils unsuited and undrained and where the quality of the wine produced has never been good. It is a sad fact that despite all the experiences of the past, it is still happening.

Ask many past and present vineyard owners 'Why did you plant here?' and the answer is still often (depressingly) 'Because it was there!'. Many growers plant land that they already own, convinced for some reason that it will be good enough and ignoring what could be learnt from past grower's mistakes. Of course, site selection is not down to just picking the most suitable piece of land in the neighbourhood and planting it. It has to be for sale, it has to be accessible, in many instances it has to come with a house to live in and some buildings to make wine in. Compromises often have to be made and one of the surprising things about English and Welsh wines – given the degree of care that went into site selection – is that some of them are as good as they are!

Overseas, where vines have been growing in some regions for centuries, site selection is less of a problem. The Old World wine regions are mapped in the minutest detail and *appellation* boundaries are based on the suitability of certain sites to produce wines true to the *appellation* ideals. In any event, in climates warmer than the UK's, the pressure to find sites where vines can fruit and grapes can ripen is less; there are many more of them. It always has to be remembered that we are growing vines in the coolest winegrowing region in the world and we must grasp whatever natural advantages there are by correct site selection. Lighter, sandy soils, with good natural drainage are to be favoured and soils that overlie even leaner sand and gravel deposits are best of all. MAFF used to publish an excellent booklet called *Soils and Manures for Fruit* (Bulletin 107) which listed all the suitable fruit soils in the UK, together with their attributes. Prospective vine growers should ignore the advice given on page 14 (of the 1975 edition) which states that vines are less susceptible to 'adverse drainage conditions than most fruit crops', but take the advice which says that 'shallow or coarse sandy soils are acceptable'. The advice on page 2 that 'aspect is not of great importance except for vines which need a southerly slope' and that 'land above 400 ft is not suitable' should also be noted. Suffice it to say that one can drag a horse to water but making it drink is another matter!

Despite the availability of advice from both books and consultants, many vineyards in the UK, both past and present, have been planted on sites unlikely to allow vines to prosper and this, sadly, has been reflected in the quality of the wine produced. The importance of choosing south facing slopes, rather than flat sites (the second choice if south facing sites are not available) or sites facing in other directions, especially north, is set out by George Ordish in great detail in his book *Vineyards in England and Wales* (1977). Any prospective vineyard owner searching for a site to grow vines on in the UK should read it. In an annex, Ordish quotes a thesis written by Nick Poulter of Cranmore Vineyards which accurately states that although the amount of sunshine reaching a 30° south facing slope compared to a level site will only be 8 per cent greater in midsummer (which is towards the beginning of the growing season), by October, when the grapes are struggling to amass sugars, it will be 70 per cent greater. To owners of level sites, let alone those with east, west or, heaven forbid, north facing sites, this is frightening information.

ROOTSTOCKS

The selection of the correct rootstock is something of a black art and wherever one goes through the winegrowing world, growers debate the matter endlessly. Most, but not all, rootstocks stem from crossings made in northern European nurseries. In France, Germany and Hungary the great vine breeders of the late nineteenth century developed many crosses using wild American vines as crossing partners to produce *phylloxera*-tolerant rootstocks. Over the intervening century or more since the aphid struck in Europe, the colleges and universities that specialise in vine breeding have clonally selected and improved those original varieties, increasing their *phylloxera* tolerance, improving their resistance to drought, to calcium rich soils and to nematodes (which spread viruses). There are hundreds of rootstocks available worldwide, with scores in regular use. (See Appendix IV, p. 497 for an annotated list.) On the UK's list of permitted rootstocks are 46 separate rootstock varieties, although probably no more than 10 are in use.

Which ones should be used in UK vineyards? This is a very debatable matter. Since most of our vines come from German nurserymen, most vines imported into the UK are only available on what would be, to a German grower, a standard rootstock. Whether these are the most appropriate for our varieties and soils is another thing altogether. Many of the UK's problems in growing and ripening grapes in sufficient quantity and quality stem from the fact that our vines suffer from excess vigour. Many of the German rootstocks in use in the UK – 5BB, SO4, 125AA and 5C – are all classed as 'vigorous' to 'very vigorous' and may not be helping this situation. Rootstocks with less vigour such as Riparia Gloire de Montpelier, 420A, 41B, 101/14 and 3309C, all of French origin, might just help in this battle. Unfortunately, very few of the varieties that we grow are grafted on to these rootstocks. Quite a few UK vineyards are planted on their own roots and although *phylloxera* is an ever present threat, some growers feel the risk worth taking.

Vines on their own roots are usually less vigorous than their counterparts on rootstocks and in many situations appear to break bud earlier, leading to a longer growing season. If a complete *cordon sanitaire* could be guaranteed around one's vineyard, these benefits (and those of cheaper home-produced rooted cuttings) might be worth the risk.

TRELLISING, TRAINING AND PRUNING SYSTEMS

Even after more than 50 years of growing vines in the UK, few in the business would claim that the question of how best to trellis, train and prune vines for our varieties and climate had been answered. Some may think that they have discovered a way in which they can just about get by, but not a way which guarantees good and consistent yields of quality fruit. Yields are still on average quite low (by the standards of other cool areas) and also very variable. If the English and Welsh wine industry is to continue for another fifty years, this aspect of production *has* to be addressed and a solution found. Very few growers can afford to subsidise their vineyards indefinitely.

In the early days of the revival there was great debate between those pre-disposed towards the wide-planted, extensive, spur-pruned Geneva Double Curtain (GDC) system and those who favoured a more European approach with more intensively planted, cane-pruned (Guyot) vines. Did GDC offer all the benefits its proponents suggested were there for the taking? Was it as cheap to establish as they said? Was the manpower required to manage a hectare of GDC trained vines really that low? Were crops really that large? The intensively planted Guyot growers claimed much earlier cropping (in year two to three, rather than year six to seven), better disease control and better wine quality. These benefits had to pay for the extra costs of establishing and growing cane-pruned vines planted relatively close together.

Since those early days, the debate over GDC versus Guyot seems to have quietened down and instead been replaced by a more technical approach to the problem using the new science of 'canopy management'. This term was invented by Dr Richard Smart and Mike Robinson whose seminal work *Sunlight into Wine – A Handbook for Winegrape Canopy Management* has become essential bedtime reading for modern viticulturalists worldwide. It covers not only how best to trellis vines for every situation, but also how to prune and care for the vines in the growing season in order to maximise both the quantity and quality of the crop. Whether all its advice is suited to UK conditions is open to debate. Our average yields are so much lower than those in many other countries (especially compared with New Zealand and Australia where much of the research work that led to *Sunlight* was done) that some of the 'Golden Rules' advocated by Richard Smart in both the book and during several Canopy Management Workshops that he has held in UK vineyards, do not really apply. However, the basic philosophy that underperforming vines with low yields can be helped by both leaving more fruiting wood per metre run of vine and by opening up the canopy to allow in as much light, heat and air as possible, still holds good, albeit to a lesser degree.

There is no doubt that in some years, GDC does work well in the UK. Whether this is because the vines are big and therefore individually stressed so that they fruit rather than grow excess canopy (known as the 'big vine' theory) is debatable. GDC trained vines in the UK seem just as vigorous as their Guyot-pruned counterparts. It may be, however, that the basal buds – which in a spur-pruned system are the only buds – are more fruitful because being close to a large body of permanent wood they are better supplied with reserves. These reserves (carbohydrates) also help the buds withstand spring frosts and in addition bring about a slightly earlier bud-burst leading to a marginally longer growing season. Disease control is still a problem in GDC vines, partly because there tends to be a lot of crossing-over of canes leading to much of the fruit getting covered up, but also because many growers do not possess sprayers of sufficient power capable of putting spray on to the target. When these two problems are addressed – by canopy management and by using more powerful air-blast sprayers – results do seem to improve.

However, there are still many Guyot growers who stick with their trellising and training systems, believing that despite the undoubted extra growing costs involved, the yields are higher, more consistent and of better quality. The additional capital costs of establishing a closely spaced, intensively planted vineyard are a reality, but taken over the twenty-five-year plus life of a vineyard, these do not add significantly to annual overheads. (GDC growers will also admit that a cheaply established vineyard, where the quality and quantity of posts and end-anchors have been skimped, is a false economy). Growing costs in closely planted Guyot vineyards can be lowered with the mechanisation of some vineyard operations – summer pruning in particular – and a more relaxed view of how often, and how severely, vines should be tucked in.

Few of the many other growing systems have found much favour in UK vineyards. There are a few growers using the Lyre system, but results show no distinct advantage over either GDC or Guyot and establishment costs are high. Some growers have found that vines trained on to a single curtain (which could be called a high Sylvoz system) achieve as much yield and as good a quality as other systems, yet growing costs can be lower. This system does have several advantages over both GDC and Guyot and with experience can be made to perform well. It seems to incorporate some of the advantages of GDC (lower capital costs, more fruitful buds, better frost resistance and lower growing costs) with the better yields and more effective disease control associated with Guyot-trained vineyards.

It is interesting to note that one fairly recent vineyard – Nyetimber – which is specialising in sparkling wine and which has been established using advice from Epernay, has planted narrow 1.6 m wide rows with single Guyot trained vines at 1.0 m apart – a planting density of 6,250 vines/hectare (2,530 v/acre). This is very near the original planting scheme that Hambledon adopted when they planted in 1951 and was followed by many others at the time. Most decided that it was an unmanageable system for UK conditions – the costs of summer pruning and training were too high – and very few vineyards survived with vines trained in this way. However, with the high quality of product coming out of Nyetimber, it cannot be long before their planting scheme is copied on the basis of 'if they can do it, so can we'. Of course quality is not the only criteria to take into account and a prudent grower would wish to be satisfied that this system can produce the correct yields (and yield means income per hectare, not just tonnes of grapes) as well as the correct quality.

How training and trellising in UK vineyards will change in the future is open to debate. Growers tend to get used to the systems they initially adopt, partly one suspects because change is either impossible or prohibitively expensive and also because no one likes to admit that they were wrong! Given that they are stuck with their chosen system, they tend to adapt and modify it to suit their individual circumstances and equipment and put up with its imperfections. Whether this attitude can be sustained is one that ultimately comes down to economics – few can support really low yields for ever.

The viticultural equipment used in UK vineyards has changed little since the early days. Tractors have got a little more powerful and four-wheel drives are now quite common. Sprayers are more efficient with low and ultra-low nozzles widespread, although not always effective for controlling diseases such as powdery mildew. A very recent introduction in two vineyards (Denbies and RidgeView) has been 're-circulation' sprayers where excess spray that passes right through the row is caught by a screen, filtered and returned to the spray tank. This is claimed to reduce the cost of the chemicals used by up to 50 per cent. Many vineyards now mechanise their summer pruning with tractor-mounted trimmers. Most vineyards control weeds below the vines with chemicals – a few do use automatic under-vine hoes – and have grass alleyways between the rows of vines which are kept mown. In general, very few new techniques of growing vines or new machinery are seen in UK vineyards, mainly because of the relatively small size of most vineyards and of the whole industry. It is simply not worth importing the latest equipment when sales levels are likely to be minute. This does put UK growers at something of disadvantage.

WINEMAKING

About the only aspect of the production of wine in England and Wales that does not really differ from other parts of the world is that of winemaking. Whilst we do have natural sugar levels that some winemakers might find discouragingly low and acid levels that would have winemakers from warmer climes rushing for their text books, in essence the task of turning UK-grown grapes into wine is much the same as it is in wineries worldwide.

When the first few vineyards of the revival started cropping, the level of winemaking knowledge was, by all accounts, fairly basic. Jack Ward at Merrydown had some technical expertise to draw on, but his staff had little experience of making wine from grapes at this time – cider and fruit wines were their specialities. Dr Alfred Pollard and Fred Beech, who ran the Cider Department at Long Ashton Research Station, near Bristol, helped Ray Brock with his wine-making. However, from what Pollard wrote in the winemaking section of the 1953 book *Vineyards in England*, he too had had little experience of working with grapes. Sir Guy Salisbury-Jones had help from some French friends for the first few Hambledon vintages and he described their results as 'encouraging'! What this meant in terms of wine quality one can only hazard a guess. About the only person who professed to really know anything about the job was Anton Massel. He quite quickly became involved with the fledgling English wine industry and supplied both advice and equipment to Salisbury-Jones, the Gore-Brownes at Beaulieu, Major Rook at Stragglethorpe Hall, as well as a number of others. Nigel Godden at Pilton Manor took a different tack: he employed a cousin of the famous opera singer Mario Lanza to help in the vineyard and winery. Since Pilton Manor won the Gore-Browne Trophy two years running (1975 and 1976) they must have been doing something right.

From all accounts, the early English and Welsh wines were, at their best, 'interesting', at their worst, fairly thin and austere. Vineyards tended to suffer from bird damage which forced growers to pick early and rely upon chemicals to remove excess acidity rather than nature. Without today's modern anti-*botrytis* and mildew sprays, the grapes suffered badly from disease which again led to growers to pick early. The equipment found in many wineries was also fairly primitive and in some cases, very unsuitable for the production of the fresh, fruity wines which today we are able to produce with regularity. There were almost no stainless steel tanks in the early wineries and until the mid-1970s, most wineries were equipped with secondhand fibreglass wine tanks, many of which had already seen 20 years, service in the cellars and railway arches of the many firms that used to bottle wines in the UK. Many wineries had small vertical screw presses, more suited to red wine production than white, although Massel did persuade Salisbury-Jones to import a Willmes airbag press in 1965 which greatly improved both the efficiency of the operation and the quality of their wines. In 1969 Ward started the Merrydown Co-operative Scheme which gave smaller growers the chance to have their wine made by professionals and greatly helped raise the general standard of UK-produced wines. The 1979 vintage was the last handled under this scheme.

Until Lamberhurst started producing wine in 1974, very few English and Welsh wines had been produced (intentionally) with noticeable residual sugar. Up until then, wines tended to be fairly dry and crisp, relying on time in the bottle to soften the acidity, rather than any added sweetness. The arrival of two German-trained winemakers (Ernst Abel and Karl-Heinz Schmitt) to make the first Lamberhurst wines marked the start of a new era. Their first wines were naturally – for they were Geisenheim trained – slightly sweetened with sterile grape juice (süss-reserve as it is usually known by UK winemakers) and bottled through sterile filters. The results were something of a revelation. The sweetness balanced the acidity and the fruity grape juice gave the wines an added dimension which pleased, if not some purists, then at least the public who were becoming increasingly interested in English and Welsh wines. With hindsight, it is easy to say that the wholesale addition of grape juice – much of it imported from Germany – was perhaps overdone and in some cases used as a mask to cover excess acidity and unripe phenolic flavours. However, at the time, when the wines were being appreciated by ordinary customers, many winemakers saw the technique as a very valuable one.

As the size and importance of Lamberhurst grew, both as an individual wine producer and as a contract winemaker for many different vineyards in the UK, so did the influence of their style of wine. Karl-Heinz Johner, another Geisenheim graduate, who took over winemaking in September 1976 and was there for twelve vintages until 1988, continued to make many wines in what one might call a 'German' style – then extremely popular. It has to be remembered that at this time, brands such as 'Blue Nun', 'Golden Oktober' and 'Black Tower', as well as a large number of generic 'hocks', 'Mosels' and 'Liebfraumilchs' dominated the lower and middle price market. More and more wine was being sold through the rapidly growing national supermarket chains and their wine-buying customers – many of them female – found this style suited their palates. Many of the newer, larger vineyards opened shops to sell wines directly to the public and it was very evident that when buyers had the chance to taste them first, wines with residual sugar found greater favour. Lamberhurst was also the first of the 'super wineries' built at a UK vineyard. With the financial clout of its proprietor, Kenneth McAlpine, behind it, the winery was lavishly equipped with the latest equipment and became something of a place of pilgrimage for vineyard owners and winemakers.

The years since Lamberhurst was the major player in the English and Welsh wine industry have seen many changes. Other large vineyards and wineries have been established, with just as impressive facilities and capable of producing wines of equal technical quality. Growers have, through a combination of better vineyard management, better chemical sprays to control *botrytis* and mildews and an appreciation that quality really does start (and often end) in the vineyard, been delivering higher quality grapes to their winery doors. Winemakers such as John Worontschak, based at Valley Vineyards, but also as a consultant to many other wineries, and David Cowderoy, at Chapel Down Wines until 1999, both of whom graduated from Australian winemaking universities, have brought with them new ideas and new techniques which have resulted in softer, more approachable wines – much more in the New World style. The fact is that whilst some would like to believe that English and Welsh wines are somehow immune from market forces, they are not. The domination of the lower and middle market by the big German and German-style brands has ended and been replaced by softer New World styles already mentioned. 'Old fashioned' English and Welsh wines, packaged as they almost always were, in brown Hock or green Mosel bottles, with 'funny' varietal names have largely disappeared.

Whilst many of the smaller wineries still retain simple equipment and use techniques suited to their scale, there are now a number of considerable size and complexity; wineries such as Battle, Biddenden, Carr Taylor, Chapel Down Wines, Chiddingstone, Davenport, Denbies, Nyetimber, RidgeView, Three Choirs, Valley and Wickham would not look out of place in any winemaking region. They are mostly well equipped with stainless steel tanks (often refrigerated), airbag presses, modern filtration equipment and good bottling lines. Those vineyards specialising in sparkling wines have presses with 'Champagne' programmes, gyro-pallets and modern disgorging and corking machinery.

In the winery too, practices have changed. Winemakers have come to appreciate the benefits of gentler handling techniques, cold maceration of fruity varieties to extract more flavour, cold settling to produce clearer juice at the point of fermentation and the use of certain yeast strains to enhance flavours or add complexity. Until 1986, the use of oak barrels for the maturation of white wines was unheard of in UK wineries, whereas today, whilst not perhaps to be found in every winery, they are quite widely distributed. As wine-makers have gained experience with barrels, learning which of the different oaks suit their wines and how long to leave them on the yeast lees, so the quality of these wines has risen. A number of wineries also now produce 'oaked' wines. This is a term used to denote the 'oaking', with oak chips or oak staves, of wines which have generally only fleetingly seen a barrel or often not seen a barrel at all. The use of oak chips and staves, made from the same wood and treated (toasted) in the same way as the wood used for making barrels, is nothing new and whilst it may not be openly admitted as such on labels, it is a common practice in wineries throughout the world. Both chips and staves can be introduced into tanks of juice or wine at any stage of the winemaking process and the amount used and the length of time they are left in contact will determine the degree of 'oakiness' imparted. Whilst these techniques do not give the same effect as using barrels, they can be very effective and impart an oaked character at a lesser cost.

The use of the malolactic fermentation (the conversion of the harsher malic acid to softer lactic acid by naturally occurring bacteria) to soften both white and red wines and add complexity during lees ageing, is also a practice that some UK winemakers have now taken to – until the late 1980s it was rarely heard of. In most cases, pHs were too low and acid levels too high for a spontaneous 'secondary fermentation' (as it is often known) to take place. Now, by picking later when acids are lower and pHs higher and by using malolactic cultures to induce the secondary fermentation, this is a technique seen very much more often.

Red wine, although still only accounting for a small proportion of the total wine produced annually (9 per cent of the total in 1999) are starting to make headway and are improving year on year. The newer varieties Rondo and Dornfelder have definitely helped to produce much deeper coloured and fuller bodied wines, and the increasing use of oak for ageing is a significant factor.

A few growers have produced successful sweet wines and whilst this is an even smaller category than red wines, it is certainly one where value can be added. Early ripening varieties such as Ortega, Optima and Siegerrebe, together with *botrytis*-prone varieties like

Bacchus and Huxelrebe, which can all produce high sugars if allowed to ripen fully, have been used to make some excellent sweet 'late harvest' style wines.

The regulations governing the production of wine from home-grown grapes have altered little since the UK joined the Common Market in 1973. The minimum natural (potential) alcohol level which grapes have to reach before they can be harvested remains at a generously low 5 per cent for Table wines and 6 per cent for Regional and Quality wines. There is a maximum total alcohol level (total alcohol is the sum of the actual plus the potential alcohol) of 11.5 per cent for white and 12 per cent for red Table and Regional wines when the wines have been enriched (chaptalised). Where Table and Regional wines have not been enriched, they may have a maximum total alcohol level of 15 per cent. Wines with more than 15 per cent total alcohol cannot be Table or Regional wines and have to qualify for Quality wine status. It is important therefore to exclude non-*vinifera* grapes from these wines as only 100 per cent pure *vinifera* wines qualify as Quality wines. Enrichment levels remain at +3.5 per cent in 'normal' years, with an additional +1 per cent allowed in years when climatic conditions are 'exceptionally unfavourable'. This extra 1 per cent allowance may be restricted to certain parts of the country or certain grape varieties. Some growers have experimented with 'cryo-extraction' or 'freeze concentration' where grape juice is concentrated by cooling and removing the resultant ice. This technique is allowed up to a point where the natural alcohol level has been raised by 2 per cent or the total volume has been reduced by 20 per cent. Table and Regional wines must have at least 8.5 per cent actual alcohol when bottled, whereas Quality wines having a natural alcoholic strength of not less than 10 per cent are allowed to be bottled with a minimum actual alcoholic strength of 5.5 per cent. These would be sweeter wines having at least 4.5 per cent potential alcohol (approximately 75 g/l residual sweetness). The more usual Quality wines must have a minimum actual alcohol of 8.5 per cent. Acid levels of finished Table wines must be at least 4.5 g/l (as tartaric acid) and of Regional and Quality wines, 5 g/l. De-acidification of juice and wines still in fermentation is allowed without limit, but finished wines may only be de-acidified by a maximum of 1 g/l. The acidification of still wines is not allowed, whereas wine for the production of sparkling wine (the *cuvée*) may be acidified by up to

1.5 g/l. These are only the very basic rules governing the production of wine in the UK.

The restrictions on total alcohol levels of enriched Table and Regional wines to 11.5 per cent for whites and 12 per cent for reds is really quite restrictive and can lead to problems. A medium dry wine with say 9 g/l of residual sugar, which equates to a potential alcohol of just over 0.5 per cent may only have an actual alcohol of, at the very maximum, 11 per cent in order to keep under the 11.5 per cent total figure. In reality winemakers have to aim slightly lower than the 11.5 per cent total alcohol figure as there are always inaccuracies in the initial measurement of sugar levels and sugar to alcohol conversion rates are never that predictable. This means that many wines are bottled with between 10 per cent and 10.5 per cent actual alcohol which, by today's standards, is low. Wines from around the world are much more likely to be bottled with 12.5–13.5 per cent actual alcohol and this relative lack of alcohol in our wines is noticeable to wine drinkers more used to modern wines from overseas. One solution to this problem is to make more Quality wines where there are no upper limits on total alcohol levels, apart from the fact that they may only be enriched by +3.5 per cent in normal years or +4.5 per cent in exceptional years. However, this does not help those wines made in whole or in part from hybrids which may not, under present EU legislation, be Quality wines. Some of our best red wines, which are perhaps the wines which above all would benefit from having actual alcohol levels in the 12.5–13.5 per cent range, may not as they have been made using hybrids; apart from Pinot noir and Pinot Meunier – both of which are mainly used for sparkling wines – three of the four most widely planted red varieties are Triomphe, Rondo and Léon Millot – all hybrids. However, a recent ruling by the German authorities that some modern hybrids (including Orion, Phoenix, Regent and Rondo) have had all their non-*vinifera* traits bred out of them, and can therefore now be considered to be *viniferas* and therefore be used for the production of quality wines, is very welcome. MAFF is currently looking at ways in which these varieties can be used for the production of quality wines in the UK. When one sees the relative laxity of production controls in many other countries (both EU and non-EU), English and Welsh winemakers do sometimes sense that their particular playing field is tilted very much against them and half-time is a long time a-coming!

The question of the use of 'süss-reserve', which seemed to exercise minds greatly in the 1980s, no longer seems to do so quite so much. Many winemakers now rely on naturally stopped fermentations, using strains of yeast that are easier to stop, as well as racking off and cooling. Süss-reserve, when it is used, is either imported (almost entirely from Germany with Müller-Thurgau and Bacchus being the most popular varieties) or is homegrown, where Müller-Thurgau and Reichensteiner are the preferred varieties. This change has come about partly because it is a requirement for Quality wines that material used for sweetening originates in the same region of production as the wine being sweetened. Stopping fermentations gets round the problem of finding suitable English or Welsh süss-reserve. In any event, residual sugar levels in English and Welsh wines have come down over the last 15 years, mainly because of the changes in taste of the wine-buying public, many of whom now prefer wines with relatively low levels of residual sugar. Geoff Taylor, Managing Director of Corkwise Ltd, which since 1988 has been the principal analyst to the wine trade and is the official analyst for the Regional and Quality wine schemes, says that most English and Welsh wines now fall into the official 'dry' and 'medium dry' categories where, with sufficient acidity, wines can have no more than 18 g/l of residual sugar. Very few English and Welsh wines are now bottled with more than 25 g/l of residual sugar which was far from the case in the 1980s. Taylor also says that in the twelve years that he has been analysing English and Welsh wines he has noticed that acidity levels have come down, due to better de-acidification and the use of malolactic fermentation, whilst alcohol levels have risen (as they have worldwide). This, he feels, is due to growers leaving their grapes to ripen more fully, coupled with the use of yeasts with better sugar to alcohol conversion rates and the wider use of refrigeration in UK wineries. This leads to gentler fermentations and less loss of alcohol. He also says that without a doubt, the overall quality of English and Welsh wines has risen over the last twelve years very substantially and many of the poorer producers now appear (thankfully) to have given up the struggle. This is surely good news for the industry.

7
Vine Varieties

━━━━━━━

The success of a winegrowing region depends, to a very large extent, on the marriage of those elements that go to make up what the French call *terroir*: climate, sites, soils and grape varieties. Whilst the first three elements remain largely fixed and unchangeable, the fourth, that of grape varieties, does not. Better varieties can be chosen and better clones of varieties selected to create wines more in tune with the market. The rise of 'varietal' wines, a phenomenon of the last twenty years, bears witness to the importance of the grape variety in determining both the style and quality of wine from any given region. The UK, while different in many ways from any other wine producing area in the world, still has to produce wines that find favour with the consumer and is not insulated against varietal changes and fashions.

EARLY VINEYARDS

Which varieties were used in British vineyards before the modern revival is open to conjecture. The monks who established vineyards following the Norman invasion of 1066 and kept them going throughout the next five centuries no doubt brought vines with them from their home monasteries and also from the nearest continental winegrowing regions – the Rhine and Mosel, the Loire, Champagne and the Paris basin (which before the railways allowed wine to be brought from much greater distances was a large centre of wine production). Belgium had a history of vineyards attached to monasteries going back to AD 854 and, with a very similar climate to ours, would have been a good place to find suitable varieties. Our medieval Bordeaux connections must also have enabled vineyard owners to gather varieties from this region.

The quest to find new and better varieties for growing in vineyards, and perhaps more importantly, in the glass roofed and walled 'vineries' which started to be built all over the country from the 1600s onwards (once it was discovered how to make glass large enough and thin enough to be used for this purpose) was one which yielded hundreds of varieties from all over the world. Table grape production became an important feature in Britain and no grand house or mansion was without its vinery to produce grapes for almost every day of the year. Britain's gardeners became adept at the cross-pollination of vines and it is quite remarkable that a few of the world's table grape varieties originated in this country (Dr Hogg's Muscat and Foster's White Seedling for instance) or were brought to this country and 'improved' through clonal selection. Varieties for outdoor ripening – whether for the table or for wine – were, however, less available. In 1666, John Rose, gardener to Charles II, wrote in his book *The English Vineyard Vindicated* that the best varieties were the 'small Black Grape, by some call'd the Cluster Grape, the white Muscadine, the Parsley Grape, the Muscadella, the Frontiniaq, both white and red' together with 'a new white grape which I found in his Majesty's garden in St. James' – which he did not name. Four years later (1670) Will Hughes wrote in *The Compleat Vineyard* that the best varieties to grow outside were 'the lesser and greater white Muscadine, the red Muscadine, the Frantinick, the Parsley-grape (more for show and rarity than profit) and the Rhenish-wine vine'. At least these two commentators seem to show some degree of uniformity in their choice of varieties!

In 1727, a 'Gentleman', known only by his initials 'S. J.', published a handbook on growing vines (as well as a wide variety of other fruits) called *The Vineyard* in which he stated that 'the Vines I would advise as most proper for this climate, and as being the hardiest, are the small black Muscadine, which are the same planted by the Champaigners and the Burgundians, in their vineyards'. No other varieties – for outdoor cultivation – appear to have met with his favour. Philip Miller, in his *Gardener's Dictionary*, the first edition of which was published in 1731, lists over 20 varieties and says 'I shall not trouble the reader with an enumeration of all the sorts of grapes which are at present known in England as this would swell this work much beyond its intended bulk, and be of little use, since many of them are not worth the trouble of cultivating'. The only one that he recommends for wine production is 'the Auverna [sic] or true Burgundy grape, sometimes called Black Morillon' (Robinson 1986 gives Morillon as a synonym for both Chardonnay and Pinot noir). Sir Edward Barry, writing in 1775, quotes his friend the Hon. Charles Hamilton who had planted the Painshill vineyard between 1740 and 1743. Barry says that Hamilton planted 'two sorts of Burgundy grapes, the Auvernat, which is the most delicate, but the tenderest, and the Miller grape, commonly called the black cluster, which is more hardy'. We can probably assume that 'the Miller grape' was what we today call Pinot Meunier.

William Speechley, writing in the 1790 edition of his *Treatise on the Culture of the Vine*, lists 50 separately identified and described varieties suitable for growing indoors for the table and adds that he has 'above 100 sorts' growing at Welbeck, the Duke of Portland's estate, where he was head gardener. In the chapter 'On Vineyards' Speechley states that 'there would be the greatest possibility of success with those kinds of grapes which have been known to thrive in the most Northern latitudes. I should therefore recommend the kinds of Vines cultivated in Germany and particularly the sort producing the grapes of which the Rhenish wine is made, in preference to any kind cultivated in France.' (It has to be said that when one looks at the selection of varieties upon which the modern revival was founded, Speechley was here giving some good advice, although sadly unheeded for another 160 years.)

As has already been related, the last vineyard enterprise of the pre-revival era, Castell Coch, was planted with Gamay noir and Millie Blanche, although the latter was soon abandoned. H. M. Tod, who grew over 40 different varieties, recommended seven as being 'absolutely safe, year by year'. They were the Miller, the Miller's Burgundy (the difference between these two is not explained), the Common or Royal Muscadine, Black Cluster, Esperione, Cambridge Botanic Garden and Brandt. None of these today is really worth considering.

Between the end of the Bute vineyards and 1946, when Brock started his experiments at Oxted, no serious attempt appears to have been made to find better varieties for the production of wine. Indeed, why should anyone have wanted to? Cheap wine was available from the colonies – Australia and South Africa especially – and no one seemed interested in planting vineyards in the UK. Viticultural activity was confined to growing grapes for the table or for home winemaking, using varieties which today would be considered most unsuitable for either purpose.

THE REVIVAL

As has already been related, the revival of commercial viticulture in the early 1950s was based on the discovery by Brock and Hyams that Müller-Thurgau and Seyval blanc were varieties that would both fruit and ripen in our climate. The early vineyards, Hambeldon, Horam Manor and Beaulieu, together with those that followed in the 1960s, were overwhelmingly planted with these two varieties. In 1970, when the first of the annual 'Vintage Reports' appeared in EVA's *Grape Press* No. 5 (based on the 1969 harvest), Müller-Thurgau, Seyval Blanc, Madeleine × Angevine 7672, Seibel 13/053, Scheurebe and Siegerrebe were still the only varieties giving crops worth reporting. By then, Jack Ward (Horam Manor) had made several forays to Germany to find better varieties and returned with Bacchus, Faberrebe, Ortega and Reichensteiner which started to make appearances in newer vineyards

Faced with a blank field and a desire to plant a vineyard, a grower in this country in the early stages of the viticultural revival was faced with the dilemma of what varieties to plant. The track record of the two major varieties – Müller-Thurgau and Seyval blanc was patchy to say the least. Both growing and winemaking skills were in short supply and most of the pioneer growers adopted a rather amateur approach to the problems – after all, in other winemaking regions, growing grapes and making wine did not appear to be too difficult and if your average French or Italian could do it seemingly with little specialist education, why shouldn't a Brit? The results of this attitude led to poorly managed vineyards, often with high levels of disease. Canopies were very vigorous and dense (as they so often are with very young vines) leading to unripe grapes. Attacks from wasps and birds – problems which the early editions of the English Vineyards Association's *Grape Press* seem to dwell on – exacerbated the problem of harvesting grapes fit for winemaking. In the cellars, lack of experience showed in the resulting wines. Whilst some good wines were made and early vineyards such as Adgestone, Pilton Manor and Wootton soon got a reputation for the quality of their wines, many wines were too acidic, too dry and lacking both fruit and body – the inevitable result of picking grapes at low levels of natural sugar and not fully appreciating how to de-acidify correctly or use low levels of sterile grape juice to balance excess acidity.

Growers looking to plant vineyards therefore tended to do two things; plant Müller-Thurgau and Seyval blanc as their core varieties, but also plant a selection of different ones, hoping that they might find one or more that would do better than the two 'standard' varieties. This inevitably led to a large number of cultivars being planted as growers sought the holy grail of British vineyard owners – the 'perfect' variety. To a certain extent, those that did have some knowledge about the subject and who also sold vines to growers – Ray Brock, Jack Ward at Merrydown and Anton Massel at Ockley – all had a vested interest in seeing as many new varieties planted in commercial quantities as possible – otherwise how was anyone going to learn what varieties really did work? Brock offered both rooted cuttings and bare wood cuttings of a large number of varieties (for both table and wine) and to start with, cornered the market. With hindsight, many of the varieties Brock offered were fairly obscure and today would not be considered as remotely suitable. His 1970/71 list (and by this time he had been growing vines for almost 25 years) offered for wine production Gamay Hâtif des Vosges and Marshal Joffre – varieties which it is doubtful anyone has ever made a good bottle of wine from in an English or Welsh vineyard. However, Brock was also offering Müller-Thurgau, Seyval blanc, Madeleine × Angevine 7672, Léon Millot, Seibel 13/053, Siegerrebe and Madeleine × Sylvaner No. 3 28/51, not all of which we might consider today when planting a vineyard, but which in their time contributed greatly to the revival. Both Ward and Massel imported grafted vines from overseas and rather looked on Brock as a bit of a renegade who sold ungrafted vines without really informing growers of the dangers of *phylloxera*, as well as a rather wide (and wild) selection of different cultivars. They, on the other hand, only imported grafted vines. They also only imported those varieties that the Germans (and to a certain extent the French) wanted us to have. There is no doubt that had it not been for German insistence that Müller-Thurgau was the only variety likely to ripen in our climate (which all Germans think is foggy for twelve months of the year) we might have discovered some of their better cultivars a bit sooner. As it was, Müller-Thurgau, which was sweeping through their own vineyards at the time, was seen as the saviour of their war-torn industry (instead of which it turned out to be the destroyer) and they felt that it would also be ideal for the UK.

A look through the EVA's 'Vintage Reports' of the early years (from the 1969 harvest) show that over 20 different varieties were being grown. This resulted in yet more problems for growers as they struggled with unknown and in many cases, unsuitable varieties, leading to yet more trouble in the winery. How it could have been managed otherwise is of course a question that has no answer. MAFF at the time had neither the experience, inclination – nor probably the power – to impose restrictions on what growers could or could not plant. However, if one looks at a 'what if' scenario where MAFF said vineyards could only be planted in the UK with say, Bacchus, Reichensteiner, Seyval blanc and Schönburger – arguably the four most successful varieties grown today – how many vineyards would have saved themselves the heartache of struggling to grow decent crops of Müller-Thurgau, Huxelrebe and Kerner – which today are slowly losing ground to better, more suitable varieties? As it was, the free-for-all approach has left us with a very wide spectrum of varieties, not all ideal for our climate, but just good enough for growers to keep them in their vineyards, rather than going to the expense of replacing them or grubbing them up altogether. The UK is often compared – viticulturally – to New Zealand which was once dominated by Müller-Thurgau and other varieties less suitable for today's market. In 1985/86 a new Labour government – hoping perhaps to find a few votes in the rural community – instigated a 'vine-pull' programme in New Zealand which paid growers to grub vineyards. In one season, over 25 per cent of all vines in the country were taken out. Over the next few years, growers replanted with varieties such as Sauvignon blanc, Chardonnay and Pinot noir which today form the basis for one of the most remarkable winegrowing regions in the world. If only our government had this type of foresight!

Before the UK joined the Common Market in 1973, MAFF was asked by the Commission in Brussels to produce a list of acceptable grape varieties for our climate. MAFF consulted the EVA and a meeting was held at the National Farmers Union's Agriculture

House in 1971 to discuss the varieties to be included. The EVA wanted Müller-Thurgau and Seyval blanc as the only 'Recommended' varieties, with a whole host of others in the lesser, 'Authorised', category. However, when MAFF produced the lists in their final form, they contained a few surprises. Auxerrois and Wrotham Pinot, despite the fact that they were only being grown in very small quantities, had been included in the 'Recommended' category and Seyval Blanc had been downgraded to 'Authorised'. Apparently, despite 'strenuous argument' by MAFF in Brussels, the Commission was not prepared to accept Seyval blanc on the 'Recommended' list as it was a hybrid variety. The EVA were told that they would have to be happy with its 'Authorised' classification although MAFF did agree that its status would be reviewed at a later date. It was not until July 1990 that Seyval blanc was raised to the 'Recommended' list.

Eventually, MAFF submitted the following list of vines to the Commission:

Recommended Varieties
 Müller-Thurgau
 Wrotham Pinot (Pinot Meunier)
 Auxerrois

Authorised Varieties
 Bacchus
 Chardonnay
 Ehrenfelser
 Faber (Faberrebe)
 Huxelrebe
 Kerner
 Kanzler
 Madeleine × Angevine 7672
 Madeleine Sylvaner No. 3 28/51
 Madeleine Royale
 Mariensteiner
 Ortega
 Perle
 Pinot noir
 Ruländer (Pinot gris)
 Seyval blanc
 Siegerrebe

The Commission was concerned about the naming of the varieties Madeleine Angevine and Madeleine Sylvaner as they felt (quite rightly as it happened) that there would be confusion. These were the names that Brock had given, for the sake of convenience and to growers when he sold them vines, to Sämling 7672 (a freely pollinated seedling of Madeleine Angevine) and Madeleine Angevine × Sylvaner No. 3 28/51. Reichensteiner, which Jack Ward felt sure was going to be a good variety for our climate, was not permitted to be classified. (Reichensteiner and Schönburger were eventually added as 'Temporarily Authorised' in 1986). The omission of Reichensteiner, however, did not really pose a problem as it was agreed with MAFF that any other varieties being grown in the UK would be considered as being 'on trial' and could continue to be used for wine production. In theory, after 1 January 1973, the only varieties permitted to be planted were those on the official 'Recommended' and 'Authorised' lists. In practice, MAFF took a fairly low key attitude to this regulation and to start with, growers continued to select varieties freely. (In fact MAFF helped confuse the situation further by issuing two publications, *Outdoor Grape Production* in 1978 and *Grapes for Wine* in 1980, both of which stated that 'any variety not in the "Recommended" or "Authorised" list may . . . be used for commercial wine production'.)

In November 1971, Wye College, the University of London's agricultural department near Ashford in Kent, which specialized in research into hops, suggested that it might undertake some research into grapevines by planting a trial vineyard. The EVA launched an appeal and the sum of £10,000 was raised towards the costs, with donations coming from members and interested organisations. Vines were donated by various German, Swiss and Austrian universities, together with some from Weingut Louis Guntrum in Nierstein. In total, 850 vines of 17 different varieties were obtained and planted in 1973, with more to follow in 1974, 1975, 1980 and 1981. The vineyard eventually covered 1.25 acres. The vines were trained on three different trellising systems: Double Guyot, Lenz Moser and Geneva Double Curtain. Bob Farrar, then in charge of the management of the College's hop gardens, took great personal interest in the vineyard, and was really responsible for seeing that it was maintained at minimal expense to the EVA, making sure that it was sprayed with any left over fungicides from the hop gardens. The yield and performance statistics gathered gave valuable information about the different varieties being grown there. The grapes harvested were either sold to Merrydown or sent to Long Ashton Research Station in Bristol to be made into wine. Eventually, the vineyard site was required by Wye College for a new hop garden and in 1984 the vines were grubbed out. Although it only lasted just over a decade, the Wye College vineyard introduced Regner, Wurzer, Bacchus, Faberrebe and Zweigeltrebe to UK vineyards.

In 1976 the categories of vines were extended to include:

Temporarily Authorised: varieties growing in the United Kingdom on 31 December 1976 and not included in any of the other lists of permitted vines. In theory, these varieties could be grown and made into wine for a further 25 years, but no new vines could be planted after this date.

Experimental: varieties that are subject to officially approved trials or are being grown for the production of cuttings or of scion wood for export to non-EC countries.

Provisionally Authorised: varieties where their suitability has been determined by approved trials and which are subject to a further 5–7 year wait until they are eligible to be added to the 'Authorised' list.

Unauthorised: varieties that do not fall into any of the permitted categories and wine from them may not be sold in an EC country, but it may be exported to a non-EC country, distilled, converted into vinegar or consumed by the winegrower and his family.

In order to comply with EU regulations, which required the relevant authority to monitor the area of vines being grown in a Member State, MAFF carried out four voluntary vineyard surveys, in 1975, 1984, 1985 and 1987. In addition it made estimates of the area of vines in 1979, 1980 and 1982 (Table 1).

The voluntary nature of the four surveys, in which growers were requested to supply details of varieties grown and yields, meant that the data collected must be viewed with some suspicion. A comparison between the 1987 and 1989 surveys, the first voluntary, the second statutory, shows that there was very considerable rise in vineyard area. Hectares not in production rose by 37 per cent, hectares in production rose by 71 per cent, overall area by 60 per cent – rises far too large to be accounted for by plantings in the spring of 1989. However, the 1975–1987 surveys probably give a

Table 1. Survey of UK Vineyard Areas 1975–1989

Year	1975	1979	1980	1982	1984	1985	1987	1989
In production (ha)	149	n/a	n/a	n/a	325	356	382	652
Not in production (ha)	47	n/a	n/a	n/a	106	132	164	224
Total (ha)	196	250	350	400	431	488	546	876

1975, 1984, 1985 and 1987 were MAFF voluntary survey areas. 1989 was the first MAFF compulsory survey. 1979, 1980 and 1982 are MAFF estimated areas.

fair indication of the rise in the level of interest in viticulture over the period.

The three later voluntary surveys (1984, 1985 and 1987) also looked at individual variety areas (Table 2) and again, although not reliable, probably give a general indication of the changes in the varietal make-up of the UK's vineyards. Varieties such as Bacchus, Huxelrebe, Reichensteiner and Schönburger rising in terms of percentage of the area with Madeleine × Angevine 7672, Müller-Thurgau and Seyval blanc falling. Müller-Thurgau showed the greatest fall, from 34.6 per cent of the total area, down to 26.7 per cent.

YIELDS OF MAJOR VARIETIES

The 1984, 1985 and 1987 surveys also looked at the yields of individual varieties. (Table 3). As with the area data (or perhaps even more so) the accuracy of these figures must be questioned. However, they probably reflect the comparative cropping levels of the individual varieties, especially the major ones such as Müller-Thurgau, Seyval blanc, Reichensteiner and Schönburger.

Since the 1987 survey there have been other surveys which have charted the progress of varietal change in UK vineyards. These have been statutory surveys, rather like the annual MAFF June Census, where farmers and growers can be prosecuted for not supplying data. However, the establishment of the Vineyard Register (Table 4), an official document listing all vineyards, the varieties in them, their rootstocks, the number in each 'parcel' and the area that they occupy, has been one of the tasks of the Wine Standards Board. The Vineyard Register is kept up to date on the

Table 2. MAFF Voluntary Surveys of Vines in the UK by Variety
1984–1987

Variety	1984		1985		1987	
	Ha	%	Ha	%	Ha	%
Auxerrois					5	0.9
Bacchus	10	2.3	14	2.9	34	6.2
Cascade (Seibel 13/053)					2	0.4
Chardonnay					7	1.3
Dunkelfelder					2	0.4
Ehrenfelser					3	0.5
Faberrebe					6	1.1
Gamay					2	0.4
Gewürztraminer					1	0.2
Gutenborner					4	0.7
Huxelrebe	23	5.3	26	5.3	30	5.5
Kerner			11	2.3	17	3.1
Léon Millot					1	0.2
Madeleine × Angevine 7672	26	6.0	26	5.3	24	4.4
Madeleine Sylvaner No.3 28/57					1	0.2
Müller-Thurgau	149	34.6	155	31.8	146	26.7
Optima					3	0.5
Ortega					16	2.9
Pinot gris (Rulander)					6	1.1
Pinot Meunier (Wrotham Pinot)					5	0.9
Pinot noir	11	2.6	13	2.7	20	3.7
Regner					6	1.1
Reichensteiner	47	10.9	55	11.3	62	11.4
Riesling					2	0.4
Sauvignon blanc					1	0.2
Scheurebe					6	1.1
Schönburger	16	3.7	27	5.5	34	6.2
Seyval blanc	46	10.7	45	9.2	53	9.7
Siegerrebe					6	1.1
Triomphe					2	0.4
Würzer					7	1.3
Zweigeltrebe					3	0.5
Miscellaneous/Unauthorised	103	23.9	116	23.8	29	5.3
Totals	431		488		546	

Table 3. MAFF Voluntary Surveys of Yields of Vines in the UK
by Variety 1984–1987
Yields given in hectolitres per hectare (hl/ha)

Variety	1984	1985	1987	Average 1984–87
Bacchus	48	13	3	21
Huxelrebe	31	19	5	18
Kerner	–	16	5	10
Madeleine × Angevine 7672	26	10	11	16
Müller-Thurgau	39	13	7	20
Pinot noir	23	12	5	13
Reichensteiner	36	15	10	20
Schönburger	43	19	13	25
Seyval blanc	40	23	13	25
Others	54	31	21	35
All varieties average yield hl/ha	42	18	11	24

Total UK Yields 1984, 1985 and 1987 – MAFF Voluntary Surveys

Year	1984	1985	1987	1984–87 Average
Total Yield	13,510 hl	6,531 hl	4,110 hl	8050 hl

basis of visits once every three years to every vineyard in the UK and in addition, by growers voluntarily supplying information about increases or decreases in the size of their vineyards.

As can be seen from Table 4, once growers were required by law to admit to exactly which varieties they were growing and how many hectares of each, a long list was produced. The 1990 survey revealed a total of 56 varieties grown in excess of 0.1 ha (approximately a quarter acre) on at least two different sites (for reasons of confidentiality, a variety which was unique to one site could not be identified). By any country's standards, let alone one so minor as the UK, it is a large number of different cultivars.

The comparison between the 1990 survey data (the first statutory survey) and the 1999 Vineyards Register figures shows how the varietal spectrum has changed in ten years. Quite a few varieties have decreased in area. Indeed, some of the very minor varieties have disappeared altogether or dropped by large percentages. The

Table 4. Wine Standards Board Vineyard Register of all UK Vine Varieties 1990 and 1999

Variety	1990		1999			Changes 1990–1999	
	Ha	% of total UK area	Ha	% of total UK area	Frequency planted in 1999*	Ha	%
Albalonga	0.1	0.01					
Auxerrois	9.1	0.98	8.6	0.99	29	−0.5	−5.5
AZ 15477	0.2	0.02					
Bacchus	76.0	8.18	86.6	9.93	156	10.6	13.9
Blauberger	0.6	0.06					
Cascade (Seibel 13053)	1.2	0.13	0.6	0.07	9	−0.6	−50.0
Chardonnay	19.9	2.14	34.2	3.92	61	14.3	71.9
Chasselas (Gutedal)	2.5	0.27	1.5	0.17	5	−1.0	−40.0
Comtessa	0.2	0.02					
Domina	0.2	0.02					
Dornfelder	5.4	0.58	11.2	1.28	40	5.8	107.4
Dunkelfelder	3.5	0.38	2.5	0.29	24	−1.0	−28.6
Ehrenfelser	2.4	0.26	1.7	0.19	9	−0.7	−29.2
Elbling (Red & White)	3.8	0.41	3.4	0.39	3	−0.4	−10.5
Faberrebe	10.3	1.11	10.8	1.24	42	0.5	4.9
Findling	3.3	0.36	2.2	0.25	12	−1.1	−33.3
Gamay	1.4	0.15					
Gewürztraminer	0.8	0.09					
Gutenborner	3.7	0.40	1.9	0.22	7	−1.8	−48.6
Heroldrebe	0.2	0.02					
Huxelrebe	43.9	4.73	41.0	4.70	94	−2.9	−6.6
Kanzler	0.2	0.02	0.2	0.02	2		
Kerner	21.4	2.30	18.5	2.12	59	−2.9	−13.6
Kernling	4.2	0.45	13.5	1.55	36	9.3	221.4
Léon Millot	2.0	0.22	3.6	0.41	32	1.6	80.0
Madeleine × Angevine 7672	54.6	5.88	59.1	6.77	164	4.5	8.2
Madeleine Sylvaner No. 3 28/51	3.7	0.40	3.4	0.39	15	−0.3	−8.1
Marechal Foch	0.3	0.03					
Marienfeldt	0.4	0.04					
Merlot	0.2	0.02					
Müller-Thurgau (Rivaner)	184.5	19.87	116.4	13.34	190	−68.1	−36.9
Optima	4.6	0.50	2.7	0.31	12	−1.9	−41.3
Orion	0.7	0.08	8.4	0.96	28	7.7	1100.0
Ortega	29.5	3.18	28.2	3.23	62	−1.3	−4.4

Variety	1990 Ha	% of total UK area	1999 Ha	% of total UK area	Frequency planted in 1999*	Changes 1990–1999 Ha	%
Perle from Alzey	0.4	0.04	0.2	0.02	4	−0.2	−50.0
Phoenix	0.4	0.04	1.9[†]	0.22	9[†]	1.5	375.0
Pinot blanc (Weissburgunder)			5.8	0.66	15		
Pinot gris (Ruländer)	2.6	0.28	5.6	0.64	18	3.0	115.4
Pinot Meunier (Wrotham Pinot)	5.5	0.59	8.2	0.94	22	2.7	49.1
Pinot noir	32.0	3.45	44.2	5.07	127	12.2	38.1
Portugieser	0.8	0.09					
Regent			2.2	0.25	6		
Regner	9.7	1.04	8.0	0.92	30	−1.7	−17.5
Reichensteiner	113.9	12.27	107.1	12.28	236	−6.8	−6.0
Riesling	5.5	0.59	2.4	0.28	7	−3.1	−56.4
Rondo (Gm 6494/5)	2.0	0.22	9.5	1.09	34	7.5	375.0
Sauvignon blanc	0.5	0.05					
Scheurebe	2.3	0.25	1.3	0.15	7	−1.0	−43.5
Schönburger	75.3	8.11	68.7	7.87	151	−6.6	−8.8
Senator	0.9	0.10	1.1	0.13	7	0.2	22.2
Seyval blanc	122.7	13.21	102.1	11.70	216	−20.6	−16.8
Siegerrebe	9.3	1.00	11.5	1.32	54	2.2	23.7
Triomphe	7.5	0.81	15.0	1.72	72	7.5	100.0
Würzer	14.3	1.54	9.8	1.12	27	−4.5	−31.5
Zweigeltrebe	3.9	0.42	2.6	0.30	15	−1.3	−33.3
Miscellaneous and Unauthorised	24.1	2.60	5.0	0.57		−19.1	−79.3
Totals	929		872			−57.0	−6.1

* 'Frequency planted' refers to the number of individual vineyard parcels that a particular vine is planted in. Some vineyards (especially larger ones) may have more than one 'parcel' of the same variety in their vineyards.

[†] 1999 figures for Phoenix are estimated.

more important varieties (those occupying more than 1 per cent of the vineyard area) that have fallen are; Müller-Thurgau (−36.9 per cent), Würzer (−31.5 per cent), Seyval blanc (−16.8 per cent), Kerner (−13.6 per cent), Schönburger (−8.8 per cent), Huxelrebe

(−6.6 per cent) and Reichensteiner (−6.0 per cent). Since varieties such as Müller-Thurgau and Seyval blanc were the very first varieties to be planted in the UK, it is not surprising that they feature more prominently in older vineyards and in the smaller, more 'amateur' vineyards, both of which are more likely to be grubbed up on the retirement of the owner.

The varieties that have prospered between 1990 and 1999 fall into several distinct camps; there are varieties such as Siegerrebe (+23.7 per cent) and Bacchus (+13.9 per cent), both showing themselves capable of producing very good wines; varieties for the production of sparkling wine such as Chardonnay (+71.9 per cent) and Pinot noir (+38.1 per cent); and varieties for red wines, Rondo (+375 per cent), Dornfelder (+107.4 per cent) and Triomphe (+100 per cent). Lesser varieties such as Madeleine × Angevine 7672 and Kernling have also risen, although the areas planted are relatively small.

Bottle-Fermented Sparkling Wines

There is no doubt that bottle-fermented sparkling wines (of all types and from all countries) are gaining in popularity with British consumers and many consider that the UK has an ideal climate in which to produce them. Much of the sparkling wine has, up to now, been produced from 'standard' varieties – Müller-Thurgau, Reichensteiner and Seyval blanc. Whilst this does not always find favour with wine writers and purists, who consider that the UK ought to concentrate on making wine from the 'classic' varieties, the results to date have in general been promising, although of course there is always room for improvement. However, the rise in the planted areas of the 'classic' sparkling wine varieties – Chardonnay, Pinot Meunier and Pinot noir – although small in terms of their share of the total planted area (9.8 per cent), represents a significant shift towards this type of wine (Table 5).

Whether in the long term these are the correct varieties to grow is open to debate for they must be considered marginal for many sites, average yields are bound to be lower and therefore the cost of grapes higher. Take the higher cost of grapes, add on the additional costs of making, storing and financing bottle-fermented sparkling wines, and the result is a product that needs a premium in the marketplace in order for it to survive. The market in non-

Table 5. UK Areas of 'Classic' Varieties for Sparkling Wine

Variety	1990 Ha	1999 Ha	1990–1999 increase Ha	1990–1999 increase %
Chardonnay	19.9	34.2	14.3	71.9
Pinot Meunier (Wrotham Pinot)	5.5	8.2	2.7	49.1
Pinot noir	32	44.2	12.2	38.1
	57.4	86.6	29.2	50.9

Champagne sparkling wines – Cava, Sekt, Cremant and a myriad of wines from other countries and regions – is a tough one and if UK produced sparkling wines are going to survive, they will have to fight hard. Having additional burdens in the shape of low yields and expensive grapes may, in the long term, prove too much. To date, the quality of wines being produced by the specialist 'classic' variety producers – most notably Nyetimber Vineyard* and RidgeView Estate – has been good, if not excellent, and one can only hope that they can find (or carve out) a niche for their premium products. They deserve to succeed, not only on a personal level, but also for the good of the whole UK wine industry.

Red Varieties

Perhaps the most interesting rise is that of red varieties (Table 6) which have increased from a total planted area of 63 ha in 1990 to 99.6 ha in 1999, a rise of 58 per cent. Red varieties now account for 11.3 per cent of the total UK area. These figures, however, do include significant rises in plantings of Pinot noir and Pinot Meunier which have mainly been for the production of bottle-fermented sparkling wine, rather than red wines. The purely red wine varieties show an even greater increase – from 25.5 ha to 47.2 ha – a rise of 85 per cent. Latest Wine Standards Board production figures show that in 1999 red wines accounted for 1,221 hl out of a total UK wine production of 13,272 hl or just over 9 per cent of the total. Considering that not too many years ago, the UK was barely considered capable of producing white wines, the fact that we are

Table 6. Red Grape Varieties in UK Vineyards 1990–1999

Variety	1990 Ha	%	1999 Ha	%	Ha Change	% Change
Cascade						
(Seibel 13/053)	1.2	0.1	0.6	0.1	−0.6	−50.0
Dornfelder	5.4	0.6	11.2	1.3	5.8	107.4
Dunkelfelder	3.5	0.4	2.5	0.3	−1.0	−28.6
Léon Millot	2	0.2	3.6	0.4	1.6	80.0
Pinot Meunier						
(Wrotham Pinot)	5.5	0.6	8.2	0.9	2.7	49.1
Pinot noir	32	3.4	44.2	5.1	12.2	38.1
Regent			2.2	0.3	2.2	
Rondo (Gm 6494/5)	2	0.2	9.5	1.1	7.5	375.0
Triomphe	7.5	0.8	15.0	1.7	7.5	100.0
Zweigeltrebe	3.9	0.4	2.6	0.3	−1.3	−33.3
Total of red varieties	63.0	6.8	99.6	11.4	36.6	58.1
White varieties	866	93.2	772	88.5	−94.0	−10.9
Total of all varieties	929		872			

now producing some interesting reds is quite remarkable. The major increases in plantings of the purely red wine varieties are of Dornfelder, Triomphe and Rondo – three varieties which if allowed to fully ripen and correctly handled in the winery (and this usually means some oak contact) – are well suited to many vineyards. Regent, a new Geilweilerhof hybrid ((Silvaner × Müller-Thurgau) × Chambourcin) is already showing promise at Three Choirs Vineyard in Gloucestershire and is being more widely planted. Why Chambourcin itself, which is a Joannes Seyve hybrid and widely planted in the Loire-Atlantique region – one of the few continental regions whose climate matches the UK's – is not planted in the UK remains a mystery. It manages – according to French sources – to produce good deep red wines in a Cabernet Franc style, as well as stylish rosés. Perhaps its day will come? There is also a number of other new red crosses which show promise – several containing *vitis amurensis* blood which could well perform satisfactorily under UK conditions. With the promise (threat?) of warmer conditions due to global warming, who knows what the future might hold for English and Welsh red wines?

CURRENT SITUATION

Over the next few years, it would be surprising if the overall planted area did not fall slightly as growers take stock of the condition of their vineyards and the market for their grapes and wines. Once the trelliswork holding up the vines requires substantial repairs or even complete replacement (which depending on the quality of the wooden stakes used, will be between the tenth and twentieth years) growers, who are perhaps experiencing low returns through a combination of poorly yielding varieties (Müller-Thurgau in particular) and low grape prices, or are having problems selling wine into what is a very competitive market, will take the decision to grub up their vines. Those growers who have been able to attend to the upkeep of their vineyards, who have managed to create a market for their wines and who have perhaps developed a niche for their 'speciality' wines – oak aged, red, dessert and sparkling wines – will continue to expand and plant more vines as they see fit.

VARIETIES FOR THE FUTURE

To pretend that no change will take place in UK vine varieties in the future would be to ignore the experience of the past. Whilst the boom in planting that occurred in the 1970s and 1980s may not happen again – at least not until global warming gives us a more Mediterranean climate – new vineyards are being planted and existing growers are increasing their plantings. There are also growers whose vineyards are now reaching the end of their lives and re-planting is being considered. If there is one thing that the past does tell us, it is that many growers believe, rightly or wrongly, that the 'perfect' variety for UK climatic conditions exists somewhere and one day someone will discover it! Varieties that have really outlived their usefulness, such as Huxelrebe, Kerner and Müller-Thurgau will probably continue to decline albeit slowly. Varieties such as Bacchus, Reichensteiner and Seyval blanc, which in quantity terms provide a large percentage of the UK's wine, will continue to be planted and will form the core of many vineyards. The production of both sparkling wines and red wines will undoubtedly increase and as the quality of both improves and gains public acceptance, more growers will be tempted to plant suitable varieties. However, the temptation to experiment with new varieties is very great.

The German viticultural colleges, crosses from which (if you include Müller-Thurgau) account for almost 75 per cent of the total UK vineyard area, are still producing new varieties and these cannot be ignored. Although the demand for new crosses has diminished in Germany as growers concentrate on their traditional varieties – Riesling, Müller-Thurgau, Silvaner and Spätburgunder (Pinot noir) – a new wave of varieties is being produced and distributed, many which of could be of interest to UK growers. For some colleges – notably Geisenheim, Geilweilerhof and Freiburg – one of their priorities over the last twenty years in breeding new varieties has been to attempt to build in natural genetic resistance to fungal diseases by cross-breeding with (mainly) French-American hybrids. The latest issue of the *Taschenbuch der Rebsorten* (Handbook of Grape Varieties) by Hillebrand, Lott and Pfaff, lists a large number of new interspecific crosses, many of which might be of interest to UK growers. Geisenheim has several new crosses which have *vitis amurensis* blood in them (apart from Rondo), as well as some that have Seibel and Seyve-Villard parentage (Hibernal, Prinzipal and Saphira). They also have a Bacchus × Reichensteiner (Gm 728-4) and a Schönburger × Reichensteiner (Gm 677-4), both of which have already showed promise in a UK vineyard and deserve to be more widely planted. Geilweilerhof, all of whose new crosses have non-*vinifera* parentage, have several of possible interest (some of which are already being grown in the UK); Phoenix, Sirius and Stauffer are all Bacchus × Seyve-Villard 12-375, Orion is Optima × Seyve-Villard 12-375 and Regent is Diana × Chambourcin – the latter a Joannes Seyve hybrid from the 1930s. Freiburg lists five new hybrids: FR 207-70, FR 946-60, Johanniter and Merzling – all of which have the blood from various Seyve-Villard varieties in them, plus a new red variety, Bronner, which has Rondo (Gm 6494/5) as one parent. These are only those varieties which have received official recognition and are available to growers – there are a large number of other interesting varieties still under wraps and still in development.

Some UK growers are against planting interspecific crosses (hybrids) because at present, only pure *vinifera* varieties may be made into Quality wine. However, there have recently been developments in Germany which may change this. Breeders of the new interspecific crosses asked the Bundessortenamt (the state body in Germany that tests and registers all new plant varieties) to study the new varieties and determine whether, apart from disease resistance, they showed any non-*vinifera* characteristics. Having looked at all aspects of the plant and its fruit, and the wine made from the fruit, they declared that they were indistinguishable from *viniferas* and could therefore be classed as such and used in the production of Quality wine. This pragmatic approach to the inflexibility of the EU winemaking regulations does not appear (yet) to have fallen foul of the Commission and it is to be hoped that this ruling can be extended to the UK. This would allow varieties such as Orion, Phoenix, Regent and Rondo – already being grown in the UK – to be used for the production of English and Welsh Quality wines.

The Eger Vine Breeding Station in Hungary has also produced some interesting interspecific crosses, also using Seyve-Villard 12-375. Bianca and Zalagyönge are two crosses that might be of interest to UK growers. They are reported to be very disease resistant (Zalagyönge is also said to be resistant to *phylloxera* when grown on its own roots), ripen early with high sugars and low acidity and have excellent wood ripening characteristics. Wine quality of both is said to be good. There are, in all probability, other varieties in use in some of the world's less sun-drenched wine-growing regions that might be usefully tested for use in the UK. Julian Jeffs (editor of this series and an expert on Iberian wines) has suggested that some of the varieties used in the north and north-west of Spain (around Vigo and Bilbao) might be useful. Whites such as Albarino and Loureira Blanco – used for making the *vinhos verdes* in Portugal – seem to thrive in Galicia which is one of the wettest and coolest parts of Spain. Another is the Ondarribi Zuri, a white variety found growing in the Chacolís, the area to the south of Bilbao, which is again fairly cool and damp. For a while I thought that the two varieties found in the *Pays Nantais*, Melon de Bourgogne (used for making Muscadet) and Gros Plant – both white – might be worth a try and did have a few vines in my collection. However, they both seemed to take an age to ripen and high acid levels were always a problem. What consumers, to say nothing of wine writers, would have made of some of these names is another matter altogether.

One also must not forget that the improvement of existing varieties through clonal selection is an ongoing process and new clones of all commercial varieties are constantly being developed by research institutes around the world. There are for instance over 80 different clones of Chardonnay and 65 of Pinot noir available to growers in France. Their attributes vary from early to late ripening, from high yield to low yield, from being suitable for sparkling wine to high quality still wine and from being suitable for warm regions to cooler ones. Many *appellations* specify which clones may be grown for the production of that region's style of wine (Champagne for instance). For UK growers to benefit from these clonal variations is not as easy as it might seem as most are developed for regions with climates considerably warmer and more suited to wine production than the UK's. However, the possibility of discovering clones of standard varieties better adapted to our conditions exists and should not be forgotten when growers are ordering vines for planting.

One problem which UK growers have to face is that of the availability of grafted vines to plant. With almost all our vines coming from overseas – German and French nurseries being the main source, although Canada has in the past supplied Seyval blanc – commercial nurserymen in these countries are by and large only interested in grafting and raising varieties which they think they can sell. The UK is such a small market that, in their eyes, it hardly exists. Even some of our mainstream varieties – Reichensteiner, Seyval blanc and Schönburger – are so little grown on the Continent, that very few grafts are made. Varieties such as Madeleine × Angevine 7672 and Triomphe which are virtually unknown overseas, are impossible to obtain and if growers need these they either have to resort to UK-produced rooted cuttings – which will have been produced from wood of uncertain provenance, possibly virus infected or not true to type – or have to send scion wood to overseas nurseries for grafting and raising. This is both long-winded and expensive, but does at least result in *phylloxera*-resistant plants, although the problems of wood quality remain.

The latest development in vine breeding to hit the headlines has been that of gene transfer. 'Gene jockeys' have been able to insert genes taken from other plants – in Germany's case the genes came from barley – into Dornfelder, Riesling and Seyval blanc, hoping that this will give them inbuilt 'natural' resistance to both powdery and downy mildew; 130 'transgenic' vines of these three varieties have been planted at Geilweilerhof and wines will be made. This will be a long-term experiment and transgenic vines from this research are not expected to be available for 25–30 years. Researchers in France, the USA, Australia, Japan and Israel have also been working on producing genetically modified vines and rumour has it that a GM Chardonnay vineyard is already cropping in Champagne. The technique of gene transfer, apart from being far more effective at building in specific resistance traits to vines than conventional sexual cross breeding, is also far quicker. Many of today's 'new' crossbred varieties were bred over 30 years ago. The results of gene transfer can be seen within three or four years after the work is carried out. There can be no doubt that if the genes that improve resistance to the mildews and *botrytis* could be inserted into say Reichensteiner or Bacchus, their ability to grow and fruit in UK conditions would be greatly increased. Not only would crops be more regular and larger, but also the costs of growing would be lower as chemical sprays would not be needed – definitely a win-win situation. However, with both the media and many politicians jumping on the 'ban GM crops' bandwagon, the future for any plant that has been genetically modified is now in doubt. The public appears to have decided the potential benefits of these plants are outweighed by the apparent risks, even though proper trials have not yet been carried out. In the present climate of opinion, it would appear doubtful that wine from GM vine varieties would be accepted by the consumer, although the risks of ingesting alcohol are probably far greater than contracting some ailment from a stray foreign gene!

THE VINE VARIETIES CLASSIFICATION COMMITTEE

Under EU legislation, each member state growing 500 ha or more of vines, has to have a committee to draw up vine variety lists (of both winemaking and rootstock varieties) and to make proposals for changes in varieties. As the 1987 survey had revealed a total of 546 ha, MAFF asked the EVA for names of growers willing to serve on such a committee. The Vine Varieties Classification Committee (VVCC) met for the first time on 3 July 1989 and at that meeting proposed a revised varieties list which took into account the findings of the 1987 survey. It also proposed that four varieties, Kanzler, Madeleine Royale, Mariensteiner and Perle, which were being grown in minute quantities and which no growers appeared to favour, be downgraded to 'Temporarily Authorised'. This allowed them a further 25 years of use, but no new vines of these varieties could be planted. The new list was as follows:

Recommended
  Huxelrebe
  Madeleine × Angevine 7672
  Müller-Thurgau
  Reichensteiner
  Schönburger
  Seyval Blanc*

Authorised
  Auxerrois
  Bacchus
  Chardonnay
  Ehrenfelser
  Faberrebe
  Kerner
  Madeleine 3 Sylvaner No. 3 28/51
  Ortega
  Pinot Noir
  Pinot gris (Ruländer)
  Siegerrebe
  Wrotham Pinot (Pinot Meunier)

*Interspecific cross or hybrid vine

The 1987 survey had also shown that thirteen 'illegal' varieties were being grown in enough volume (see Table 2 for areas) for them to be noticed by the Commission and therefore had to be legalised. The varieties were:

  Dunkelfelder
  Gamay noir
  Gewürztraminer
  Gutenborner
  Optima
  Léon Millot

Regner
Sauvignon blanc
Scheurebe
Cascade (Seibel 13/053)
Triomphe
Würzer
Zweigeltrebe

Apart from Gamay noir, Gewürztraminer and Sauvignon blanc, which most growers accepted were very marginal for UK conditions, the VVCC proposed that over the course of the next three years, the ten remaining varieties be proposed for the 'Provisionally Authorised' category. The ten have all since been accepted.

The work of the VVCC is ongoing, with the more established varieties being upgraded from 'Authorised' to 'Recommended' (only Bacchus to date) and from 'Provisionally Authorised' to 'Authorised'. Newer varieties, which have been on unofficial trial in UK vineyards, are proposed for introduction into the lists as 'Provisionally Authorised' and data sheets showing full details about the variety in question are prepared and submitted to the Commission. The current list is a good reflection of the varieties actually being used in the UK today. However, for the lesser grown varieties, one could argue that they are included simply to satisfy bureaucracy as a wine made from a variety *not* on the lists may only be labelled as 'United Kingdom Table Wine' and can (in theory) bear neither the name(s) of the grape variety nor a vintage. The current list of permitted vine varieties for UK wine production, 1999/2000 is as follows:

Recommended
  Bacchus
  Huxelrebe
  Madeleine × Angevine 7672
  Müller-Thurgau (Rivaner)
  Reichensteiner
  Schönburger
  Seyval Blanc*

Authorised
  Auxerrois
  Cascade (Seibel 13/053)*

Chardonnay
Dunkelfelder
Ehrenfelser
Faberrebe
Gutenborner
Kerner
Léon Millot*
Madeleine × Sylvaner No. 3 28/51
Optima
Ortega
Pinot gris (Ruländer)
Pinot Meunier (Wrotham Pinot)
Pinot noir
Regner
Scheurebe
Siegerrebe
Triomphe*
Würzer
Zweigeltrebe

Provisionally Authorised
Chasselas (Gutedal)
Dornfelder
Elbling Red
Elbling White
Findling
Kernling
Orion*
Perle (Perle from Alzey)
Pinot blanc
Phoenix*
Regent*
Riesling
Rondo (Gm 6494/5)*
Senator

Temporarily Authorised
Kanzler
Mariensteiner
Madeleine Royale

*Interspecific cross or hybrid vine; permitted synonyms in brackets.

AVAILABILITY OF ACCURATE PERFORMANCE FIGURES

With even the most widely grown variety in the UK (Müller-Thurgau) only occupying 116.4 ha (288 acres) and with no official performance recording system (as can be found in almost all other winegrowing countries), the collection of evidence on which to base individual variety descriptions can sometimes be quite daunting. Until 1993, the English Vineyards Association collected valuable yield figures which were submitted when growers entered their wines for the 'Seal of Quality'. This scheme, which was in many respects like the Quality Wine Scheme (QWS), required growers to give individual variety area and yield data when they submitted applications. Whilst these figures only related to those growers and those wines entered for the 'Seal', it did give a valuable guide to the actual yields being achieved in the better managed vineyards. Since the demise of the 'Seal', no accurate yield data that reflects what is happening across a range of vineyards has been collected and collated. That it was not a requirement of the QWS for actual harvest data – yields, natural alcohol and acidity levels – to be submitted with applications and, after collating, made available to the industry, was a great pity. That it is also not a requirement for this type of data to be submitted by every grower along with the mandatory 15 December 'Production Declaration' is also a loss to the industry. Without accurate figures of at least yields (but hopefully other data as well) it becomes very difficult to assess which varieties are performing well. No doubt the already stretched Wine Standards Board would have other views about the collection and collation of even more figures!

Yields

The actual yield from a vineyard will depend on many factors and it is almost impossible to be dogmatic about the matter. Yields in vineyards, especially under UK growing conditions, can vary widely and inconsistency of harvests is one of the problems that has to be faced. The annual yield figures collected by the Wine Standards Board demonstrate this dramatically (Table 7). Taking only the reliable post-1989 figures, the two lowest annual yields, 1995 and 1997, were both years in which late spring frosts did tremendous damage across much of the country. Many vineyards harvested

Table 7. UK Vineyard Areas and Yields 1975–1999

Year	Total hectares of vineyards	Hectares in production	Total yield in hectolitres	Total hectolitres per hectare	Yield tonnes per acre	Number of vineyards*	Number of wineries
Surveys before 1989 were voluntary and data is therefore not reliable. The year is that to which the data refers – not the year in which the survey was carried out or the results published.							
1975	196	149					
1979	250	n/a					
1982	400	n/a	7000				
1984	431	325	13510	41.57			
1985	488	356	6531	13.38		281	120
1987	546	382	4110	7.53		378	
Surveys from 1989 have been compulsory							
1989	876	652	21447	32.89	1.9	442	147
1990	929	629	14442	22.96	1.3	445	147
1991	992	650	15429	23.74	1.4	454	150
1992	1055	701	26428	37.70	2.2	457	157
1993	1065	767	17502	22.82	1.3	479	148
1994	1035	733	18327	25.00	1.4	435	123
1995	984	745	12795	17.17	1.0	413	115
1996	965	775	26572	34.29	2.0	408	123
1997	949	791	6523	8.25	0.5	386	114
1998	901	842	11358	13.49	0.8	382	112
1999	872	835	13272	15.89	0.9	370(est)	110 (est)
Average harvests and yields:							
1989–1999		738	16736	22.67	1.3		

From 1994, figures exclude 'abandoned' vineyards, i.e. those not in active production.
* A 'vineyard' to be registered must be 10 ares or quarter of an acre (one are = 100 sq m).

virtually nothing, yet returned a production declaration which would have been included in the figures. Crops in those vineyards that escaped frost damage were actually quite good. The two highest yielding years, 1992 and 1996, followed years when early summer growing conditions had been good for fruit bud initiation and show how close to the margin of success UK growers are. A national average crop for these two years of 36 hl/ha compares quite favourably with the long-term average yields of France – 44 hl/ha, Italy – 43 hl/ha and Spain – 20 hl/ha. However, compared to Germany – 60 hl/ha, New Zealand – 61 hl/ha, Australia –

Table 8. 1983–1992 EVA 'Seal of Quality' Yields of
'Recommended' Varieties

Variety	Hl/ha	Tonnes/acre
Müller-Thurgau	36.6	2.1
Reichensteiner	40.6	2.3
Seyval blanc	51.8	3.0
Bacchus	31.3	1.8
Schönburger	32.7	1.9
Madeleine × Angevine 7672	35.9	2.1
Huxelrebe	32.8	1.9

61 hl/ha and South Africa – 67 hl/ha, the situation does not look quite so rosy!

Accurate yield figures are perhaps the hardest (and possibly the most meaningless as they ignore wine quality) to collect and compile. Even when the EVA collected data for the 'Seal', they were always open to question. The figures included all vineyards, young or old, well managed or badly managed, frost-prone or frost-free, and very often the results required a degree of interpretation before they made any sense. With the lesser varieties only being grown in small – sometimes minute – quantities, the results from these were of little value. However, for the seven major varieties – now all 'Recommended' – the following figures were collected over the ten-year period 1983–1992. Despite the inbuilt inaccuracies of the system, the most problematic being that of returning yield data from immature or very badly performing vineyards, the results do show a consistency in line with the expectations of vineyard owners. As can be seen from Table 8, most varieties average around the 35 hl/ha (2 tonne/acre) mark, apart from Seyval blanc which can claim another 50 per cent, bringing it up to nearer 52 hl/ha or 3 tonne/acre. In reality, given a mature vineyard and good management (especially pest and disease control) capable growers would expect to better these figures on all varieties by a further 30–50 per cent. Indeed, the economics of growing grapes and making wine in the UK would suggest that for most 'standard' wines, i.e not sparkling, red, oak-aged, late-harvest or other speciality wines, 52 hl/ha or 3 tonnes/acre would be considered the bare minimum for the long-term viability of the enterprise.

Natural sugar and acidity levels

Most growers in the UK record natural sugar levels using the German system of degrees Oechsle (°OE) – mainly because wine-makers in the early days were very often guided and helped by both German trained winemakers and by German textbooks and most of our varieties have origins in that country. The Wine Standards Board issues conversion tables for winemakers to convert °OE into a figure of potential alcohol in order to calculate amounts of sugar required for enrichment. Whilst this may be confusing to growers and winemakers used to using Brix, Baumé, Ballung, Klosterneuberg or any other system, it is the one which all UK vineyards and winemakers accept. Acidity levels are always recorded in grammes per litre of total acidity expressed as tartaric acid which – apart from France and French influenced winemaking regions – is the universal way of recording acid levels.

Having said that yield figures can be difficult to obtain and when obtained, open to interpretation, the same has to be said about natural sugar and acid levels. Again, as with the yield figures, the industry would have benefited greatly had these figures been requested as part of the annual 'production declaration' required to be completed by all growers. The figures for sugar and acid given for the various varieties must therefore be seen as only a *very* general guide. Many factors will influence both sugar and acid levels. The most significant influences on these – apart from the general warmth and length of any particular growing season – will be the general 'quality' of the vineyard in all aspects, as well as the level of yield obtained. Some sites consistently produce grapes with significantly higher natural sugar levels than the average and this can be put down to a variety of factors; the height above sea-level, the angle of the vineyard to the sun, the amount of shelter, the date bud-burst occurs, the quality of the management in all respects, the trellising and pruning systems employed, plus several more. Yield levels, especially in more marginal areas and vineyards, can have a very marked effect on both sugar and acid levels. This, of course, is not a particular UK phenomenon and is something that all growing regions encounter. However, under our very cool growing conditions there would appear to be a definite 'cut-off' level of yield for any given site, variety and year. Over and above this point, natural sugar levels will be lower and acid levels higher by far more than can be explained by say, a 20 per cent increase in yield. It would appear that the limited amount of heat and light that we have in our vineyards can only be spread so far.

8

Vine Variety Descriptions A–Z

VINE VARIETIES

The following variety descriptions cover all varieties in the 'Recommended', 'Authorised' and 'Provisionally Authorised' lists – a total of 42 varieties. The three varieties on the 'Temporarily Authorised' list – Kanzler, Madeleine Royale and Mariensteiner – are not covered as they are barely grown and, furthermore, may no longer be planted. The eighteen most widely planted varieties (those each covering 1 per cent or more of the UK planted acreage) which together account for almost 90 per cent of the planted area, have been covered in greater detail than the remaining 24. A description for Phoenix has also been included, even though it does not appear as a separate variety in the WSB's lists.

Notes on vine variety names

MADELEINE × ANGEVINE 7672

The confusion surrounding this variety will (in my view) never be cleared up until a completely new name is chosen for the variety originally sent to Ray Brock by Dr Zimmerman from Alzey in 1957. It is most definitely *not* the French table grape Madeleine Angevine (also sometimes spelt Madeleine d'Angevine or Madeleine angevine) and this was confirmed by Dr Alleweldt in 1992 (then head of the Geilweilerhof Institute for Grapevine Breeding) who reported that Scheu's old breeding books showed it to be an 'open pollinated progeny of Madeleine Angevine'.

I have therefore referred to the variety as 'Madeleine × Angevine 7672' which is not really correct (Az 7672 would be a more correct name), but at least it differentiates it from Madeleine Angevine which is most certainly incorrect. Where I have referred to wines labelled as 'Madeleine Angevine' I have left the spelling alone.

MADELEINE ANGEVINE × SYLVANER No. 3 28/51

Again, as with Madeleine × Angevine 7672, the name Madeleine Sylvaner is most definitely incorrect, although likely to cause less confusion as there is no 'original' variety of the same name and it is also a far less important variety. However, it would have been better to give it a completely new name. The official name in the EU Regulations is Madeleine Sylvaner.

PINOTS

I have generally stuck to the French names for the Pinots – blanc, gris, Meunier and noir – even though Ruländer is the 'official name' for Pinot gris in the UK and Wrotham Pinot for Pinot Meunier. This is more in line with the names used by winegrowers on their bottles.

SYLVANER/SILVANER

I have generally used the old spelling of Sylvaner when referring to both Madeleine Sylvaner and Riesling Sylvaner (Müller-Thurgau or Rivaner) in preference to the modern German spelling *Silvaner* which has only been used when referring to crossings made in Germany. The Swiss continue to use Riesling Sylvaner, in the main, as their name for wines made from Müller-Thurgau.

Grape varieties

The information on each grape variety is presented as follows:

Variety synonym
Type / colour / official category
Origin / crossing

Natural alcohol levels are given as per cent potential alcohol. Acidity levels are expressed in grammes per litre (g/l) as tartaric acid. Comparisons to 'M-T' refer to Müller-Thurgau which is taken as the UK's standard variety. A 'vineyard parcel' is a separately identifiable plot of land planted with a single variety of vine. Individual vineyards may have more than one 'parcel' of the same variety.

Auxerrois *syn.* Pinot Auxerrois (non-EU)
Vinifera / white / Authorised
Very old variety of unknown origin. Thought to be related to Chardonnay.

Auxerrois was included on the original list of 'Recommended' varieties submitted to the EU in 1973, even though it had not been one suggested by the EVA. It is grown in Alsace where it is usually blended into 'Edelzwicker' (although, curiously, it can also be labelled as Pinot blanc) or used for sparkling wine (Cremant d'Alsace). Also to be found in Luxembourg and Burgundy in the Old World, and Canada, New Zealand and the USA in the New. Geisenheim has produced some more productive clones and there are now 70 ha in Germany.

It is a variety of moderate vigour, fairly resistant to *botrytis* and ripens its wood well. It is quite a late variety, after Müller-Thurgau, but before Seyval blanc. As a neutral Pinot blanc/Chardonnay style variety which would be useful for barrel-ageing or for sparkling wine base, it should be more widely planted in the UK. It has lower acid levels than other similar varieties and yields steadily. In 1999 it occupied 0.99 per cent of the UK vineyard area and was planted in 29 vineyard parcels.

Bacchus
Vinifera / white / Recommended
(Silvaner × Riesling) × Müller-Thurgau

Crossing made by Peter Morio and Professor Husfeld at the Geil-weilerhof Institute for Grapevine Breeding in the Pfalz, Germany. First registered in 1972 and known locally in the Pfalz as the 'Early Scheurebe'. It is the second most popular 'new-crossing' variety in Germany (after Kerner) and in 1998 3,316 ha were planted. It first appeared in the UK in the Wye College vineyard in 1973 and was upgraded to 'Recommended' in 1998. In 1999 it occupied 9.93 per cent of the UK vineyard area and was planted in 156 vineyard parcels.

Viticulture: Less vigorous than M-T and requires less summer pruning. Leaf removal around the grape zone aids flavour development. Subject to poor fruit set in cold/wet flowering conditions.

Disease susceptibility: Needs a full spray programme, although less disease prone than M-T.

Harvesting period: Mid-season. Slightly earlier than M-T.

Natural sugar level: 7.5 per cent–9.5 per cent.

Acidity level: 9.5 g/l–10.5 g/l.

Wine type: When picked at slightly lower sugar levels, has good New World (Marlborough style) Sauvignon blanc characters with excellent fruit definition, good length and crisp acidity. When riper, tends more towards Sancerre. Well made Bacchus wines age well and develop interesting tertiary flavours. Has also been used for late-harvest wines when *botrytis* affects grapes.

Advantages: Excellent wine quality.

Disadvantages: Yields not that high. Needs good flowering conditions.

Summary: One of the UK's better varieties, capable of being turned into world-class wines. More yield would be an advantage.

Cascade *syn.* Seibel 13/053
Hybrid / red / Authorised
Seibel 7042 × Seibel 5049

An old red hybrid variety that found favour in the USA and Canada owing to its early ripening habit and frost resistance. Named 'Cascade' in 1972 by the Finger Lakes Wine Growers Association (New York), it has now more or less disappeared from commercial vineyards there and Galet says that it has virus problems. It was grown by Brock at Oxted and subsequently by the Gore-Brownes at Beaulieu. Margaret Gore-Browne had heard that 'it was prohibited by the Common Market as it is said to have an injurious effect upon the liver', so felt that they ought not to plant it any more. However, they continued to grow it and their first vintage, the 1961, was a rosé, made in part from Cascade.

Like most red hybrids, the variety tends to extreme vigour, with large leaves, long canes and multiple side shoots. Cordon pruning is preferred. It is almost disease free, although a light spray programme is probably the best policy and it ripens its wood well.

It has an early bud-burst and can therefore be caught by the frost but produces good flowers from secondary buds.

The grapes have coloured flesh and juice and wines can be very dark red. Although the wines do not have a proper 'foxy' or hybrid flavour, there is something slightly non-*vinifera* about them, especially when made from grapes not fully ripe and acids can be very high. Perhaps best kept for blending with lower acid whites for making rosé wines. In reality, it is an older hybrid variety that has now been superseded and will eventually disappear from UK vineyards. In 1999 it occupied 0.07 per cent of the UK vineyard area and was planted in 9 vineyard parcels.

Chardonnay
Vinifera / white / Authorised
Original variety

With its origins lost in the Middle East, Chardonnay is now found in virtually every grapegrowing region in the world from the hottest parts – Australia, South Africa and California – to the coolest of all growing regions, the UK. With it being almost the only white variety used in Burgundy, Chablis and Champagne, it is not surprising that early vineyard owners in Britain were seduced into thinking that it would do well here. Brock had it in his collection at Oxted, but could never get it to ripen properly. Salisbury-Jones planted it at Hambledon in the late 1950s and had the same problems: excessively high acid levels and low natural sugars. This was a common finding among those growers who persevered with it, although most decided to give up and removed the offending variety. Only in really hot years would it produce anything like ripe grapes and tolerable wine. For still wines it remains a marginal variety for all but the very best sites and years. In 1999 it occupied 3.92 per cent of the UK vineyard area and was planted in 61 vineyard parcels.

In the late 1980s, some growers (most notably – but not only – Nyetimber Vineyard and RidgeView Estate) started to plant Chardonnay for the production of bottle-fermented sparkling wines, using better clones, ones perhaps more suited to our climate. Through a combination of good site selection and traditional training systems (perhaps aided by a slight degree of global warming) they have started to produce some excellent and interesting results.

Whilst acids are still high at harvest (15 g/l is not uncommon), the combination of a full malolactic-fermentation and the traditional secondary bottle fermentation, renders them manageable.

Viticulture: Early bud burst makes it liable to spring frost damage, but it recovers well with fruitful secondary buds. Quite vigorous and needs routine trimming and careful canopy management.
Disease susceptibility: Needs full spray programme. *Botrytis* can be a problem, especially in wet years.
Harvesting period: Late. Early November not unknown.
Natural sugar level: 7 per cent–9 per cent.
Acidity level: 12 g/l–16 g/l.
Wine type: Neutral and usually high in acid when made into still wines (which are rare in UK). Develops well in bottle when made into sparkling wine and picks up typical nutty/yeasty characters with extended lees contact. Full malolactic fermentation recommended to soften acidity and improve normally rather lean mouth-feel.
Advantages: Can be good when use in bottle-fermented sparkling wines.
Disadvantages: Late. High acidity. Low yields. Needs hard work in the winery.
Summary: Many growers have found Chardonnay far too high in acidity, too low in yield and have abandoned it. A new wave of sparkling wine producers appear to be having success and one can only wish them well. In UK vineyards it remains one for the brave and patient.

Chasselas *syn.* Gutedal or Fendant
Vinifera / white / Provisionally Authorised
Original variety of great antiquity

Said to be one of the oldest varieties known to man and once very widespread, Chasselas is now confined to southern Germany, where it is known as Gutedal, and Switzerland, where it is known as Fendant. The wines at best are light and appealing, often with some dissolved carbon dioxide in them to give an extra bite. They are rarely of very high quality.

The Chasselas family has many different sub-varieties and clones, especially amongst table grapes. Chasselas – under various guises – was grown by Brock at Oxted and he thought quite highly of it.

However, it was never widely taken up and has seldom produced wines of any real style or character in the UK. At best, a lowish acid blending variety and not really suited to the UK. Jon Leighton at Valley Vineyards considers that Chasselas rosé (a different variety from plain Chasselas) is worth trying and uses it for sparkling wine. In 1999 it occupied 0.17 per cent of the UK vineyard area and was planted in only 5 vineyard parcels.

Dornfelder
Vinifera / red / Provisionally Authorised
Helfensteiner × Heroldrebe

Crossing made in 1955 by August Herold at Weinsberg Research Institute in Würtemburg, Germany. Helfensteiner is Early Pinot noir × Black Hamburg and Heroldrebe is Portugieser × Limburger. Released in 1980.

One of the new(ish) wave of German crossings, bred in the heart of Germany's red wine producing region, Würtemburg. Traditional varieties grown there – Trollinger (Black Hamburg) and Limburger – suffer from a lack of colour and substance and Dornfelder was bred to produce more of both. Now quite widely grown in Germany (1998, 3,218 ha) and capable of producing some very fine wines, albeit in a spicy 'Rhone' style, rather than a classic Bordeaux style. First appeared in the UK in the late 1980s and has proved itself able to produce some interesting red wines, especially in combination with other varieties. It is being planted more widely and is definitely one of the most promising red varieties being grown in the UK. In 1999 it occupied 1.28 per cent of the UK vineyard area and was planted in 40 vineyard parcels.

Viticulture: Fairly vigorous, but has good upright canes which make summer canopy management easier.
Disease susceptibility: Needs a good spray programme, especially if *botrytis* is to be avoided.
Harvesting period: Later than M-T.
Natural sugar level: 7 per cent–9 per cent.
Acidity level: 12 g/l–14 g/l.
Wine type: With skin contact will produce deep red wines without huge tannins. Usually fresh and fruity, more like Syrah or Gamay than Cabernet Sauvignon.
Advantages: Good red colour when fully ripe.

Disadvantages: Needs better than average site to get acids down to acceptable levels.

Summary: One of the best of the reds for UK conditions.

Dunkelfelder
Vinifera / red / Authorised
Unknown parentage

Crossing made by G. A. Froelich in Edenkoben, Rheinland-Pfalz, Germany in early 1900s. Exact parentage unknown. Discovered in the table grape selection at the Geisenheim Institute for Grapevine Breeding in the 1930s. Clonally selected in the 1970s and officially classified for wine production in Germany in 1980 where there are now 263 ha (1998) and where few varietal wines are made from it. It first appeared in UK in mid-80s.

Dunkelfelder is culturally undemanding with fairly low vigour, but does not usually run to large crops. It needs regular spraying and *botrytis* can be a problem. It ripens very early and is susceptible to bird and wasp attack. It is the best *teinturier* (colouring) variety grown in the UK and can produce massive colour. On its own, the wine is fairly neutral with low acidity and is best blended with other red varieties. Certainly should be considered as part of any UK red wine blend. In 1999 it occupied 0.29 per cent of the UK vineyard area and was planted in 24 vineyard parcels.

Ehrenfelser
Vinifera / white / Authorised
Riesling × Silvaner

Crossing made at the Geisenheim Institute for Grapevine Breeding by Professor H. Birk in 1929. In Germany (1998, 278 ha) it is used as a substitute for Riesling on less favourable sites for making both still and sparkling wines. First appeared in the UK in the Wye College Vineyard in the mid-1970s.

Ehrenfelser is a relatively undemanding variety, requires a regular spray programme and ripens fairly late. Natural acid levels can be very high. The wines are fruity and usually quite high in acid and probably best blended with other lower acid varieties. It is a variety not really suited to UK conditions and is slowly disappearing. In 1999 it occupied 0.19 per cent of the UK vineyard area and was planted in 9 vineyard parcels.

Elbling, Red
Vinifera / red / Provisionally Authorised
Clonal selection from an original variety

This is a clonal selection from the White Elbling, said to be the *vitis alba* of pre-Roman times. The red variant is grown along the Mosel in both Germany and Luxembourg, but only in limited quantities. First planted in the UK at Denbies in the late 1980s. Probably not a variety ideally suited to UK conditions, although it is said to survive poor flowering conditions. In 1999 it occupied 0.15 per cent of the UK vineyard area and was planted in only 1 vineyard parcel.

Elbling, White
Vinifera / white / Provisionally Authorised
An original variety

A very old variety, said to be the *vitis alba* of pre-Roman times. Widely grown along the Mosel in both Germany (1998, 1,072 ha) and especially Luxembourg. Planted in the UK at Denbies in the late 1980s.

Elbling is a difficult variety to ripen in the UK and acid levels can be very high. It is not ideally suited to UK conditions and at best could be used for sparkling wine. In 1999 it occupied 0.24 per cent of the UK vineyard area and was planted in only 2 vineyard parcels.

Faberrebe
Vinifera / white / Authorised
Pinot blanc × Müller-Thurgau

Crossing made by Georg Scheu in 1929 at the Alzey Institute for Grapevine Breeding. Popular in Germany (1998, 1,657 ha) for its high natural sugars and crisp fruity acidity and widely used for blending with Müller-Thurgau. First introduced to the UK in the Wye College Vineyard in the late 1970s and subsequently planted by a number of growers. In 1999 it occupied 1.24 per cent of the UK vineyard area and was planted in 42 vineyard parcels.

Viticulture: Vigorous with copious side shoots making canopy management labour intensive. Probably best grown on a high wire cordon system like Sylvoz or Geneva Double Curtain (GDC).

Disease susceptibility: Requires a good spray programme to keep it clean. Will suffer from *botrytis* and stem rot if not well managed.
Harvesting period: Mid–late season, after M-T.
Natural sugar level: 7 per cent–9 per cent.
Acidity level: 10 g/l–12 g/l.
Wine type: Very fruity with crisp acidity. Full flavours, somewhere between Bacchus and Huxelrebe.
Advantages: When fully ripe, wine quality can be good and makes a good blending partner to more neutral lower acid varieties. Yields exceed M-T.
Disadvantages: Too vigorous
Summary: Given the choice, Bacchus is probably a better variety to grow if this style of wine is required. Not one to pull out, but perhaps not one to plant any longer.

Findling
Vinifera / white / Provisionally Authorised
Müller-Thurgau mutation

A Müller-Thurgau mutation, i.e. a 'sport' of M-T, selected by Franz Kimmig from Baden, Germany. Registered in 1971. In Germany, it is said to give a higher natural sugar level, lower acidity and more neutral wine than M-T. Introduced into the UK with the hope that it might prove better than M-T, but results to date suggest that it may not. Until a more positive track record has been established, growers should only plant it experimentally. In 1999 it occupied 0.25 per cent of the UK vineyard area and was planted in 12 vineyard parcels.

Gutenborner
Vinifera / white / Authorised
Müller-Thurgau × Chasselas Napoleon

Crossing made at the Geisenheim Institute for Grapevine Breeding, Germany in the 1930s. Now found in Germany only in very small amounts. First introduced into the UK in the mid-1970s. With less vigour overall than M-T, smaller leaves and more resistance to disease, this variety is a much easier variety to grow. Wine quality is good, with a pronounced fruity muscat flavour. Unfortunately, it has now been discontinued and stock is impossible to obtain. Another one for the history books and not likely to be around much in the future. In 1999 it occupied 0.22 per cent of the UK vineyard area and was planted in 7 vineyard parcels.

Huxelrebe
Vinifera / white / Recommended
Chasselas × Courtillier Musqué

Crossing made by George Scheu at the Alzey Institute for Grapevine Breeding, Germany in 1927. Named after Fritz Huxel, a grower from near Worms, who first recognised its potential. In Germany (1998, 1,332 ha) it can produce very large yields of grapes with high natural sugars. First introduced to the UK via the Wye College vineyard in 1972 and on account of its higher yielding ability, was quite widely planted. In 1999 it occupied 4.7 per cent of the UK vineyard area and was planted in 94 vineyard parcels.

Viticulture: Extremely vigorous, with fat canes and very large leaves. Probably best grown on a spur system where vigour can, to a certain extent, be tamed. Bunches are very large and contain an unusually high number of seedless grapes which ripen readily and achieve very high natural sugars. Benefits from thinning and pre-harvest leaf removal.
Disease susceptibility: Very susceptible to *botrytis*, mainly on account of the small seedless berries that ripen early. These are also attacked by wasps and birds
Harvesting period: Mid-season. After M-T.
Natural sugar level: 8.5 per cent–11 per cent.
Acidity level: 10 g/l–12 g/l.
Wine type: Very fruity with pronounced Sauvignon blanc character. Acid levels can be high and to obtain the best wines, the grapes must be allowed to ripen as fully as possible. Unripe examples can be rather too herbaceous and catty. Has been used for late-harvest sweet wines to good effect.
Advantages: High yields, high natural sugars and, when ripe, excellent wines.
Disadvantages: Too susceptible to disease which forces early picking of grapes which may not all be fully ripe.
Summary: A variety that is probably worth persevering with on account of its good quality wine and higher than average yields. With the new generation of anti-*botrytis* fungicides available, perhaps Huxelrebe will become more viable to grow.

Kerner
Vinifera / white / Authorised
Trollinger × Riesling (Trollinger is Black Hamburg)

Crossing made in 1929 by August Herold at Weinsberg Research Institute in Würtemburg, Germany. Very popular in Germany where it has several advantages over Riesling: it ripens more easily, has a lower acidity and better frost resistance, yet still retains the wine quality of the noblest of its parents, Riesling. Now Germany's fourth most planted white variety (1998, 7,011 ha) and the most popular of the 'new crosses'. First appeared in the UK in the Wye College vineyard in the mid-1970s and widely promoted as a quality variety, but experience has shown that it is difficult to ripen and makes wines of uneven quality. In 1999 it occupied 2.12 per cent of the UK vineyard area and was planted in 59 vineyard parcels.

Viticulture: Very dense foliage and vigorous side-shoots make this a demanding variety.
Disease susceptibility: Better than M-T. Needs a full spray programme to keep it clean. Dense leaf-wall make spray applications difficult.
Harvesting period: Late to very late.
Natural sugar level: 7 per cent–9 per cent.
Acidity level: 12 g/l–14 g/l.
Wine type: Quite racy, Riesling style fruity wines, but unless really ripe, they suffer from excess acidity. Can be long-lasting.
Advantages: Few. Could be a used as a blending partner for lower acid, more neutral varieties, but this is hardly a reason to plant it.
Disadvantages: Late ripening and high acidities.
Summary: Its high acid levels and late ripening make it unsuitable for the UK and there are better varieties.

Kernling
Vinifera / white / Provisionally Authorised
Kerner mutation

A 'sport' of Kerner selected by Ludwig Hochdorfer from the Pfalz, Germany. First registered in 1974. Said to be similar to Kerner, but without the excessive side-shoots that make Kerner difficult to grow. Introduced into the UK in the late 1980s as an alternative to

Kerner. Despite the relatively large area planted, the number of single varietal wines available is small, although some have been very good. Whether it is a variety that will do well in the UK over the long term is another matter as acids can be high and yields are not that distinguished. In 1999 it occupied 1.55 per cent of the UK vineyard area and was planted in 36 vineyard parcels.

Viticulture: Fairly vigorous with an upright habit.
Disease susceptibility: Less prone to disease than Müller-Thurgau.
Harvesting period: Mid to late season.
Natural sugar level: 7 per cent–9 per cent.
Acidity level: 10 g/l–12 g/l.
Wine type: Fruity in a steely, Riesling style. Acidities can be high.
Advantages: Easier to ripen than Kerner and better yields.
Disadvantages: Difficult to ripen fully in some years leading to unripe characters.
Summary: A variety to treat with caution until more positive results have been achieved.

Léon Millot
Hybrid / red / Authorised
riparia-rupestris × Goldriesling (Goldriesling is Riesling × Courtillier Musqué)

An old French-American variety bred by Kuhlmann in the late 1890s and popular at one time in both France and the eastern USA. Introduced into the UK by Brock at Oxted in the early 1950s, it was one of the first red varieties to be grown commercially. It is, like many red hybrids, very vigorous and canopies can be dense. However, it is very resistant to disease and can be grown with minimal spraying. Both the bunches and the grapes on them are small and yields are never high.

Colour is good – the skin, flesh and juice are all red – and the variety is useful for adding colour to blend of different red varieties or for a rosé with other white varieties. Its flavour, whilst not 'foxy', does have a certain non-*vinifera* element which must be counted against it. For the UK, it has probably now been superseded by better red varieties and one would not think of it as a first-choice for red wines. Some growers report a lot of clonal variation and it might be that the good clones will survive. Difficult to obtain stock except as rooted cuttings. In 1999 it occupied 0.41 per cent of the UK vineyard area and was planted in 32 vineyard parcels.

Madeleine × Angevine 7672 *syn.* Madeleine Angevine
Vinifera / white / Recommended
Freely pollinated seedling of Madeleine Angevine

In 1957, Brock at Oxted was sent hardwood cuttings of several varieties by Dr Zimmerman from the Alzey Institute for Grapevine Breeding, Germany. One of them was labelled 'Sämling [seedling] 7672'. When this crossing was made is not known, although the timing would suggest that it was whilst Georg Scheu – responsible for varieties such as Huxelrebe, Faberrebe, Kanzler, Regner, Scheurebe, Septimer, Siegerrebe and Würzer – was the Institute's Director.

By 1960, Brock was able to report that it was 'giving large crops which ripen with Riesling Sylvaner. Considered to be a promising variety.' Not having been given the crossing details of Sämling 7672, Brock wrote to Zimmerman and asked him for them. He was informed that it was a 'freely pollinated seedling of Madeleine Angevine'. (In 1992, Professor Dr Alleweldt, then head of the Geilweilerhof Institute for Grapevine Breeding, confirmed that Scheu's old breeding books stated that Sämling 7672 was an 'open pollinated progeny of Madeleine Angevine'.) Brock started to sell cuttings of the variety, giving it the name Madeleine × Angevine 7672 and it was under this name that he continued to sell it for many years. As it became quite popular, the name became shortened to simply 'Madeleine Angevine'. This was unfortunate as a variety already existed under this name.

Madeleine Angevine itself (also written as Madeleine d'Angevine), is a female only table grape variety, a crossing of Précoce de Malingre and Madeleine Royale, made by Vibert in Angers in 1859. It is one of the earliest table grape varieties for open cultivation. Having only female flowers and being very early it has been used by plant breeders in a number of crosses over the years; Morio and Husfeld used it for Forta and Noblessa and it is one grandparent of Reichensteiner. Scheu himself also used it to produce Siegerrebe and interestingly, this variety, which at one time was credited with being a Madeleine Angevine × Gewürztraminer crossing, was unmasked by Heinz Scheu – Georg's son – as also being a freely pollinated Madeleine Angevine seedling. It is conceivable that the variety we now grow in the UK as Madeleine × Angevine 7672 comes from the same crossing programme that produced Siegerrebe.

The variety found favour with many of the early growers (Gillian Pearkes was a great fan) and it was planted widely and at one time was the third most popular variety after Müller-Thurgau and Seyval blanc. Unfortunately, owing to the confusion over the name and the fact that this variety was not available from any other source other than Brock's original stock or vineyards planted with cuttings from it, some growers were sold vines of the true table grape variety Madeleine Angevine, which was barely suitable for the UK, except in the very best years. Unless it was being grown in proximity to other early varieties for pollination, it seldom set a good crop and in some years, ripened at the end of August. The wines from this table grape variety were flabby and never really acceptable, except for blending.

The confusion over this variety – foreseen in a rare moment of sanity (as far as rules and regulations governing UK viticulture is concerned) by the EU Commission in 1973 when we submitted vine varieties for classification – has meant that it gained something of a chequered reputation. Now that the confusion over the variety has (hopefully) been cleared up and growers are not being offered vines of dubious provenance, it is regaining some of its reputation and the area under this variety has been rising. In 1999 it occupied 6.77 per cent of the UK vineyard area and was planted in 164 vineyard parcels.

Viticulture: Undemanding. Not excessively vigorous and takes to both cane and spur pruning. Good open leaf wall. Bud-burst occurs early and variety will flower and set fruit under poor conditions. Ripens its fruit very rapidly and needs picking on time to preserve acidity.

Disease susceptibility: Better than M-T. Susceptible to *botrytis* especially in a wet year.

Harvesting period: Early. Two to three weeks before M-T.

Natural sugar level: 7 per cent–8.5 per cent.

Acidity level: 6.5 g/l – 8.5 g/l.

Wine type: Light and fruity with a pronounced muscat bouquet and palate. Low in acidity and suitable for blending with higher acid varieties.

Advantages: Easy to grow. Early budburst and ripening and ability to set fruit under adverse conditions. Low acidity.
Disadvantages: Wine can be rather soft and flabby if picked too late.
Summary: An interesting variety and if good true-to-type stock can be obtained, worth planting. It needs good management, especially at harvest time and needs picking before acids get too low and flavours disappear

Madeline Sylvaner No. 3 28/51 *syn.* Madeleine Sylvaner
Vinifera / white / Authorised
Madeleine Angevine × Silvaner

In 1950 Edward Hyams, who had a small vineyard at Molash near Canterbury, Kent, was sent three new crossings, including Madeleine Angevine × Sylvaner No. 3 28/51, by Professor Husfeld, then head of the Geilweilerhof Research Station in the Pfalz, Germany. Hyams sent cuttings to Brock to put in his collection at Oxted. In 1955, Brock sent a report on these three varieties to Husfeld which set out how each had fared and ended by saying that only the Madeleine Angevine × Sylvaner No. 3 28/51 was really worth continuing with and the other two crosses had been abandoned. For convenience sake when vines were sold, the name was shortened to 'Madeleine Sylvaner'. It is a variety similar in many ways to Madeleine × Angevine 7672 having an early bud-burst, capable of setting fruit in adverse conditions, a low acidity and can be turned into light, fruity wines. Owing to the fact that vines for planting are difficult to obtain, it is unlikely to become popular, although growers who do have it, are very supportive. If stock was available, could be worth trying. In 1999 it occupied 0.39 per cent of the UK vineyard area and was planted in 15 vineyard parcels.

Müller-Thurgau *syn.* Rivaner (EU) Riesling Sylvaner (non-EU)
Vinifera / white / Recommended
1882 Uncertain parentage. Now generally thought to be Riesling × Riesling

Professor Dr H. Müller, a Swiss from Thurgau near Zurich, produced the crossing in 1882 while working at the Geisenheim Institute for Grapevine Breeding in Germany. Returning to Switzerland in 1891 to become Director of the Wädenswil Research

Institute, Müller asked for 150 of his best crossings to be sent to him at Wädenswil, including No. 58, which was to become, eventually, Müller-Thurgau. Owing to some confusion with the labelling at the time the crossings were delivered, the true parentage of No. 58 was never discovered and it became known as Riesling Sylvaner on account of its wine style – said to resemble a blend of Riesling and Sylvaner. Professor Becker, head of the Geisenheim in the 1970s and 1980s, attempted to recreate the variety by crossing Riesling and Sylvaner, but failed. He was of the opinion that it more resembled a Riesling x Riesling crossing than any other combination.

In 1912, wet-sugaring (the use of sugar in solution to chaptalise wines) was forbidden in Switzerland and Müller-Thurgau started to replace Elbling, up until then a common variety used for this purpose, but high in acid. It began to find favour in Germany and in the early 1920s, was taken up by Georg Scheu, then working at the Alzey Research Station in the Rheinland-Pfalz. He subjected it to clonal selection and helped improve its yield. Following the Second World War, when many old vineyards were re-structured and new vineyards established, it was widely planted and its large yields, early ripening and soft wines, lower in acidity than either Riesling or Sylvaner, were much appreciated. It is today Germany's second most widely planted white variety (1998 – 20.4 per cent of total area) and is to be found in several other countries. EU regulations forbid the use of the name Riesling Sylvaner, although it can still be found in non-EU countries under this name. Rivaner is an official EU synonym and is used in Luxembourg where it is a popular variety (1998 – 35 per cent of total area). Until 1987, it was New Zealand's most widely planted variety and accounted for 42 per cent of their vineyard area. This has now dropped to 7 per cent of the NZ vineyard area, although it accounted for 13.5 per cent of their total yield in 1998.

Its introduction into the UK stems from Brock's visit to Switzerland in 1946 when he met Mr Leyvraz at the Swiss Federal Vine Testing Station at Caudoz sur Pully. In 1947 vines of various varieties were sent to Brock, including 'Riesling Sylvaner' as it was then known in Switzerland. Brock trialled it for a number of years, gave cuttings to Edward Hyams in 1949 and first harvested it on 14 October 1950. In Hyams' 1953 book *The Grape Vine in England*, Brock wrote in his chapter on varieties, 'Riesling Sylvaner is known to give an outstandingly fine wine in cool climates'.

Jack Ward, who spoke fluent German (having been a music student at the Frankfurt Conservatoire before the war), was recommended it when he looked for vines for the Horam Manor vineyard which he planted in 1954. Ward was a very influential figure in the early days of the revival (first Chairman of the English Vineyards Association) and undoubtedly did much to persuade growers to plant Müller-Thurgau. Ward's company – the Merrydown Wine Company – sold vines and gave advice and ran a winemaking co-operative between 1969 and 1979 to which many of the early growers belonged.

With hindsight, it was a variety that the UK could probably have done without, although one has to bear in mind that the most popular wine style in the UK at the time it was being planted widely was the light, fruity 'Liebfraumilch' style that Müller-Thurgau makes so well. Its extreme vigour, especially in the early years, coupled with its on-off cropping pattern, makes it a difficult variety to grow economically. In 1999 it occupied 13.34 per cent of the UK vineyard area, making it the most widely planted, and it was planted in 190 vineyard parcels.

Viticulture: A very vigorous variety, especially in its early years, with thick canes and large leaves leading to excess shading. This often results in poor cropping, especially in years with low light and heat levels in the previous season. Benefits from leaf removal to expose fruit.

Disease susceptibility: High. Will suffer from *botrytis* and *oidium* and requires regular spraying. In heavy years stem-rot can be a problem. Not for organic growers. Wood often ripens poorly and does not overwinter well.

Harvesting period: Mid-season. Usually second–third week of October.

Natural sugar level: 7.5 per cent–9.5 per cent.

Acidity level: 9.5 g/l–10.5 g/l.

Wine type: When ripe, fruit flavours are good with muscat hints and at its best, the wine can be very good. When less than fully ripe, can tend towards the herbaceous and catty. Acidity is usually average to low and with balancing residual sugar, wine can be very attractive and fresh when young. Can keep, although probably best 2–3 years after bottling.

Advantages: Can produce good crops, especially in years when weather during bud formation in previous year was good. Wines can be excellent.

Disadvantages: Low yields. Excess vigour can lead to shaded fruit and buds causing both unripe grapes. Too susceptible to disease.

Summary: A variety that has now been superseded in the UK and is no longer being planted by commercial growers. It is capable of producing fine wines, but its low yields and propensity to fungal attack make it a difficult variety from which to earn a living.

Optima
Vinifera / white / Authorised
(Silvaner × Riesling) × Müller-Thurgau

Crossing made by Peter Morio and Professor Dr B. Husfeld at the Geilweilerhof Institute for Grapevine Breeding, Germany. First registered in 1970. Germany has 266 ha (1998).

This is a very early ripening variety, capable of reaching high natural sugars – even under UK conditions – and is therefore suitable for 'late-harvest' style dessert wines. Birds and wasps are always going to be a problem with this type of sweet, early variety and may preclude it being grown widely. Not very resistant to disease (about the same as M-T) and needs a full spray programme to keep it clean. Will get *botrytis* easily which might be an advantage if sweet wines are required. Optima is not likely to become very widespread in the UK, although it has its admirers. In 1999 it occupied 0.31 per cent of the UK vineyard area and was planted in 12 vineyard parcels.

Orion
Hybrid / white / Provisionally Authorised
Note: Classified by Germany's Bundessortenamt as *Vitis vinifera*
Optima × Seyve Villard 12–375 (SV 12-375 is Villard blanc)

Crossing made by Professor Dr Alleweldt at the Geilweilerhof Institute for Grapevine Breeding, Pfalz, Germany. First registered in 1984. One of a new generation of hybrid varieties bred both for wine quality and disease resistance. Not as resistant to fungal attack as some of the older hybrids (Seyval blanc for instance) and usually requires spraying against *oidium*. Ripens its wood well, shows better resistance to winter frost damage than Müller-Thurgau and its basal buds are said to be very fruitful. A very recent introduction to the UK and it is really too early to tell whether it has a future, although early reports are encouraging. Wines can be fruity and quite aromatic. The increase in area shows that it is achieving some limited popularity. One to watch with interest, especially as it has now been classified by Germany's Bundessortenamt as being of the species *Vitis vinifera*, making it eligible for UK Quality Wines psr. In 1999 it occupied 0.96 per cent of the UK vineyard area and was planted in 28 vineyard parcels.

Ortega
Vinifera / white / Authorised
Müller-Thurgau × Siegerrebe

A crossing made by Dr H. Breider at the Würzburg Viticultural Institute, Franken, Germany. First registered in 1971 and named (somewhat curiously) after the Spanish philosopher José Ortega y Gasset. It is popular on the Mosel and there were 1,073 ha in the whole of Germany in 1988. There, it ripens early, achieves high natural alcohol levels and low acidity levels and with its rich spicy tones, makes a good blending partner for higher acid varieties such as Riesling. First introduced to the UK by Jack Ward at Horam Manor in 1971 and has achieved a limited success. Wine quality is good and it ought to be more widely planted. In 1999 it occupied 3.23 per cent of the UK vineyard area and was planted in 62 vineyard parcels.

Viticulture: An early bud burst makes it susceptible to spring frost damage. It is sensitive to poor flowering conditions and will suffer from *coulure* in poor years. Quite vigorous and canopy management needs to be good to get the best fruit.
Disease susceptibility: About the same as M-T. Will get *botrytis* towards the end of ripening which will turn to 'noble rot' if sugar levels are high enough. Needs good spray programme to keep it clean.
Harvesting period: Early to very early.
Natural sugar level: 9 per cent–11 per cent.
Acidity level: 7.5 g/l – 9.5 g/l.
Wine type: When fully ripe, wines are rich and zesty with good balance. Warm years may result in wines with rather low acidity and care needs to be taken. Good for blending with more neutral varieties. Surprisingly it takes new oak well. Has been used for

'late-harvest' dessert wines to good effect and flavours are quite concentrated and rich.

Advantages: Early ripening. High natural sugars. Excellent wine quality.

Disadvantages: Yields not very good, especially in cooler years. Disease can be a problem.

Summary: Given good canopy management and attention to disease control, Ortega can provide high quality grapes. Useful for both normal still wines and dessert wines. A variety that should be planted more widely and, with the use of new-generation fungicides, should become easier to grow.

Perle of Alzey

Vinifera / white / Provisionally Authorised
Gewürztraminer × Müller-Thurgau

Crossing originally made by Georg Scheu at the Alzey Vine Breeding Station and then subjected to clonal selection by Dr H. Breider at Würzburg. First registered in 1961 and allowed to be planted in Germany in 1968 where only 127 ha (1998) are grown. First planted in the UK in the early 1970s. Some confusion over this variety has been caused because of an old table grape variety – still used in Europe – called Perle from Czaba (sometimes spelt Csaba) and it may be that some of the UK plantings were originally made with this variety, thus giving it a bad reputation. It was in fact relegated to the 'Temporarily Authorised' list, but was re-instated in 1998 on the 'Provisionally Authorised' list. It is said to be an early ripening variety with a lower acidity and higher sugars than Müller-Thurgau. As it is now almost impossible to obtain grafted stock, its future as a variety for the future in the UK looks limited. In 1999 it occupied 0.02 per cent of the UK vineyard area and was planted in only 4 vineyard parcels.

Phoenix

Hybrid / white / Provisionally Authorised
Note: Classified by Germany's Bundessortenamt as *Vitis vinifera*
Bacchus × Seyve Villard 12-375 (SV 12-375 is Villard blanc)

Crossing made by Professor Dr Alleweldt at the Geilweilerhof Institute for Grapevine Breeding, Pfalz, Germany. First registered in 1984. One of a new generation of hybrid varieties bred both for wine quality and disease resistance and although not as resistant to fungal attack as some of the older hybrids (Seyval blanc for instance), it ripens its wood very well. Only planted on a very few sites in the UK and in small quantities. Wine quality is said to be good, with higher sugars and lower acids than Müller-Thurgau. Wine is Bacchus-like, although not as powerful. Could be a very interesting variety, especially as it has now been classified by Germany's Bundessortenamt as being of the species *Vitis vinifera*, making it eligible for UK Quality Wines psr. In 1999 it occupied 0.22 per cent of the UK vineyard area and was planted in 9 vineyard parcels (estimated figures). One to watch.

Pinot blanc *syn.* Weissburgunder
Vinifera / white / Provisionally Authorised
Original variety with many clones

Pinot blanc is widely distributed across Europe and is one of the vast family of Pinots. It is often confused (one suspects mostly on purpose) with Chardonnay – the style of wine they produce can be similar. In general terms it is less demanding than Chardonnay, will ripen more easily and has a higher yield. In the UK it is a very new introduction, mainly used for the production of sparkling wine base, and few varietal wines exist. Like Chardonnay, it requires a good site and careful management to fully ripen. An interesting variety to watch. In 1999 it occupied 0.66 per cent of the UK vineyard area and was planted in 15 vineyard parcels.

Pinot gris *syn.* Ruländer (Germany)
Vinifera / white / Authorised
Original variety with many clones

Pinot gris is one of the large Pinot family that appears to have almost as many clones as there are winegrowing regions that use it. In Alsace, its most respected home where it is known as Tokay d'Alsace, it is capable of producing exceptionally fine late-harvest dessert wines; in Germany (1998, 2,565 ha) – where it is known as Ruländer – it makes an easy-drinking soft wine; in Italy it makes a very neutral, quite crisp wine – ideal with food. It seems to change style to suit the region. In the UK, where it has been grown since the late 1970s, it is an unexceptional variety and although it has a lower acidity than Pinot blanc, really has few other attributes. Not a variety to stir too many British hearts. In 1999 it occupied 0.64 per cent of the UK vineyard area and was planted in 18 vineyard parcels.

Pinot Meunier *syn.* Wrotham Pinot (UK), Müllerrebe and Schwarzriesling (Germany)
Vinifera / red / Authorised
Original variety

Pinot Meunier is the most widely grown variety in Champagne and whilst it is seldom spoken about in the same breath as its nobler companions – Chardonnay and Pinot noir – it is used in some of the finest cuveés (Krug for example). In the UK it has a somewhat chequered career. In the early 1950s, Edward Hyams launched an appeal in one of his many magazine articles to try and discover neglected varieties already growing in British gardens and greenhouses. He was told of a vine growing on a cottage wall at Wrotham in Kent and took cuttings. In appearance, the cuttings resembled Pinot Meunier, having the typical 'dusty' leaf, and Hyams named the variety 'Wrotham Pinot'. It was in all probability the variety known as 'Miller's Burgundy' which had been widely grown in Britain for many years. Barron, writing in the standard Victorian work on grape growing, *Vines and Vine Culture*, states that the variety was discovered by the famous horticulturalist Sir Joseph Banks in a vineyard at Tortworth in Gloucestershire – a county well known for its mediaeval vineyards. Brock ran a trial on Hyam's discovery at Oxted and reported that it had 'a higher natural sugar content and ripened two weeks earlier' than supplies of Pinot Meunier obtained from overseas. Brock sold cuttings and it became quite popular with early growers.

Today, it is doubtful whether any cuttings from Hyams or Oxted still survive in British vineyards and all plantings of Pinot Meunier stem from France or Germany. However, the name Wrotham Pinot is still the official name for this variety in the lists of allowable varieties. In 1973, when we joined the EU and MAFF had to submit a list of acceptable varieties to Brussels, Wrotham Pinot was one of the three 'Recommended' varieties on it, despite the fact that the EVA had not asked for it to be included and it was not widely grown at the time.

Although it has been grown for over 40 years in UK vineyards, it has never really shone as a variety capable of making interesting wines on its own and most of it has been blended with other varieties. It needs a very good site and year to get it to ripen properly for still wine production and most of the upsurge in planting in recent years is for making sparkling wine base. In this role it may be more successful, especially if blended with other, lower acid varieties. It is not suitable for the production of red wines in the UK. The amount of colour in the skins, except in very exceptional years, is not high, it ripens late and there are other better varieties. In 1999 it occupied 0.94 per cent of the UK vineyard area and was planted in 22 vineyard parcels.

Pinot noir *syn.* Blauer Spätburgunder (Germany)
Vinifera / red / Authorised
Original variety with many clones

Pinot noir is one of the most ancient of all varieties and probably has more clones and variants than any other variety. It sometimes seems as if every grower and every site spawns its own sub-variety. Whilst its home is often thought of as Burgundy, where undoubtedly many of the finest examples can be found, it seems to thrive in both very warm and very cool climates and good wines can be found from Chile, California, Australia, Spain and New Zealand. Norway's only vineyard – yes, Norway – is planted with Pinot noir and the wine can be good. It is also of course one of the classic sparkling wine grapes, found not only in Champagne, but wherever good sparkling wines are made.

In the UK it was one of the earliest varieties to be grown. Brock ran trials of it at Oxted, but was not pleased with it and by 1961, when he issued *Report No. 3 – Progress with Vines and Wines* he stated 'appears to be very much later [than on the Continent] in this climate . . . and has been discontinued'. His lack of success was probably due to the fact that at the vineyard's elevation of 400/450 ft above sea level, the site was just too marginal. In addition, Brock was not, in the early years of his vinegrowing, looking to make sparkling wines, the use to which it is probably most suited in the UK. Jack Ward was likewise somewhat dismissive of the variety and also thought it too late.

Despite the reservations of these pioneers, it seems to have been planted quite widely, if not in any great quantity. Many of the early growers seemed to limit their investigation of continental vineyards to a quick visit to Champagne and returned enthused with the idea that Pinot noir (and for that matter Chardonnay) were naturals for our climate. The truth of the matter is that they are not – except in the best sites and with careful management in the vineyards and winemaking skills in the winery. The upsurge in recent plantings (up 38 per cent from 32 ha to 44 ha between 1990 and 1999) is due to the rise in interest of bottle-fermented sparkling wines and the results to date, from those vineyards that have gone into the job seriously, is impressive. There have also been a number of very creditable red wines made from the variety in recent times – it has to be said only in the warmer years – but it is an interesting trend. In 1999 it occupied 5.07 per cent of the UK vineyard area and was planted in 127 vineyard parcels.

There are several factors which make Pinot noir a more acceptable variety for the UK now. There is no doubt that vine breeders have done much to change Pinot over the last 50 years. Clones are available that ripen earlier, crop more consistently, produce better quality wines and are more disease resistant. The upsurge in interest in making bottle-fermented sparkling wines seems set to continue and Pinot noir must be considered as a major variety in this respect. Today's fungicides, especially for the control of *botrytis*, are markedly better than they were only a decade ago and this undoubtedly allows growers to leave their grapes to hang for longer and to ripen more fully. Whether or not global warming is affecting the UK now – or will do so in years to come – is open to debate. However, most winegrowers sense that weather patterns are changing and we are now experiencing earlier bud-bursts (although this is coupled with a higher incidence of spring frost damage) and therefore longer growing seasons. This does mean that the more marginal varieties – of which group the Pinots and Chardonnay are members – may fare better in the next decade than the last. One other factor to be considered is that of marketing. There is no doubt that the public will buy wines bearing names that they recognise and Pinot noir is one that has many devotees.

Viticulture: Not over-vigorous and performs well on canes or spurs. Usually has enough fruitful buds – especially basal buds near to the older wood – after frost damage to give a crop.

Disease susceptibility: Needs regular spraying, especially against *botrytis*. Ripens wood well.

Harvesting period: Late, although timing will depend on whether grapes are for sparkling or red wine.

Natural sugar level: 7 per cent–8.5 per cent.

Acidity level: 10 g/l–12 g/l.

Wine type: In good years, acceptable – even better than acceptable – red wines can be made, although grapes do need to be really ripe to get full colour and low acidity. Takes new oak well. In sparkling wines, it adds good background flavour and appears to help yeast autolysis characters.

Advantages: Quality name with good public awareness and acceptance. Dual purpose variety – red/rosé in ripe years, sparkling wine base in lesser years.

Disadvantages: Needs a good site to be at its best. *Botrytis* prone.

Summary: A variety that is probably going to be more widely planted, especially as some of the better clones show their paces. If the UK's climate improves, it would undoubtedly become one of our standard varieties.

Regent

Hybrid / red / Provisionally Authorised

Note: Classified by Germany's Bundessortenamt as *Vitis vinifera* (Silvaner × Müller-Thurgau) × Chambourcin (Chambourcin is a Joannes Seyve hybrid bred in the 1930s. Its parentage is not known)

Crossing made by Professor Dr Alleweldt at Geilweilerhof Institute for Grapevine Breeding, Pfalz, Germany. First registered in 1989. There were 178 ha in Germany in 1998. One of a new generation of hybrid varieties bred both for wine quality and disease resistance and although not as resistant to fungal attack as some of the older hybrids (e.g. Seyval blanc), it is still more resistant than *viniferas*. It is a very new introduction to the UK and although varietal wines are few and far between, those few that have appeared show distinct promise. Has good colour and acids are not too high. One to watch, especially as it has now been classified by Germany's Bundessortenamt as being of the species *Vitis vinifera*, making it eligible for UK Quality Wines psr. In 1999 it occupied 0.25 per cent of the UK vineyard area and was planted in 6 vineyard parcels.

Regner
Vinifera / white / Authorised
Luglienca bianca × Early Gamay (Luglienca bianca is known as
Gelbe Seidentraube in Germany)

Crossing made by Georg Scheu at the Alzey Institute for Grapevine
Breeding in 1929. First released in 1978. This is another of
Scheu's crossings that used a commercial table grape as one parent
and a standard wine grape as the other. Regner first appeared in the
UK in the Wye College vineyard and quickly proved itself capable
of good yields and bore grapes that ripened early with high sugars
and low acid levels – in short – an ideal variety for our climate. As
it is barely grown in Germany (1998, 157 ha), stock is hard to
find which is a pity as it deserves to be more widely grown in UK
vineyards. Wine quality can be excellent. In 1999 it occupied
0.92 per cent of the UK vineyard area and was planted in 30
vineyard parcels.

Reichensteiner
Vinifera / white / Recommended
Müller-Thurgau × (Madeleine Angevine × Calabreser Fröhlich)

Crossing made at the Geisenheim Institute for Grapevine Breeding
by Professor H. Birk in 1939 by crossing Müller-Thurgau with a
variety which was a crossing of two table grapes; Madeleine
Angevine, the female French table grape used by Scheu (amongst
others) for a number of crosses and Early Calabrese, an Italian early
table grape. Together, these have combined to produce an early
ripening variety, capable of producing large crops of relatively
neutral grapes, high in natural sugars. In Germany, it was seen as a
substitute to the practice of 'wet-sugaring' (where up to 20 per cent
by volume of water could be added to grape juice in order to stretch
it and lower acidity) – a practice that only came to an end in the late
1970s. In Germany (1998 268 ha) Reichensteiner is capable of
producing massive crops – up to 200 hl/ha (12 tonnes/acre) is not
uncommon – and it is used as a blending partner for varieties with
more acidity. Apart from a small, but highly productive area in
New Zealand (where in 1998, 57 hectares cropped at an average of
29.7 tonnes/ha or 12.02 tonnes/acre) its only other home is the UK.
In 1999 it occupied 12.28 per cent of the UK vineyard area and was
planted in 236 vineyard parcels, the highest number of any variety.

Only Müller-Thurgau, at 13.34 per cent of the national area, is more widespread.

Reichensteiner was first introduced into the UK by Jack Ward when he extended the 'Brickyard' vineyard in Horam in 1971. Early results showed that it was a consistent cropper, had good yields and high natural sugars. Although it can be quite vigorous in its youth, it settles down after a few years and is far less vigorous than Müller-Thurgau at the same age. It has a good open habit and a leaf-wall that is more open and airy, which helps disease control. As a single varietal wine it does not have the character of fruitier varieties, but has the advantage of lower acid levels with more body and extract. It is probably best used in a blend. It has also been used for sparkling wine, as well as for the production of 'sweet-reserve' for the pre-bottling sweetening of dry wines.

Viticulture: Vigorous in its youth, but will settle down. Open leaf-wall and smaller leaves than M-T, make it less disease prone.
Disease susceptibility: Less prone to *botrytis* than M-T. Stem-rot can be a problem. Needs full spray programme.
Harvesting period: Earlier than M-T.
Natural sugar level: 8.5 per cent–11 per cent.
Acidity level: 9 g/l–11 g/l.
Wine type: Not as fruity as M-T, but with better body and mouth-feel. Acids lower than M-T. Best used for blending.
Advantages: High yield and high natural sugars. Good blending variety. Can be used for making sweet-reserve.
Disadvantages: Neutrality of wine.
Summary: Should be considered as a standard variety in all but the most specialist of vineyards. Crops well and wine quality is good, especially in a blend.

Riesling
Vinifera / white / Provisionally Authorised
Original variety

According to some commentators, Riesling is one of the world's most underrated varieties and due for a long awaited revival. In fact it has been used – some would say abused – in a wide number of diverse winegrowing regions and performs surprisingly well in some of the warmer parts of the world (California and Australia) as well as some of the coolest (Germany). In warm regions it was often used to make wines with considerable sweetness and much of its intrinsic flavour was lost. In cooler regions, grapes struggle to achieve alcohols in double figures and acids can be frighteningly crisp. However, at their best, properly aged low alcohol (7 per cent–9 per cent) Mosel Spätlese wines can be superb. Riesling is Germany's most widely planted variety, accounting for 28 per cent (1998) of their white wine vines. On the Mosel it accounts for 54 per cent of the area.

In the UK it has even more problems than it does in Germany and apart from a very few growers with exceptional sites, it does not do well over here, although recent examples from Denbies are encouraging. It ripens late and acids are high. In short, a variety to treat with caution. In 1999 it occupied 0.28 per cent of the UK vineyard area and was planted in 7 vineyard parcels.

Rondo *syn.* Gm 6494/5
Hybrid / red / Provisionally Authorised
Note: Classified by Germany's Bundessortenamt as *Vitis vinifera*
Saperavi Servernyi × St Laurent (Saperavi Servernyi is a crossing of Précoce de Malingre × *vitis Amurensis*)

If ever there was a variety with a complicated history, Rondo has to be one of the best. The original *vitis Amurensis* vines stem from Manchuria, in the north of China, where the River Amur marks the border with Russia. Here, on account of the early onset and severity of the winters, wild vines need to ripen their fruit early and the vines need to be able to withstand deep winter temperatures. A crossing of Précoce de Malingre and a wild *vitis Amurensis* was made at the 'Michurin Central Genetic Laboratory' (somewhere in central Russia) in 1936 and was named Saperavi Servenyi. This crossing then found its way to Czechoslovakia where it came to the notice of Professor Dr Kraus and thence to Geisenheim where Professor Helmut Becker used it as a crossing partner with a number of other varieties, including St Laurent – an old Austrian wine variety. The resultant cross, then only known by its breeding number Gm 6494/5, was trialled at Geisenheim and proved capable of producing good crops of early ripening, deeply coloured grapes. In 1983 Professor Becker gave 50 vines each to three vineyards in England – Adgestone, Lamberhurst and Tenterden – to see what the results would be. From its first harvests, it showed itself well adapted to UK conditions and plantings have been increasing since then. In 1999 it occupied 1.09 per cent of the UK vineyard area and was planted in 34 vineyard parcels.

Viticulture: Fairly to very vigorous, it grows long canes with large leaves. Needs careful summer leaf work to expose fruit so that air and light can get to the fruit. Buds tend to be very fruitful. Berries start to drop when fully ripe and picking can be problematic.

Disease susceptibility: It is not as resistant to *botrytis* as some of the older hybrids (a regular spray programme is advised) and grapes will start to rot quite readily once sugar levels rise. Fairly resistant to powdery and downy mildews.

Harvesting period: Early

Natural sugar level: 8 per cent–10 per cent.

Acidity level: 11 g/l–12.5 g/l.

Wine type: Rondo has very good red colour and above all, has very good vinous flavour – there is no trace of non-vinifera parentage. It blends well with other varieties (such as Dornfelder and Pinot noir) and can be likened to a cross between Tempranillo and Syrah. Whilst acid levels at harvest can be quite high (12 g/l), by the time the wine has gone through both a primary and a malolactic fermentation, it softens to acceptable levels. Takes oak well.

Advantages: Good colour, early ripening, regular yields.

Disadvantages: Prone to *botrytis*. Over vigorous.

Summary: Without doubt this is a good variety for red wine production in the UK. If properly managed and *botrytis* is kept under control, it can produce fine, deeply coloured wines. It is probably best used in a blend with other red varieties.

Scheurebe
Vinifera / white / Authorised
Silvaner × Riesling

Crossing made by Georg Scheu at the Alzey Institute for Grapevine Breeding in 1916. Known as Sämling 88 (or S88 for short) for many years. In Germany (1998, 3,294 ha) it is grown mainly in Rheinhessen and the Rheinpfalz and is, after Kerner, Bacchus and Morio-Muskat, the fourth most popular new cross-bred variety. Good German examples have a typical grapefruit character and some wines, especially dry Spätlese and Auslese wines, can be superb. Can also make very good late-harvest sweet dessert wines (Beerenauslese and Trockenbeerenauslese).

In the UK, it has never really found its feet and few varietal wines of note have been made from it. It ripens too late, acids are too high and wines can be too herbaceous. Other Scheu crosses – Huxelrebe, Faberrebe and Würzer – are better bets. In 1999 it occupied 0.15 per cent of the UK vineyard area and was planted in only 7 vineyard parcels.

Schönburger
Vinifera / white / Recommended
Pinot noir × IP1 (IP1 is Chasselas rosa × Muscat Hamburg)

Crossing made at the Geisenheim Institute for Grape Breeding, Germany, by Professor Dr H. Birk in 1939 and first registered for use in 1979. Like many of the crosses from this era, it combined an early ripening table grape variety (in this case a cross-bred by an Italian, I. Pirovano, called IP1), with a classic winemaking variety in the hope that a unique German table grape could be produced. Schönburger is planted sparsely in Germany (in 1994 there were only 49 ha) and countries such as Canada, New Zealand and the UK have more – some can even be found in South Africa!

In the UK, it has been grown since the late 1970s and on account of its quality grapes, low acidity and regular crops, it has become the fifth most planted variety. It is an undemanding variety, more disease resistant than Müller-Thurgau and not so on-off in its cropping habits. Yields are never large, but what is picked is almost always of excellent quality. As they ripen, the grapes change colour from a light lime green to at first a light pink and then, when fully ripe, to an almost tawny brown colour. This gives a very good visual indication to the pickers as to which bunches are ripe and allows for some selective picking. This can only aid wine quality.

The wines are almost always light and very fruity, with some good muscat tones (some resemble a less powerful version of Gewürztraminer) that are best balanced with a slight amount of residual sugar. Wines do age well and have been known to keep for up to 7 years. Schönburger is also one of the few varieties grown in the UK that can be eaten with pleasure as table grapes and although the berries are small, they are packed with flavour. In 1999 it occupied 7.87 per cent of the UK vineyard area and was planted in 151 vineyard parcels.

Viticulture: Not as vigorous as M-T with a more open habit. Crops well on both canes and spurs.
Disease susceptibility: More disease resistant than M-T, although downy mildew can be a problem. Needs full spray programme to keep it clean.
Harvesting period: Mid-season. Just after M-T.
Natural sugar level: 7.5 per cent–9.5 per cent.
Acidity level: 7.5 g/l–9.5 g/l.
Wine type: Very fruity with good muscat tones. Can resemble a light Gewürztraminer. Very often at its best with a little residual sweetness.
Advantages: Wine quality excellent. Better disease resistance than M-T. Regular crops. Eats well as table grape, although berries are small. Can be selectively harvested as riper berries turn dark pink.
Disadvantages: Very few. Yields could be larger.
Summary: A good all-round variety for the UK. A bit more yield would be nice, but not at the expense of wine quality.

Senator
Vinifera / white / Provisionally Authorised
Silvaner mutation

A Silvaner mutation selected by August Lerch from his vineyard in Langenlonsheim on the Nahe in Germany in 1968. Said to be considerably lower in acidity than Silvaner. To date, has not set the world alight, either in Germany or the UK, but one lives in hope. A variety to be treated with caution. In 1999, it occupied 0.13 per cent of the UK vineyard area and was planted in 7 vineyard parcels.

Seyval blanc *syn.* Seyve Villard 5/276
Hybrid / white / Recommended
Seibel 5656 × Seibel 4986 (S.4986 is known as Rayon d'Or in France)

A crossing made in 1921 by Bertille Seyve (the younger) at his nursery in St Vallier on the Rhône. Originally known as Seyve-Villard 5/276. At one stage there were over 1,300 ha in France (1968) but plantings have declined since then. It can be found in many different parts of North America, most notably in New York State and Ontario. In some references, the crossing is given as Seibel 4996 × Seibel 4986, but according to Pierre Galet, Bertille Seyve's son stated in the 'Viticulture Nouvelle' of 1961 (p. 182) that it was S.5656 × S.4986.

It was first grown in the UK by Edward Hyams who, in 1947, obtained vines directly from the Seyve-Villard nurseries (so called because Seyve married the daughter of another vine-breeder, Victor Villard and took over his nursery). Hyams planted them in his small vineyard at Molash near Canterbury, Kent. Brock also imported the variety from the Swiss Federal Vine Testing Station at Caudoz sur Pully a year later in 1948. These two pioneer growers tested it and soon found that it was a very suitable variety for our climate and together with Müller-Thurgau, it became the standard variety for almost all the early vineyards. When Salisbury-Jones planted his vineyard at Hambledon in 1951 he chose Seyval blanc, he said 'on the advice of a helpful Burgundian grower', but no doubt also because Brock and Hyams had had good results with it.

It has many attributes. It sets good crops even in cooler years, is not vigorous and has a good open habit. It is almost totally resistant to disease, although *botrytis* can occur in riper years. Although the grapes are never very high in natural sugar, wine quality can be good and usually yields are high. On the downside, apart from the low natural sugars, the wine can be very neutral, high in acidity and if not pressed with care, can get a rather grassy, herbaceous tone. However, it takes to lees and oak ageing well and is useful for sparkling wine. In 1999, it occupied 11.70 per cent of the UK vineyard area, making it the third most widely planted, and was planted in 216 vineyard parcels.

Viticulture: Very easy to grow. Low in vigour with a good open leaf-wall. Will set fruit in poor flowering conditions. Cropping can become biennial. In very heavy years, thinning improves quality.
Disease susceptibility: Resistant to almost all diseases. Will get *botrytis* especially in riper years, but does not usually suffer from stem-rot and so grapes continue to hang well. Superb wood ripening.
Harvesting period: Late. Early November not uncommon.
Natural sugar level: 6.5 per cent–8.5 per cent.
Acidity level: 10 g/l–12 g/l.

Wine type: Wine usually has crisp acidity and is quite neutral. Drinks well in medium-dry style with some residual sugar, especially if a fruity sweet-reserve is used. Takes to oak ageing well and some growers add flavour via lees contact. Ideal for sparkling wines.

Advantages: Reliability, disease resistance and good yields. 85–120 hl/ha (5–7 tonnes/acre) is not unknown. Can be used for several different styles of wine. Takes lees-ageing and oak well.

Disadvantages: Wine quality not always of the very highest and needs a winemaker who knows the variety. Low natural sugars, especially in years with heavy crops and cool autumns.

Summary: One of the UK's most reliable varieties, capable of producing yields more like those found in overseas vineyards. With care, very saleable, attractive wines can be made and unless Brussels outlaws it, destined to be a part of UK viticulture for the foreseeable future. As someone who has twice won the Gore-Browne Trophy with wines made from it, I am perhaps rather biased in my opinions.

Siegerrebe
Vinifera / white / Authorised
Freely pollinated seedling of Madeleine Angevine

Crossing made by Georg Scheu at the Alzey Institute for Grapevine Breeding, Germany, in 1929 and released to growers in 1958. The variety was originally said to be Madeleine Angevine × Gewürztraminer, but it was later revealed by Scheu's son, Heinz, to be a freely pollinated seedling of Madeleine Angevine (which is the same parentage as the UK's Madeleine × Angevine 7672). In Germany (1998, 170 ha) it is capable of reaching very high natural sugar levels and consequently sometimes used for making sweet dessert wines. The grapes have a strong muscat character and when ripe, can be very concentrated and almost overpowering. Consequently it is more often used for blending with other, less distinctive, varieties.

It has been in the UK since 1957 when Brock was sent cuttings from Alzey. By 1960 he was able to report 'Exceptionally early and the grapes have a strong bouquet'. It was strongly recommended by Brock as suitable for both the table and winemaking. Despite its attributes of early ripening, low acidity and strongly flavoured grapes, it has really failed to be planted in anything like serious amounts and although one or two vineyards do make interesting varietal wines from it, it mainly gets lost in blends. Maybe because it ripens very early, it falls so far outside what most growers consider to be their normal harvest time, that it is rather disruptive to their slow build-up to harvest? Wasps are a particular problem and good wasp-nest control needs to be practised if real damage is to be avoided. Birds likewise, tend to be a nuisance. In 1999, it occupied 1.32 per cent of the UK vineyard area and was planted in 54 vineyard parcels.

Viticulture: Undemanding variety. Crops well on both canes and spurs.
Disease susceptibility: Needs standard spray programme. Wood ripens well.
Harvesting period: Very early. Mid-September in average years, even earlier in warm ones.
Natural sugar level: 10 per cent–11 per cent.
Acidity level: 7 g/l–9 g/l.
Wine type: Very fruity with moderate acidity and a noticeable muscat/Gewürztraminer tone. Needs some residual sugar to be at its best.
Advantages: Early ripening. High natural sugars. Excellent fruity flavours.
Disadvantages: Wasp and bird attack.
Summary: A variety that should be more widely planted as it has several distinct advantages.

Triomphe *syn.* Triomphe d'Alsace (non-EU)
Hybrid / red / Authorised
Unknown parentage

An old French-American hybrid bred by Eugene Kuhlmann from Alsace in the late 1900s. Its breeding number is Kuhlmann 319.3. It was originally known as 'Triomphe d'Alsace' and for many years was labelled as such. When, in 1992, the UK tried to register it under that title, the EU Commission objected (because it contained the name of an *appellation contrôlée* region) and the name was shortened to 'Triomphe'. Its exact parentage appears to be unknown, but is probably from the same *riparia-rupestris* × Goldriesling selections that produced two other Kuhlmann crosses, Léon Millot and Maréchal Foch. Triomphe has the small berries and dark red skin, flesh and juice of the other Kuhlmann red hybrids.

First introduced into the UK by Brock at Oxted and quite widely planted by the early growers. Plantings have recently grown as the interest in red wines has increased. In 1999 it occupied 1.72 per cent of the UK vineyard area and was planted in 72 vineyard parcels.

Viticulture: Early bud-burst and appears to be quite tolerant of poor flowering conditions. Berries and bunches are small. Colour is good. Vines usually very vigorous and spur pruning may be an advantage
Disease susceptibility: Low. Almost resistant to most diseases. Maintenance sprays advised as *botrytis* can affect fruit.
Harvesting period: Early to mid-season.
Natural sugar level: 9 per cent–10 per cent.
Acidity level: 12 g/l–14 g/l.
Wine type: Very deep red colour and firm tannins. If not really ripe, can be slightly non-*vinifera*, but if blended with other *viniferas* makes a useful contribution. Acids can be high.
Advantages: Good deep colour. Disease resistant. Regular yields.
Disadvantages: Some clones said to be poor. Perhaps not best as a single varietal.
Summary: Although an old hybrid, it should not be dismissed as one to grow for the production of a deep red in the UK. Probably best blended. Some clonal selection would be beneficial.

Würzer
Vinifera / white / Authorised
Gewürztraminer × Müller-Thurgau

Crossing made by Georg Scheu at the Alzey Institute for Vine Breeding, Germany in 1932. Released to growers in 1978. Another of Scheu's spicy crosses (Scheurebe, Faberrebe and Huxelrebe being the other ones used in the UK) and in a similar mould. There were 110 ha in Germany in 1998. For the UK it is really rather too late for most sites and does not show any real advantages over several other varieties (Bacchus for instance). The declining area is probably a good indication of its usefulness. In 1999, it occupied 1.12 per cent of the UK vineyard area and was planted in 27 vineyard parcels.

Viticulture: Can be quite vigorous. Tends to have lots of side shoots and needs good canopy management to keep the leaf-wall open.

Disease susceptibility: As with other *viniferas*. Needs full spray programme to remain clean.

Harvesting period: Late. After M-T.

Natural sugar level: 7 per cent–9 per cent.

Acidity level: 11 g/l–12.5 g/l.

Wine type: Fresh and fruity. Tends towards high acidity. Best blended if not really ripe.

Advantages: Very few. When ripe, wine can be very spicy and useful in a blend.

Disadvantages: Too late. Acids can be high.

Summary: A variety that has probably had its day. If this is the style of wine required, try Bacchus.

Zweigeltrebe *syn.* Blauer Zweigelt
Vinifera / red / Authorised
Blaufrankisch × St Laurent

Crossing made at Klosterneuberg in Austria by Dr Fritz Zweigelt. Quite popular there with over 6,000 acres planted. First introduced to the UK in the Wye College Vineyard in the late 1970s and subsequently planted by a number of growers. Jack Ward (Merrydown/Horam Manor) championed it on the advice of the Austrian grower, Lenz Moser. The colour is not really deep enough for red wine and in many years it struggles to ripen. It is often picked with very high acid levels. Now superseded by better red varieties and unlikely to be planted in the future. In 1999, it occupied 0.30 per cent of the UK vineyard area and was planted in 15 vineyard parcels.

9
Vineyards by Region

EAST ANGLIA VINEYARD REGION

Vineyards are listed alphabetically by county. The counties appear in the following order: Cambridgeshire, Norfolk, Suffolk, Hertfordshire, Essex.

The East Anglia region is the second smallest of the five regions in this guide with 39 vineyards growing 84 hectares of vines. In my 1989 book, *The Vineyards of England*, there were 45 vineyards growing 121 ha.

Fruit, especially apples, pears and soft fruit, have always been a feature of this region's agriculture, and large commercial fruit farms can still be found along the coastal areas of Norfolk, Suffolk and Essex. Many of the soils are well suited to fruit growing and, especially in north Essex and Suffolk, there are plenty of sheltered slopes where one might consider vines would grow well. The region is the driest in England and would therefore appear to be a very suitable one for vines. However, it can suffer from cold winds from the north and east and if these coincide with the all-important flowering period (late June to mid-July) significant crop loss will follow. In inland sites, frost can be a problem and in the heavily frosted years such as 1995 and 1997, East Anglian vineyards were amongst the hardest hit. Many early vineyards in the region were planted with the Müller-Thurgau grape variety and this is probably a major reason why so many small vineyards have, over the last decade, been grubbed up. It is not a variety that is tolerant of poor flowering conditions. Many of the smaller growers have found the task of marketing their wines in today's crowded, highly competitive market, just too difficult. Some tell me that there are now so many different tourist and visitor enterprises vying for

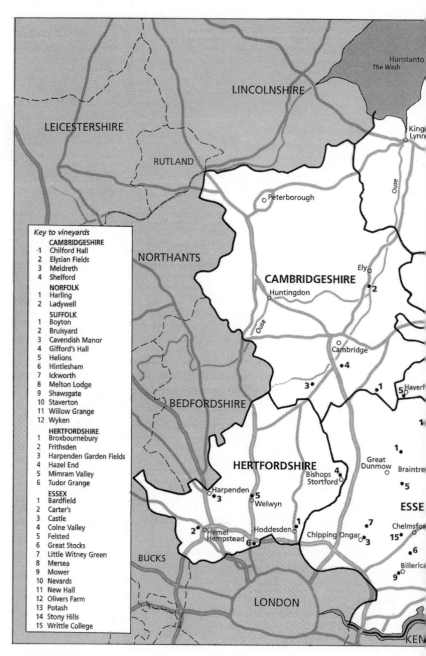

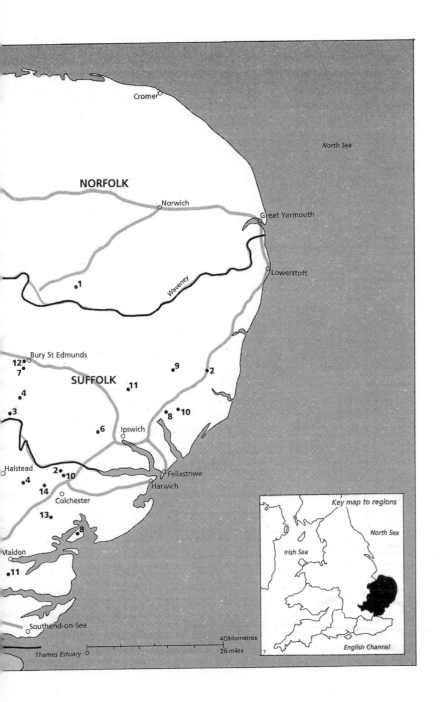

NORFOLK

Cromer

Norwich

Great Yarmouth

Lowerstoft

Waveney

•1

Bury St Edmunds

12••

7•

SUFFOLK

•4

•3

•9

•2

•11

•8 •10

•6

Ipswich

Halstead

2•

•10

•4

14

Colchester

13•

•8

Felixstowe

Harwich

Maldon

•11

Southend-on-Sea

Thames Estuary 0

40 kilometres

25 miles

Key map to regions

North Sea

Irish Sea

English Channel

customers that they – and their wallets and purses – are spread very thinly, making farm-gate sales less attractive than they used to be.

Vineyards have been planted in East Anglia since the very early days of the revival. Elmham, planted by Master of Wine, Robin Don, in 1966 (now grubbed) and Felsted, planted in 1967 by Graham and Irene Barrett, were both pioneer vineyards and their owners did much to publicise English wine growing in the early days. Other vineyards such as Chilford Hall and Cavendish Manor, were also early entrants. Pulham Vineyard near Diss in south Norfolk and Kelsale, a Suffolk vineyard (both now grubbed out), were respectively winners of the Gore-Browne Trophy for the best wine of the year in 1977 and 1978. Pulham won it again in 1980. These early successes certainly put the region on the map as far as vineyard planting was concerned.

Today, the region has one very large vineyard, New Hall (36 ha) which is situated on the south Essex coast, well sheltered from cooling northerly winds and protected from the worst of the spring frosts by the proximity of the sea. New Hall manages to produce well above average crops of quality grapes, almost all of which are sold to other wineries around the country. Other significant vineyards such as Chilford Hall near Cambridge and Bruisyard and Shawsgate in Suffolk, have built up, over the years, a loyal following of visitors and customers. Wyken won the Gore-Browne Trophy in 1995.

The best places for growing grapes in this region are undoubtedly in the south-eastern part of Suffolk and along the Essex coast. Here, sheltered sites which can escape both spring frost and damaging cold winds at flowering, can produce viable crops. Marketing will always be an issue in less populated rural areas, and the most successful vineyards will be planted where they can be easily accessed by visitors and tourists.

Chilford Hall Vineyard

Balsham Road, Linton, Cambridgeshire, CB1 6LE

T: 01223 892641. F: 01223 894056
E: simonalper@chilfordhall.co.uk. W: www.chilfordhall.co.uk

Owner: Simon Alper
Winemaker: Chris Durrant
Directions: Take B1052 Linton to Balsham road. Vineyard will be found on the left-hand side.
Vineyard Details: 7.42 ha of vines, planted between 1972 and 1976 with substantial re-plantings in 1993 and 1995. The south-west facing site, protected from the north and east, lies between 65 m and 75 m above sea level and the soil varies; some light loam and gravel, some pure sand, some chalk and some heavier loam. The vines are planted between 2.9 m and 3.2. m row width and between 1.25 m and 1.4 m between vines. They are mainly Double Guyot pruned but some are in the process of being converted to Scott Henry training.

CHILFORD HUNDRED 1996

Juror of the Chilford Hundred 1086

WALTER DE CLA

11.5% VOL
e75cl

Schönburger
English Table Wine

Estate bottled at Chilford Hall, Cambridge. Produce of the United Kingdom

Grape Varieties: Huxelrebe, Dornfelder, Ortega, Müller-Thurgau, Reichensteiner, Schönburger, Siegerrebe.
Wine Sales: Good Friday to 1 November, daily, 11 am to 5.30 pm. Remainder of the year during office hours or by appointment.
Vineyard Visits: Groups by appointment. Tours on the hour during the season. Free tastings and souvenir glass included in tour price.

Chilford Hall is one of the oldest and largest wine producers in East Anglia and is now in the hands of a second generation English wine-grower, Simon Alper. His father, Sam Alper, was one of the first to have a large commercial vineyard in the UK. Today, wine is but a small part of the operation and Chilford Hall is also home to a major conference, exhibition and banqueting centre.

The winery is housed in an attractive eighteenth-century timber-framed barn, with marble and slate floors. Equipment includes two Vaslin presses, a Seitz Compacta filler, Velo lees filter and stainless steel and glass fibre tanks. There are also some oak barrels. The wine store is housed in a half-buried building, built mainly from reclaimed materials; the pillar facings from the Long Bar at Waterloo Station are incorporated into it!

Their individual style of winemaking is due in part to the use of naturally occurring yeasts to ferment their still wines, extended lees contact and frequent lees stirring – in some cases as frequently as every ten days. Their wines have regularly won awards at the UKVA's annual competition. Some of their wines are now exported and they have recently been taken up by the Norwegian State Monopoly and are selling to France, Holland and California. They have a growing reputation for their sparkling rosé Aluric de Norsehide (named after a juror of the Chilford Hundred in 1086). Jilly Goolden praised it in 'Out and About' on BBC East, as did Sarah Jane Evans on the Jimmy Young Show on Radio Two and in the BBC Good Food Magazine of which she is Editor.

Elysian Fields

Bedwell Hey Farm, Little Thetford, Ely, Cambridgeshire, CB6 3HJ

T: 01353 662722. F: 01353 663774. M: 0860 663510
E: bedwell.hey@farmline.co.uk

Owner: John Parish
Winemaker: Wines made at Shawsgate Vineyard

ELYSIAN FIELDS

English table wine of character   Medium Dry 75cl Alc 10% bv
Produced at Bedwell Hey,   Lt. Thetford, Ely Cambs

Directions: Vineyard not open to the public.
Vineyard Details: 0.06 ha of vines planted in 1991. The south west facing site is 9 m above sea level on a greensand soil. The vines are planted at 2 m × 1.5 m and are Double Guyot trained.
Grape Varieties: Ortega, Schönburger + others.

Meldreth Vineyard
Malton Lane, Meldreth, Cambridgeshire
Address for correspondence:
12 Pump Lane, Hardwick, Cambridge, CB3 7QW

Owner: Dr Alan Buglass
Directions: Vineyard not open to the public.
Vineyard Details: 0.23 ha of vines planted between 1995 and 1999. The south-facing site is between 10 m and 12 m above sea level and it has a marl soil. The vines are planted at 2 m × 1.5 m and are Double Guyot trained.

Grape Varieties: Dornfelder, Madeleine × Angevine 7672, Kernling, Pinot blanc, Pinot Meunier, Pinot noir, Seyval blanc + others.

This is a small experimental vineyard, growing a wide range of varieties, including several Kuhlmann hybrids (Léon Millot, Maréchal Joffre, Triomphe etc). 'Genuinely keen' individuals can contact Dr Buglass on 01994 212156.

Shelford Vineyard

13 High Green, Gt Shelford, Cambridge, Cambridgeshire, CB2 5EG

T: 01223 845544
E: ken@realnet.ltd.uk

Owner & Winemaker: Ken Sewell
Directions: Vineyard not open to the public.
Vineyard Details: 0.07 ha of vines planted in 1993 on a 1.4 m × 1.2 m Double Guyot system. The south-west facing site is 15 m above sea level.
Grape Varieties: Auxerrois, Dornfelder, Dunkelfelder, Reichensteiner.

Harling Vineyards

Eastfield House, Church Road, East Harling, Norwich, Norfolk, NR16 2NA

T: 01953 717341. F: 01953 718663

Owner: David Issitt
Winemaker: Wines made at Shawsgate Vineyard
Directions: From the A11, Thetford to Norwich road, take the B1111 to East Harling. Vineyard by church.
Vineyard Details: 2.63 ha of vines planted between 1972 and 1993. The gently sloping site is between 27 m and 30 m above sea level and the soil is a light loam with some sand and gravel over flint and limestone. The vines are planted at 1.8 m × 1.5 m and are Double Guyot trained.
Grape Varieties: Bacchus, Müller-Thurgau.
Wine Sales: Daily, all year round. Telephone for times.
Vineyard Visits: As above. Guided tours for groups by arrangement. Tasting of six wines £2.50 per person.

Herling

English White Table Wine

SERVE CHILLED

MEDIUM

*Produced from selected Müller Thurgau grapes grown in
Harling Vineyards, Eastfield House, East Harling, Norfolk NR16 2NA, U.K.
by D. & J. Issitt & Son*

10% vol.   Bottled for the Producers – W 1565   *75cl* e

Harling Vineyards were originally established by the Milkovics in 1972 and were taken over by the Issets in 1992. Since then the vineyards have been expanded and Bacchus planted. Their 1992 Late Harvest Dry and Off-dry and their 1995 Medium Sweet were all Commended in the EAVA's regional competition.

Ladywell Vineyard
Brookdale, Church Lane, Sedgeford, Hunstanton, Norfolk, PE36 5NA

T: 01485 572399. F: 01485 572399
E: valhughford@ladywell.demon.co.uk

Owner & Winemaker: Hugh Ford
Directions: Vineyard not open to the public.
Vineyard Details: 0.03 ha of vines planted on a 2 m × 1.8 m Double Guyot system. The south facing site is 25 m above sea level and has a light soil over chalk.

Grape Varieties: Madeleine × Angevine 7672, Schönburger, Seyval blanc.

Boyton Vineyard
Hill Farm, Boyton End, Stoke-by-Clare, Sudbury, Suffolk, CO10 8TB

T: 01440 761893. F: 01440 761893

Owners: Roy L & C M Williams
Winemaker: Wines made at Shawsgate Vineyard
Directions: Take A1092 Stoke-by-Clare to Clare road and follow vineyard signs.
Vineyard Details: 0.81 ha of vines, planted in 1977, on a 3 m × 1.5 m Double Guyot system. The site is between 61 m and 73 m above sea level and faces south. The soil is loam with some sand over clay.

1996

Boyton Vineyard

HUXELREBE
DRY ENGLISH TABLE WINE

Grown by R. L. & C. M. Williams
Boyton Vineyard, Stoke-by-Clare, Sudbury, Suffolk
Telephone / Facsimile 01440 761893

Bottled by Shawsgate Vineyard, Suffolk

75cl e   PRODUCE OF THE UNITED KINGDOM   11.5% vol

Grape Varieties: Huxelrebe. Müller-Thurgau.
Wine Sales: Open all year round 11 am to 6 pm.
Vineyard Visits: The vineyard is open to visitors from April to October 11 am to 6 pm for tours of the vineyards and gardens and tastings. There is no charge.

Boyton Vineyards was established by a Mr Crisp in 1977 and taken over by Roy Williams in 1984. Their wines are now made by Rob Hemphill at nearby Shawsgate Vineyard and over the years have been consistent medal and award winners. Recent awards include the 1996 Macrae Trophy for the best wine from East Anglia with their 1994 Huxelrebe and the 1997 East Anglian Wine of the Year with their 1996 Huxelrebe.

Bruisyard Vineyard
Church Road, Bruisyard, Saxmundham, Suffolk, IP17 2EF

T: 01728 638281. F: 01728 638442. M: 07990 523344
E: 106236.463@compuserve.com

Owners: Ian & Eleanor Berwick
Winemaker: Robert Capp
Directions: 18 miles north east of Ipswich. Take A12 towards Lowestoft. At Saxmundham bypass, take B1119 towards Framlingham and follow signs.
Vineyard Details: 4.05 ha of vines planted in 1974 and 1975, all on a 2.44 m by 1.22 m Double Guyot system. The vineyard is 30 m above sea level in the Alde Valley, south facing, with a sandy clay loam soil.
Grape Variety: Müller-Thurgau.
Wine Sales: Vineyard open for wine sales daily, 16 January– 24 December, 10.30 am to 5 pm. The vineyard has an off-licence for single bottle sales and wines may be tasted free-of-charge.
Vineyard Visits: Vineyard open to visitors at times as above. Self-guided tour with Walkman: adults £3.50, Senior Citizens £3.00, children under 16, £2.00. Visitors can see the vineyard and winery, as well as established herb and water gardens. Also children's play and picnic areas. Meals may be obtained at the vineyard in the licenced restaurant. Guided tours for groups of 20+ people can be arranged in advance and include a walk through the vineyards, a talk on winemaking in the winery and a winetasting. The charge for

HALCYON – 1994

Dry White Wine

11.5% VOL   *English Vineyards Quality Wine psr*   75Cle

Bottled by Bruisyard Wines, Nr. Saxmundham, Suffolk, United Kingdom

SERVE lightly chilled. Delicious with most fish dishes.

guided tours is £3.00 per person. Meals for groups can be arranged. Ample parking for cars and coaches.

The area was chosen for its lower than average rainfall and the site at Bruisyard for its gentle sheltered aspect. The vineyard is unusual in this country in that it only has one variety, Müller-Thurgau, and it would appear from the results that it was a wise choice. There are no plans to expand or change to other varieties.

The winery at Bruisyard is housed in a group of red brick farm buildings, roofed with the traditional pantiles of the region. Winery equipment is very much up-to-date, and includes a KTM crusher/destalker, Willmes UP 1200 pneumatic press and Howard screw press. There is a semi-automatic bottling line. The winery also makes wines for a number of other growers in the area.

The visitor facilities at Bruisyard have been developed over the years and apart from the vineyard and winery, there are well established herb and water gardens, a children's play area and a picnic area. The licensed restaurant serves good home-made food and is open for lunches and teas during opening hours and for groups at other times by appointment.

Over the last 25 years, Ian and Eleanor Berwick have established Bruisyard as one of the major vineyards in the UK. They are regular winners of awards and medals and their 1987 Bruisyard St Peter Medium Dry won the Best English Wine in the 1988 IWSC. Their range of wines now covers oaked, un-oaked, still and sparkling from dry to medium sweet. Bruisyard wines are also regularly awarded Quality Wine status.

Cavendish Manor Vineyard
Nether Hall, Cavendish, Sudbury, Suffolk, CO10 8BX

T: 01787 280221

Owner: Basil Ambrose
Winemaker: Wines made at Pulham Vineyards
Directions: Vineyard not open to the public.
Vineyard Details: 0.36 ha of vines planted in 1970 on a south facing site, 52 m above sea level. The vines are planted at 3.66 m × 1.22 m and GDC trained.
Grape Variety: Müller-Thurgau.
Wine Sales & Vineyard Visits: By appointment only.

Basil Ambrose was one of the first in Suffolk to grow vines and the vineyard once extended to 1.21 ha. Nether Hall is an interesting property and houses a collection of bygones and it, together with the village of Cavendish, are well worth a visit.

Gifford's Hall
Hartest, Bury St Edmunds, Suffolk, IP29 4EX

T: 01284 830464. F: 01284 830964
E: wines@giffordshall.co.uk. W: www.giffordshall.co.uk

Owners: John & Jeanie Kemp
Winemaker: Jonathan Kemp
Directions: Take B1066 from Bury St Edmunds to Hartest. Turn left at village green, over bridge and up hill for three-quarters of a mile. Gifford's Hall on right just before T-junction.
Vineyard Details: 3.62 ha of vines planted between 1986 and 1990. The south-west facing site is between 85 m and 91 m above sea level

and the soil is a sandy loam over clay over chalk. The vines are planted at 2.29 m × 1.52 m and trellised on a single high wire spur pruned system.

Grape Varieties: Bacchus, Madeleine × Angevine 7672, Pinot noir, Reichensteiner, Rondo.

Wine Sales: April to end of October, daily, 11 am to 6 pm.

Vineyard Visits: The vineyard is open during the above times. Admission is charged depending on the time of the year (£2.50–£3.25. Less for OAPs). Meals available in the Tea Rooms. Groups welcome by appointment and a wide selection of meals is available. In addition to the vineyards and winery, Gifford's Hall has much for the visitor to see; a sweet pea collection, a rose garden, wild flower meadows, rare breed sheep, goats, pigs and domestic fowl. There is a 'Rose and Sweet Pea Festival' at the end of June, a 'Potato Tasting Day' at the beginning of September and a 'Wine Festival' at the end of September. Telephone for brochure for full details.

Although the vineyards at Gifford's Hall are at one of the highest points in Suffolk, the vineyard is usually frost free and well ventilated which helps cut down on fungal problems. The winery, in a converted 1950's grain store, features the usual equipment for this size of operation, with a 1 tonne horizontal press, glass fibre tanks, a Seitz 9 head bottler and 'two pairs of size ten feet'. The Kemps must be the only UK winemakers who actually tread their grapes (up to 90 per cent). Despite this (the Kemps claim because of this) the wines have won a number of awards including 'Best Dry Wine' for their 1995 Estate Reserve, 'East Anglian Wine of the Year' for

GIFFORDS

75cl ℮   10% alc

HARVEST BLEND 1997

Grown, made and bottled at Gifford's Hall, Hartest, Suffolk IP29 4EX

Our site on one of the highest points in Suffolk certainly proved its worth in 1997. Frosts as low as -7c in May caused huge damage to many English vineyards. Happily for us it mostly rolled down the hillside and left us virtually unscathed. What's more the long hot summer ripened the grapes handsomely. This medium dry wine is a blend of grapes left on the vine into mid October to allow acidity to fall. It has a bouquet which reminds me of apples with a hint of lemon.

John Kemp   April 1998

their 1996 Medium Dry and the 'MacRea Challenge Trophy' for the 1997 Medium Dry in the EAVA annual competition.

The 13.4 ha smallholding is home to a wide variety of different activities and the vineyard and winery is but part of the enterprise. A wide range of dryish fruit liqueurs is also produced using local fruit including raspberries, sloes, damsons, blackcurrants, apples and hedgerow fruit. These were featured on BBC's Food and Drink programme by Oz Clarke. The Kemp family also have a selection of rare breed animals for visitors to see, a covered area growing sweet peas, wild flower meadows and a rose garden. Visitors can take trailer rides through the estate and there are good walks to be had. Much of the produce from the farm – honey, eggs and vegetables – finds its way into the tea rooms and is served to guests. There is also a children's play area and picnic site. Altogether, Gifford's Hall offers visitors one of the better days out at an English vineyard.

Helions Vineyard
The Old Vicarage, Helions Bumpstead, Haverhill, Suffolk, CB9 7AS

T: 01440 730316

Owner: Jasper Grinling CBE
Winemaker: Wines made at Shawsgate Vineyard
Directions: Telephone for directions.
Vineyard Details: 0.23 ha of vines planted in 1980. The site is level and the soil a meadow top soil with clay subsoil. The vines are Single Guyot trained and planted at 1.52 m × 1.37 m.
Grape Varieties: Müller-Thurgau, Reichensteiner.
Wine Sales & Vineyard Visits: Visitors welcome at any time!

The 1992 Helions was awarded a gold medal and the 1996 a bronze medal in the EAWG's regional competition.

Hintlesham Vineyard
Tythe Cottage, Duke Street, Hintlesham, Suffolk, IP8 3QP

T: 01473 652355

Owner: J. Robinson
Winemaker: Wines made at Carters Vineyard
Directions: Telephone for directions.
Vineyard Details: 0.09 ha of vines planted in 1995 on a 1.8 m ×

1.5 m Double Guyot system. The south-east facing site is between 15 m and 18 m above sea level on a clay soil.
Grape Varieties: Bacchus, Pinot noir, Rondo.
Wine Sales & Vineyard Visits: By appointment only.

Ickworth Vineyard
Ickworth House, Hollinger, Bury St Edmunds, Suffolk
Address for correspondence:
3 Wyken Road Cottages, Stanton, Bury St Edmunds, Suffolk, IP31 2DW

T: 01359 251173. F: 01359 251173
E: aihusr@smtp.ntrust.org.uk

Owners: Charles Macready & Jillian Simms
Winemaker: Wines made at Carter's Vineyard
Directions: Vineyard is within grounds of Ickworth House, a National Trust property.

ICKWORTH
VINEYARD

Walled Garden
White
1998

Vineyard Details: 0.8 ha of vines planted in 1995 and 1996. The site, within a 2 ha old walled kitchen garden, is between 75 m and 80 m above sea level. The soil is heavy loam. The vines are planted at 2.5 m × 1.75 m and 2.5 m × 1.4 m and are mainly two cane Scott Henry trained.
Grape Varieties: Auxerrois, Bacchus, Pinot noir, Rondo.
Wine Sales: Available from the National Trust shop and restaurant. Open from Easter to end October, Tuesdays, Wednesdays, Fridays, weekends and Bank Holidays, 1 pm to 5 pm. Weekends in November and December, 11 am to 4 pm.
Vineyard Visits: Self-guided tours and winetastings on the first Sunday of the month, June to October 11 am to 4 pm. Also guided tours of the vineyard with supper in Ickworth House during the year. Telephone for full details. Park open all year round except Christmas Day 7 am to 7 pm. Admission is charged.

Jillian Simms started her viticultural life by planting and managing the nearby Wyken vineyards. There she met Charles Macready (who now manages Wyken) and together they have very enter-prisingly persuaded the National Trust to let them establish a vineyard within the walled kitchen garden that is in the grounds of Ickworth House. This eccentric eighteenth-century building, which has a magnificent central rotunda, was built by the equally eccentric Bristol family. The 2 ha walled garden runs down to a large lake in front of which is the first Earl's summerhouse, built in 1703, some 80 years before the main house was constructed. Table grapes had once been grown in the walled garden and stored in the summer-house.

Planting started in April 1995 and despite a severe mid-May frost of −4°C which killed about a quarter of the vines they had just planted, the remainder produced their first crop in 1997. Since then they have re-planted and expanded the vineyard and it now extends to 0.8 ha. They are now making both red and white wines and these are exclusively available from the shop and the restaurant attached to Ickworth which has over 80,000 visitors a year.

Melton Lodge Vineyard
Melton Lodge, Melton, Suffolk, IP12 1LU

T: 01394 387322. F: 01394 387366
E: leggettjjr@aol.com.

Owner: Jeremy Leggett
Directions: Vineyard not open to the public.
Vineyard Details: 0.67 ha of vines planted between 1996 and 1999. The south facing site, within an old walled kitchen garden, is between 15 m and 20 m above sea level and has a light soil. 1996/97 plantings are at 1.5 m × 1.5 m; 1999 planting at 2 m × 2 m. All are Double Guyot trained.
Grape Varieties: Bacchus, Pinot noir, Reichensteiner, Siegerrebe.

This vineyard produced its first crop in 1999. Further plantings of Pinot noir are planned.

Shawsgate Vineyard

Badingham Road, Framlingham, Woodbridge, Suffolk IP13 9HZ

T: 01728 724060. F: 01728 723232
E: wines@shawsgate.co.uk. W: www.shawsgate.co.uk

Owner: Shawsgate Ltd
Winemaker: Rob Hemphill

Directions: On A12, 15 miles north-east of Ipswich, take the B1116 to Framlingham. Leave Framlingham on the B1120 Badingham Road and vineyard will be found in one mile on the left-hand side.
Vineyard Details: 5.05 ha of vines planted between 1973 and 1998. The level site is 91 m above sea level, the rows are planted north–south and the soil is a medium to heavy clay. The vines are planted at 2.1 m × 1.3 m and 2.4 m × 2m Guyot trained and 4 m × 2 m GDC trained.
Grape Varieties: Bacchus, Müller-Thurgau, Reichensteiner, Rondo, Schönburger, Seyval blanc.
Wine Sales: 15 January to 24 December, daily, 10.30 am to 5 pm. Telephone for other times.
Vineyard Visits: As above for casual visitors. Teas and coffees, children's play area and picnic facilities available. Tours and meals for groups of all sizes by arrangement with general interest and specialist tours available. Prices depending on group size and tour taken, from £3.25 per person.

Shawsgate vineyard was established in 1973 and purchased by Ian Hutchinson in 1985. He invested in it heavily and planted vineyards and built a new winery in 1987. In early 2000 it was sold to a consortium of investors headed by a majority shareholder, Ray Cross, and further investment is under way. It is good to see this major East Anglian vineyard prospering.

The 1.62 ha of GDC trained vines (1989 and 1998 plantings) are not sprayed against weeds at all and the ground cover is maintained by mowing. This has allowed several species of rare orchids and wild flowers to naturalise. The winery is equipped with 87,000 litres of Möschle stainless steel tanks, a Willmes UP 1200 pneumatic press, and a six-head filler. Wines are also made for some fourteen other local vineyards. The winery is housed in an all-timber building designed to look like a traditional Suffolk barn with a fully insulated and temperature controlled bottle store.

Shawsgate has also been one of the pioneers of 'vine leasing' where individuals may rent a row (or more) of vines from which they are entitled to take the crop and have it turned into wine. This enables the wine to be returned to them without payment of Excise Tax.

Over the years, wines from Shawsgate have won an impressive number of awards and medals including the IWSC English Wine

Trophy with their 1994 Bacchus Dry. Recent successes include an IWSC silver for the 1996 Bacchus Dry in 1998 and two silvers and two commendeds in the 1998 EAWGA competition.

Staverton Vineyard
The Rookery, Eyke, Woodbridge, Suffolk, IP12 2RR

T: 01394 460271. F: 01394 460818
E: rsheeps@aol.com

Owners: Robin & Lilias Sheepshanks
Winemaker: Wines made at Shawsgate Vineyard
Directions: From the A12 take the B1084, Woodbridge to Orford road. After 4 miles, turn north where signed to Rendlesham. Vineyard in approx. half mile on right.
Vineyard Details: 0.52 ha of vines planted in 1973 and 1989 on a level site. The soil is a sandy loam. The vines are planted at 3.4 m × 1.8 m and 2.4 m × 1.8 m and are all Double Guyot trained.
Grape Varieties: Bacchus, Müller-Thurgau, Ortega, Reichensteiner, Seyval blanc.
Wine Sales & Vineyard Visits: The vineyards are open on alternate Sundays from April to July. At all other times by appointment.

Staverton Vineyards (named after the family who were Lords of the Manor in the fourteenth century) are part of the Rendlesham Estate. The present owners, who took over the estate in 1951, have developed and expanded the gardens which are open to the public in the summer. They extend to 3.24 ha of shrubs, trees, roses, rhododendrons and include a Japanese garden and ornamental ponds. When the gardens are open, they are almost always open for charity. Telephone for details.

Staverton make both still and sparkling wines and have won a number of awards including an EAWGA gold for their 1992 Extra Dry Sparkling and a silver for their 1995 Dry.

Willow Grange Vineyard
Street Farm, Crowfield, Suffolk, IP6 9SY

T: 01449 760612. F: 01449 760612

Owners: Peter & Jill Fowles
Winemaker: Peter Cook
Directions: The vineyard is adjacent to Street Farm which is located at the southern end of Crowfield village, some 15 km north of Ipswich and east of the A140.

Vineyard Details: 0.4 ha of vines planted between 1980 and 1982. The west facing site is 70 metres above sea level and has a clay loam soil. The vines are planted at 2.16 m × 1.25 m and are Double Guyot trained.
Grape Varieties: Müller-Thurgau, Optima, Ortega.
Wine Sales & Vineyard Visits: Open by appointment only. Wine sold in local village store.

Wyken Vineyards
Wyken Hall, Stanton, Bury St Edmunds, Suffolk, IP31 2DW

T: 01359 250240. F: 01359 252256

Owners: Kenneth & Carla Carlisle
Winemaker: Wines made at Shawsgate Vineyard
Directions: 8 miles north east of Bury St Edmunds off the A143. Follow brown tourist signs from Ixworth.
Vineyard Details: 2.12 ha of vines planted in 1988. The south facing site is some 85 m above sea level and the soil is a sandy loam

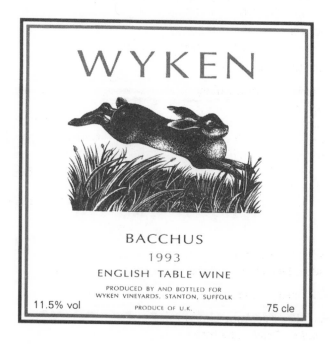

WYKEN

BACCHUS

1993

ENGLISH TABLE WINE

PRODUCED BY AND BOTTLED FOR
WYKEN VINEYARDS, STANTON, SUFFOLK

11.5% vol   PRODUCE OF U.K.   75 cle

over chalk. The vines are planted at 1.8 m × 1.2 m and are all Double Guyot trained.

Grape Varieties: Auxerrois, Bacchus, Kernling, Léon Millot, Madeleine × Angevine 7672, Senator, Triomphe.

Wine Sales: 12 January to 24 December, Wednesday to Sunday plus Bank Holiday Mondays, 10 am to 6 pm. Open at all other times by appointment.

Vineyard Visits: Open for individuals during above hours. The 'Leaping Hare' café (3 stars, Good Food Guide and 1998 Vineyard Restaurant of the Year) is also open. Guided tours by appointment. Wyken Hall is described as 'a garden-lover's paradise' and boasts rose, herb, kitchen and knot gardens as well as a nuttery, copper beech maze and wildflower meadows. Garden is *not* open on Saturdays.

The 1991 Bacchus won gold in 1993 and the 1992 Bacchus the Gore-Browne Trophy in 1994 in the UKVA's national competition.

Broxbournebury Vineyard

Cock Lane, Hoddesden, Hertfordshire
Address for correspondence:
35, Park Avenue, Palmers Green, London, N13 5PG

T: 0208 8862168

Owner: W D Martin Knight
Directions: Vineyard not open to the public.
Vineyard Details: approx. 1.21 ha of vines planted between 1979 and 1990. The south facing site is between 40 m and 49 m above sea level and the soil is mixed gravel and clay. The vines are planted on a modified Double Guyot system at 2.50 m × 1.22 m and 3.05 m × 1.22 m.
Grape Varieties: Huxelrebe, Reichensteiner, Pinot noir, Seyval blanc.

Frithsden Vineyard

Frithsden, Hemel Hempstead, Hertfordshire, HP1 3DD

T: 01442 864732. F: 01442 864732

Owners: Peter & Anne Latchford
Winemaker: Peter Latchford

Frithsden

English Medium White
Table Wine

Estate Grown and Bottled by

P. and A. Latchford • Frithsden Vineyard • Hemel Hempstead • Herts. • UK
Telephone 01442 864732

10.5 % vol   75 cl

Directions: From Hemel Hempstead town centre take the A4146 Leighton Buzzard road towards Water End. After three miles, take the second left-hand turning signposted Frithsden and Nettleden and continue for one mile to road junction. Turn left and after a quarter mile turn right into Frithsden. After 100 yards turn right immediately after the Alford Arms. Vineyard is 120 yards up the lane on the right.

Vineyard Details: 0.81 ha of vines planted between 1971 and 1979. The south facing site is 122 m above sea level and the soil is a silty loam over chalk. The vines are all planted at 2 m × 1.4 m and are Scott Henry pruned.

Grape Varieties: Kerner, Madeleine × Angevine 7672, Müller-Thurgau, Ortega, Pinot Noir, Siegerrebe.

Wine Sales: Open all year round, Wednesday to Saturday 10 am to 5 pm, Sunday, noon to 3 pm. At all other times by appointment.

Vineyard Visits: Guided tours of the vineyard and winery by appointment.

The vineyard was planted by the Latchfords in 1971 at a time when they were uncertain as to its viability. A vist to Geisenheim and a consultation with Professor Helmut Becker convinced them that they did have a good site. It is in a well sheltered valley in the

Chilterns and over the years, 2000 trees have been planted to provide additional protection from the wind. This has greatly helped the vineyard's microclimate and has resulted in better wines. The winery at Frithsden, built in 1985 in the Mediterranean style with white walls and 'Roman' tiles, produces a range of wines. Their 1996 Ortega was awarded 'Best wine from a small vineyard' and their 1997 Kerner 'Best Dry White' in the T&CVA annual competition.

Harpenden Garden Fields Vineyard

Dark Lane, Harpenden, Hertfordshire
Address for correspondence:
66 Cowper Road, Harpenden, Herts, AL5 5NG

T: 01582 769695
E: irene_boogerman@bigfoot.com

Owners: Irene Boogerman & Ralph Martin
Winemaker: Ralph Martin
Directions: Vineyard is not open to the public
Vineyard Details: 96 sq.m of vines planted in 1999. The south-west facing site has a clay soil over chalk.
Grape Varieties: Bacchus, Ortega.
Wine Sales: Vineyard not yet in production.

Hazel End Vineyard

Hazel End Farm, Bishop's Stortford, Hertfordshire, CM23 1HG

T: 01279 812377. F: 01279 815894. M: 07768 264766
E: corylus@aol.com

Owners: Mr and Mrs Charles Humphreys
Winemaker: Wines made at Tenterden Vineyards
Directions: Vineyard not open to the public.
Vineyard Details: 0.83 ha of vines planted between 1990 and 1993. The level site is 73 m above sea level and the soil is a flinty silt. All vines are planted at 2.44 m × 1.22 m and are Double Guyot trained.
Grape Varieties: Bacchus, Huxelrebe, Müller-Thurgau, Reichensteiner.
Wine Sales & Vineyard Visits: By appointment only from the vineyard. Wine also sold from Hazel End Farm Shop at Gypsy Lane,

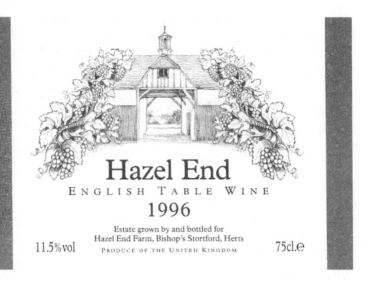

Hazel End
E N G L I S H   T A B L E   W I N E
1996
Estate grown by and bottled for
Hazel End Farm, Bishop's Stortford, Herts
11.5%vol   PRODUCE OF THE UNITED KINGDOM   75cl.℮

Bishop's Stortford and by the glass from the Three Horseshoes PH, Hazel End.

Charles Humphreys has been attempting to grow vines at Hazel End for over 20 years and this site is the third attempt and by far the most successful.

Mimram Valley Vineyard
The Garden House, Tewin Water, Welwyn, Hertfordshire, AL6 0AB

T: 01438 714395. F: 01438 714395
E: keith.cox@talk21.com

Owner & Winemaker: Keith Cox
Directions: Take the B1000 towards Hertford from the A1(M) and A1000 (J6). At the second small roundabout at the bottom of New Road in Digswell Village, turn left and immediately right into a drive. The vineyard is half a mile east down this drive.
Vineyard Details: 0.48 ha of vines planted between 1986 and 1990. The south south-west facing site is between 55 m and 69 m above sea level and the soil is a very fine sandy loam. The vines are planted at varying distances; 3 m × 1.5 m and 1.2 m Double Guyot and 2.5 m × 1. 5 m modified GDC.

Grape Varieties: Bacchus, Huxelrebe, Madeleine × Angevine 7672, Reichensteiner.
Wine Sales & Vineyard Visits: At any time by prior appointment.

The winery is in part of a Victorian apple barn – there are still old apple racks and evidence of the lighting system – which keeps a good temperature and is therefore ideal for wine storage. Keith Cox likes to keep his winemaking simple – sulphur dioxide kept to a minimum, as little movement as possible, no finings and a nitrogen atmosphere over the stainless steel vessels. Equipment is simple, but serviceable.

Tudor Grange Vineyard
Barnet, Hertfordshire
Address for correspondence:
81 Cedar Lawn Avenue, Barnet, Hertfordshire, EN5 2LP

T: 020 8449 9654

Owner & Winemaker: Anthony de Naeyer
Directions: Vineyard not open to the public.
Vineyard Details: 0.024 ha of vines planted between 1984 and 1994. The site – on an allotment – is south facing and has a London Clay soil.
Grape Varieties: Gagarin Blue, Kuibishevski, Müller-Thurgau, Orion, Seyval blanc, Triomphe.

This is a small non-commercial vineyard planted on an allotment. Although it is not generally open to the public, those interested in setting up a similar venture can telephone to talk and arrange a visit. The vineyard produces up to 250 bottles of wine a year (from 99 vines).

Bardfield Vineyard
The Great Lodge, Great Bardfield, Braintree, Essex, CM7 4QD

T: 01371 810776. F: 01371 811398

Owner: Alan Jordan
Winemaker: Wines made at Shawsgate and Chapel Down Wines
Directions: Take the A120 from Great Dunmow towards Braintree. Turn left at the Saling Oak towards Great Bardfield and four and a half miles later, Great Lodge will be found on the right-hand side.

BARDFIELD

·

VINEYARD

English Table Wine

DRY

1996

11% Vol.   75cl.

ESTATE GROWN AND BOTTLED BY:
BARDFIELD VINEYARD, GREAT BARDFIELD, ESSEX, UK

Vineyard Details: 1 ha of vines planted in 1989 and 1990 on a Double Guyot system. The site is 90 m above sea level, south facing and on sandy loam soil.
Grape Varieties: Bacchus, Reichensteiner.
Wine Sales: Open all year, Monday to Friday, 10 am to 4 pm. Weekends by appointment only. To arrange a tasting or for wine sales, telephone Mrs Penny Lacy on 01787 210430 or 07971 464396.
Vineyard Visits: Vineyard visits and tours are available by appointment.

The site of Bardfield vineyard was once in the ownership of Ann of Cleves and the current owner is reviving the tradition of wine-growing in the Essex countryside. Mr Jordan says of his wines, which are made at Shawsgate vineyard in Suffolk and Chapel Down Wines in Kent, that they 'range from the dry to the fruity and have character and balance which makes them eminently drinkable as an apéritif or with white fish and meat dishes'.

Carter's Vineyards
Green Lane, Boxted, Colchester, Essex, CO4 5TS

T: 01206 271136. F: 01206 271136, M: 07802 988609
E: mary@carters.prestel.co.uk. W: www.englishwines.com

Owner & Winemaker: Mary F Mudd

Directions: From Colchester take the A134 towards Sudbury. After Great Horkesley, turn right into Boxted Church Road. Take second right into Green Lane and vineyard is on the left after a quarter mile.

Vineyard Details: 1.71 ha of vines planted between 1990 and 1994. The site between 40 m and 43 m above sea level, south facing and has a sandy loam and gravel soil. The vines are all planted on a 2.2 m × 1.52 m spacing, with both Pendlebogen and Scott Henry training systems.

Grape Varieties: Bacchus, Chardonnay, Dornfelder, Dunkelfelder, Orion, Phoenix, Pinot noir, Reichensteiner.

Wine Sales: Open daily, Easter to end of September 11 am to 5 pm. At other times by appointment.

Vineyard Visits: During opening hours as above. Visitors may follow a vineyard and nature trail through woodland, around lakes and wild flower meadows. Picnic area available. There is also an exhibition of renewable energy ideas. Group visits and meals available by appointment and candle lit wine tasting evenings with a buffet are suggested. School parties are welcome.

Carter's Vineyard was set up to make the most of renewable energy sources and the winery is not connected to mains drainage, water or

English Table Wine

CARTER'S BACCHUS

DRY

Produced by and bottled for
Carters Vineyards, Green Lane,
Boxted, Colchester, England

Produce of United Kingdom

11%   75cl

electricity. A reed bed takes care of waste. Wind and bio-mass fuelled generators looks after the energy requirements. Despite this, the winery manages to produce some interesting wines, including a still white from Bacchus, which in 1998 won the East Anglian Wine of the Year, and red, rosé and sparkling. Mary Mudd reckons that Dornfelder and Bacchus are her two most successful varieties. The winery is well equipped with a Velo air-bag press and monoblock filler/corker. Tanks are all stainless and there are also a few *barriques*. The vineyard is to be expanded slowly with more Bacchus, Dornfelder and Pinot noir.

Castle Vineyard
Vine House, Castle Street, Ongar, Essex, CM5 9HP

T: 01277 364364. F: 01277 364364

Owners: The vineyard is an investor's and worker's co-operative
Winemaker: Mr David Parrish
Directions: Vineyard not open to the public.
Vineyard Details: 0.2 ha of vines planted in 1991. Site is between 25 and 30 metres above ea level and the soil is a fertile loam over boulder clay. Vines are spaced at 2 m × 1.4 m on a 'Castle' system of spur pruned laterals.
Grape Varieties: Huxelrebe, Ortega, Schönburger, Triomphe.

Castle Vineyard is probably unique in that it is owned and run by a co-operative of investors and workers, all members of the Ongar Wine Circle. It is financed by a subscription of £50 per year per member. Crops have been up to 4.75 tonnes in a good year (off only 0.2.ha) and the wine is distributed amongst the participants. It is described as a 'relaxing enterprise, done for fun, but run on strict business lines'. The vines, now eight years old, are pruned on the 'Castle' system of five permanent lateral rods which can produce up to 5 kg a fruit per vine.

Colne Valley Vineyard
Toad Hall, Colchester Road, White Colne, Colchester, Essex, CO6 2PW

T: 01787 224294. F: 01787 222753. M: 078600 557766
E: tim_scorer@lineone.com

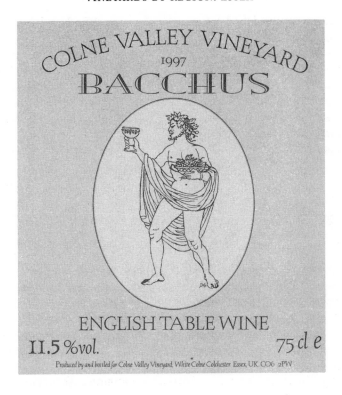

Owner: Tim Scorer
Winemaker: Wines made at Shawsgate Vineyard
Directions: Vineyard not open to the public.
Vineyard Details: 0.58 ha of vines planted in 1991. The south facing site is 27 m above sea level and has an alluvial soil over clay. Vines are all trained on a 4 m × 2 m GDC system.
Grape Varieties: Bacchus, Reichensteiner, Pinot noir.
Wine Sales: By appointment.

Felsted Vineyard
Crix Green, Felsted, Great Dunmow, Essex, CM6 3JT

T: 01245 361504. F: 01245 361504
E: felstedvineyard@supanet.com

Owners: Marcello Franco & Sarah-Jane Davanzo
Winemaker: Marcello Davanzo

Directions: Take the A120 Great Dunmow to Braintree road and follow signs.

Vineyard Details: 4.25 ha of vines. The south west facing site is between 49 m and 55 m above sea level and the soil is clay over flints. The vines are spaced at 1.5 m × 1 m and 2 m × 0.75 m and are GDC trained.

Grape Varieties: Chardonnay, Madeleine × Angevine 7672, Madeleine Sylvaner, Müller-Thurgau, Pinot Meunier, Pinot Noir, Seyval Blanc.

Wine Sales: March until Easter, weekends only, 10 am to 6 pm. Easter until September, Tuesday to Sunday, 10 am to 6 pm. October to Christmas Eve, weekends only 10 am to dusk.

Vineyard Visits: Individuals during above hours. Group visits for 12 or more people available by arrangement from £3.50 per person. A wide range of meals is available by arrangement.

Felsted Vineyards occupies a special place in the history of English Wine and was one of the first commercial vineyards to be planted. In 1965, Graham and Irene Barrett bought 4.25 ha of land at Cricks Green (as it was then known) just outside the village of Felsted. At that time, Graham was working full time, and it was not until 1967 that the job of planting the first of their vines got under way. Their first third of an acre (0.13 ha) was followed in successive years by

more vines, and by the time they had their first commercial crop in 1970, they had over 2 ha planted. The varieties they chose at first were the two standards, Müller-Thurgau and Seyval Blanc, together with a less usual variety, Scheurebe. More varieties followed and by the time they expanded to the full 4 ha in 1972, they had over 14 different varieties. The first 2 ha were planted on a 5 ft by 4 ft Guyot system, but in order to cut back on the labour requirements, the next acreage was planted on a wider spaced Lenz Moser system.

When the Barretts bought the site, it was bare land with no accommodation. After a two-year battle, planning permission for a house was eventually obtained, and once completed, they were able to move on to the vineyard and take up winegrowing full time. At first the wines were made at Merrydown which involved a journey of some distance, but in 1975 a winery was installed, and Graham started making some of the wine at Felsted.

Being one of the first commercial vineyards in East Anglia, they received some good early publicity, and the wines, sold under the 'Felstar' label (so-called because they were advised by MAFF that the wine could not bear the name of their village) soon became well known. In 1973 they had their most successful harvest to date, picking over 9 tons of grapes, including a very small quantity of the first English 'Ice-Wine', made from Scheurebe and Riesling grapes picked on 29/30 November when the temperature dropped to $-4.5°C$.

1979, their tenth commercial vintage, was a good one, second only to 1976 in terms of quantity, with Seyval Blanc cropping at 11 tons/acre. They decided that the costs and labour demands of the 5 ft by 4 ft Guyot system were too great, and they decided to convert all their vines onto the wider spaced Lenz Moser system. This involved the removal of one out of three rows, leaving a 10 ft gap, followed by two rows 5 ft apart. The winter of 1981/82 was extremely severe and hard frosts did a lot of damage to the vines. Yields in 1980 and 1981 were not good and as the costs of running the vineyard were still too high they decided to convert their vines on to GDC.

In 1985, Graham and Irene decided that retirement from wine-making was due and they sold the vineyard. Over the 18 years that they had been at Felsted, the vineyard and its wines had become one of the best known in the country and together they had played a big part in the revival of viticulture. In the early years of the English

Wine of the Year Competition their wines achieved several awards and medals, including a Silver Medal in 1978 for their 1976 Felstar Méthode Champenoise Sparkling Wine. Irene Barrett was Secretary of the English Vineyards Association from its founding in 1967 until 1980 and Graham a Director from 1969 until 1985.

Since the Barretts left Felsted, the vineyard has been through several changes of ownership. It was first bought by Bill Garner, who went on to buy Tenterden Vineyards. It was then owned by a Mr Lilley and then Mr and Mrs Fells. In March 2000 it was bought by the present owners. Marcello and Sarah have been making wine in the Piave region, near Venice where Marcello was born.

Today, the vineyard and winery is undergoing something of a revival under the Davanzo's ownership and is open for tours and tastings for groups and individuals. There are five wines on their current retail list; a Chardonnay, a Madeleine blend, a medium dry 'Crix Green' Müller-Thurgau, a medium 'Black Notley Müller-Thurgau and a rosé made from Pinot's Meunier and noir.

Great Stocks Vineyard
Downham Road, Stock, Ingatestone, Essex, CM4 9RB

T: 01277 841122. F: 01277 841122. M: 07775 875025
E: gtstocks@aol.com.

Owners: Brian & Gillian Barnard
Winemaker: White wines made at Davenport Vineyards, red wines at Carters Vineyard
Directions: Leave the A12 Chelmsford by-pass at exit for Galleywood and Billericay and take the B1007 exit towards Billericay. After three quarters of a mile turn left into Downham Road and the vineyard will be found 100 yards on the left-hand side.
Vineyard Details: 2.63 ha of vines planted between 1993 and 1999. The south facing site is 70 m above sea level and has a 225 mm of topsoil over calciferous clay. The vines are planted at various planting distances and two different training systems; 3 m × 1.5 m, 1. 8 m and 3.7 m spur pruned bi-lateral cordons and 2.5 m × 1.4 m spur pruned single cordons.
Grape Varieties: Orion, Phoenix, Regent, Rondo, Siegerrebe, Sirius, Triomphe.

ORION FUMÉ

GREAT STOCKS

VINE YARD

11% VOL   75cl ℮

TÊTE DE CUVÉE

ENGLISH TABLE WINE

ESTATE GROWN AT
GREAT STOCKS VINEYARD, STOCK, ESSEX, ENGLAND.
PRODUCE OF THE U.K

BOTTLED BY W1708 TN6 3RR. U.K.

Wine Sales: Daily, 10 am to 6 pm.
Vineyard Visits: Self-guided tours for individuals during opening hours as above. Guided tours for groups (12 people minimum) by arrangement £3.50 inc. wine tasting, cheese and biscuits. Meals for groups available by arrangement. Homemade food from £8.50 per person.

The Barnards bought this 8½ ha site in 1992 and planted their first vines a year later. Their choice of varieties is an interesting one and they have chosen with care. Not for them the usual Müller-Thurgau, Reichensteiner and Seyval blanc, but they have opted for some of the newer and potentially more exciting varieties – mainly hybrids – that are now available. Orion, Phoenix and Sirius (white) and Regent (red), the Geilweilerhof new varieties which are gradually becoming better known both here and in Germany; Rondo, the proven Geisenheim *vitis Amurensis* red which has been used for some of the best of the UK's red wines; Triomphe, the rather neglected but underrated, red hybrid; and Siegerrebe, probably the earliest ripening (and most wasp prone) variety grown in the UK, but capable of making fine aromatic wines in a light Gewürztraminer/Muscat style. These are the choices of a thinking man (and probably woman) and of all the vineyards in this book, this must be one that both existing and potential vineyard owners should follow as these may well be the varieties for the future.

Not only have the varieties been chosen with some thought, but so too have the training and pruning systems. Again, no Double Guyot or GDC systems, but a simple spur pruned system with either single or double cordons. Most of the vines are grown to organic status in respect of sprays used. All this thought and care has paid dividends and their tally of awards and medals to date has been good. They won a gold medal in the UKVA's 1997 competition for their 1995 Symphony medium sweet. A winery is at the planning stage and will be operational for the 2001 harvest.

Little Witney Green
Fyfield, Ongar, Essex
Address for correspondence:
Vine House, Ongar, Essex, CM5 9HF

T: 01277 364364. F: 01277 364364

Owner & Winemaker: David Parrish
Directions: Vineyard not open to the public.
Vineyard Details: 0.45 ha of vines planted in 1978. The site is 30 m above sea level, south facing and the soil is a boulder clay. The vines are planted at 3 m × 1.5 m and spur pruned.
Grape Varieties: Huxelrebe, Müller-Thurgau, Seyval blanc, Zweigeltrebe.

1996 Topaz Rosé awarded 'Commended' in the EAWG 1998 competition.

Mersea Vineyard
Rewsalls Lane, East Mersea, Colchester, Essex, CO5 8SX

T: 01206 385900. F: 01206 383600
E: merseawine@btinternet.com

Owners: Roger & Jacqui Barber
Winemaker: Wines made at the vineyard and by Chapel Down Wines and Valley Vineyards

Mersea

1997

ENGLISH TABLE WINE

Produced & bottled for Mersea Vineyard
by Valley Vineyards UK.

12 % Vol   75 cl.

Directions: Take B1025 from Colchester. On entering the island, fork left, and take the third turning on the right. Vineyard is on right after half a mile.

Vineyard Details: 2.67 ha of vines planted between 1985 and 1991. The south facing site lies between 1 m and 8 m above sea level and the soil is mainly clay. The vines are all planted at 2 m × 1.4 m and Single Guyot trained.

Grape Varieties: Müller-Thurgau, Ortega, Reichensteiner.

Wine Sales: Easter to October, retail shop and tea rooms open every day. At other times only open at the weekends.

Vineyard Visits: Available for a minimum of four people. Telephone for details. There is also a function room available for up to 50 people as well as some bed-and-breakfast rooms with en-suite facilities.

The wines from this vineyard have consistently done well in competitions. The 1994 won the UKVA's Wine Guild Trophy in 1996 and their 1996 a silver and 1997 a gold medal and the 'Bruisyard Trophy' in the EAWGA's regional competition.

Mower Vineyards
9 Glenside, Billericay, Essex, CM11 2LY

T: 01277 624132

Owner & Winemaker: Bert Mower
Directions: Vineyard not open to the public.
Vineyard Details: 0.08 ha of vines planted between 1976 and 1984. The site is on east and south facing slopes, is between 91 m and 107 m above sea level and has a clay soil. The vines are all on their own roots, planted at 1.9 m × 0.9 m and either Bordeaux Lyre or GDC trained.
Grape Varieties: Madeleine × Angevine 7672, Müller-Thurgau, Pinot noir.

This small non-commercial vineyard has its own winery with cellar attached and all wines are fermented in glass carboys. Vintages are delayed to obtain higher natural sugar levels and low temperature fermentation techniques are employed. Skin contact is limited, some wines are left *sur lie* and some have oak treatment. Mr Mower, a

member of the National Guild of Wine and Beer Judges, has achieved two firsts and a second with his wines in the National Association of Wine and Beermakers competitions in 1998 and 1999. In both 1998 and 1999 his wines were the Judge's Conference 'Wine of the Year'. He rates Müller-Thurgau highly, which although prone to disease, still makes good wines.

Nevards Vineyard
Boxted Road, Boxted, Colchester, Essex
Address for correspondence:
Fletchers, Fletchers Lane, Middleton, Saxmundham, Suffolk, IP17 3NZ

T: 01728 648471. F: 01728 648471

Owners: DW & T E Cooper
Winemaker: Donald Cooper
Directions to vineyard: Take the A134 Colchester to Sudbury road heading north. Shortly after the village of Great Horkesley, turn

English Table Wine

Nevards

MEDIUM DRY

Lightly Oaked

Estate bottled by Carters Vineyards
Boxted · Colchester · England
11.5% Vol   Produce of the United Kingdom   75cl e

right into Boxted road and take the second on the left (public house on corner). Vineyard is half a mile on the right.
Vineyard Details: 0.35 ha of vines planted in the early 1980s at 3.5 m × 1.5 m and *'Cordon de Royat'* trained. The site is south facing, 50 m above sea level and has a gravel soil.
Grape Varieties: Huxelrebe, Regner, Reichensteiner.
Wine Sales: Wines sold from Carter's Vineyard – see separate entry.
Vineyard Visits: By appointment.

This vineyard was taken over by Donald Cooper in 1998 and has been reduced in size by removing internal rows to allow for the passage of standard tractors. There are high hedges around it which give it the effect of a walled garden and the well drained soil and the dry East Anglian climate combine to give reliable crops. The grapes are taken to Carter's Vineyard (where Donald is joint licensee with Mary Mudd). The 1997 Nevards Lightly Oaked won bronze at the EAVA's regional competition.

New Hall Vineyards
Chelmsford Road, Purleigh, Near Maldon, Chelmsford, Essex, CM3 6PN
T: 01621 828343. F: 01621 828891
W: www.newhallvineyards.fsbusiness.co.uk

Owner & Winemaker: Piers Greenwood
Directions: From the A12 Chelmsford by-pass take A414 Maldon road. Go through Danbury and at first roundabout go straight across on to B1010 to Burnham. Vineyard two and a half miles on left-hand side in Purleigh village. Follow Tourist Board signs.
Vineyard Details: 36.3 ha of vines all planted on a wide spaced Guyot trellising system between 1969 and 1998. Row widths are between 2.74 m and 3.96 m and vines are spaced between 1.22 m and 1.52 m in the row. The site is between 11 m and 24 m over sea level, mainly facing south or south-west and the soil is fairly heavy London clay.
Grape Varieties: Bacchus, Chardonnay, Huxelrebe, Müller-Thurgau, Ortega, Perle, Pinot blanc, Pinot gris, Pinot noir, Reichensteiner, Schönburger, Zweigeltrebe.
Wine Sales: The vineyard is open for wine sales on Mondays to Fridays 10.30 am to 5.30 pm, Saturdays and Sundays 10.30 am to 1.30 pm. At all other times by appointment.

Vineyard Visits: The vineyard is open to visitors as above. There is no entry charge. Guided tours for groups (16–120 people) are available from £4 per person. Tours must be booked in advance. Teas, coffees and ploughman's lunches and suppers are available for groups. Visitors will see the vineyards, winery and cellars, see a slide show on winegrowing at New Hall, and have a tasting. There are also special Champagne Tours.

Each year over the first full weekend in September, New Hall Vineyards hold their annual English Wine and Craft Festival with a wide range of attractions for the whole family, including Country Dancing, Vineyard Tours and Wine Tastings, musical entertainers, traditional Essex food such as oysters and sea food and a variety of entertainments for children. The charge is £4 for adults, 50p for children. No booking required, 10.30 am to 5.30 pm each day over the weekend. Telephone for dates.

New Hall Vineyards is one of the oldest and largest vineyards in the country and in an area climatically ideal for growing vines; frost is seldom a problem. Purleigh is 4 miles from the River Blackwater

estuary and has an annual rainfall of only 43 cm. Bill Greenwood, Pier's father, first planted vines on his 249 ha arable farm in 1969. Despite initial drainage problems with the heavy clay soil, crops are now usually very good and consistent. The first harvest at New Hall was a modest 2½ tons in 1973 and in those days, with no winery on the farm, the grapes were shipped to Merrydown to be vinified. Today, New Hall has its own winery, fully equipped with two Vaslin 1200 litre presses, a 12 head Seitz Velox filler and all the other usual equipment. The winery has a capacity of 150,000 litres, about half in stainless steel, the balance in glass fibre.

New Hall is not the village of Purleigh's first vineyard as records show that there was one at nearby Purleigh Hall in the twelfth century. In 1169 the 'vintager', as the winegrower was called, received 19s 10d for repairs to the vineyard for two years. In 1187 the cost of making and transferring the wine to London was 11/- and in 1207, two 'tuns' or barrels were taken to Bury St Edmunds in readiness for the arrival of King John. The vineyard crops up in the records throughout the next two hundred years, with a final mention being in 1402, when 8 men were employed at 1.5d per day to dig the vineyard and cart manure from the rectory. The carting was a separate item and cost 4/- for two four-horse carts for two days!

Today, Purleigh's vineyards are under a more modern management regime. The wide-spaced Guyot system suits the equipment on the farm and makes for a more open growth of vines than one sees in other vineyards. In 1988 approx. 20 ha of vines were established, planted under contract by Lamberhurst Vineyards, using a Wagner planting machine brought over specially from Germany. This new acreage was planted at the unusual row width of 3.96 m but with a very good reason. The vineyards had been interplanted with lucerne which was destined for a local grass drying plant and the forage harvester needed to cut the crop required this distance to get down the rows. The trellising system is also of interest. The wide rows enable a proportion of the growth to grow without being tucked in, which is unusual for Guyot systems and makes for both savings in labour and a well ventilated leaf canopy. Crops at New Hall must be amongst the best in the country and are usually high in natural sugars. Quite a large proportion of the New Hall crop is sold under contract to other wineries and some of the major UK producers source grapes here.

Olivers Farm Vineyard

Olivers Farm, Toppesfield, Halstead, Essex, CO9 4LS

T: 01787 237642. F: 01787 237602

Owner & Winemaker: James Blackie
Directions: Vineyard not open to the public.
Vineyard Details: 0.02 ha of vines planted between 1980 and 1990. The south facing site is between 70 m and 73 m above sea level and the soil is a chalky boulder clay. The vines are on their own roots, planted at 1.2 m × 1.2 m and Double Guyot trained.
Grape Varieties: Madeleine × Angevine 7672.

Toppesfield is one of the few vineyard sites in Essex recorded in the Domesday Book. It is on the north side of an east–west running valley with about two miles of south facing slope which runs down to the Toppesfield Brook. This is a private vineyard and wine is not sold.

Potash Vineyard

Potash, Abberton Road, Layer de la Haye, Colchester, Essex, CO2 0JX

T: 01206 734734. F: 01206 734734

Owner: Peter Rowe
Directions: Vineyard not open to the public.
Vineyard Details: 0.10 ha of vines planted in 1995. The south facing site is 40 m above sea level and the soil is a sandy loam over gravel. The vines are planted at 2 m × 1.5 m and are Double Guyot trained. The vineyard is managed organically.
Grape Varieties: Bacchus, Chardonnay, Dornfelder, Dunkelfelder, Pinot noir, Reichensteiner.

Stony Hills Vineyard

Fossets Lane, Fordham, Colchester, Essex
Address for correspondence:
25 Partridge Drive, Fordham, Colchester, Essex, CO6 3NH

T: 01206 241198

Owner: Peter Codd
Winemaker: Wines made at Carter's Vineyard

Directions: Vineyard not open to the public.
Vineyard Details: 0.99 ha of vines planted in 1993 on a south facing site between 30 m and 37 m above sea level. The soil is a clay loam. The vines are planted at 3 m × 1.5 m and are Double Guyot trained.
Grape Variety: Schönburger
Wine Sales & Vineyard Visits: By appointment.

Writtle College Vineyard
Writtle Agricultural College, Writtle, Chelmsford, Essex, CM1 3RR

T: 01245 420705. F: 01245 420456
E: ctp@writtle.ac.uk

Owner: Writtle Agricultural College
Winemaker: Wines made at New Hall Vineyards
Directions: On the western outskirts of Chelmsford.
Vineyard Details: 0.28 ha of vines planted in 1987 and 1988 at 3 m × 1.5 m. There are several different training systems used; GDC, Double Guyot and Bordeaux Lyre. The site is 30 m above sea level and the soil is a sandy clay above gravel.
Grape Varieties: Bacchus, Reichensteiner, Schönburger.

SOUTH EAST VINEYARD REGION

Vineyards are listed alphabetically by county. The counties appear in the following order: Surrey, Kent, West Sussex, East Sussex.

The 'South East' region contains the largest number of both vineyards, 75, and hectares of vines, 312, in this guide. In my 1989 book, *The Vineyards of England*, there were 113 vineyards covering 350 hectares. The region has always had the most area under vines and the average size of vineyards is larger than in other parts of the UK (4.28 ha compared with a UK average of 2.40 ha) although this is in part accounted for by the presence of one vineyard, Denbies Wine Estate, which has almost 106 ha of vines.

The region is large and has a diversity of sites and soils. It contains both the South and North Downs – chalk hills that bisect the area from east to west – and a large region known as the Weald which lies between the Downs. Kent is known as the 'Garden of England' mainly because of its proximity to London and good transport links to the capital made it a centre for both fruit growing and market gardening in the nineteenth century. Today, Kent has lost many of the hop gardens and apple and pear orchards that made it famous and its farming enterprises are, as in most parts of the region, very mixed. There are plenty of sheltered south-facing sites in the region with suitable freely-draining soils that make them ideal for vines. Rainfall in the main is neither excessive nor too little and if the region has a fault, it is that it can be prone to spring frosts, especially on sites away from the coast.

The first modern vineyard to be planted in this region was at Horam Manor where, in 1954, Jack Ward pioneered the growing of vines for the commercial production of wine. His company, Merrydown, did much to help organise growers, supplying vines and equipment and making wine under the Merrydown Co-operative Scheme which ran for ten years from 1969. Ward's enthusiasm certainly rubbed off on both farmers and growers looking for an alternative crop, as well as infecting local business-men with land to spare who fancied the idea of owning a vineyard. Other early vineyards include Biddenden, Nettlestead, Rock Lodge and Flexerne. One businessman who wanted to own a vineyard was Kenneth McAlpine who established Lamberhurst in 1972. Lamberhurst expanded rapidly and became the major English wine producer of the mid-1970s. Its high profile and apparent

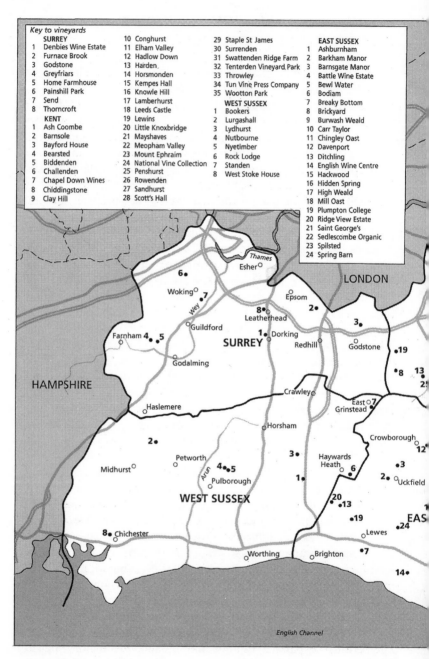

Key to vineyards

SURREY
1 Denbies Wine Estate
2 Furnace Brook
3 Godstone
4 Greyfriars
5 Home Farmhouse
6 Painshill Park
7 Send
8 Thorncroft

KENT
1 Ash Coombe
2 Barnsole
3 Bayford House
4 Bearsted
5 Biddenden
6 Challenden
7 Chapel Down Wines
8 Chiddingstone
9 Clay Hill
10 Conghurst
11 Elham Valley
12 Hadlow Down
13 Harden
14 Horsmonden
15 Kempes Hall
16 Knowle Hill
17 Lamberhurst
18 Leeds Castle
19 Lewins
20 Little Knoxbridge
21 Mayshaves
22 Meopham Valley
23 Mount Ephraim
24 National Vine Collection
25 Penshurst
26 Rowenden
27 Sandhurst
28 Scott's Hall
29 Staple St James
30 Surrenden
31 Swattenden Ridge Farm
32 Tenterden Vineyard Park
33 Throwley
34 Tun Vine Press Company
35 Wootton Park

WEST SUSSEX
1 Bookers
2 Lurgashall
3 Lydhurst
4 Nutbourne
5 Nyetimber
6 Rock Lodge
7 Standen
8 West Stoke House

EAST SUSSEX
1 Ashburnham
2 Barkham Manor
3 Barnsgate Manor
4 Battle Wine Estate
5 Bewl Water
6 Bodiam
7 Breaky Bottom
8 Brickyard
9 Burwash Weald
10 Carr Taylor
11 Chingley Oast
12 Davenport
13 Ditchling
14 English Wine Centre
15 Hackwood
16 Hidden Spring
17 High Weald
18 Mill Oast
19 Plumpton College
20 Ridge View Estate
21 Saint George's
22 Sedlescombe Organic
23 Spilsted
24 Spring Barn

South East

230

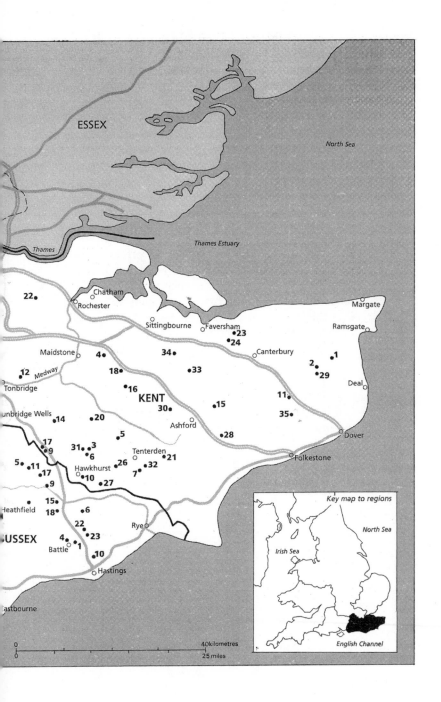

ESSEX

North Sea

Thames Estuary

Thames

22

Chatham
Rochester

Sittingbourne

Faversham

Margate

Ramsgate

23
24

Maidstone

4

34

Canterbury

2
1

Medway
12

18

33

29

Tonbridge

16

KENT

30

11

Deal

Tunbridge Wells

14

20

15

35

5

Ashford

Dover

31
9

3

28

Folkestone

6

Tenterden

21

5

11

26

32

Hawkhurst

7

17

10

9

27

15

18

6

Heathfield

22

Rye

SUSSEX

4

23

1

Battle

10

Hastings

Eastbourne

0   40 kilometres
0   25 miles

Key map to regions

North Sea

Irish Sea

English Channel

commercial success persuaded many in the region that they too should plant up. The first Gore-Browne Trophy awarded to the 'English Wine of the Year' was won by Brede Vineyard, near Rye in East Sussex in 1974. Subsequent Gore-Browne Trophy winners from the region included myself at Tenterden in 1981 and 1991 and Lamberhurst in 1983, 1985 and 1990, Biddenden in 1987, Carr Taylor in 1989 and Chapel Down Wines in 1999. These important successes have helped cement the region's reputation as one of the best to grow vines and make wine in.

Today, apart from Denbies Wine Estate, the region has a number of big vineyards and 22 of the 34 vineyards in the UK of 4 ha or over are in the region. Two of these are relatively new entrants to the English wine scene and both are exclusively producing sparkling wine: Nyetimber and RidgeView Estate. The latter won the 2000 Gore-Browne Trophy and has done much to publicise the region. The presence of Chapel Down Wines, the country's largest wine producer, in this region means that the South East produces very much more wine than any other area. Although accurate statistics on wine production by region are not available, it is my estimate that the four counties that make up the South East between them account for almost 75 per cent of total UK wine production. There is still plenty of scope for increasing production in the region. The closeness of large conurbations, as well as the constant passage of overseas visitors through the channel ports, means that growers who are on suitable routes and get their marketing right can be assured of worthwhile levels of farm-gate sales.

Denbies Wine Estate
London Road, Dorking, Surrey, RH5 6AA

T: 01306 876616. F: 01306 888930
Information: 01306 742002
Group Bookings: 01306 742224
E: denbies@denbiesvineyard.co.uk. W: www.denbiesvineyard.co.uk

Owners: A E & G D White
General Manager: Mike Allen
Directline: 01306 742225
Mobile: 07785 283576
Consultant Winemaker: John Worontschak
Winemaker: Nick Patrick
Vineyard Manager: Tony Potter
Visitor Centre Manager: Val Chapman
Directions: Take junction 9 off the M25 and follow A24 towards Dorking. Vineyard is on the right-hand side and is well signposted.
Vineyard Details: 105.58 ha of vines planted between 1986 and 1990. The large site, between 50 m and 100 m above sea level, is split between lower lying level ground and the surrounding slopes. The soil is a fertile loam, interspersed with flints, overlying a chalk strata. Most of the slopes face south.
Grape Varieties: Auxerrois, Bacchus, Chardonnay, Dornfelder, Dunkelfelder, Ehrenfelser, Huxelrebe, Müller-Thurgau, Optima, Ortega, Pinot blanc, Pinot gris, Pinot Meunier, Pinot noir, Red Elbling, Reichensteiner, Riesling, Schönburger, Seyval Blanc, White Elbling.
Wine & Gift Shop: January to March, Monday to Friday, 10 am to 4.30 pm. Saturday, 10 am to 5.30 pm. Sunday, 11.30 am to 5.30 pm. April to December, Monday to Saturday, 10 am to 5.30 pm. Sunday, 11.30 am to 5.30 pm.
Vineyard Visits: Vineyard open as above. They can be seen at will and there is a trail that can be followed. The public facilities are superb and there are extensive catering facilities for all levels of eating and drinking and a very well stocked shop. Guided tours on the hour during most of the above opening hours starting at 11 am and continuing throughout the day except at 1 pm – although on Sundays there is a tour at 1 pm. The tour includes a visit to the 3-D time lapse film show, a ride on the 'people mover' which takes you through the winery and cellars and ends with a winetasting. £5 for

adults with reductions for senior citizens and children. Groups welcome by appointment. There is a 3.66 m (12 ft) height limit for coaches entering the site. Full facilities for functions, conferences, company presentations, product launches etc. Telephone Lesley Heard on 01306 742224 for details.

It is difficult to know quite where to start in describing Denbies Wine Estate, such is the scale and scope of the undertaking. When Adrian White (head of Biwater, the very successful company based in Dorking) who is the prime mover behind this remarkable venture, let it be known that he was preparing to plant over 100 ha of vineyards, most in the industry – and probably many outside it – questioned his sanity. The UK, with, at that time, around 750 ha of vines (figures are approximate as at the time no official records were kept) was not really ready for one vineyard to be planted that would increase the area under vine, and the production of wine, by that amount. However, undeterred by any criticism, over the four years between 1986 and 1989, the bulk of the vineyards were planted. A laser-guided machine planter was imported from Germany, the first (and only) one to be used in the UK.

The Denbies Estate was once the property of the Cubitt family (the nineteenth century builders and property developers) and there used to be a very large mansion on the estate, overlooking the town of Dorking. This mansion was demolished after a war-time fire and initially there were plans to excavate the old basements, cover the roof over with soil and grass so that the whole building would blend in with the countryside and put a winery in there. However, the Mole Valley District Council did not view this as the correct place for a winery and were frightened that it might become 'another Lamberhurst' as the Planning Committee put it. The access to that part of the estate was poor and they were concerned about the large number of vehicles that would visit the winery.

The land which was planted to vines stretches from the top of the hills overlooking the town of Dorking, right down to the A24 which defines the southern limit of the site. Cutting across the lower end of the vineyards is the London–Dorking railway line, at this point raised up on an embankment some 5 m above the surrounding land. Apart from making access to the site impossible for anything over 3.66 m (12 ft), the embankment traps any downward rolling frost which might otherwise escape. Parts of the site are ideal south-facing slopes, some undulating sections which are warm in the summer, but frost-pockets in the spring and much of the lower section, that surrounding the winery and running down to the main road, is relatively flat.

Advice from the Trier Viticulture Institute on the Mosel was sought before planting and a selection of varieties chosen, some of which at the time were seen as rather wild cards. Since the first issue of this book, Gewürztraminer, Kerner and Siegerrebe have gone and Chardonnay, Dornfelder, Huxelrebe, Reichensteiner and Ortega have been introduced. Elbling, an ancient variety only planted on the Mosel in Germany and Luxembourg, which was in the original planting scheme, is however still there. The vines are planted at either 2.9 m × 1.2 m or 2.5 m × 1.2 m and are trained to both Double and Single Guyot training. It is said that the fairly wide row spacings were chosen to cope with the Braud grape harvesting machine although I do not quite understand this as models are available to cope with narrower rows. To my mind the wide spacings do not really make best use of the available land and crops are lower (on a per hectare basis) than in more closely planted vineyards. The harvester is the only one in use in UK vineyards

at the present time, although several of the larger growers are considering using one.

A vineyard of this size and complexity can never be planted – especially in a country as marginal as the UK – without problems, and with hindsight one can always see the pitfalls. The vineyards have suffered from frost – especially in the last few years – and efforts to overcome these have not been without difficulties. Anti-frost 'windmills' – large two bladed propellers which stir up the colder air that sinks to the valley floor with the warmer air that remains above it (an 'inversion' frost) – were imported from California (where they are widely used in both vineyards and citrus orchards) and installed across the lower vineyard areas in preparation for the next frost. Unfortunately, the powers of the local authority's enforcement officer had not been reckoned with (planning permission should have been obtained) and after one night of noise and alarm when these giant noisy blades stirred up the air and the nearby residents in about equal amounts, a halt was called to their use. The windmills disappeared and were sold – some of which ended up in a New Zealand vineyard (Palliser Estates in Martinborough)! The next (and current idea) is to use oil powered burners that sit silently amongst the vines in the dangerous mid-April to mid-May period, waiting for the temperature to drop, whereupon all hands set to and light them in ever increasing numbers as the temperature sinks. These can be effective if the number of burners and the depth of the frost are matched, although a really deep frost might defeat them. Their big drawback is that they need physically placing out each year, filling with oil and lighting at very unsociable hours. Inversion frosts usually strike after midnight and keep going until 9 am in the morning. To date, they are using several hundred of these and more are on order. They do give off a rather eerie glow and when they are all alight at the dead of night, there is a touch of Dante's Inferno about the place!

For the first harvest, in 1989 a winery was installed in the old cattle buildings and for three years it remained there whilst the new winery was in both the planning and building stage. Mole Valley Council again had views about the desirability of the whole enter-prise and whilst they could do nothing about someone wanting to plant vineyards, they could – and did – put objections in the way of building the winery. In the end, planning permission was gained and a magnificent flint and brick building, complete with central tower and viewing gallery, atrium-cum-conservatory style servery, superb visitor centre and of course, well appointed wine making areas and underground storage cellars, was constructed. Today it is the very busy nerve centre of the operation. The shop and restaurant seem always to be filled with both local visitors and tourists, there are good conference facilities and it is widely used for this purpose.

The winery must be the finest in the UK in terms of facilities and equipment. Glass, tiles and stainless steel dominate and the place has the look of the Napa Valley, rather than the outskirts of leafy Dorking. It is magnificently equipped with over 500,000 litres of temperature controlled stainless steel tanks (mainly made in South Africa), two 8 tonne Sharfenburger Europresses, RDV and DE filters, a GAI fully automatic filler and Bertani labeller, a Clemens sparkling wine disgorging line and a whole host of other wine-making paraphanalia. Running through the winery are the hidden tracks of the 'people mover' that ferries visitors across its floors and down into its cellars.

The winemaking at Denbies has, over the years since the first harvest, been something of a roller coaster with winemakers coming and going at rather frequent intervals. The first winemaker was a German, Hans Schleifer, who arrived just at a time when most UK winemakers were attempting to shed the ersatz-Liebfraumilch image that English and Welsh wine had achieved for itself. Although some good wines were made – most noticeably some sweet wines and those made from the Bacchus grape – many did not really live up to the quality that the trade had been expecting. The General Manager at this time was a South African living in the UK, Michael Trull, whose marketing skills were brought to bear on selling the first few vintages. Special crested bottles were created and the presentation was (and remains) very good, but without the quality in the bottle, sales were slow and Denbies' reputation suffered.

The second winemaker was an Australian called Keith Bown. He supervised the 1995 vintage before returning home in 1996 just before the harvest. The third was Christopher Lindlar (a well-known English winemaker who had recently closed his own winery and was fortuitously available to take over) who was retained almost minutes before the first grapes of the 1996 season were harvested. He acted on a consultancy basis for two seasons, until the fourth arrived – a young New Zealand trained Englishman,

Nick Patrick, who is still there. However, for vintage 1999, the omnipresent flying winemaker, UK born but Australian trained, John Worontschak, was brought in to oversee production. Worontschak's style is – as one would imagine – more New World than Old, with an accent upon appealing, fresh fruity whites. His list of achievements in the field of English Wine (to say nothing of his overseas ventures) is impressive. His winemaking skills have won him the Gore-Browne Trophy five times, the President's Trophy three times, the Bernard Theobald (best red) four times, the Vintner's Trophy once and the Jack Ward Salver twice, to say nothing of the other awards and medals that wines either made by him or from wineries where he is a consultant, have won. However, despite making some exellent wines for them in both 1999 and 2000 (including the Bernard Theobald Trophy winner) his services were dispensed with in early 2001. Owner Adrian White has decided to concentrate on the visitor and tourist market and effectively withdraw Dendies' wines from sale to the trade and retailers.

Denbies most successful wines to date (in terms of award winning) have been ones that I am sure were never contemplated when the vineyards were planted. These are the 'Late Harvest' and 'Noble Harvest' dessert wines, made from a selection of varieties depending on the vintage and sugar content of the grapes. Their best to date, the 1992 'Noble Harvest' has a natural alcohol level of almost 22 per cent, an actual alcohol of 16½ per cent and was made from Optima and Ortega. Other dessert wines have been made from blends of Bacchus, Huxelrebe, Red Elbling and White Elbling. Wines made from Bacchus have also been relatively successful. Less successful have been the early oak aged and red wines although later vintages are much improved. The problem of having twenty different varieties, all cropping at different times and at different qualities and then trying to produce wines that the UK wine trade – always ready to knock English and Welsh wines whenever the opportunity presents itself – liked, was bound to be difficult. To do so on a scale such as this was never going to be easy.

With all the changes in the winemaking department, it is hardly surprising that the style of wines produced at Denbies in the past has changed with some regularity. It is to be hoped that with Worontschak's guiding hand – and he is without doubt one of the most experienced and arguably the most successful winemaker in the UK today – they will settle down. His immediate post-vintage harvest report for the 1999 wines tells of both excellent quantities and qualities of wines; 'over 15,000 litres of ink-black and full bodied red, 7,000 litres of velvety Pinot noir undergoing malolactic in new *barriques*, 30,000 litres of top MC [*méthode Champenoise*] base with great structure and finesse and near 2,000 litres of *botrytis* sweet with a natural potential alcohol of 28 per cent'. At the 2000 UKVA Wine of the Year Competition, Denbies walked away with a silver medal, the Jack Ward Memorial Salver and the Bernard Theobald Trophy for their 1999 Redlands, an oak aged 80 per cent Dornfelder and 20 per cent Pinot noir red and a clutch of bronzes and highly commendeds for the other 1999 wines they entered. On this result, Worontschak's appointment looks like it is paying off.

The final paragraph of Worontschak's harvest report perhaps sums up for the whole industry and not just for Denbies, the state of UK wines today:

'With the far greater understanding we now have of how to handle the viticulture and winemaking in this climate, a greater desire by the general public to buy local produce and the past and future investments of this industry, I am sure that finally wine of interest, quality and volume can be profitably produced in this country.'

There are perhaps a few winemakers who will chuckle at Worontschak's inclusion of the word 'finally' – but in essence he is correct. We have all been learning how to grow grapes and make wines and it has taken time. What is also certain is that Denbies, as the biggest vineyard in the UK and one of its most visited and noticed, must produce wines of real quality and interest if English and Welsh wines are to be taken seriously. It is to be hoped that, despite Worontschak's departure, they can continue to produce the standard seen with their 1999 and 2000 wines.

Furnace Brook Vineyard
Uphill, How Lane, Chipstead, Surrey, CR5 3LL

T: 01737 553600. F: 01737 553600

Owner: Colin Vaughan
Winemaker: Wines made at Chapel Down Wines
Directions: Vineyard not open to the public.

Vineyard Details: 1.08 ha of vines planted between 1990 and 1997. The south facing site is between 46 m and 53 m above sea level and the soil is Tunbridge Wells sand. The vines are all trellised on a 3 m × 1.5 m Scott Henry system.
Grape Varieties: Bacchus, Cabernet Franc, Kernling, Pinot noir, Reichensteiner.

Godstone Vineyard
Quarry Road, Godstone, Surrey, RH9 8DE

T: 01883 742367. F: 01883 743847. M: 07836 534112

Owners: Peter & June Deeley
Winemaker: Robert Deeley
Directions: From the M25 take the A22 north and Quarry Road is the first turning on the right (across the dual-carriageway).
Vineyard Details: Approx. 1.5 ha of vines planted between 1986 and 1993. The steeply sloping south facing slope overlooks the M25 and is between 183 m and 213 m above sea level and has an upper greensand soil. Vines are planted at 2.5 m × 1.25 m on a Double Guyot system.

Greyfriar's Vineyard
Quality Sparkling Wine
1996

"Produced by Traditional Methods"
CHARDONNAY / PINOT NOIR

Vinified and bottled by Lurgashall Winery for
GREYFRIARS VINEYARD
12% vol.   HOGS BACK, PUTTENHAM, GUILDFORD, SURREY   75cl.e.

Grape Varieties: Dornfelder, Schönburger, Seyval blanc.
Wine Sales & Vineyard Visits: Shop and restaurant open Monday to Friday, 10.30 am to 4.30 pm, Weekends, 10 am to 5.30 pm. Closed Christmas, Boxing and New Year's Days.

Godstone Vineyards must be one of the most widely seen vineyards in the country, perching as it does on steep hills overlooking Junction 6 of the M25. Whether all the motorists who see it realise what they are looking at is another matter! The vineyard has its own well stocked shop and a coffee house which offers morning coffee, light lunches teas etc. It also has an 'Adopt-a-Vine' scheme where members of the public can 'own' a vine for a year (or longer) and receive wine from vines of that variety.

Greyfriars Vineyard
Greyfriars Farm, The Hog's Back, Puttenham, Guildford, Surrey, GU3 IAG

F: 01483 811074

Owner: William Croxson
Winemaker: Wines made at Lurgashall Winery
Directions: Vineyard is situated on the Farnham bound carriageway of the Hog's Back, about 2 miles from Guildford before the Puttenham turning is reached.
Vineyard Details: 0.46 ha of vines planted in 1989 and 1990. The south facing site is between 100 m and 114 m above sea level and the soil is a clay loam over chalk. The vines are planted at 1.83 m × 1.52 m and Double Guyot pruned.
Grape Varieties: Chardonnay, Pinot noir.
Wine Sales & Vineyard Visits: The vineyard is not open on a regular basis. However, wine tastings and sales are arranged by personal contact. Fax for details. Greyfriars makes both still and sparkling wines.

Home Farmhouse Vineyard
Puttenham, Guildford, Surrey, GU3 IAR

T: 01483 810632

Owner & Winemaker: Dr Jonathan Whitaker
Directions: Take A31 Guildford to Farnham road travelling south

(Hog's Back) and then the B3000. Take the first right towards Puttenham. Vineyard is 200 yards on the right, opposite the church. *Vineyard Details:* 0.157 ha of vines planted between 1972 and 1990. The site is between 91 m and 107 m above sea level, south facing and mainly on a belt of clay between chalk and sand. The vines are planted at 1.83 m × 1.22 m and mostly single Guyot trained.

Grape Varieties: Chardonnay, Gagarin Blue, Gamay, Madeleine × Angevine 7672, Seyval blanc, Siegerrebe.

Wine Sales & Vineyard Visits: Only open by private arrangement for village 'Open Gardens' days. Interested growers are also welcome by appointment.

Dr Whitaker says that his vineyard is too small for commercial production – but too large for home consumption. Fearing unproductive years, more vines were planted in the 1970s in a fit of enthusiasm, but since his first harvest in 1975, only three years – 1980, 1981 and 1997 – have had such small crops that they were not worth bird netting. The wines are made on-site in an old brick and tile shed and is equipped with the usual small scale equipment found on a vineyard of this size. Of his varieties, Dr Whitaker prefers the Seyval blanc for reliability, the Siegerrebe for flavour (despite its vulnerability to wasp damage and the predations of pickers) and the Chardonnay *'pour acuter un peu de noblesse'* as Guy Salisbury-Jones used to say. His wines keep well and the 1989 is the current vintage!

Painshill Park Vineyard

Painshill Park, Portsmouth Road, Cobham, Surrey, KT11 1JE

T: 01932 868113. F: 01932 868001.
W: www.briansys.com/cobham/painshill

Owner: Painshill Park Trust Ltd
Vineyard Manager: Mark Ebdon
Winemaker: Wines made at Valley Vineyards
Directions: Take J10 off M25 (Painshill Junction) and take A245 towards Cobham. Entrance to the park is opposite the Territorial Army Centre, 200 metres east of the A245/A307 roundabout.
Vineyards Details: 0.73 ha of vines planted between 1992 and 1994 on a steeply sloping south facing site. The soil is a very light sandy

loam. The vines are spaced at 2.13 m × 1.2 m and are Single Guyot trained up individual poles.

Grape Varieties: Chardonnay, Pinot noir, Seyval blanc.

Wine Sales: Not yet available.

Vineyards Visits: April to October, Tuesday to Sunday and Bank Holidays 10.30 am to 6 pm (last entry 4.30 pm). November to March, telephone for details. Admission: Adults £3.80, OAPs, Students, UB40s, £3.30. Special group rates.

Painshill Park is one of Europe's finest eighteenth-century landscape gardens and was created by the Hon. Charles Hamilton between 1738 and 1773. He transformed barren heathland into ornamental pleasure grounds and parkland of dramatic beauty and contrasting scenery, dominated by a six hectare lake fed from the river by an immense waterwheel. The lake is overlooked by a steeply facing slope upon which is planted the vineyard. I had first seen the site in the early 1980s when I had accompanied Anthony Goddard (at that time owner of Barton Manor vineyard on the Isle of Wight) who had been invited to visit the site to advise on the possible replanting of the vineyard. Owing to the demands of the many other restoration projects in the park, the replanting of the vineyard was left for several years.

The establishment of the modern Painshill vineyard was part of the overall re-creation of Hamilton's masterpiece and as such, had to be as true to the original as possible. The only real record of how the vineyard looked were two paintings which show closely planted vines, trained up thin single poles, a type of training and pruning still seen on the Mosel and in vineyards in other steeply sloping regions. The modern vineyard, in order to accommodate a tractor and mower, was more widely spaced with rows at 2.13 m wide, although the vines were trained up individual poles at 1.2 m apart, but with pruning and training wires as in a normal vertically shoot positioned system.

The original varieties were said by Hamilton to be 'two sorts of Burgundy grapes, the Auvernat, which is the most delicate, but the tenderest, and the Miller grape, commonly called the black cluster, which is more hardy' and that the wine 'had a finer flavour than the best Champaign [sic] I ever tasted'. The decision therefore was taken to plant varieties suited for the production of bottle fermented sparkling wine. As a gesture to history, Chardonnay and Pinot noir were planted, but supplemented with Seyval blanc – a reliable variety with a good track record for producing sparkling wines in this climate.

The first task to be undertaken before the vineyard could be re-planted was the clearing of the site which was covered with immense Scot's Pines which had established themselves over the intervening two centuries. At that time I was winemaker at Lamberhurst Vineyards, then owned by Kenneth McAlpine, a member of the Sir Robert McAlpine construction company family, who volunteered, in the winter of 1989, to provide some heavy earth moving equipment and operators. (Kenneth, who at one time owned, and drove for, the 'Connaught' motor racing team, knew the site as he had once been part of a consortium who were considering buying it in order to build a racing circuit.) The site was duly cleared of trees and undergrowth, graded to a uniform slope and then sown with grass seed to stabilise the site. After two years the site was ready for replanting and in 1992, the first of the vines were planted (by me) some 230 years after the original vines had been put in. To my knowledge, it is the only vineyard today that occupies exactly the same site as an original pre-revival one.

The vines have been slow to establish – badgers, deer and rabbits have all had to be contended with – and over 1000 vines have had to be replanted. The first very small harvest of Pinot noir was taken in 1996 and was blended with some bought in Dunkelfelder to make a rosé. In 1997 and 1998 spring frosts affected the site and very few grapes were harvested. Yields in 1998 and 1999 were better, with the Seyval blanc producing most of the crop. They have been made into sparkling wine at Valley Vineyards and the first release was due for mid-2000. Vineyard manager Mark Ebdon says that his major problem is getting the acids of the Chardonnay down to a manageable level and keeping the birds off. Netting was tried once, but the costs proved prohibitive.

(A fuller history of this vineyard and its origins can be found in the historical section of this book.)

Send Vineyard
Tannery Lane, Ripley, Surrey
Address for correspondence:
Valley Vineyards, Stanlake Park, Twyford, Reading, Berkshire, RG10 0BN

T: 0118 9340176. F: 0118 9320914
E: vvineyards@aol.com

Owner: RMC Ltd
Winemaker: This vineyard is leased by Valley Vineyards
Directions: Vineyard not open to the public.
Vineyard Details: 1.89 ha of vines planted in 1976 and 1978. The level site is 20 m above sea level and the soil is a light loam over sand.
Grape Varieties: Gamay, Pinot noir, Seyval blanc.

This vineyard was one of two (the other was Kingsley Vineyard at Eversley near Basingstoke) which Bernard Theobald persuaded Ready Mixed Concrete's leisure division to plant on land that they had in their land 'bank'. Being situated above free-draining sand and gravel, the sites were thought very suitable for vines. Bernard – a doyen of the early vineyard revivalists who thought that (a) the Thames Valley had a climate superior to that of Bordeaux's and (b) GDC was the only planting system worth considering – had some strange ideas about vine varieties and did tend to persuade growers to put in reds which were hard to ripen. The Kingsley vineyard was fairly short lived as RMC decided to start quarrying, but the Send vineyard survives and is today leased by Jon Leighton from Valley Vineyards. All the grapes go into various Valley Vineyards blends and varietals.

The Pinot noir at Send has produced some very good fruit – especially in ripe years – and grapes from here were a major constituent of some of Valley Vineyards' award winning wines. The 1995 Valley Vineyards Clocktower Selection Pinot noir which won the Gore-Browne Trophy and Wine Guild of the UK Trophy in 1997 and the 1997 Valley Vineyards Clocktower Selection Pinot noir which won the President's Trophy and (fittingly) the Bernard Theobald Trophy, both had Send fruit in them.

Gamay (and here we are dealing with the Gamay Noir à Jus Blanc – not Gamay *teinturier* which is a different animal altogether and is to be found on only one site in the UK) is a difficult variety to ripen in a cool climate. In France it is most commonly found in the Mâcon *appellation* and of course Beaujolais – where temperatures are considerably warmer than in the UK – and along the Loire where it appears as Gamay de Touraine and in Anjou Rosé. It also appears in high-altitude Swiss vineyards, but is often blended with softer

Chasselas as high acids are a problem endemic to the variety. In the UK it is seldom found and to my knowledge, Send, with 0.78 ha of it, is the only vineyard with anything approaching a commercial area of the variety (although Biddenden in Kent have 0.40 ha of Gamay *teinturier* which is a clonal variant). Valley Vineyards have used the Gamay at Send to make some of their sparkling wines and the 1994 Clocktower Selection Gamay Sparkling won a bronze medal in the 1997 UKVA competition. This is probable its best use, except in a really hot year when more colour will develop and acids will be lower.

Jon Leighton likes the Send vineyard and says that its grapes are a useful addition to his portfolio of varieties. How long the vineyard will remain in existence is another matter as I am sure the returns from sand and gravel will be higher than from viticulture!

Thorncroft Vineyard
Thorncroft Drive, Leatherhead, Surrey, KT22 8JD

T: 01372 372159. F: 01372 363074
E: guywoodall@cs.com

Owner & Winemaker: Guy Woodall
Directions: Vineyard not open to the public.
Vineyards Details: Approx. 3.44 ha of vines planted in 1986 and 1988 on a 3.66 m × 2.44 m GDC system. The site is between 27 m and 30 m above sea level, sloping gently to the south-east.
Grape Varieties: Ortega. Pinot Noir. Reichensteiner. Schönburger.

Thorncroft have been producing wine since 1988 and are known for their late harvest wine made from Ortega. Whilst waiting for their first crop, they developed a range of non-alcoholic drinks based on elderflowers and are perhaps better known for their Elderflower Cordial and Elderflower 'Champagne' – over which a celebrated court case was fought and lost.

Ash Coombe Vineyard
Coombe Lane, Ash, Canterbury, Kent, CT3 2BS

T: 01304 813396

Owners: Paul & Isabel Lucas
Winemaker: Paul Lucas

Directions: The vineyard is signposted from the centre of Ash village. It is 10 miles from Canterbury and 3 miles from Sandwich.
Vineyard Details: Approx. 1.4 ha of vines planted between 1987 and 1989. The site is 200 m above sea level, south facing and the soil is a sandy loam. The vines are mainly planted on a 2 m × 1.5 m Double Guyot system.
Grape Varieties: Dornfelder, Kernling, Schönburger, Seyval blanc.
Wine Sales: The vineyard is open for wine sales at weekends from Easter to Christmas and during all school holidays. Monday to Saturday 11 am to 6 pm. Sunday 12 noon to 6 pm.
Vineyard Visits: Dates and times as above. £1 per person. Group tours by arrangement. Meals not available.

Ash Coombe is very much a working vineyard, run entirely by the proprietors. The winery is purpose built and equipped with stainless steel and high density polyethylene tanks, small crushing and pressing equipment, a filter and bottler. Total capacity is 15,000 litres. The wines are made into varietals, with the Dornfelder making both rosé and red. Red wines are something of a speciality and future plantings would definitely include more Dornfelder.

Barnsole Vineyard
Fleming Road, Staple, Canterbury, Kent, CT3 1LG

T: 01304 812530. M: 0370 482883
E: john@danilewicz.freeserve.co.uk. W: www.barnsole.co.uk

Owners: Dr John & Mr Adam Danilewicz
Winemaker: Dr John Danilewicz
Directions: Take the A257 from Canterbury and the first turning off the Ash bypass for the village. Turn first right into Durlock Road and after one mile, in the village of Staple, turn sharply left at the T-junction. The vineyard is on the left, a little past Leyham Garden Centre.
Vineyard Details: 1.39 ha of vines planted in 1993 on a south facing site between 17 m and 20 m above sea level. The soil is a heavy loam on clay. The vines are planted on a 2 m × 1.8 m Double Guyot system.
Grape Varieties: Huxelrebe, Madeleine × Angevine 7672, Reichensteiner, Schönburger.

Wine Sales: Open daily from April to October, 10.30 am to 6 pm. In the winter will close at dusk.

Vineyard Visits: Free 'mini-tours' available. Visitors will be shown how the vines are grown and tended, as well as the winery and how the wine is made. Full guided tours are available for groups at £1.50 per person. Group discounts available by prior arrangement. Meals are not available.

Barnshole vineyard was planted by the Danilewicz brothers after some 16 years of research into both varieties and growing systems. There is a well equipped insulated winery with a WP 500 Willmes pneumatic press, Rauch crusher, GAI eight head rotary filler and stainless steel tanks. There are also two separate insulated wine stores. Every effort is made to achieve high fruit quality by developing a large leaf area and by careful canopy management to compensate for the cooler UK climate. The grapes are all treated with pectinase and given 12–24 hrs skin contact prior to pressing to obtain as much varietal character as possible. All wines are entered

English Vineyards
Quality Wine psr

1996

Dry

Canterbury

Choice

11% vol

75cl e

Reichensteiner

Estate grown & bottled by
Barnsole Vineyard
Staple, Canterbury, Kent UK. CT3 1LG

Produce of the United Kingdom

248

for the UK's Quality Wine Scheme and to date only one has not passed. Further plantings will include Rondo.

Bayford House
Queen Street, Sandhurst, Cranbrook, Kent, TN18 5HR

T: 01580 850177

Owners: R F and F M Graham
Winemaker: Wines made at Tenterden Vineyard
Directions: Vineyard not open to the public.
Vineyard Details: 0.07 ha of vines planted in 1990 and 1994. The site is 90 m above sea level, south and south-east facing and the soil is Weald clay. The 360 vines are planted on a 2 m × 1 m Double Guyot system.
Grape Varieties: Schönburger, Seyval blanc.
Wine Sales and Vineyard Visits: The wine is not sold and visits are not possible.

This is a classic small amateur vineyard, planted on the site of an old orchard devastated by the 1987 hurricane. With the assistance of Chris Nicholas, from nearby Sandhurst Vineyards and Fred Hedger, around 300–400 bottles of wine are produced annually.

Bearsted Vineyard
24 Caring Lane, Bearsted, Maidstone, Kent, ME14 4NJ

T: 01622 736974. F: 01622 736974
E: enquiries@bearstedwines.co.uk. W: www.bearstedwines.co.uk

Owners: Dr John & Elizabeth Gibson
Winemaker: Dr John Gibson
Directions: Take junction 8 off the M20 and head west back towards Maidstone. After one mile turn south off the A20 into Caring Lane towards Langley. The vineyard will be found on the right-hand side after half a mile.
Vineyard Details: 1.6 ha of vines, planted between 1986 and 1995 on a south-west facing site, 49 m to 55 m above sea level. The soil is a fine sandy loam overlying Kentish ragstone. The vines are all trained on a modified Sylvoz system with 2.5 m wide rows and vines planted either at 1.8 m or 3.6 m apart in the row. Two thirds of the shoots are allowed to hang down either side of a high cordon (at

1.5 m from the ground), the remainder train themselves up through catch wires.

Grape Varieties: Bacchus, Dunkelfelder, Faberrebe, Kerner, Léon Millot, Seyval Blanc, Triomphe.

Wine Sales: Open all year, Monday to Saturday 10 am to 6 pm. Sundays by appointment only between noon and 5.30 pm.

Vineyard Visits: Individuals may walk the vineyard during opening hours at no charge. Guided tours of the vineyard and winery for groups of between 10 and 50 people are available by prior arrangement. A tutored tasting is part of the tour and the charge is £3 per person. Under 18's are free, but may not taste wine. Meals are not available.

Since their first vintage in 1989, the Gibsons have established themselves as one of the best 'boutique' vineyards in the country and ex-research chemist John Gibson (who is a Fellow of the Royal Society of Chemistry) has been making an ever increasing range of wines which consistently win awards and medals. In 1990 they won the prestigious Wine of the Year Trophy in the South East Vineyards

ENGLISH TABLE WINE

BEARSTED

75cl e   11.5% vol

**1996 BACCHUS
DRY**

Estate Bottled by JF and ER Gibson
Bearsted Vineyard Caring Lane Maidstone Kent
Produce of the United Kingdom

Association's annual competition with their Bacchus Dry and in the 1999 UKVA annual competition, the Vintner's Trophy for sparkling wines with their NV Bearsted Vineyard Brut.

Initially, the Gibsons wanted to plant Schönburger, but problems with obtaining stock of this variety led them to plant Bacchus. This variety is now their favourite owing to its excellent wine quality. The public also like its non-Germanic name and its Sauvignon blanc-like flavour. The grapes are picked in small batches and the vineyard will be passed through two to three times as the grapes ripen.

The winery is housed in old apple and pear cold stores which are well insulated with 4 in thick cork. The small pear store still has the original cooling equipment and can be refrigerated for the cold stabilization of wines. Equipment in the winery consists of a 500 litre Zambelli horizontal hydraulic press, Vigo crusher/destemmer and GAI monobloc filler. All wines are membrane filtered before bottling. Whenever possible, nitrogen pressure is used for filtering and bottling rather than pumps. Red, very dry and sparkling base wines are put through a malolactic fermentation in order to soften them.

There are eight wines on their current list including a red reserve, made from Léon Millot and Triomphe, a non-vintage bottle fermented sparkling and 'Bearsted Pimpernel' – a 'fresh and lively' rosé. This latter wine is named after the book, *The Scarlet Pimpernel* whose author, the Hungarian born Baroness Orczy, settled in Bearsted soon after its publication in 1905. There is also grape juice from the vineyard.

Biddenden Vineyards
Little Whatmans, Gribble Bridge Lane, Biddenden, Ashford, Kent, TN27 8DH

T: 01580 291726. F: 01580 291933
W: www.biddendenvineyards.co.uk

Owner & Winemaker: Richard Barnes
Directions: From Biddenden take the A262 towards Tenterden. After one and a half miles turn right on to the Benenden road. Take the next left and the vineyards and winery will be found after 150 m.
Vineyard Details: 8.1 ha of vines planted between 1972 and 1987. The site is between 52 m and 65 m above sea level, south and

south-east facing, in a small, sheltered valley. The soil is a sandy loam over Weald clay. Most of the vines are trellised on a 3.35 m × 1.22 m GDC system, although some are on a single curtain at the same spacing.

Grape Varieties: Dornfelder, Gamay *teinturier*, Huxelrebe, Müller-Thurgau, Ortega, Pinot noir, Reichensteiner, Schönburger.

Wine Sales: The vineyard is open for wine sales at the following times: March to December, Monday to Friday, 10 am to 5 pm. Saturday, 10 am to 5 pm. Sunday, 11 am to 5 pm. Bank Holidays 11 am to 5 pm. January and February, Monday to Friday, 10 am to 5 pm. Saturday, 11 am to 5 pm. Sundays, closed. The shop also closes from noon on Christmas Eve until 2 January. The vineyard has an off-licence for single bottle sales and wines may be tasted free-of-charge. In December the shop is stocked with a wide range of Christmas gifts and complimentary mince pies and mulled cider are served to all visitors.

Vineyard Visits: Visitors are welcome to look around the vineyards during the above opening times and free self-guided tour leaflet and map is available. Guided tours can also be arranged by appointment for groups of at least 15 adults at a charge of £2.85 per person. Tea, coffee, biscuits and ices are available at weekends and daily during

the summer. Meals for groups are available on request. A visit can be combined with a trip on the Kent & Sussex Steam Railway which runs from Tenterden Town Station or to the Brogdale Horticultural Trust at Faversham.

The Barnes came to Kent from their native Lancashire in 1958. Little Whatmans was at that time a fruit farm growing apples and in 1969 a small one third of an acre of vines was put in as an experiment. The first vintage was in 1974. Biddenden is the oldest vineyard in the south east and has been the inspiration for many of the region's other growers. It is also one of the largest farm cider makers in the country, making a wide range of apple products, including ciders, apple wines and apple juice. Today, the second (and in the school holidays, the third) generation of Barnes is fully involved with running the enterprise. Their cider was awarded the CAMRA 'Cider of the Year' award.

The winery is housed in a building formerly used for apple storage and grading, with the fermentation and storage tanks in the old cold stores. The winery is well equipped with a 22 hl Vaslin press, Imma separator and GAI monobloc filler. Most tanks are glass fibre. For the apples, a 6 tonne per hour Voran continuous belt press is used. The total capacity of the winery, for all products, is almost 500,000 litres. Over the years that Biddenden has been producing wines, it has achieved many awards and commendations, including in 1987, a gold medal and the Gore-Browne Trophy for the 'English Wine of the Year' with their 1986 Ortega. They also make a bottle fermented sparkling wine.

Challenden Vineyard
Sponden Lane, Sandhurst, Cranbrook, Kent, TN18 5NR

T: 01580 850522

Owner: Tom Hughes
Winemaker: Wines made at Tenterden Vineyard
Directions: Telephone for directions.
Vineyard Details: 0.62 ha of vines planted in 1991. Site is 30 m above sea level and the soil is a sandy clay loam. The vines are trellised on a 2 m × 1.4 m Pendlebogen system.
Grape Varieties: Faberrebe, Huxelrebe
Wine Sales & Vineyard Visits: By appointment only.

This vineyard no longer makes wine and the grapes find their way into Sandhurst Vineyard's wines. Challenden still has a 1993 sparkling wine for sale.

Chapel Down Wines Ltd

Tenterden Vineyard Park, Small Hythe, Tenterden, Kent, TN30 7NG

T: 01580 763033. F: 01580 765333
E: sales@chapeldownwines.co.uk
W: www.chapeldownwines.co.uk

Owner: Chapel Down Wines Ltd
Winemaker: Owen Elias
Directions: From A28 in Tenterden, take the B2082 Rye road. Vineyard is 2 miles on right-hand side.
Vineyard Details & Grape Varieties: See under Tenterden Vineyard Park.
Wine Sales & Vineyard Visits: See under Tenterden Vineyard Park.

This company traces its origins back to Chapel Farm vineyard on the Isle of Wight, owned by Anthony Pilcher. This vineyard had been planted and managed by Ken Barlow of nearby Adgestone vineyard and for a number of years the grapes had been incorporated into his wines. However, owing to a drop in sales, the arrangement had ended and Pilcher was contemplating what to do with his grapes. Jan Trzebski, owner of neighbouring Morton Manor vineyard, suggested that a close friend of his, David Cowderoy, with whom he had been at Wye College, might be interested in taking the grapes. David, son of Norman Cowderoy who had been growing grapes at Rock Lodge Vineyard since 1965, had recently returned from Australia where he had been studying winemaking at Roseworthy College.

David's idea was to start a winery, which would source its grapes from a number of vineyards and make wines on a much larger scale than most vineyards. This would bring about economies of scale in production and enable the wines to be professionally marketed. The company was formed in 1992 with Anthony Pilcher as Chairman, Nicky Branch, an accountant, as Managing Director, Carl Koenen, whose family had been in the wine trade since 1925 and who had become interested in English wines, as Sales Director and David as winemaker. The winery would concentrate on making a new style of English wine and would also specialise in making sparkling wines, a product they felt was very suited to our climate. They would also offer contract winemaking services for making both still and sparkling wines.

To start with, the winery at Rock Lodge vineyards was used as a base and grapes from both Chapel Farm and other vineyards were purchased and made into wine. The company soon outgrew these premises and in 1993 a building on a factory estate in Burgess Hill was rented and speedily transformed into a winery. For the next two vintages this was home to the fledgling enterprise. As volumes grew and as stocks of maturing wines, especially sparkling, became larger, it was obvious that another move would have to be made. A chance conversation between myself and Carl Koenen in February 1995 about the search for new premises led eventually to the company buying Tenterden Vineyards, the 25 ha farm, vineyards and winery that I had started in 1977. In September 1995, with the harvest already under way, the complete winery was shipped to Tenterden and re-assembled as best it could be, in between loads of grapes arriving to be pressed.

Since then, Chapel Down Wines has made a significant investment in both premises and facilities at Tenterden and today the winery is

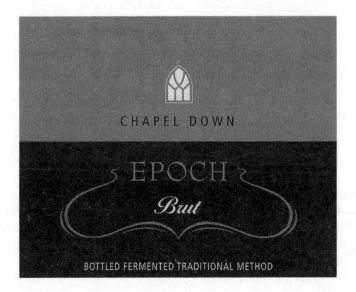

one of the best equipped in the UK. It has a bulk storage capacity of over one million bottles, all in stainless steel and mostly temperature controlled; presses are a Europress 8 tonne, a Diemme 6 tonne and a Willmes UP 1800 – all pneumatic; a Velo crusher/destemmer, a Velo Rotary Drum Vacuum filter and a Seitz fully automatic bottling line. It has three inclined plane drainage tanks for cold-soaking to extract maximum flavours from varieties such as Bacchus and Schönburger. It has eight computer controlled Gyro pallets for riddling sparkling wines, together with semi-automatic disgorging and dosage equipment. Storage capacity for finished product and maturing sparkling wines is in excess of 500,000 bottles. The vineyard has a well stocked shop, a café and very good function facilities. It is one of the most visited vineyards in the country.

Grapes are sourced today from a very wide selection of vineyards around the UK; 1999 saw grapes from 26 different vineyards arrive at the winery. Amounts purchased vary according to the vintage and stock requirements, but is usually in the 500–600 tonnes range. Some of the vineyards are under long-term contract to supply grapes, whereas some are bought on the spot market when the opportunity arises. Contract sparkling wines are also quite a speciality and are made for over twenty different vineyards.

From the outset, Chapel Wines decided to try and break the mould of English winemaking and refused to make the easy drinking ersatz-Liebfraumilch that other major vineyards seemed to think was what mass-market English wines ought to be. Wines are today slightly drier than many English wines, more akin to modern New World styles. Oak is used in all its forms – barrels, staves and chips – with considerable success. Wines made from Bacchus have become something of a trademark and its reds are a definite hit. Made from a blend of Rondo and Dornfelder, their Epoch and Epoch Reserve are amongst the very best of UK reds. The Epoch Brut sparkling, both vintage and non-vintage, is probably the most widely distributed English sparkling wine. The standard of winemaking at Chapel Down has always been very high and this is reflected in the number of awards and medals received over the years. Their tally in the 1999 UKVA competition is but a pointer to the past: the Gore-Browne Trophy, Jack Ward Memorial Salver and Dudley Quirk Memorial Trophy – all for their 1998 Bacchus, the

Wine Guild of the UK Trophy for their 1997 Schönburger and the McNie Trophy for their non-vintage Downland Oak. In the 2000 UKVA competition, they again won the McNie Trophy as well as the Dudley Quirk Memorial Trophy with the Downland Oak.

In late 1999, Cowderoy, who had always spent some of the spring months winemaking in the southern hemisphere, decided to leave Chapel Down to work full time as a flying winemaker. His long-time assistant, Owen Elias, has now taken over, assisted by two young winemakers, Andy Hollis and Hugh Girling. Together, they are continuing where David left off. Chapel Down's products are to be found in some of the major UK multiples – Tesco, Safeway, Sainsbury's and Waitrose – as well as a very wide variety of other outlets. Their largest customer is British Airways for whom they supply a medium dry white in quarter bottles.

In July 2000, a merger was announced between Chapel Down Wines, Lamberhurst Vineyards and Carr Taylor Vineyards. These three major players have joined together to form English Wines plc. All winemaking operations will be concentrated at the Tenterden site and the wineries at both Lamberhurst and Carr Taylor will no longer be used for winemaking. Lamberhurst's temperature controlled underground cellars will become the main storage area for the maturation of both Chapel Down's and Carr Taylor's bottle fermented sparkling wines. The combination of these three vineyards, with over 100 ha of vines under their ownership or contractual control and a million bottles worth of winemaking capacity, should give them the economies of scale to make a significant impact on the market with their products

The struggle to make commercial quantities of sound (and some-times really quite exciting) wine in this climate for sale in the very price-sensitive UK market is never ending and will always be a challenge. Chapel Down is still a young operation and the challenge continues. As part of English Wines plc and with the other two similarly sized operations (Three Choirs and Denbies) they have the chance to open up the market to English wines and show both trade winebuyers and retail consumers that really good quality and good value wines can be made in this climate. As someone who has been deeply involved with both this company and with the industry as a whole, I can only admire what has been achieved and wish them all the best for the future.

Chiddingstone Vineyard
Vexour Farm, Chiddingstone, Edenbridge, Kent, TN8 7BB

T: 01892 871400. F: 01892 870878. M: 07887 780574
E: sales@chiddingstone.demon.co.uk. W: www.winespy.co.uk

Owners: Mr J P Quirk & Mr M Quirk
Winemaker: Charles Capbern-Gasqueton
Directions: Take Chiddingstone Causeway to Chiddingstone road. Entrance to vineyard through wrought iron gates by humpback bridge over river.
Vineyard Details: 14.43 ha of vines planted between 1978 and 1992 on various sites between 61 m and 76 m above sea level. Soils vary from alluvial silty clay near to the river to mottled clay on higher ground. The vines are almost all planted on a 4 m × 1.4 m GDC system.
Grape Varieties: Bacchus, Brandt, Chasselas, Faberrebe, Kerner, Kernling, Madeleine × Angevine 7672, Pinot blanc, Pinot Meunier, Pinot noir, Reichensteiner, Rondo, Seyval Blanc, Triomphe.
Wine Sales & Vineyard Visits: Visitors are welcome by appointment. Telephone 01892 871400.

Chiddingstone Vineyards is on a 400 acre arable and stock farm situated in the valley of the River Eden. The countryside in this part of Kent is some of the county's finest and the nearby village of Chiddingstone, lovingly protected by the National Trust, is well worth a visit.

The vineyard was established by Dudley Quirk, who sadly died in 1999 and is today owned by his two sons, who together with a French winemaker and a (Scottish sounding) manager, Alastair Maclean, manage what is one of the UK's largest winegrowing enterprises.

The winery at Chiddingstone Vineyards is in converted brick and tile cattle buildings, situated around an attractive cobbled courtyard, now roofed over with a 'vast plastic dome'. The winery is well equipped with a Willmes hydraulic press, Chemo harvest trailer and GAI automatic filler which can handle both PET and glass quarter bottles. Fermentation is in glass fibre and stainless tanks and some wines are matured in 225 lt French oak barrels.

The emphasis at Chiddingstone is very much on producing wines in the French style, dry with plenty of body, and with a good keeping potential and over the years they have scored some significant sales successes, especially where the Royal family is concerned. Their wines have found their way onto the menu at the House of Commons when the Speaker hosted a dinner for the Queen Mother in 1990, at Buckingham Palace when the Queen entertained the G7 leaders in 1991, at the British Embassy in Paris in 1992 when the Queen hosted a dinner for President Mitterand and again by the Speaker when the Prince of Wales came to dine in 1992. They also supply a number of other British Embassies, as well as quarter bottles to Air UK. They make quite a wide range of wines including a red from Triomphe which gets good reviews, an oak aged Pinot noir and Pinot Meunier and a varietal Chasselas.

Clay Hill Vineyard
Shepherds Lodge, Clay Hill Road, Lamberhurst, Kent, TN3 8LT

T: 01892 891356. F: 01892 891356

Owner: Carole Lamond
Winemaker: Wines made at Davenport Vineyards
Directions: Not open to the public.
Vineyard Details: 2.63 ha of vines planted in 1987 and 1988. The

south facing site is between 50 m and 61 m above sea level with a sandy clay/loam topsoil and clay subsoil. Most vines are trellised on a 2.5 × 1.6 m Double Guyot system.
Grape Varieties: Bacchus, Huxelrebe, Pinot noir, Reichensteiner, Schönburger, Zweigeltrebe.

Clay Hill (formerly Bayham Abbey) vineyard was taken over by the present owners quite recently and is at present undergoing extensive re-trellising and refurbishment after some years of neglect. It is hoped to be back in full production in 2000/2001.

Conghurst Vineyard
Conghurst Lane, Hawkhurst, Kent, TN18 4RW

T: 01580 752634. F: 01580 752634

Owner: Miss Julia Bridgwater
Winemaker: Wines made at Battle Wine Estate
Directions: Conghurst Lane runs between the A268 and A229 and the vineyard is about half way along on a sharp corner.
Vineyard Details: 0.2 ha of vines planted in 1978 on GDC.
Grape Variety: Chasselas.
Wine Sales & Vineyard Visits: By appointment.

Elham Valley Vineyards
Breach, Barham, Canterbury, Kent, CT4 6LN

T: 01227 831266. F: 01227 456963

Owner: Vale of Elham Trust
Winemaker: Mathew Gurney
Directions: On B2065 between Elham and Barham on left-hand side.
Vineyard Details: 0.72 ha of vines planted between 1980 and 1998. The site is mainly level and approx. 64 m above sea level. The soil has a high chalk and flint content.
Grape Varieties: Müller-Thurgau, Reichensteiner, Seyval blanc.
Wine Sales: January to December, Monday to Friday, 9.30 am to 5 pm (or dusk if earlier). Weekends, noon to 6 pm (or dusk if earlier).
Vineyard Visits: At above times. Guided tours for groups (min. 10 people) available by appointment. Also pottery workshop, arts and crafts shop, tea room.

This vineyard is now owned by the Vale of Elham Trust, a registered charity providing learning facilities and working opportunities for the disabled, some of whom live on site. In the past its wines have done well in competitions. The 1992 Canterbury Celebration sparkling wine was the South East Wine of the Year in 1994.

Hadlow Down Vineyard
The Brooms, Tinkers Lane, Hadlow Down, East Sussex, TN22 4ET

T: 01825 830420

Owners: Tony & Brenda Honess
Winemaker: Tony Honess
Directions: Take A272 Maresfield to Hadlow Down road. Turn right into Tinkers Lane. Vineyard is 100 yds on left-hand side.
Vineyard Details: 0.56 ha of vines planted between 1980 and 1999. The south facing site is between 107 m and 114 m above sea level and the soil is a sandy loam over Tunbridge Wells sandstone. The vines are all planted at 2.13 m × 1.37 m and Double Guyot trained.
Grape Varieties: Müller-Thurgau, Pinot noir, Reichensteiner, Triomphe.
Wine Sales & Vineyard Visits: By appointment only. Guided tours for groups available.

Wines from this vineyard include both varietals and blends, a red from the Triomphe and a bottle fermented sparkling wine.

Harden Vineyard
Grove Road, Penshurst, Nr Tonbridge, Kent, TN11 8DX

T: 01892 870221

Owners: Robert & Mrs K Cole, Mrs J Patty, Mrs D Gray
Winemaker: Wines made at Chapel Down Wines
Directions: Take the Fordcombe road from Penshurst village
(B2188) and turn right 150 yards past a narrow bridge into Grove
Road. Go up the hill, past Penshurst Vineyards entrance, and
Harden Farm will be found on the right-hand side.
Vineyard Details: 5 ha of vines planted between 1986 and 1988.
The south and southwest facing site is between 46 m and 53 m
above sea level and has Tunbridge Wells sand and Wadhurst Clay
soils. The vines are all GDC trained and planted at 3.66 m × 2.44 m.
Grape Varieties: Bacchus, Huxelrebe, Regner, Reichensteiner,
Schönburger.
Wine Sales & Vineyard Visits: By appointment only.

This vineyard's 1996 Schönburger came third in the Country
Landowners English and Welsh wine competition. It is also a
member of Partnership Wines Ltd.

Harden Vale

TABLE WINE OF ENGLAND

DESSERT WINE
1995

IN ASSOCIATION WITH PARTNERSHIP WINES

Produced by Harden Vineyard, Penshurst, Kent
Bottled by W1464

37.5cl ℮   9.5% vol

Produce of the United Kingdom

Horsmonden Vineyards
Hazel Farm, Horsmonden, Kent
Address for correspondence:
Davenport Vineyards, Limney Farm, Castle Hill, Rotherfield,
Crowborough, East Sussex, TN6 3RR

T: 01892 852380. F: 01892 852781
E: will@davenportvineyards.co.uk
W: www.davenportvineyards.co.uk

Owner: Will Davenport
Winemaker: Wines made at Davenport Vineyards
Directions: Vineyard not open to the public.
Vineyard Details: 2.03 ha of vines planted in 1991. The south
facing site is between 80 m and 90 m above sea level and the soil is
a clay sand loam. The vines are all planted at 2.7 m × 1.5 m, mainly
Double Guyot trained, but the Ortega is single cordon pruned and
the Triomphe is Scott Henry trained.
Grape Varieties: Bacchus, Faberrebe, Huxelrebe, Ortega, Siegerrebe,
Triomphe.
Wine Sales & Vineyard Visits: see details under Davenport Vineyards.

The vineyards are farmed using minimum inputs of fungicides and
no herbicides, insecticides or any artificial fertilisers are used.

Kempes Hall Vineyard
Kempes Corner, Ashford, Kent, TN25 4ER

T: 01233 812217. F: 01233 813109

Owner: Tony Denne
Winemaker: Wines made at Tenterden Vineyard
Directions: Vineyard not open to the public.
Vineyard Details: 0.10 ha of vines planted in 1976. The site is level and
the vines are planted at 1.83 m × 1.37 m and Double Guyot trained.
Grape Varieties: Chardonnay, Schönburger, Seyval blanc.

This vineyard was planted by the late Charles Laughton (not the
actor!), one of the very early pioneers and great supporters of
English wine, who bravely introduced it onto the wine list of the
Commonwealth Club when he was on their wine committee.
Charles is remembered by a trophy named after him which is
awarded to the runner-up in the South East Wine of the Year

competition. Today, it is owned by Tony Denne and the grapes usually go into the collective blend produced at Tenterden Vineyards for smaller growers.

Knowle Hill Vineyard
Ulcombe, Maidstone, Kent
Address for correspondence:
159 Kennington Park Road, London, SE11 4JJ

T: 020 7735 5135. F: 020 7735 1470

Owner: Ian Grant
Winemaker: Wines made at Tenterden Vineyards
Directions: Vineyard not open to the public.
Vineyard Details: 0.05 ha of vines planted in 1978 on a 2 m × 1.5 m Double Guyot system. The site is south facing, some 60 m above sea level and has a clay soil.
Grape Varieties: Müller-Thurgau, Pinot noir.

Lamberhurst Vineyards
Ridge Farm, Lamberhurst, Kent, TN3 8ER

T: Office: 01892 89000, Shop: 01892 890412. F: 01892 891137
E: chris.brown@stenoak.co.uk

Directions: Take A21 London to Hastings road. In centre of Lamberhurst village, turn right onto B2100 and follow signs for vineyard. Entrance is in Bayham Abbey Road.
Vineyard Details: 10.64 ha of vines planted between 1975 and 1990 on 2 m × 1 m, 2m × 1.4 m and 2.6 m × 1.5 m Double Guyot and 3.66 m × 2 m GDC. The site is predominantly north facing between 50 m and 86 m above sea level. The soil is a clay loam over Tunbridge Wells sandstone.
Grape Varieties: Bacchus, Kerner, Müller-Thurgau, Reichensteiner, Rondo, Schönburger, Seyval blanc.
Wine Sales & Vineyard Visits: Open daily, 10 am to 5 pm.

The Lamberhurst story started in 1971 when Kenneth McAlpine, a member of the Sir Robert McAlpine construction company family, thought that some land that had just been purchased overlooking the village, would be suitable for vines. Although the land was north facing, it was well sheltered from the prevailing south-westerly winds, quite steeply sloping and had often produced early crops of raspberries, strawberries and other fruit. Vines would fit in well with some of the other crops being grown on the McAlpine farms, which included both hops and fruit. Bob Reeves, his farm manager, who was fluent in German from his time in the services, visited Germany and went to Geisenheim to see Professor Kiefer who suggested varieties and trellising systems that could be used. In 1972 an initial 3.64 ha were planted; Müller-Thurgau, Seyval Blanc and Madeleine Angevine, all on a 2.6 m by 1.3 m Pendlebogen training system. In 1974 Professor Kiefer came over from Geisenheim to see how the first plantings were coming along, and encouraged by his advice, another 1.6 ha were planted the following year.

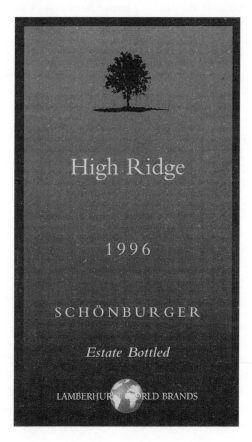

High Ridge

1996

SCHÖNBURGER

Estate Bottled

LAMBERHURST WORLD BRANDS

In the spring of 1974, Ridge Farm was purchased and a winery installed in what had been the old apple grading room. Reeves had always looked more to Germany than to France for help and encouragement and for the first vintage in 1974, two young Germans, Ernst Abel, who worked at Geisenheim and Karl-Heinz Schmitt, a young graduate, came over for the vintage. Abel returned soon after the harvest, leaving Schmitt to carry on. Only 700 bottles of 1974 wine were produced, with quite a few grapes having been lost before harvest to birds and *botrytis*. The following year, 1975, was generally a good year for English vineyards and some 7000 bottles were made from their own vineyards. In addition they began taking in grapes from other vineyards, and making wines under contract.

In 1976, Schmitt decided to return home, and another young winemaker was sought. In September, just before the harvest, Karl-Heinz Johner, also a graduate from Geisenheim, came over with his wife and two young children, and took over as winemaker.

The 1976 harvest was large and showed that the existing winery was far from adequate, and for the next harvest a brand new winery, certainly the largest in the United Kingdom, and equipped to a better standard than many on the Continent, was built. On two floors, with underground fermentation and storage cellars capable of holding 300,000 litres, with an insulated bottle store with a capacity of 500,000 bottles, with its presses, centrifuge and fully automatic bottling line, it was, for many, the proof they needed that English Wine had arrived.

In 1977 another 5.24 ha of vines were planted, bringing the total up to 10 ha and in 1979 another 4 ha making them by far and away the largest vineyard in the country. It was not all plain sailing, however. The initial acreage of Madeleine Angevine proved very unsatisfactory, with many plants dying and the remainder refusing to crop. They were grubbed up in 1975. They were replaced with Ortega which a neighbour promptly sprayed with 2-4-5-T weed-killer, killing over half of them! During 1975, areas of newly planted vines appeared to be dying for no apparent reason. Professor Stelwag-Kittler was brought over from Geisenheim to see if he could see what the problem was. A flight for him in McAlpine's helicopter over both Lamberhurst's and some nearby vineyards failed to pinpoint the cause. However, one of the women working in the vineyards noticed a small grub emerging from a dead vine and it transpired that the dock sawfly had taken to laying its eggs in the stems of the young vines, and the hatching larvae were the problem. This was put right by getting rid of the docks in the vineyards and covering the grafts of newly planted vines with grafting wax.

Harvests during the period from 1977 to 1981 were generally poor, and it was at this time that the spare capacity in the new winery was put to good use by the production of a 'British Wine'. The first batch was made from a quantity of table grapes destined for Covent Garden that had become over ripe in transit and the resulting wine was known as 'Olympus', named after the variety of grape used. As production grew, it was decided to use fresh grape juice from Germany, and the name was changed to 'Festival'. At this time, British Made-Wines (as they were officially called) carried a lower rate of duty to either imported or home produced wines, and this enabled Festival to be sold at a very competitive rate.

With the advent of the huge 1983 crop in England however, the decision was taken to drop the production of Festival, much to the relief of many growers of English Wines who felt that too much confusion was being caused. This relief was short lived, as in 1984, with another large crop of grapes harvested from vineyards all over the country, and over 1 million bottles in store in both tank and bottle, McAlpine took the decision to cut the retail price of his basic English Wine, the blended 'Lamberhurst White', to an unheard of price of £1.99, together with matching wholesale prices! Sales of this wine naturally took off and suddenly there was an English Wine which could be found on the shelves of wine merchants all over the country, spreading the word that the product was good, available, and at that price, no longer the elitist product it had seemed to be to many wine drinkers and, perhaps more importantly, wine merchants as well.

The harvests between 1982 and 1986 were relatively good for the south-east, and during this period Lamberhurst was able to consolidate its position as the leading vineyard in the country. The vineyards were extended to over 20 ha and the output of wine increased; a Grape Purchase Scheme was started which contracted growers in other parts of the country to supply grapes on a regular basis and a range of services from winemaking to vineyard management as well as a wide variety of supplies for both vineyards and wineries were offered for sale.

In 1988, Johner, who since 1982 had been commuting weekly between Lamberhurst and his home and vineyards in Baden, decided to leave. He had recently started selling wines from his German vineyards here in England and this was taking more and more of his available time. He decided that he could no longer devote enough time to the Lamberhurst operations and, after an exchange of views with the management, thought it best to leave. His 12-year period as winemaker had been one of remarkable changes for both Lamberhurst and English Wine in general. Whilst he was winemaker, the winery won many awards and medals for both its own wines and the many it made under contract. Their 1982 Huxelrebe (made with grapes purchased from Bill Ash's Staple Vineyards) and their 1984 Schönburger both won the Gore-Browne Trophy. Their wines were regularly awarded the EVA's Seal of Quality. During Johner's time at Lamberhurst he started experimenting with oak aged, bottle fermented sparkling and red wines. With the generous backing of McAlpine he was able to use techniques and equipment unavailable to most UK wineries at the time and did much to pave the way for today's wine styles. Lamberhurst's wines from this era were sometimes criticised for being too 'Germanic' and for their over-reliance on imported 'suss-reserve' which was used quite liberally in most of the more popular and widely distributed wines. With hindsight, this is probably a fair observation, but the popular market for wines was then very different to today's and almost all the top selling brands were Liebfraumilch or of a similar style. He also started production of their successful range of fruit liqueurs. Lamberhurst's success during these halcyon days was due in a large measure to the support given it by McAlpine who invested heavily in all aspects of the business. He was an enthusiastic and generous supporter of many aspects of the English wine industry and without this support, its wines would not be as well know as they are today. He was awarded the OBE in the 1997 New Year's Honours list for 'Services to English Wine'.

In July 1988 I was asked by McAlpine to take over from Johner. After considerable deliberation and a promise from McAlpine that I would be free for three months at the start of 1989 to write the first edition of this guide to vineyards in the UK, I agreed. It was not an easy decision to make because only two years before I had sold my vineyard and winery at Tenterden with the intention of spending my time writing in the summer and contract winemaking in the winter. However, running Lamberhurst, then the largest producer of English wines, was a challenge I felt I could not let pass. For the three years that I was there, things more or less continued where Johner had left off. More vineyards were planted including 0.75 ha of the new red *vitis Amurensis* hybrid Rondo which had been on trial from Geisenheim and 5 ha of Seyval blanc which had proved over its years the most productive variety on the farm. I also like to think that I, together with Stephen Donnelly (Assistant Winemaker since 1987) made some interesting wines and we were all pleased, in 1990, to win both the Gore-Browne Trophy and Wine Guild of the UK Trophy with the 1988 Schönburger. It was also during this time that Lamberhurst launched the first brandy made from English Wine – an event which seemed greatly to interest the media. In 1991, after three years as both General Manager and Winemaker, during which time substantial improvements to both the visitor and office facilities had been carried out, I decided that I would continue where I left off – making wine under contract and writing.

At the same time, McAlpine decided that as he was now approaching retirement age he would like to retire from active management of the business and started to look for a purchaser for the whole enterprise. Perhaps not surprisingly, this took a considerable while – an undertaking of this size was bound to take time to find the right buyer – and it wasn't until late 1994 that buyers emerged and then not for all of the property. The area of vineyards had already been reduced during the three years that the winery was up for sale and only the 10.6 ha of vines at Ridge Farm, which surround the winery, were purchased by the new owners, Paul Cooper and Derek McMillen. They proposed to use the facilities and the well-known name of Lamberhurst to import and sell a range of foreign wines, in addition to continuing the English wine business. Unfortunately, trading conditions did not favour them and in March 1998 their company was put into administration and although it continued to trade, the property was once again sold at the end of 1999.

The new owners are the locally based major fencing contractor, Stenoak Fencing, who have established their offices and depot there and who are in the process of revitalising the vineyard. A shop has once again been opened and there are plans to build a new shop and visitor centre. In July 2000, a merger was announced between Lamberhurst Vineyards, Chapel Down Wines and Carr Taylor Vineyards. These three major players have joined together to form English Wines plc and with over 100 ha of vines under their ownership or contractual control and a million bottles worth of winemaking capacity, it should have the economies of scale to make a significant impact with its products. Although the winery at Lamberhurst will no longer be used for winemaking, the temperature controlled underground cellars will become the major storage area for Chapel Down's and Carr Taylor's bottle fermented sparkling wines.

Before Lamberhurst Vineyards was a force on the English Wine scene, the industry used to be thought of as one dominated by retired servicemen, the gentleman farmer, and the enthusiastic amateur. The wines in the early days were made to appeal to an elitist consumer and not for the generality of High Street wine buyers. The Lamberhurst operation however, was something else. It was big and professional, it made wines to appeal to ordinary wine drinkers, and what was more, ordinary wine drinkers seemed to want to buy them. More than any other vineyard in modern times, it helped establish English Wine as a commercial product.

Leeds Castle Vineyard
Leeds Castle, Broomfield, Maidstone, Kent, ME17 1PL

T: 01622 765400. F: 01622 735616
E: derekhorton@leeds-castle.co.uk. W: www.leeds-castle.co.uk

Owner: Leeds Castle Enterprises Ltd
Winemaker: Wines made at Tenterden Vineyards
Directions: Exit 8 off the M20. Entrance to Leeds Castle off B2163.
Vineyard Details: 1.31 ha of vines planted in 1980 and in 2000. The south facing site is between 85 m and 105 m above sea level and the soil is a sandy clay loam. The vines are planted at 2 m × 1.5 m and are all Double Guyot trained.
Grape Varieties: Müller-Thurgau, Reichensteiner, Schönburger, Seyval blanc.
Wine Sales & Vineyard Visits: Vineyard is within Leeds Castle grounds. Open daily except Christmas Day, the last Saturday in June and the first Saturday in July, March to October, 10 am to 5 pm, November to February 10 am to 3 pm. Admission is charged.

Wine is available from the Castle shop and catering outlets. Telephone 0870 600 8880 for recorded information of up-to-date news. Guided tours of the vineyard are available by arrangement. Telephone Mrs Judy Murray 01622 765400.

The Domesday Book of 1086 recorded that there was a vineyard of one acre at Leeds Castle, planted by Bishop Odo, half brother to William the Conqueror. Further evidence of viticulture at Leeds Castle is to be found in a register of the expenses of King Edward I and his queen, Eleanor of Castile, dated 1291–3 which states that 'Arnold the vinedresser' was to be paid 20 shillings 'for his outgoings and expenses at the vineyards of Leeds'. The present vineyard was planted in 1980 and was formally opened by Mr Peter Walker, the then Minister of Agriculture. The vineyard today produces on average 5000/6000 bottles a year, all of which is used at Castle functions or sold from the Castle shop. The vineyard was expanded in 2000 with an additional 0.27 ha of Reichensteiner and Schönburger. In 2000, their 1998 Seyval blanc was awarded the Charles Laughton Trophy in the SEVA's annual competition. Their 1998 Müller-Thurgau was also highly praised by the judges and

MEDIUM DRY WHITE WINE
Estate grown in the
Leeds Castle Vineyard
Müller-Thurgau 1998

was one of the final six wines in the competition. I am happy to say that I had a hand in making both these wines!

Leeds Castle is also the home of the Leeds Castle Festival of English Food and Wine, held in mid-May, which features many vineyards from the south-east of the country. Leeds Castle offers a wide variety of attractions to visitors, and apart from the beautiful Castle, has Aviaries, a Maze and Secret Grotto, Dog Collar Museum, superb catering facilities in the Fairfax Hall and a Golf Course. Throughout the year there are a number of special events including a Celebration of Easter, International Balloon Fiesta, Open Air Concert, November Firework Display and the famous Open Air Concerts held in mid-summer.

Lewins Vineyards

Lewins, Main Road, Crockham Hill, Edenbridge, Kent, TN8 6RB

T: 01732 867788

Owner & Winemaker: Derek Roberts
Directions: Vineyard not open to the public.
Vineyard Details: 0.13 ha of vines mainly planted in 1982. The south facing site is approx. 110 m above sea level and the soil is a sandy clay loam. The vines are planted at 1.5 m × 1.5 m and both GDC and Double Guyot trained.
Grape Varieties: Dornfelder, Müller-Thurgau, Pinot noir, Seyval blanc.

This is a small vineyard making (when harvests permit), white, rosé, light red and sparkling wines.

Little Knoxbridge Vineyard

Little Knoxbridge Barn, Knoxbridge, Staplehurst, Kent, TN12 0EU

T: 01580 893643

Owner: Paul Loftus
Winemaker: Wines made at Tenterden Vineyard
Directions: One mile south of Staplehurst on A229, Maidstone to Cranbrook road, on right-hand side. Vineyard not open to the public.
Vineyard Details: 0.16 ha of vines planted in 1983. The site is 60 m

above sea level, flat and the soil is a silty clay. The vine are planted at 2 m × 1.3 m and are all Double Guyot trained.
Grape Variety: Auxerrois.

This vineyard was for many years owned by Bob Grilli, but sold to the present owner in 1996. Paul Loftus now runs it as a partnership with three friends and both still and sparkling wine are made, mainly for home consumption.

Mayshaves Vineyard
Mayshaves Farm, Woodchurch, Kent, TN26 3PT

T: 01233 820286

Owners: Roy & Violet Adams
Winemaker: Wines made at Davenport Vineyards.
Directions: Vineyard not open to the public.
Vineyard Details: 0.16 ha of vines planted in 1982. The north facing site is 40 m above sea level and the soil is Wealden clay. The vine are all GDC trained at 3.66 m × 2.44 m.
Grape Varieties: Müller-Thurgau, Reichensteiner, Seyval blanc.

Meopham Valley Vineyard
Wrotham, Kent
Address for correspondence:
Norway House, Wrotham Road, Meopham, Kent, DA13 0AU

T: 01474 812727. F: 01474 812727
w: www.yell.co.uk/sites/meopham-valley-wines

Owners: Pauline & David Grey
Winemaker: Wines made at Sedlescombe Organic Vineyard and Chapel Down Wines
Directions: Take the A227 from Gravesend. In Meopham village turn left by cricket green, go down the track by the old oast house and the vineyard is on the left-hand side when entering the valley.
Vineyard Details: 1.93 ha of vines planted in 1991. The south east facing site is between 107 m and 137 m above sea level and the soil is loam with a limestone subsoil. The vines are planted at 1.83 m × 1.23 m and Double Guyot trained.
Grape Varieties: Chardonnay, Léon Millot, Madeleine × Angevine 7672, Pinot noir, Pinot gris, Reichensteiner, Triomphe.

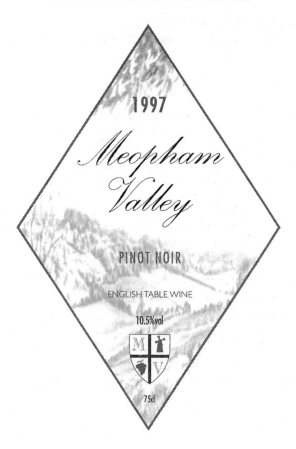

Wine Sales: By appointment.
Vineyard Visits: Group tours available (max. 25 people) by arrangement.

Accountant David Grey and his wife Pauline set this vineyard up with the help and encouragement of the late Gillian Pearkes and attended a course at her vineyard in Devon (Yearlstone). Only sulphur and copper are used to guard against disease and no other fungicides, pesticides or herbicides are used in the vineyard. The vineyard is fertilised by mulching the vine prunings and using the 'services' of a flock of sheep from the adjacent farm between harvest and the start of pruning. The first harvest was in 1994 and they now sell a range of wines including a red and a sparkling.

Mount Ephraim Vineyard

Mount Ephraim Gardens, Hernhill, Faversham, Kent, ME13 9TX

T: 01227 751496. F: 01227 750940
W: www.mistral.co.uk/hammerwood/ephraim

Owner: Sandys Dawes
Directions: Follow signs to Boughton from A2 or to Hernhill from A299.
Vineyard Details: 0.43 ha of vines planted in 1985. The north-east facing site is 30 m above sea level, has a brickearth soil and the vines are planted at 2.59 m × 1.52 m and Double Guyot trained.
Grape Varieties: Müller-Thurgau, Reichensteiner.
Wine Sales & Vineyard Visits: Easter to mid-September, daily 1 pm to 6 pm, except closed on Tuesdays and Fridays. Cream Teas are served in the Edwardian kitchen. There is also a craft centre. Entry fee charged. Guided tours and meals for groups, including morning coffee, lunches, teas and supper available by arrangement.

Mount Ephraim has been home to the Dawes family for over 300 years and the current house is a splendid Victorian mansion built in 1870. It is situated in beautiful north Kent countryside with views over the Swale and Thames estuaries. The vineyard is within over 9 acres of superb gardens open to the public, including a Japanese rock garden, topiary garden, rose terraces and a lake.

National Vine Collection

Brogdale Horticultural Trust, Brogdale Farm, Brogdale Road, Faversham, Kent, ME13 8XZ

T: 01795 535286 & 535642. F: 01795 531710
E: info@brogdale.org.uk. W: www.brogdale.org.uk

Owner: Brogdale Horticultural Trust
Chief Executive: Lady Jane Garrett
Directions: Take M2 and leave at J6 Faversham (A251). Join A2 towards Sittingbourne and take second on left into Brogdale Road. Continue for 1 mile.
Vineyard Details: 0.24 ha of vines, first planted in 1992, as a varietal collection. The site is level, situated at 48 m above sea level and the soil is colluvium and mixed drift over chalk (a mixture of brickearth and clay with flints).

Grape Varieties: Over 100.
Vineyard Visits: Brogdale's gift shop, plant centre and tea rooms are open daily all year round from 9.30 am to 5.30 pm. The orchards are open for tours from Good Friday until late November. See website for current details.

The vineyards at Brogdale were established in 1992 when they planted 50 vines each of every recommended and authorised variety permitted to be grown in the UK. They also inherited a collection of vines – mainly table and ornamental – from the Royal Horticultural Society's Wisley gardens and another collection from the late Gillian Pearkes's Yearlstone vineyard. The Ministry of Agriculture, Fisheries and Food contributed to the initial establishment costs of the vineyard and the Vintner's Company to its expansion.

The vineyard is intended to be experimental and as a gene bank for the future and is not run as a vineyard for the production of wine. There are at least two other vineyards and/or nurseries that claim to have national vine collections – Hales Nursery of Loddon in Norfolk have a collection of greenhouse grapes and Yearlstone a collection of outdoor vines. Brian Edwards at Sunnybank Vineyard and Vine Nursery, whilst not claiming National Collection status, probably has the best collection of vines and has many of them for sale. Plumpton College has a collection of rootstock cultivars.

Penshurst Vineyards

Grove Road, Penshurst, Tonbridge, Kent, TN11 8DU

T: 01892 870255. F: 01892 870255. W: www.penshurst.co.uk.

Owner & Winemaker: David Westphal
Directions: Take the Fordcombe road from Penshurst village (B2188) and turn right 150 yards past a narrow bridge into Grove Road. Go up the hill and the entrance will be found on the right-hand side.
Vineyard Details: 5 ha of vines planted between 1972 and 1991. The south and south east facing site is between 37 m and 41 m above sea level. Planting distances are 2.74 m × 1.30 m and 3.05 m × 2.44 m and all are GDC trained.
Grape Varieties: Ehrenfelser, Müller-Thurgau, Reichensteiner, Scheurebe, Seyval Blanc.

Wine Sales: January and February, Monday to Friday, 10 am to 4.30 pm. March to December, daily, 10 am to 5 pm.
Vineyard Visits: Self-guided tours during above hours. Guided tours, tastings and meals for groups (min 15 people) are available by appointment. From £3 for adults, OAPs £2.75. There is also a wildlife park where visitors can see wallabies, rare breed sheep and exotic waterfowl.

Penshurst Vineyards was established by Bob Westphal, an Australian by birth, who spent his war years in the Royal Air Force. Today, the vineyard is run by his youngest son, David and his Danish wife, Kirsten, while Bob lives in retirement in Sydney. From an initial 1.62 ha acres which gave them 300 bottles in 1975, they now have 5 ha in production.

The first vines were trellised on the Guyot system, but poor harvests in the late '70s convinced them that on their site, which is often subject to frosts, the vines would be better if grown on the high-wire GDC system, and the trellis work was converted. Penshurst was one of the first vineyards to use overhead netting to protect the crop against birds, and with woods surrounding many of their vineyards, it has proved to be the only secure way of retaining the harvest. Crop thinning is carried out and bunches reduced to one per cane in order to concentrate on quality. Further plantings are planned and varieties will include Dornfelder, Pinot noir and Schönburger.

At first, the grapes from Penshurst Vineyards were sent to Lamberhurst Vineyards to be made into wine, but when David decided to take the vineyard over in 1980, a winery and bottle store were built and adjacent buildings converted into a shop and wine bar. The winery is one of the best in the country and has modern equipment including a Chemo grape trailer, Willmes UP press, Romicon cross-flow filter, Seitz filter and Sterilus 6 head filler. Tanks are all Möschle stainless steel and the centrepiece of the winery is a magnificent 4,000 litre oak barrel with a carved end depicting the Penshurst Label, used for ageing the Ehrenfelser wine. All wines are whole berry pressed, no finings are used and the wines are suitable

for vegetarians. The Australian theme runs through the vineyard, with a kangaroo hidden on the label (three-quarters of the way up on the right-hand side), wallabies in the park and black swans on the lake.

Rowenden Vineyard
Sandhurst Lane, Rolvenden, Cranbrook, Kent, TN17 4PQ

T: 01580 241255. F: 01580 241164
E: bellnote@tlindlar.freeserve.co.uk

Owner: Trevor Lindlar
Winemaker: Wines made at RidgeView Estate
Directions: From A28 in Rolvenden take the B2086 road towards Benenden and Cranbrook. After windmill take Sandhurst Lane on left, vineyard on left-hand side after three-quarters of a mile.
Vineyard Details: 0.15 ha of vines planted in 1988 and 1999. The south facing site is between 40 m and 43 m above sea level and the soil is clay. The vines are planted at 2.13 m × 1.37 m and are single Guyot trained.
Grape Varieties: Faberrebe, Huxelrebe, Kerner, Regner, Reichensteiner.
Wine Sales: All year round except Mondays 10 am to 6 pm.
Vineyard Visits: By appointment.

Rowenden Vineyard once covered almost 2 ha, but has been gradually reduced in size over the past few years. The wines, once made at High Weald Winery, then owned by winemaker Christopher Lindlar, son of Trevor, are now made at RidgeView.

Sandhurst Vineyards
Hoads Farm, Crouch Lane, Sandhurst, Cranbrook, Kent, TN18 5PA

T: 01580 850296. F: 01580 850296

Owners: J F & C A Nicholas
Winemaker: Wines made at Tenterden Vineyards
Directions: Take A268 Rye to Hawkhurst road. Turn right just before Sandhurst village, opposite the playing fields.
Vineyard Details: approx. 5.5 ha of vines planted between 1988 and 1996. There are three different sites and the soil is generally a

fine sandy loam above Wealden Clay. The vines are all Double Guyot trained and planted at 2 m × 1.4 m and 1.3 m.
Grape Varieties: Bacchus, Dornfelder, Reichensteiner, Rondo, Schönburger, Seyval blanc.
Wine Sales: Easter to Christmas, weekdays, 2 pm to 6 pm, Saturdays, 11.30 am to 6 pm and Sundays, noon to 3 pm.
Vineyard Visits: Self-guided tour with free leaflet available during above opening hours. Guided tours by appointment.

Sandhurst Vineyards was established in 1988 (when I helped plant the first plot of Seyval blanc) on a family owned mixed farm, which has over 32 ha of hops as well as apple orchards, sheep and cereals. Much of the crop is grown under contract for other local vineyards. Christopher Nicholas, who looks after the vineyards, always manages to produce excellent yields of high quality, clean fruit. He must be one of the best grape growers in the country. The vineyard's own wines have won a number of awards including a silver medal from the SEVA in 1999 for their 1996 Bacchus Dry. The vineyard intends to plant more red varieties including Rondo, Dornfelder and Regent. Their first red was released in mid-2000.

Scott's Hall
Smeeth, Ashford, Kent, TN25 6ST

Owner: J O Davies
Winemaker: Wines made at Tenterden Vineyards
Directions: Vineyard not open to the public.
Vineyard Details: 0.20 ha planted in 1988 on 3 m by 1.6 m a spur-pruned Single Curtain (Sylvoz) system and 1.8 m by 1.3 m Guyot (double and single) system. The site 66 m above sea level and the soil a medium loam with clay subsoil.
Grape Varieties: Bacchus, Blauer Früburgunder (early Pinot noir), Dornfelder, Gm 6495/3, Huxelrebe, Madeleine Angevine, Müller-Thurgau, Reichensteiner, Rondo, Schönburger, Seyval Blanc + trial varieties.

After we sold Tenterden Vineyards in 1986, Scotts Hall and its ten acres of grounds, was the house I moved to with my family and was 'home' for almost ten years. The vineyard was established as a small commercial vineyard and as a test bed for new varieties. The major planting was of the six UK 'Recommended' varieties (with more

Seyval blanc than any other variety) together with some newer varieties provided by Geisenheim including two very interesting varieties: Bacchus × Reichensteiner and Schönburger × Reichensteiner. The trellising system used for the majority of the Seyval blanc was a single curtain spur pruned Sylvoz system which proved economical and fruitful. The vineyard is planted on the site of the 'Ladies Walk', the formal gardens once attached to Scott's Hall, a large mansion which dated from 1429 and was the home of the Scotte or Scot family, but was demolished in 1808. In 1996 the house and land were bought by the Davis family.

The 1992 Scott's Hall Sparkling Rosé won the UKVA's President's Trophy in 1994 and the 1994 Scott's Hall Sparkling was awarded a bronze medal in the 1998 UKVA national competition.

Staple St James Winery
Church Farm, Staple, Canterbury, Kent, CT3 1LN

T: 01304 812571

Owner & Winemaker: Bill Ash
Directions: From the A257 in Wingham take the B2046 by the Red Lion and then second on the left, signposted to Staple. Vineyard

will be found after 2 miles on right-hand side, nearly opposite church.

Vineyard Details: 1.30 ha of vines planted in 1979 and 1980 on a 1.52 m × 1.23 m Double Guyot system. The level site is 23 m above sea level and the soil is a deep sandy brickearth overlying a chalk bed.

Grape Varieties: Huxelrebe, Müller-Thurgau, Reichensteiner.

Wine Sales: Easter to end September daily, 10 am to 6 pm. By appointment at all other times.

Vineyard Visits: Self-guided tours during opening times as above. £1.50 per person. Guided tours for groups (min. 14 people) by appointment. £2 per person. Meals not available.

Staple vineyards was one of the first to be planted in East Kent. Over the years since it first cropped in 1981, it has always produced high quality grapes and its wines have won several awards. The winery, housed in an old brick-built barn, is equipped with a Chemo Harvest Trailer, Willmes WP 1200 pneumatic press, Seitz Velox 12 head bottler and fibreglass fermentation and storage tanks.

Surrenden Vineyard

Walnut Tree Farm, Swan Lane, Little Chart, Ashford, Kent, TN27 0PS

T: 01233 840214. F: 01233 840703

Owner: Martin Oldaker

Winemaker: Wines made at Valley Vineyards

Directions: Between Little Chart and Pluckley. Telephone for further details.

Vineyard Details: approx. 1.2 ha of vines planted in 1986 and 1987. The north east facing site is 91 m above sea level and has a greensand and marle soil. The vines are all pruned according to the classic Champagne system.

Grape Varieties: Chardonnay, Pinot Meunier, Pinot noir.

Wine Sales: By appointment.

Vineyard Visits: The vineyard and gardens have been open under the National Gardens Scheme and may be in the future. Look under 'Walnut Tree Farm'.

This vineyard, which Tom Stevenson in his masterly book on sparkling wines claims was the first in the UK to be planted with the classic Champagne varieties, now only produces bottle fermented sparkling wines. (In fact, Guy Salisbury-Jones planted these varieties back in the early 1960s and they were still there when the first edition of this book was written in 1989.) Chardonnay is Mr Oldaker's most successful variety and 'makes a superb still wine if you can lay it down for a few years'. His sparkling wines are gaining recognition and are bottled under the Merret Method label.

Swattenden Ridge Farm Vineyard
Swattenden Lane, Cranbrook, Kent, TN17 3PR

T: 01580 712327

Owner & Winemaker: William Strutt
Directions: From the A29 Cranbrook to Hawkhurst road, take the B2086 Benenden road. Vineyard on right-hand side after approx. 1 mile.
Vineyard Details: 0.25 ha of vines planted in 1992 and 1994 on a 2 m × 1.4 m Double Guyor system. The south facing site is between 88 m and 91 m above sea level and the soil is a heavy clay over sandstone.
Grape Varieties: Reichensteiner, Schönburger, Seyval blanc.
Wine Sales & Vineyard Visits: By appointment.

Tenterden Vineyard Park
Small Hythe, Tenterden, Kent, TN30 7NG

T: 01580 763033. F: 01580 765333
E: sales@chapeldownwines.co.uk
W: www.chapeldownwines.co.uk

Owner: Chapel Down Wines Ltd
Winemaker: Owen Elias
Directions: From A28 in Tenterden, take the B2082 Rye road. Vineyard is 2 miles on right-hand side.
Vineyard Details: 7.57 ha of vines planted between 1977 and 1999. The site is between 9 m and 18 m above sea level, mainly south facing and well sheltered from the south west. The vines are planted on several different spacings and pruning systems; 2 m × 1.3 m to 1.5 m Pendlebogen, 2 m × 1 m single Guyot, 3.7 m × 2.6 m GDC and 2.45 m × 1.3 m high wire spur pruned Sylvoz. The soil is a fine to very fine sandy loam.

Grape Varieties: Auxerrois, Bacchus, Dornfelder, Gutenborner, Müller-Thurgau, Pinot noir, Reichensteiner, Rondo, Schönburger, Seyval blanc.

Wine Sales: January and February, Monday to Saturday 10 am to 5 pm. March to December, daily, 10 am to 5 pm.

Vineyard Visits: Self-guided tours during opening hours as above. Guided tours throughout the day for individuals and small groups daily in June to September, weekends only in May and October and daily over Easter inc. Good Friday and Easter Monday. Vineyard café with terrace open Easter to October 10 am to 5 pm for light meals and refreshments. Also specialist plant nursery, children's adventure playground, herb garden, picnic area etc. No entry charge. Guided tours at any time by appointment. Full range of meals available in large function room. Also available for meetings, weddings, wakes etc.

The first vines were planted at Tenterden by me in 1977. I had spent the previous two years in Germany, working in a vineyard and winery (Schloss Schönborn in the Rheingau), studying at Geisenheim and formulating my plans for planting vines in England. The farm at Tenterden, at that time called Spots Farm, was purchased by my then father-in-law in 1976 and was chosen for its closeness to sea level, good light soil, its well sheltered sites and the presence of buildings suited for conversion into a winery, wine store, farm shop etc. An initial 2.33 ha of vines were planted with varieties selected in consultation with the late (and much lamented) Professor Dr Helmut Becker, Professor of Vine Breeding at Geisenheim. They were Müller-Thurgau, Reichensteiner, Gutenborner and Seyval blanc.

For the first vintage, the 1979, a winery was installed in the old oast house on the farm and equipped with mainly second-hand equipment – the press being a 25-year old Willmes pneumatic (now in use at Staple St James vineyard). The next harvest, although not large, proved to be something of a milestone. The 1980 Spots Farm Seyval blanc, of which only 1250 bottles were made, was awarded the Gore-Browne Trophy for the English Wine of the Year. One of the features of this wine was its high level of natural carbon-dioxide, achieved by stopping the fermentation before it was completely finished and sterile filtering it to retain some residual sugar.

Over the next few years more vineyards were planted, a shop, tasting bar and functions room built in the barn where the hop-picking machine once stood and the farm opened to visitors. In 1980 my then wife, Linda, planned and planted a large herb garden as an additional visitor attraction. After the massive 1983 harvest it became obvious that the winery needed upgrading and expanding and a Chemo Harvest Trailer and Willmes UP1800 press with central filling were purchased.

In 1986 we took a decision, which surprised many in the industry, to sell the farm as a going concern to two business men – Bill Garner and Derek Todd – who had already dipped their toes in the water by buying Felsted Vineyard the year before. At Easter 1986 the new owners took over retaining me as winemaker and consultant. Garner and Todd immediately embarked on an impressive spending spree, making substantial investments in both the winemaking and visitor facilities, as well as expanding the vineyard acreage. The winery was equipped with Möschle stainless steel tanks, all housed in the existing temperature controlled cold-store, a new Seitz Tauch-Stella bottle steriliser and a Tirax 8 head filler and a dozen new French *barriques* were bought. A large insulated bottling hall and wine store was erected, the shop was

enlarged and the catering facilities improved. I was retained as a consultant and as winemaker.

During the period between 1979 and 1989, the wines made at Tenterden had their fair share of success in competitions. The Gore-Browne Trophy was won twice; in 1981 with the 1980 Seyval blanc and in 1991 with the 1989 Seyval blanc Special Reserve. UKVA gold medals were gained in 1983 with the 1982 Müller-Thurgau Dry, 1982 Spots Farm medium dry and 1982 Gutenborner. The President's Trophy went to the 1988 Tenterden Rosé in 1989 and the Wine Guild of the UK Trophy to the 1989 Seyval blanc Special Reserve. The wines were served at Downing Street and Lancaster House for a G8 summit and by the Queen at the Commonwealth Prime Minister's Conference.

Towards the end of 1989, Garner and Todd decided that the English Wine business was not for them and the establishment was put on the market. Just before the 1990 harvest it was bought by Malcolm Kay who already owned a large vineyard near Battle (Ashburnhams) and needed processing facilities. Kay owned the vineyard until 1995, during which time more investment was made in the visitor facilities, in packaging, presentation and in marketing. Unfortunately, Kay's other business interests (property, hotels and restaurants) suffered badly in the recession and by mid-1992 he was effectively bankrupt. In early 1993 Kay entered into an Individual Voluntary Arrangement (IVA) with his creditors and the farm was in the hands of the banks that had made loans on the property.

For the next two years the vineyards suffered badly as money for sprays and general maintenance was short and little wine was made. However, the visitor facilities remained open and I continued to make wine there for contract customers and to bottle the stock of Tenterden wines from the 1990 and 1991 harvests. In September 1995, after over six months of negotiations with Kay and the banks, Chapel Down Wines Ltd purchased the business and property and proceeded to move their entire operation from Burgess Hill to Tenterden (see Chapel Down Wines entry).

Since 1995, substantial investments have been made (yet again!) in all aspects of the business. A total of 1.77 ha of new red vineyards have been planted using Dornfelder, Rondo and three clones of Pinot noir – including a *teinturier* clone called 'Tête du Nègre'. The winery has been expanded and improved to cope with the much larger Chapel Down operation and the visitor facilities – shop, restaurant, functions room, new conservatory and kitchens – have all been improved and upgraded. The marketing of the vineyard as a visitor attraction has also been tackled and today, 'Tenterden Vineyard Park', as it is now known, is probably one of the most visited vineyards in the UK.

Throwley Vineyard
The Old Rectory, Throwley, Faversham, Kent, ME13 0PF

Owner: Duncan Wilson
Directions: Vineyard not open to the public.
Vineyard Details: 1.38 ha of vines planted in 1986. The site is between 61 m and 76 m above sea level, faces south west and has a predominantly chalk soil. The vines are planted at 3.35 m × 1.83 m and GDC trained.
Grape Varieties: Chardonnay, Ortega, Pinot noir.

The wines from Throwley have done well in competitions over the years since the first vintage. Their 1989 Chardonnay sparkling won gold at the 1992 IWSC, the 1990 Pinot noir and Chardonnay sparkling won silver at the 1994 IWSC, the 1991 Ortega won gold at the 1993 Wine Challenge, the 1992 Rosé Brut sparkling won bronze at the 1995 IWSC and the 1994 Ortega bronze at the 1997 IWSC – an impressive tally. The first winemaker was Kit Lindlar of High Weald Winery, but since 1998 when Lindlar closed his winery, the grapes have been bought by Mike Roberts at RidgeView Estate.

Tun Vine Press Company
Parsonage Farm, Newnham, Sittingbourne, Kent, ME9 0NA

T: 01795 426871. F: 01795 410808. Bar Bistro: 01795 890711

Owners: J H Abbs and Partners
Winemaker: Jonathan Abbs
Directions: Vineyard is in the village of Newnham, situated between Lenham and Faversham.
Vineyard Details: 3.29 ha of vines planted between 1976 and 1978 on a 3.34 m × 1.52 m GDC system. There are various sites facing north, east and south, situated between 61 m and 79 m above sea level. The soil is a medium loam over Pleistocene clay with flints and chalk.
Grape Varieties: Maréchal Foch, Müller-Thurgau, Ortega, Pinot

blanc, Pinot Meunier, Pinot noir, Reichensteiner, Rondo, Seyval blanc, Würzer, Zweigeltrebe.

Wine Sales: All year round, Monday to Saturday, 10 am to 5 pm, Sunday, 11 am to 4 pm. Bar Bistro open all year round, daily, 10 am to 11 pm.

Visits to Vineyards and Lavender Fields: Self-guided tours around vineyards, cider orchard, hop gardens and lavender fields during opening hours as above. Guided tours by arrangement. 'Vintners' oak beamed rooms featuring inglenook fireplaces open to casual visitors all year round. Private parties and coach parties welcome. Wide selection of meals available in Bar Bistro.

Jonathan Abbs has been interested in English Wines since he was ten years old and as a child he and his mother, Paula, helped pick grapes in 1969 with Jack Ward in the Horam Manor vineyards. They also helped with the harvest at Felsted for Graham and Irene Barrett. Jonathan's parents originally came from North Yorkshire where his great-grandfather on his mother's side had a brewery business at Darlington. Being born profoundly deaf, Jonathan went to a school for the deaf at Weybridge in Surrey. In 1971, having left school, he decided to become a taxidermist and went to college at

PRODUCE OF THE UNITED KINGDOM

Syndale Valley Vineyards
Newnham St. Peter

REICHENSTEINER
ENGLISH MEDIUM DRY WHITE TABLE WINE

75 cl (e)

ESTATE GROWN AND BOTTLED BY
J. H. ABBS & PARTNERS, Newnham, Sittingbourne, Kent, U.K. Tel. (0179 5890) 693/711

Rowland Ward in Woodgreen, North London. This, however, did not suit him and he went instead to Hadlow Horticulture College near Tonbridge. On leaving Hadlow, he decided that his passion was to plant a vineyard in England and after spending some time looking for an ideal site, moved with his parents to Newnham, near Faversham, a well known fruit and hop growing area and one that he thought would be suitable for his venture. Soon, Parsonage Farm came on the market, and, after checking that the soil and its structure looked hopeful, it was purchased and he began thinking about planting a vineyard. He subsequently discovered that there had been a vineyard called 'Little St John's Vineyard' on a meadow next to the current one and that another adjacent field had been called 'Wineycock' which means 'man of wine' in medieval English.

The initial acreage was planted in 1976 on a Guyot system, but in an effort to reduce the vigour of the vines which are on the vigorous 5BB rootstock and to cut labour costs, the vines have been re-trellised on to GDC. There are plans to replace the Müller-Thurgau, Reichensteiner, Zweigeltrebe and Maréchal Foch with Rondo and Pinots on SO4 rootstock.

At first, wines were made at Lamberhurst, with surplus grapes in years with heavy crops being sold. In 1986 a winery was installed, and since then Jonathan has been in charge of winemaking. The winery is fully equipped with Chemo Harvest Trailer, destemmer, Willmes UP 700 pneumatic press and stainless steel fermentation and storage tanks. There is also an Italian Rossi Giaguaro 80 1 tonne cider press, together with a Bucher apple mill. Jonathan makes both white and red wines, still and sparkling, as well as fruit wines and cider. In early 2000, the vineyard – formerly known as the Syndale Valley Vineyard – was amalgamated with the Swale Brewery to form the Tun Vine Press Company.

Wootton Park Vineyard
The Gables, Wootton, Canterbury, Kent, CT4 6RT

T: 01303 844334

Owners: Mr & Mrs B H Prichard
Directions: Vineyard not open to the public.
Vineyard Details: Approx. 0.81 ha of vines planted between 1982 and 1990. The site is between 91 m and 107 m above sea level

and the soil is clay over chalk. The vines are planted at 1.83 m ×
1.37 m and are Double Guyot trained.
Grape Varieties: Chardonnay, Madeleine Angevine, Seyval blanc.

Bookers Vineyard
Foxhole Lane, Bolney, West Sussex, RH17 5NB

T: 01444 881575. F: 01444 881399
E: bookersvineyard@btinternet.com
W: www.btinternet.com/~bookersvineyard

Owners: Rodney & Janet Pratt
Winemaker: Samantha Linter & Rodney Pratt
Directions: From the A23 turn west on to the A272 at Bolney. Take
Foxhole Lane which is the second turning on the right, go up a hill,
down a hill and the vineyard is the second drive on the left.
Vineyard Details: Approx. 2.43 ha planted between 1973 and 1998
on both 1.83 m × 1.52 m and 2.44 m × 1.52 m four-arm Double
Guyot systems. Conversion to Sylvoz is being carried out on some
vines. The south west facing site is 150 m above sea level and the
soil is a sandstone and clay mixture.
Grape Varieties: Chardonnay, Dornfelder, Dunkelfelder, Kerner,
Müller-Thurgau, Pinot noir, Schönburger, Würzer, Zweigeltrebe.
Wine Sales: Vineyard open all year round, Monday to Friday 10 am
to 5 pm, Sundays 1 pm to 5 pm. Not open on Saturdays, Easter
Day, Christmas Day or Boxing Day.
Vineyard Visits: Tours for individuals are available at above times.
A recorded commentary is supplied. Group tours are available by
appointment. The 'Buttinghill Room' is also available for meetings,
conferences etc. for up to 80 people.

Bookers Vineyard has consistently produced wines since their first
vintage in 1983. This wine won a Silver in the International Wine
and Spirit Competition. The winery is well equipped with mainly
stainless steel tanks, a 500 kg Vaselin press and a small bottling line.

Lurgashall Winery
Dial Green, Windfallwood, Lurgashall, Petworth, West Sussex,
GU28 9HA

T: 01428 707292. F: 01428 707654
E: jerry@lurgashall.co.uk. W: www.lurgashall.co.uk

Owner: Jerry Schooler
Winemakers: Hans Schleifer & Ian Morris
Directions: Turn right off A283 Guildford to Petworth road. Follow tourist signs.
Vineyard Details: No vineyard. Grapes purchased from local vineyards.
Wine Sales: Monday to Saturday, 9 am to 5 pm, Sundays, 11 am to 5 pm all year round except Christmas Eve to New Year. Well stocked shop with range of both grape and fruit wines and liqueurs, together with many other regional foods and gifts.
Winery Visits: Self-guided tours at weekends for individuals. Groups from 15–50 people by prior arrangement. Tours and tutored tastings with or without biscuits and cheese, from £5.95 per person.

Lurgashall Winery is housed in a complex of converted and restored seventeenth- and nineteenth-century barns which have received several awards for their restoration. They make English wines from locally grown grapes and currently have a Müller-Thurgau and Seyval blanc still wine and a Chardonnay and Pinot noir sparkling. Ex-Denbies winemaker, Hans Schleifer, is one of the winemakers and wines are also made under contract for local vineyards.

Lydhurst Vineyard
Lydhurst Estate, Warninglid, West Sussex, RH17 5TG

T: 01444 461247

Owner: Lady J Hayward
Directions: Vineyard not open to the public.
Vineyard Details: 0.27 ha of vines planted in 1977. The south facing site is between 70 m and 75 m above sea level and the soil is a sandy loam. The vines are planted at 1.98 m × 1.37 m and Double Guyot trained.
Grape Variety: Müller-Thurgau.

Nutbourne Vineyard
Gay Street, Pulborough, West Sussex, RH20 2HH

T: 01798 815196. F: 01798 815179
E: james@partyingredients.co.uk

Owners: Bridget & Peter Gladwin

Winemaker: Wines made at Chapel Down Wines
Directions: Via A283 Pulborough, signposted West Chiltington-
Nutbourne. Right turning before Nutbourne village then left into
Gay Street. Vineyard entrance is half a mile up Gay Street on the
left-hand side.
Vineyard Details: 6.06 ha of vines planted between 1981 and 1988.
The south east facing site is approx. 107 m above sea level and soil
is greensand. Most vines are planted at 3.66 m × 2.44 m on a GDC
system; some of the earliest plantings are at 1.52 m × 1.37 m and
Double Guyot trained.
Grape Varieties: Bacchus. Huxelrebe. Müller-Thurgau. Reichensteiner, Schönburger.
Wine Sales: May to October, weekdays 2 pm to 5 pm. Weekends
and Bank Holidays, 11 am to 5 pm.
Vineyard Visits: Casual self-guided tours for individuals or small
groups of up to 12 people as above and free of charge. Guided tours
available for larger groups (12+) by appointment between April
and October from £2 per person. Food not available, but group
tours can use marquee for own catering.

Nutbourne Manor vineyard was originally established by Jeff
Sanger and bought by the Gladwins in 1991. In past years, the
grapes have been made into wine at various wineries around the

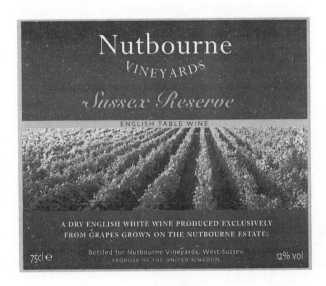

south east, but now find their way to Chapel Down Wines. Their wines have done well in both local and national competitions and recent accolades include an IWSC silver for the 1996 Sussex Reserve and IWSC bronze for their Late Harvest Dry. This last wine was served at the Golden Wedding lunch for the Queen given her by the Mayor and Corporation of the City of London at Guildhall. Their wines have also been served at Buckingham Palace and the Foreign Office. Peter Gladwin – when not tending vines – runs the major London caterers 'Party Ingredients' as well as his eponymous restaurants in the City and St James's.

Nyetimber Vineyard
Gay Street, West Chiltington, West Sussex, RH20 2HH

T: 01798 813989. F: 01798 815511

Owners: Stuart & Sandra Moss
Winemaker: Sandra Moss
Directions: Vineyard not open to the public.
Vineyard Details: 15.8 ha of vines planted between 1988 and 1991. The south facing site is 60 m above sea level and is on greensand. The vines are planted at 1.6 m × 1 m and are single Guyot pruned, low to the ground, with a no-cultivation total herbicide regime.
Grape Varieties: Chardonnay, Pinot Meunier, Pinot noir.
Wine Sales & Vineyard Visits: By appointment. Case sales only.

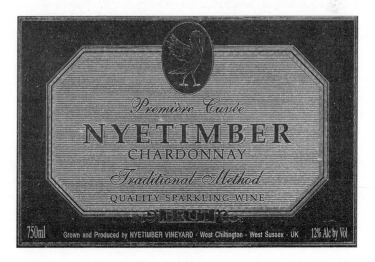

Over the 50 years since the revival in UK viticulture started and the first modern commercial vineyard was planted at Hambledon, there have been many brave adventurers who, bitten by milady vine, have taken the plunge and planted substantial vineyards. Many of these have chosen the most unlikely places, planted the wildest of varieties and forged ahead with seemingly little regard for the work involved. When it was heard that there were some 'crazy Americans' planting acres of Chardonnay high up in the hills near Pulborough, many in the industry (including myself I will admit) said 'not another one' and waited for the inevitable outcome.

This time, however, it was different. Tales were told of the dedication which the two from Chicago were putting in to the venture, of the French consultants drafted in to help and of the serious equipment bought to make the wine and temporarily established at a Kent winery whilst their's was being designed and built. Even more fascinating was the fact that even after a winery had been built at Nyetimber and several harvests had taken place, no wines were forthcoming. What was going on? The answer was that the Moss's were slowly, painstakingly 'getting it right'. They were determined to come to the market with a product that was as good as they had ever hoped it would be and with packaging that lived up to the product.

Nyetimber's winery, in a purpose built steel framed building, is clean and functional and contains the latest French Champagne making equipment: a 4000 litre whole berry Magnum press, temperature controlled stainless steel tanks, cold stabilisation unit, a double cage Gyro-pallet for riddling and semi-automatic disgorging and dosage line. Bottling is still done under contract by a team from Epernay who come over once a year.

Their first release, the 1992 Nyetimber Première Cuvée (a *blanc de blanc* made only from Chardonnay) was entered into the 1997 IWSC and promptly nabbed a gold medal and the English Wine Trophy. Their second release, the 1993 Classic Cuvée (Chardonnay and Pinot noir) went one better; a gold medal, the English Wine Trophy and the International Trophy for the best (non-Champagne) sparkling wine in the 1998 IWSC; their third, the 1993 Nyetimber Première Cuvée 'Blanc de Blanc' was again awarded a gold medal, the English Wine Trophy and – just to ring the changes – the IWSC 'Most Impressive Wine Presentation Trophy'. These awards, not given lightly, attest to both the quality in the bottle and the excellence of the packaging. There can be no doubt that whatever the cost, whatever the hard work and single mindedness that has gone into getting this whole project off the ground, the overall quality of the product is *not* in doubt. Occasionally one has to admit that one was wrong – I do now.

Rock Lodge Vineyard

Lewes Road, Scaynes Hill, Haywards Heath, West Sussex, RH17 7NG

T: 01444 831567. F: 01444 831567

Owner: J N P Bellière
Winemaker: Wines made at Chapel Down Wines
Directions: On A272, just outside village of Scaynes Hill. Vineyard not open to the public.
Vineyard Details: 2.83 ha of vines planted between 1965 and 1990. The south facing site is between 61 m and 67 m above sea level and it has a sandy loam and clay soil over bedrock. The vines are planted at several different planting distances and systems; 3.05 m × 1.52 m and 3.05 m × 2.44 m single high curtain (Sylvoz); and 1.83 m × 1.22 m Double Guyot.
Grape Varieties: Bacchus, Pinot noir, Reichensteiner, Schönburger, Seyval blanc + others.

Rock Lodge Vineyards is one of the oldest vineyards in the country (possibly the oldest still producing grapes) and vines were first planted on trial as early as 1961 by Norman Cowderoy, described in the EVA Journal No. 1 as 'a Sussex viticulturist'. In 1965 the first commercial plantings were made at Rock Lodge, the first harvest being in 1970. In the beginning, as was quite usual then, the grapes were sent to Merrydown to be turned into wine but in 1976 a winery was built and equipped with the necessary machinery and equipment. The vineyard became one of the best known in the UK and, in its day, won many awards and medals for its wines.

Norman was also instrumental in helping to found the English Vineyards Association (in 1965). He asked his local MP, William Straubenzee, who was also a solicitor, to help him negotiate with MAFF to set the company up. Norman's son David, who studied agriculture at Wye College and winemaking at Roseworthy in Australia, helped found Chapel Down Wines which, for one season, used the winery at Rock Lodge before moving to larger premises, firstly in Burgess Hill and then at Tenterden Vineyard. In 1999, having previously sold the house off, Norman decided to retire from active winegrowing and sold the vineyard and winery. He is currently Editor of the UKVA's *Grape Press* quarterly magazine. The vineyard was bought by John Bellière of East Mascalls, Lindfield in 1999.

Standen Vineyard
Standen Farm, Standen, East Grinstead, West Sussex, RH19 4NE

T: 01342 328835. F: 01342 317704

Owner: Jill Develin
Winemaker: Wines made at Sedlescombe Organic Vineyard and Chapel Down Wines
Directions: Vineyard not open to the public.
Vineyard Details: 1.04 ha of vines planted in 1995 on a gently sloping, south-west facing site. The soil is a light sandy loam. The vines are planted at 1.83 m × 1.83 m and are Double Guyot trained.
Grape Varieties: Auxerrois, Seyval blanc, Reichensteiner.

Standen Vineyard is aiming to specialise in bottle fermented sparkling wines. Their first vintage – a still wine – was made in 1998.

West Stoke House Vineyard
Downs Road, West Stoke, Chichester, West Sussex, PO18 9BN

T: 01243 575413. F: 01243 573203. M: 0802 397083
E: richard.elwes@farming.co.uk

Owner: Richard Elwes
Winemaker: Wines made at Chapel Down Wines
Directions: Vineyard not open to the public.
Vineyard Details: 2.4 ha of vines planted in 1990. The site faces south-west and is between 107 m and 122 m above sea level. The vines are planted at 4 m × 2 m and Double Guyot trained.
Grape Varieties: Reichensteiner, Schönburger, Würzer.
Wine Sales & Vineyard Visits: By appointment. Case sales only.

The wine from this vineyard is called 'Jupiter's Field' – named after

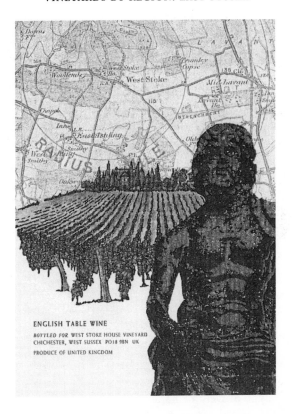

ENGLISH TABLE WINE

BOTTLED FOR WEST STOKE HOUSE VINEYARD
CHICHESTER, WEST SUSSEX PO18 9BN UK

PRODUCE OF UNITED KINGDOM

a Roman statuette of Jupiter now in the British Museum – which was discovered there in the 1870s.

Ashburnham Vineyard
Court Lodge, Ashburnham, Nr Battle, East Sussex, TN33 9PJ

Owner: David Braxton
Directions: Vineyard not open to the public.
Vineyard Details: Approx. 4 ha of vines planted in 1984 on a 3.66 × 2.44 GDC system. The vineyard is some 46 m above sea level.
Grape Varieties: Huxelrebe, Schönburger, Pinot noir.

This vineyard was planted by Malcolm Kay, who owned Tenterden Vineyards between 1991 and 1995. The crop is now sold to local wineries.

BARKHAM MANOR

PREMIUM ESTATE

11.5%

Produce of U.K

75cl℮

Estate Produced & Bottled
ENGLISH TABLE WINE

Barkham Manor Vineyard, Piltdown, East Sussex, U.K

PE 497-1

Barkham Manor Vineyard
Piltdown, Uckfield, East Sussex, TN22 3XE

T: 01825 724440

Owners: Wayne & Debra Channon
Directions: Vineyard not open to the public.
Vineyard Details: 14 ha of vines, planted between 1985 and 1987.
Early plantings are on a 3.66 m × 2.44 m GDC system, later ones
on a 3.66 m × 1.83 m GDC system. The site is some 25–35 m above
sea level, on a slight south facing slope. The soil is predominantly
well drained Tunbridge Wells sand.
Grape Varieties: Bacchus, Huxelrebe, Kerner, Müller-Thurgau,
Pinot noir, Schönburger.

The history of Barkham Manor is an interesting one and goes back
to well before the Norman Conquest. More recently, in 1911, an
amateur archaeologist Charles Dawson, claimed to have found the
skull of 'Piltdown Man', the missing link between humans and apes,
at Barkham Manor. Later dating of the skull proved that it was a
hoax and of a relatively modern origin. The vineyard was planted
by Mark Lambert in 1985 who owned it until 2000. Mark used

the services of Karl-Heinz Johner, winemaker at Lamberhurst Vineyards, to assist in winemaking and achieved considerable success. The house and vineyard were then sold, as was the winery equipment. The vineyard is now leased to another winery.

Barnsgate Manor Vineyard
Herons Ghyll, Nr Uckfield, East Sussex, TN22 4DB

T: 01825 713366. F: 01825 713543. M: 07889 966500

Owners: Keith & Linda Johnson
Winemaker: Linda Johnson
Directions: On the A26, Uckfield to Crowborough road on left-hand side.
Vineyard Details: 3.55 ha of vines, planted between 1975 and 1996. All vines were originally planted on a 1.68 m × 1.37 m Guyot system, but spacings are now said to be 'very variable'. The vineyard is situated between 100 m and 150 m above sea level, south and south-west facing and on a mixture of clay and sand.

75cl
11% vol
1995

Barnsgate
WEALDEN DRY
(Reichensteiner)
ENGLISH TABLE WINE

Produced and bottled by - BARNSGATE MANOR VINEYARD
Herons Ghyll Nr. Uckfield East Sussex U.K.

PRODUCE OF ENGLAND

Grape Varieties: Kerner, Reichensteiner, Rondo, Seyval Blanc.
Wine Sales: Open daily all year round 10 am to 5 pm (or dusk if earlier). There is a well stocked vineyard shop.
Vineyard Visits: Tours for groups only. £100 + VAT fixed charge per group which includes a vineyard and winery tour, plus a tasting. Meals are available in either the tea room or restaurant. The latter is available for wedding receptions, dinner-dances, private parties etc. and can seat up to 200 people. There is also an air conditioned discotheque below the restaurant, as well as an outside patio and barbeque area. There are also two conference rooms.

At the time it was planted in the mid-1970s, Barnsgate Manor was almost certainly the largest vineyard in the country. The first owner, a gentleman named William Ross, put in something like 50 acres of vines, planting them in double quick time using a cabbage planter, with both the row and vine spacings being calculated more with the eye than the ruler. The posts consisted of lengths of plain steel angle-iron, notched to take the support wires, which were run out down the rows by being towed behind a motorbike! The trelliswork was very low, in the Champagne style. The Ministry of Agriculture, who almost had shares in the place in view of the amount they must have given in drainage grants, organised a memorable farm walk. During this, the enthusiastic Ross, who was wholly convinced of Barnsgate's possibilities, spoke confidently of employing a grape harvesting machine, so large were the crops going to be! This was in 1977, when the memories of the previous summer were still fresh, and many believed that England had a truly Meditteranean climate. Unfortunately, this dream never materialised, and the vineyard was placed on the market.

In 1980, it was taken over by Pieroth, one of Germany's largest wine companies, whose immediate task it was to grub out a large quantity of vines and re-trellis what remained of the rest. Pieroth invested heavily in all aspects of the enterprise, putting in superb visitor facilities, as well as planting new vineyards with varieties more suitable to our climate. However, the company was involved in the di-ethylene glycol (anti-freeze) scandal and decided to reduce its commitments in the UK. The vineyard was put on the market and purchased by the Johnsons in 1985. Since then, the hard-working Johnsons have put a tremendous amount of effort into the enterprise and under their ownership it has at last flourished. Today it is well known for its superb dining, functions and conference facilities.

The wines are all made on site by Linda Johnson and the winery is well equipped with stainless steel tanks, Vaslin press and a Pedia Cryer heat exchanger. Wines are bottled by an outside contractor. The site is probably the highest in the country and although never troubled by spring frosts, ripening is usually 10–14 days behind most vineyards. They currently have six grape wines on their list (they also make apple wine) including oak aged and bottle-fermented sparkling. The wines are all sold on the premises and are not available to the trade.

As well as vines, Barnsgate also has donkeys, llamas and alpacas and the Johnsons own the Ashdown Llama Farm at nearby Wych Cross.

Battle Wine Estate
Leeford Vineyards, Whatlington, Battle, East Sussex, TN33 0ND

T: 01424 870449 or 773183. F: 01424 870449 or 773183
E: info@battlewineestate.co.uk
W: www.battlewineestate.co.uk

Owner: Battle Wine Estates Ltd.
Winemaker: David Sax
Directions: Vineyard not open to the public.
Vineyard Details: 13.36 ha of vines planted between 1983 and 1989. The site is mainly south facing, between 20 m and 40 m above sea level and the soil is Ashdown Sand. The vines are all planted on a 3.66 m × 2.44 m Single Curtain system (converted from GDC in 1999/2000).
Grape Varieties: Huxelrebe, Kerner, Reichensteiner, Schönburger, Würzer, Zweigeltrebe + others.
Wine Sales: Full range of wines available from 'The Food Rooms', 53–55 High Street, Battle, TN33 0EN.
Vineyard Visits: Private tours by appointment only.

Up until 1994, the wines were made under contract at other local wineries. In 1995, David Sax returned from New Zealand where he had been at Lincoln University studying viticulture and winemaking

and working vintages at Geisen Wine Estate in Canterbury and Villa Maria in Auckland, to set up a new winery at Battle Wine Estate. This is in a purpose-built modern building and is well equipped with temperature-controlled stainless steel tanks, a Willmes TP 2,500 lt tank press, DE filter and the usual range of modern equipment. Great emphasis in the winemaking process is put upon the use of inert gas at all stages of production to produce clean fresh wines with pronounced fruit characters.

Battle Wine Estate's wines have done well in both local and national competitions. Their 1995 Reserve Schönburger and 1996 Reserve Late Harvest were both awarded silver and their 1995 Reserve Pinot noir and Zweigeltrebe bronze by the UKVA and their 1995 Reserve Pinot noir bronze by the SEVA. They also produced a wine for Marks and Spencer. Two other local vineyards, Spilstead and Court Lodge at Ashburnhams, are leased and the grapes used in Battle Wine Estate's wines.

Bewl Water Vineyard
Little Butts Lane, Cousley Wood, Wadhurst, East Sussex, TN5 6EX

T: 01892 785045. M: 0468 557600

Owners: David & Carol Somers
Directions: Vineyard not open to the public.
Vineyard Details: 6.5 ha of vines planted in 1990 on a Lyre system. The site is south facing and overlooks the Bewl Valley reservoir.
Grape Varieties: Bacchus, Faberrebe

Grapes from this vineyard are sold to local wine producers.

Bodiam Vineyards
Bodiam, East Sussex, TN32 5UJ
Address for correspondence:
Sedlescombe Organic Vineyard, Cripps Corner, Sedlescombe, Robertsbridge, East Sussex, TN32 5SA

Owner: Castle Vineyards Ltd
Directions: Vineyard not open to the public.
Vineyard Details: 1.82 ha of vines planted between 1979 and 1989 on 2.90 m × 1.22 m four arm replacement cane (Guyot) system. The site is 15 m to 32 m above sea level, on a steep south-west facing slope and the soil is a fine sandy loam.
Grape Varieties: Auxerrois, Bacchus, Blauberger, Faberrebe, Kerner, Optima, Ortega, Pinot noir, Regner, Reichensteiner, Seyval Blanc.

Sited on a steep south-west facing slope overlooking the River Rother and Bodiam Castle, this vineyard must occupy one of the most attractive sites in the country. For many years the region around Bodiam was noted for its production of fine hops, and until the late 1970s Guinness had large hop gardens in the area. The vineyard site and soil are ideal for vines and have consistently produced good fruit. Initially it produced its own wines, but since 1988 it has been rented out, first to Sandhurst Vineyards and, since May 1994, to Roy Cook of Sedlescombe Organic Vineyard. The grapes are incorporated into Sedlescombe's wines.

Breaky Bottom Vineyard
Rodmell, Lewes, East Sussex, BN7 3EX

T: 01273 476427. F: 01273 476427
E: breakybottom@talk21.com. W: www.breakybottom.co.uk

Owners: Peter & Christine Hall
Winemaker: Peter Hall
Directions: Take Lewes to Rodmell road. five miles from Lewes turn right into Northease Farm. Continue down concrete farm track for about one and a quarter miles until vineyard is discovered. Do not give up before you get there!
Vineyard Details: 2.23 ha of vines planted between 1974 and 1987. Original plantings at 2.1 m × 1.5 m, later plantings on 2.1 m × 1.2 m spacing. The site is approx. 50 m above sea level on both sides

Breaky Bottom

Dry White Table Wine

Estate grown and bottled by Peter Hall
Breaky Bottom Vineyard, Rodmell, Sussex, UK

Produce of United Kingdom

75cl   11% vol

of a gently sloping valley bottom and the soil is a free-draining chalk loam. The vines are all trellised on a two-cane Double Guyot system.

Grape Varieties: Müller-Thurgau, Seyval blanc.

Wine Sales: The vineyard is open for wine sales every day except Christmas and Easter from 10 am to 6 pm or dusk. The vineyard has an off-licence for single bottle sales and wines may be tasted free-of-charge. It is best to telephone in advance.

Vineyard Visits: Visitors are welcome to look at the vineyard and winery at the above times. Guided tours for groups of up to 50 people can be arranged and will include a wine tasting of at least four wines. The access is not suitable for coaches.

To call Breaky Bottom an archetypal English vineyard would be to do a disservice to its indefatigable owner, Peter Hall, but for many this particular vineyard does seem to be a classic. It is picturesque, situated down the end of a rough track, appears small in a compact, cosy way and manages (usually) to produce wines of real interest and quality. As always, there is more behind the image than meets the eye.

Peter Hall, a sometime graduate of Newcastle University and pig farmer, started the vineyards at Breaky Bottom in a fit of enthusiasm in 1974, planting three main varieties; Müller-Thurgau, Reichensteiner and Seyval blanc. His first vintage in 1976 was ruined by another winery into whose hands he had delivered his grapes and since then he has always made his own wines. The winery is housed in a lovely old Sussex flint barn (built in 1827) that sits square in the middle of his vines, waiting for the harvest. Today, there are stainless steel tanks, a 1½ tonne Vaslin press, a seven-head filler and all the other paraphernalia required in a small winery. Over the years, only the Seyval blanc has really cropped in anything like a viable fashion, and he has gradually replaced some of the Müller-Thurgau and all of the Reichensteiner with Seyval blanc.

The history of calamities that have struck Breaky Bottom seem to have induced a Job like patience in Peter and he doggedly refuses to give in; chemical spray drift from a neighbouring farmer; underground fungal attacks on the roots of young vines; infestations of grape eating badgers and pheasants; extensive flooding and soil deposits from further up the valley; and damage from supposedly beneficial chemical sprays which did more harm than good. All these have been endured, grapes have been harvested and wines made.

Peter's approach to winemaking is a simple one, possibly inherited from the French half of his family. Let the grapes ripen fully, netting the whole vineyard so that the birds don't pick the grapes first; vinify the grapes with the minimum of physical disturbance and leave them on the lees to gain some extra character; and bottle the wines in as natural a way as possible. Both de-acidification and the use of süss-reserve are avoided. This style of winemaking brings individual results and over the years he has been making wine he has built up a loyal following of customers. Some of the wines are 'oaked', i.e. made with the use of oak chips and this adds yet another layer of complexity to them. Since 1994, a bottle fermented sparkling wine has been made from Seyval blanc and the current vintage, the 1995, shows very well and demonstrates what can be done in this climate. To me his best wines have an austere, Loire-like quality, with plenty of body and character, rather like their maker. Many Breaky Bottom wines age exceptionally well and can be even better after ten years in bottle. Those made from Seyval blanc have a *goût de terroir* not found in other English wines from this variety.

Over the years, Breaky Bottom wines have notched up quite an impressive list of medals and awards and although Peter is not one to set great store by winning competitions, they are some sort of recognition that his wines do have commercial appeal. The 1989 Seyval blanc won the 1990 South East Wine of the Year Competition, the 1990 Seyval blanc won gold at the 1993 IWSC and the 1992 Seyval blanc Oaked Fumé won silver in the 1996 IWC and silver in 1996 and gold in 1997 in the UKVA's annual competition. The 1995 Seyval blanc won a silver and the 1996 won a bronze in the UKVA's 2000 competition, together with the UKVA's 'Best Presentation' Trophy.

Yields at Breaky Bottom have been very variable and occasionally non-existent and those that know Peter wonder at his stamina. However, he and his new wife Christine managed to buy the farm in 1994 (he was previously a tenant) and I do not think that he is ready to give up just yet. I have no doubt that he will be making his individual wines, smoking his roll-ups and doing his best to keep Messrs Gordon and Bell in business for a few years yet. He has been a great friend of mine since we first met in 1977 and I wish him well for the future.

Brickyard Vineyard
Kingston Villas, Chiddingly Road, Horam, East Sussex

T: 07714 718980. F: 01189 344910
E: john@4corners.co.uk

Owner & Winemaker: John Worontschak
Directions: Vineyard not open to the public.
Vineyard Details: Approx. 1.78 ha of vines planted between 1981 and 1986 on a 2.13 m × 1.23 m Pendlebogen system. The site is slightly north facing, well sheltered and has a soil mainly composed of broken bricks left over from the brickworks that once occupied the site.
Grape Varieties: Kerner, Müller-Thurgau, Reichensteiner, Schönburger.

The full history of this site, and the vineyard on it, is told in Chapter 3, in the early section concerning Jack Ward and Horam Manor. The vineyard was bought from Kenneth McAlpine (Lamberhurst Vineyards) by John Worontschak – winemaker at Valley Vineyards and for many other vineyards in the UK – in 1992. Although John claims never to have visited the site, his plans for it include grubbing half and grafting the remaining vines over to Pinot noir to produce a barrel aged red 'two to three times in five years' (frost and poor flowering accounting for the missing years). Subject to planning permission, he hopes to build a small winery on the site.

Burwash Weald Vineyard
Burnt House Farm, Burwash Weald, Etchingham, East Sussex, TN19 7LA

T: 01435 883119. F: 01435 883119. M: 0836 655570

Owner: Peter Etherton
Directions: On A265, 2 miles west of Burwash. Entrance to farm on left-hand side.
Vineyard Details: 1.2 ha of vines planted in 1983 on south facing site between 78 m and 88 m above sea level. The soil is Wealden clay and sandstone. The vines are all trained on a 3.6 m × 2.4 m GDC system.

Grape Varieties: Bacchus, Huxelrebe, Pinot noir.
Wine Sales & Vineyard Visits: Vineyard only open by appointment.

This vineyard is situated in an Area of Outstanding Natural Beauty and is near Batemans, a National Trust property, that was the home of Rudyard Kipling. This is delightful countryside and there are many good walks in the area. At present, grapes from this vineyard are sold to other local producers, but there are plans to start producing wine. Cider and apple wine is also produced. The winery is well equipped with both 5 hl and 3 hl Vaslin presses, stainless steel and glass fibre tanks, Seitz Velox 6 head filler and a large amount of additional equipment.

Carr Taylor Vineyards
Wheel Lane, Westfield, Hastings, East Sussex, TN35 4SG

T: 01424 752501. F: 01424 751716
E: sales@carr-taylor.co.uk
W: www.carr-taylor.co.uk. www.englishvineyards.co.uk

Owner: Carr Taylor Ltd
Directions: Just off the A28. Follow signs to vineyard from Westfield village.
Vineyard Details: 7.40 ha of vines planted between 1973 and 1980.

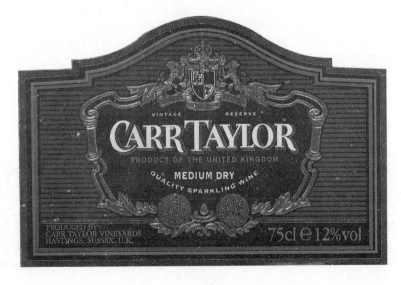

All vines planted on a 3.66 m × 2.44 m GDC system. Site 46 metres above sea level, south east facing. Sandy soil overlying ironstone and clay shale.

Grape Varieties: Bacchus, Gutenborner, Huxelrebe, Kerner, Müller-Thurgau, Ortega, Pinot Noir, Reichensteiner, Schönburger.

Wine Sales: January and February, Monday to Saturday 10 am to 5 pm. March to December, daily 10 am to 5 pm.

Vineyard Visits: Vineyard open to visitors as above. Vineyard trails, Adults £1.50, OAPs £1.25. Guided tours for groups (minimum 20 people) are available by appointment. The charge for guided tours is £3 for adults, £2.50 for OAPs. Meals for groups are available at the vineyard by appointment. There is ample car parking for both cars and coaches. Premises also available for functions, events etc.

Carr Taylor Vineyards is one of the better known vineyards in the country and their wines will be found in a wide variety of outlets. With a background in engineering, David Carr Taylor took what many at the time thought was an unorthodox approach to viticulture and planted 20 acres in the space of two years, all trellised on the wide spaced Geneva Double Curtain (GDC) system. Although not the first to use this system in the UK (Bernard Theobald at Westbury claimed that distinction), Carr Taylor has certainly been one of its greatest protagonists and his enthusiasm for it persuaded many to follow his example. Despite a troubled patch in the mid 1990s when the recession forced the vineyard to look for additional backers, the vineyard is now incorporated as a limited company and back making a wide range of wines, as well as a number of other drink products.

The site at Westfield is less than 6 miles from the coast at Hastings and is well sheltered by both the gentle rolling countryside as well as windbreaks positioned strategically throughout the vineyard. The initial plantings in 1973 consisted of Müller-Thurgau and Reichensteiner, and these gave their first crops in 1976. There was at that time no winery at Carr Taylor Vineyards and the grapes were processed at Lamberhurst Vineyards. Crops continued to be modest up until 1982, when a good crop of 56,000 bottles coincided with the installation of a winery at the vineyard. 1983 followed and was a huge year with Reichensteiner cropping at 15 tonnes per acre and a total harvest of some 186,000 bottles! This rapid increase in wine stocks enabled the Carr Taylors to really get to grips with their marketing, and since those days, their wines have seldom been out of the news.

Carr Taylor Vineyards is today probably best known for its bottle-fermented sparkling wines. Their first year of production was in 1983 when the ample crop gave them sufficient wine to start putting stocks away. Although not the first to make this type of wine – both Pilton Manor and Felsted produced very modest amounts in the early days of English wine production and Lamberhurst a bit later on – Carr Taylor was certainly the first to make serious commercial quantities of it and paved the way for many current producers.

In July 2000 a merger was announced between Chapel Down Wines, Lamberhurst Vineyards and Carr Taylor Vineyards who have joined together to form English Wines plc. All winemaking operations will be concentrated at the Tenterden site and the wineries at both Lamberhurst and Carr Taylor will no longer be used for winemaking. Lamberhurst's temperature controlled underground cellars will become the main storage area for the maturation of both Chapel Down's and Carr Taylor's bottle-fermented sparkling wines. Quite what this means for the Carr Taylors personally is at the time of writing less than 100 per cent clear although it looks like the vineyards and retail shop will continue to be run by David.

Over the years since production started in 1976, Carr Taylor wines have been successful in many national and international competitions winning awards, medals and commendations in abundance. Their sparkling wines in particular have done well and in 1998, their NV Quality Sparkling was joint winner of the Country Landowners English and Welsh wine competition. In 1998 David Carr Taylor was awarded a gold medal at the Challenge International du Vin in Bordeaux for his sparkling wines and in 1999 the Carr Taylor's son, Alexander, was also awarded a gold medal at the same competition. It is good to see that despite ups and downs, the irrepressible David and his very supportive wife, Linda, are still there, promoting the cause of English wine.

Chingley Oast Vineyard
Chingley Manor Oast, Nr Flimwell, Wadhurst, East Sussex, TN5 7QA

T: 01580 879528. F: 01580 879788, M: 07775 928442

Owner: Mr Graham Bowden
Directions: Vineyard not open to the public.
Vineyard Details: 0.69 ha of vines planted in 1991. The site is between 90 m and 98 m above sea level, south east facing and the soil is a sandy loam. The vines are all planted on a 3.66 m × 1.83 m Double Guyot system.
Grape Varieties: Reichensteiner, Würzer.

Apart from a small amount of wine for home consumption, most of the output from this vineyard is sold to other local wineries. Damage from birds is forcing a reduction in size in 2000 to a 'nettable' area.

Davenport Vineyards

Limney Farm, Castle Hill, Rotherfield, Crowborough, East Sussex, TN6 3RR

T: 01892 852380. F: 01892 852781
E: will@davenportvineyards.co.uk
W: www.davenportvineyards.co.uk

Owner & Winemaker: Will Davenport
Directions: From Crowborough take the Jarvis Brook road and after going under the railway bridge in Jarvis Brook, take the second turning on the right and follow this road until the T junction at the end. Turn right and Limney Farm is the second farm on the right.
Vineyard Details: 1.67 ha of vines planted in 1993. The west facing site is between 77 m and 100 m above sea level and the soil is a heavy loam. The vines are all planted on a 2.7 m × 1.5 m Double Guyot system.
Grape Varieties: Auxerrois, Pinot noir.
Wine Sales: By appointment (tasting and sales facilities planned for 2000).
Vineyards Visits: By appointment. The farm (see below) is open for educational visits and there is plenty of picnic space.

Will Davenport, who also runs Horsmonden Vineyards (see separate entry) is one of the more serious and talented (and younger) winegrowers in the UK today. After training at Australia's Roseworthy College, assisting in cellars in Alsace, California and Australia, helping at the International Wine Challenge and two

years in the wine trade in London, he planted vineyards on his parents' farm at nearby Horsmonden in 1991 and at Limney Farm, a 15 ha traditional cattle farm (managed under MAFF's 'Countryside Stewardship Scheme' which helps promote wildflower meadows, traditional hedges etc.) in 1993. The vineyards are farmed using minimum inputs of fungicides and no herbicides, insecticides or any artificial fertilisers are used. Some bio-dynamic techniques are being evaluated.

The winery, set up in the farm's old dairy buildings, contains some of the best facilities and equipment in the UK. It has a Willmes WCP 1500 press (the only one in the UK), a Rotary Drum Vacuum filter, GAI monoblock filler and labeller and full bottle-fermented sparkling wine facilities. All fermentations and storage of wine are in temperature-controlled stainless steel. Will's approach to wine-making is to combine nature with technology, letting wines ferment and clarify slowly – sometimes this can take until the summer following the harvest – using as little sulphur dioxide as possible and allowing the natural fruit flavours to shine through. All wine are made to organic and vegetarian/vegan standards, finings are kept to a minimum and some experimental ferments are being carried out using natural yeasts. Natural methods of de-acidification are also being tried. Will also makes wine for several vineyards that do not have wineries and has achieved success with many of their wines as well.

About half the production from the Horsmonden vineyard goes into the Horsmonden Dry, the remainder going into blends or varietals as required. A rosé is also made. A bottle-fermented sparkling wine, made from the Pinot noir and Auxerrois planted at Limney Farm specifically for the purpose, is now in production and will be available from 2001. Several of Davenport's wines have done well in both regional and national competitions. The 1995 Horsmonden Dry won second prize in the Country Landowners Association's (CLA) competition, the 1996 Davenport Medium Dry and Horsmonden Dry were both awarded bronze by the SEVA and highly commended by the UKVA and the 1996 Davenport Bacchus, a Seal of Approval at the International Wine Challenge (IWC). This last wine is also a 'Quality Wine'. The 1997 Horsmonden Dry won third prize in the 1999 CLA competition, a bronze in the 1999 SEVA competition and highly commended in the 1999 UKVA competition. The 1997 Bacchus won a seal of approval in the 1999 IWC and their 1998 Rosé won first prize in the Rosé category at the 1999 English Wine Festival at Plumpton College. Many of their wines (Bacchus and Horsmonden Dry) have been awarded Quality Wine Status.

Will Davenport (together with his Australian born wife Kathleen) have established one of the brighter stars in the English and Welsh wine firmament. They have tackled the planning and establishment of both the vineyard and winery in a thoroughly professional manner and deserve to succeed. If you can find it – it must be one of the most tucked away vineyards in the country – it is well worth a visit.

Ditchling Vineyards
Beacon Road, Ditchling, East Sussex, BN6 8XB
Address for correspondence:
9 Church Close, Burgess Hill, West Sussex, RH15 8EZ

T: 01444 233243

Owner: David Mills
Directions: Vineyard not open to the public.
Vineyard Details: 2 ha of vines planted between 1981 and 1983 on

a 1.8 m × 1.2 m Double Guyot system. The soil is clay and clay/loam with chalk over a greensand sub-soil and is 75 m above sea level. It slopes gently to the east and is just below the South Downs. Part of it is being re-planted with red varieties.

Grape Varieties: Dornfelder, Kerner, Optima, Ortega, Müller-Thurgau, Regner, Reichensteiner.

Until 1987, Ditchling Vineyards produced wine under its own label and achieved some success with its wines. Their 1983 won a silver medal in the EVA's Wine of the Year competition. Since 1988 it has been leased by several other wineries and today is managed by Plumpton Agricultural College into whose wines the crop goes.

English Wine Centre
Alfriston, East Sussex, BN26 5QS

T: 01323 870164. F: 01323 870005
E: bottles@englishwine.co.uk. W: www.englishwine.co.uk

Owner: Christopher Ann
Directions: Take A27 Polegate to Lewes road. Turn left signposted Alfriston and entrance is immediately on the left-hand side.
Vineyard Details: 0.01 ha of vines planted in 1972.
Grape Varieties: Mixed
Wine Sales & Vineyard Visits: The English Wine Centre is open daily from 2 January to 23 December, 10 am to 5 pm. A wide range of tours, tastings, meals etc. is available. There is also a Wine Museum, a restored seventeenth-century barn which is available for receptions, weddings, seminars, wine tastings etc. Telephone for full details.

The English Wine Centre occupies a special place in the history of English Wine. Christopher Ann has been involved with many aspects of the business; as a wine-merchant specialising in English Wines; as a Director of the English Vineyards Association from 1983–88 looking after the publicity and promotion of English Wines; as Chairman of the Weald and Downland Vineyards Association from 1978–81; and lastly as the organiser of the English Wine Festival for 21 years from 1975 to 1995. This Festival, held over the first weekend of September, was the focal point for both producers and consumers and helped spread the word about English and Welsh Wines. (The Festival then moved to

Eastbourne for two years and in 1999, to Plumpton Agricultural College.)

The English Wine Centre today stocks probably the widest range of English and Welsh wines available at any single outlet, arranges tours, tastings and meals and supplies 'own label' wines for both individuals and companies. It has a Wine Museum on site, filled with interesting artifacts which help explain the history of wine production in the UK, as well as that of cider and ale. It is also home to 'Walton's Barn' – a barn built in Epsom in 1670, rescued from demolition and moved to this site in 1982 – and this is available for receptions, weddings, seminars and wine tastings. Christopher prides himself on the quality of the food and wine served to guests.

Hackwood Vineyard
Hackwood Farm, Ludpit Lane, Robertsbridge, East Sussex, TN32 5ER

T: 01580 881281. F: 01580 880640

Owners: Michael & Ruth Edwards
Winemaker: Wines made at Tenterden Vineyards
Directions: Vineyard not open to the public.

11·0%vol   75cl℮

Hackwood
MULLER THURGAU/SEYVAL BLANC
Oak
1·9·9·6

ESTATE GROWN BY AND BOTTLED FOR MICHAEL AND RUTH EDWARDS
HACKWOOD VINEYARD, ROBERTSBRIDGE, EAST SUSSEX
ENGLISH TABLE WINE PRODUCED IN THE UNITED KINGDOM

Vineyard Details: 1.64 ha of vines planted in 1980. The south-east facing site is between 46 m and 61 m above sea level. The vines are planted at 2 m × 1 6 m and Double Guyot trained.
Grape Varieties: Müller-Thurgau, Schönburger, Seyval blanc.

The vines in this vineyard are leased to interested individuals who participate in the growing and harvesting of the grapes and take the crop from their leased vines. Both still and sparkling wines are produced.

Hidden Spring Vineyard
Vines Cross Road, Horam, Heathfield, East Sussex, TN21 0HF

T: 01435 812640. F: 01435 812640. M: 07802 862497
E: hidden-spring@eastbourne.org

HIDDEN SPRING
VINEYARD
1996

ENGLISH
TABLE
WINE

Produce of UK

11.5% VOL
75 CLe

Grown by
and bottled for
Hidden Spring
Vines Cross Road
Horam, E. Sussex, UK
Tel/Fax: 01435 812640

Owners: Graham & Sue Mosey
Winemaker: Wines made at Valley Vineyards
Directions: Take A267 Heathfield to Horam road. Turn left into Vines Cross road. Vineyard on left-hand side. Follow the brown tourist signs.
Vineyard Details: 3.04 ha of vines planted in 1987 and 1988 at 2.29 m × 1. 37 m and both Double and Single Guyot trained. The site is between 46 m and 76 m above sea level on a gently sloping south facing slope and has a medium loam soil over Tunbridge Wells sandstone.
Grape Varieties: Dunkelfelder, Faberrebe, Ortega, Müller-Thurgau, Pinot Noir, Reichensteiner, Seyval blanc.
Wine Sales: 1 April to Christmas Eve, Saturdays and Wednesdays 11 am to 5 pm, Sundays and Bank Holidays, noon to 5 pm. At all other times by appointment.
Vineyard Visits: As above. Apart from the vineyards, there is a nature trail, water garden, blossom trail, bluebell walk, organic orchard and picnic site. Group tours, tastings and either lunch or supper available by appointment.

Hidden Spring, under its two creators Martyn Doubleday and Chris Cammel, built for itself an enviable reputation through a combination of flair and flamboyance, good design and (perhaps most importantly) interesting wines. The pair had bought the farm in 1987 and the October hurricane of that year did its best to flatten the 6000 vines they had planted that spring. Undeterred, they carried on and their first harvest was in 1989.

The quality of their wines has always been high and they have mainly been made by John Worontschak at Valley Vineyards. Their 1993 Dark Fields red won the Bernard Theobald Trophy in 1995, their 1996 Sussex Sunset Rosé won the Jack Ward Memorial Salver in 1997 and their 1996 Dark Fields the Wine Guild Trophy in 1998, all in the UKVA's national competition. The vineyard has also been producing sparkling wines and their 1990 Brut has been well received – as has their Pinot noir ('a wine I would like to enjoy for the millennium' said Jancis Robinson!).

The vineyard and farm was bought by the present owners in 1997 and continues the high standards previously set. Their wines all have interesting names and their labels – love them or hate them – are always colourful and inventive. Their 1998 'Sussex Sunset' Rosé gained a bronze at the Wine Challenge and put it 'in the top ten rosés in the world' (or at least of those put forward for tasting!). The Moseys have made improvements to the establishment and it is now 'an even easier place for visitors to get around and soak up the relaxed atmosphere'. This vineyard is well worth a visit.

High Weald Vineyard
Birchenwood Farm, Pashley Road, Ticehurst, East Sussex

T: 01435 883119. F: 01435 883119. M: 07836 655570
E: grapewine@burwash40.freeserve.co.uk

Owner: Peter Etherton
Directions: On B2099, 2 miles from A21.
Vineyard Details: 1.51 ha of vines planted between 1972 and 1992 on a 3.66 m × 2.44 m GDC system. The site is 100 m above sea level and gently south facing.
Grape Varieties: Kerner, Müller-Thurgau, Pinot noir, Reichensteiner. Seyval blanc.

This vineyard, firstly owned by Pam Cleere who for many years sold the output to Lamberhurst Vineyards, was bought in the first instance by Filipo Molinari who owned the nearby Coombe House Vineyard, then leased by Peter Etherton (Burwash Weald Vineyard) in 1995 and bought by him in 1999. The grapes are usually sold to Chapel Down Wines.

Mill Oast Vineyard
Sedlescombe, East Sussex
Address for correspondence:
Sedlescombe Organic Vineyard, Cripps Corner, Sedlescombe, Robertsbridge, East Sussex, TN32 5SA

T: 01580 830715. F: 01580 830122

Owner: Mr M Pierce
Directions: Vineyard not open to the public.
Vineyard Details: Approximately 1 ha of vines planted in 1986 on a south-west facing slope.
Grape Varieties: Auxerrois, Bacchus, Faberrebe, Huxelrebe, Müller-Thurgau, Optima, Ortega, Pinot noir, Regner, Reichensteiner.

This vineyard is leased by Sedlescombe Organic Vineyard.

Plumpton College Vineyard
Plumpton Agricultural College, Ditchling Road, Plumpton, Lewes, East Sussex, BN7 3AE

T: 01273 890454. F: 01273 890071
E: chris.foss@plumpton.ac.uk. W: www.plumpton.ac.uk

Owner: Plumpton College Corporation
Winemaker: Chris Foss and course students
Directions: On the B2116 Lewes to Hassocks road.
Vineyard Details: 0.46 ha of vines planted on a level site in 1988. The site is 70 m above sea level and the soil is a poorly drained clay loam with a clay subsoil. The vines are planted mainly at 3.6 m × 1. 8 m and GDC trained and at 2 m × 1.3 m and Double Guyot trained. This vineyard was extended in 1994 with a trellis trial area (Bordeaux Lyre, R2T2, Scott Henry, Smart-Dyson) and planted with Schönburger. There is also a 0.1 ha varietal collection of 26 cultivars on a variety of rootstocks, plus 22 specimens of different rootstocks.
Grape Varieties: Bacchus, Regner, Schönburger, Seyval blanc.
Wine Sales: Available from the College Plant Centre, open during

Plumpton College

Medium
Dry
Table Wine

1997

Estate bottled by
Plumpton College, Plumpton,
Nr Lewes, East Sussex, UK
Telephone (01273) 890454

10%vol   75cl

term times. Monday to Friday 9 am to 5 pm. Saturdays, 9 am to 12.30 pm. Closed at all other times.
Vineyard Visits: No individuals. Groups by prior arrangement.

Plumpton College was founded in 1926 and is at the centre of a 647 ha farm which is used to teach many different land-based courses. The vineyards were established in 1988 when the college started offering courses in viticulture and winemaking. At first these were taught in conjunction with Brighton College of Technology and offered a City and Guilds qualification, but today the whole course is run by Plumpton and students can gain an HND in Wine Studies. This is a two-year course, approved by the University of Brighton, which can lead on to a BSc Biological Sciences (Wine Studies) degree course. In addition, part-time courses are offered such as: An Introduction to Vine Growing, An Introduction to Winemaking, The Vinegrower's Course, The Winemaker's Course, and The Sensory Evaluation of Wine. Students can also study for the Wine and Spirit Education Trust's (WSET) Higher Certificate and WSET Diploma.

In 1998, a new winery (in buildings that previously had housed a chicken slaughter house) was established with the help of sponsors including the Vintners' Company. This is both a teaching and a semi-commercial winery with its own laboratory and tasting and seminar room. Winemaking is carried out by the students under the supervision of qualified teaching staff. The winery is well equipped with a Fabri 5.5 hl pneumatic press, mainly variable capacity stainless steel tanks and the usual range of small winery equipment. Bottling facilities are hired in when needed. Some wines are oak aged in 115 litre barrels. Their 1996 Medium Sweet won a bronze at the SEVA's regional competition and their 1996 Dry came third in the Sky News Trophy competition. The college also now leases two other local vineyards; Ditchling and St George's at Waldron.

Plumpton College has also taken over the staging of the annual English Wine Festival which is held over the first weekend in September.

RidgeView Estate Winery
Fragbarrow Lane, Ditchling Common, Hassocks, East Sussex, BN6 8TP

T: 01444 258039. F: 01444 230757. M: 070701 WINES (94637) or 070701 VINES (84637)

E: ridgeview@compuserve.com
W: www.ridgeview.co.uk. www.ridgeviewestate.com

Owner: RidgeView Estate Winery Ltd
Winemaker: Mike Roberts
Directions: Lying a quarter of a mile to the west of the B2112, one and a half miles north of the village of Ditchling.
Vineyard Details: 6.48 ha of vines planted between 1995 and 2000. The south facing site is between 40 m and 50 m above sea level and the site lies on a Paludina limestone ridge on sandstone with clay loam over clay alluvial drift. The vines are planted at 2.2 m × 1.2 m and are Single Guyot pruned.
Grape Varieties: Chardonnay, Pinot noir, Pinot Meunier.
Wine Sales & Vineyard Visits: By appointment.

RidgeView estate was created by Christine and Michael Roberts, both previously in the computer industry, who wished to establish a vineyard for the production of high quality bottle-fermented sparkling wine. With advice from both French consultants and Christopher Lindlar, who used to run High Weald Winery, thirteen different clones of the classic Champagne varieties were planted, each variety on two different rootstocks. Drainage on the site is not

CUVÉE
MERRET

CHARDONNAY-PINOT NOIR-PINOT MEUNIER

BLOOMSBURY
Quality Sparkling Wine
TRADITIONAL METHOD
1996

75cl℮ GROWN AND PRODUCED BY RIDGEVIEW ESTATE 12%vol
DITCHLING, WEST SUSSEX UK

naturally good and land drains have been installed at five-metre intervals. The site is only seven miles from the sea and the high hills to the south create a rain shadow which gives RidgeView a dry microclimate and helps keep fungal diseases at bay.

For their first vintage, the 1996, a modern winery was built. It is in a purpose-built building with an underground maturing cellar which will hold 150,000 bottles. The winery has been equipped with the latest sparkling wine making equipment so that the complete 'méthode Champenoise' can be followed from harvesting to sale. It has two computer controlled presses, forty-four temperature controlled stainless steel tanks which can be heated or cooled, a dedicated cold stabilisation unit, a bottling line and a complete sparkling wine disgorging, corking and muzzling line. Giro-pallets are used for riddling. Their 1998 harvest amounted to 24,000 bottles, in line with expectations.

To date the results from RidgeView Estate have been impressive. Their first shipment was in June 1999 to the *Sunday Times* Wine Club, who have since made reserves for releases 2000 and 2001. The name 'Cuvée Merret' was first introduced in a release to members of Bordeaux Direct Wine Club in October 1999. The trademark 'Merret' has been registered and to keep the London connection, each style of wine will be named after an area of the city. RidgeView's most recent success has been with their 'Cuvée Merret Bloomsbury 1996' which, released in early 2000, has won a number of major awards. In May it won the South East Wine of the Year Trophy and in June the IWSC Perkins Closures English Wine Trophy. Considering that this trophy has been won three years running by RidgeView's only real competitor at the top end of the English sparkling wine business – Nyetimber Vineyard – the Roberts must be very pleased to have scooped this particular award. In July it was awarded the UK's highest award, the Gore-Browne Trophy, together with the Wine Guild Trophy, the Vintner's Cup and a gold medal. It also picked up a silver at the IWC, a competition which uniquely judged the wine alongside Champagnes as well as sparkling wines from around the world.

This wine, a 53 per cent Chardonnay, 36 per cent Pinot noir and 11 per cent Pinot Meunier blend, which underwent a full malolactic conversion and spent 27 months on the lees in bottle, has been rated highly by noted Champagne and sparkling wine writer Tom Stevenson, who gave it 85 points and Anthony Rose (*The*

Independent) who put in it in his top five sparkling wines under £20. Mike Roberts was asked to present this wine at the 2000 International Cool Climate Symposium held in Melbourne which, he says, 'shows how seriously other countries are taking English sparkling wine'.

Cuvée Merret is named after Christopher Merret – whose name is at times spelt with two t's – who described how to make bottle fermented sparkling wines in a paper given to the Royal Society in 1662, thirty years before the French claimed that Dom Pérignon 'invented' the system! Tom Stevenson – who uncovered the Merret story – said of the RidgeView 1996 South Ridge Cuvée Merret 'I have no hesitation in awarding this wine . . . a high score'. RidgeView Estate are the owners of the Registered Trade Mark 'Merret' and are considering the creation of a scheme through which they will license the use of the term 'Merret' to other English wine producers who follow their 'recipe' and whose wines pass both an analytical and organoleptical test.

This is an exciting venture and one that will be watched with interest. RidgeView, together with the other large scale specialist sparkling wine producer, Nyetimber, must be viewed as pioneers in what possibly may become the way forward for winegrowing in the UK. If it can be shown that the classic Champagne varieties will succeed here and that crops are of sufficient size and quality to make the standard of sparkling wine that the market requires, then others will doubtless follow. The Roberts have approached the task with a high degree of professionalism and have not been put off by the scale of the investment required to create a viable business. One can only wish them *bonne chance*.

Saint George's Vineyard
Waldron, Heathfield, East Sussex, TN21 0RA

T: 01435 812156. F: 01435 813185

Owners: Mr & Mrs P Biddlecombe
Directions: Vineyard not open to the public.
Vineyard Details: 4.49 ha of vines planted between 1989 and 1985. The south and south east facing site is approx. 76 m above sea level and the soil is Tunbridge Wells sand and Wadhurst clay. Earlier plantings (1980/84) are spaced at 1.6 m × 1.2 m; 1985 plantings at 3.6 m × 1.6 m. All are Double Guyot trained.

Grape Varieties: Kanzler, Kerner, Müller-Thurgau, Ortega, Pinot noir, Reichensteiner, Schönburger, Seyval blanc.

St George's, once one of the best known vineyards in the UK through the marvellous publicity generated by its owners, has been on the market for some while and is now leased to Plumpton College.

Sedlescombe Organic Vineyard

Cripps Corner, Sedlescombe, Robertsbridge, East Sussex, TN32 5SA

T: 01580 830715. F: 01580 830122
E: rcook91137@aol.com. W: www.tor.co.uk/sedlescombe

Owner & Winemaker: Roy Cook
Directions: On B2244 one and a half miles north of Sedlescombe village.
Vineyard Details: 3.24 ha of vines planted between 1979 and 1985. The south facing slope is between 60 m and 120 m above sea level and the soil is a sandy loam. The vines are spaced at 3 m × 1.4 m and 2.5 m × 1.4 m and both Scott Henry and Double Guyot pruning systems are used.
Grape Varieties: Az.15477, Gutenborner, Huxelrebe, Ortega, Müller-Thurgau, Reichensteiner, Rondo.
Wine Sales: Easter to Christmas, daily 10 am to 6 pm. Christmas to Easter, weekends only, noon to 5 pm.
Vineyard Visits: Self-guided tours available during above opening hours. Adults £3. Guided tours for groups available by appointment (contact Irma Hartmann-Cook) and will include a woodland walk as well as a visit to the vineyards and winery. 12–30 adults £4 each, 30+ £2.50 each. For groups of less than 12 there is a £25 minimum charge.

Sedlescombe Organic Vineyard is one of the very few vineyards in the country to grow vines and make their wines organically; all its wines and other products (apple juice, cider and fruit wines) bear the Soil Association organic symbol. The vineyards are cared for using only natural manures and mineral sprays against diseases, weeds are kept at bay by mechanical and thermal means and parts of the vineyard are intercropped with fruit and vegetables. Roy Cook is also a supporter of WWOOF or Working Weekends On Organic Farms, which aims to satisfy 'those who are interested in manual participation in the organic movement', and some of the work in the vineyard is carried out by this organisation. In 1987 WWOOF helped Roy and his wife, German-born Irma Hartmann, build a house on the site.

In the winery too, Roy Cook sticks to his organic principals, and uses only techniques and materials approved by the Soil Association. The aim in the winery is to treat the grapes as gently as possible, avoid mechanical handling as much as possible so as to avoid unwanted astringent phenols and keep sulphur dioxide levels low. He makes a range of wines, both still and sparkling, red and white. Competitions are not entered into. Roy also rents Bodiam and Mill Oast vineyards.

Spilsted Vineyard
Stream Lane, Sedlescombe, East Sussex, TN33 0PB

T: 01424 870422

Owner: Mr & Mrs Donald Clay
Directions: Stream Lane runs between the A21 and the A229 at the northern end of Sedlescombe village. Vineyard is on the right-hand side.
Vineyard Details: Approximately 4 ha of vines planted between 1984 and 1988 on a 3.66 m × 2 m GDC system. The site is 30 m above sea level, facing south-east.
Grape Varieties: Bacchus, Pinot noir, Pinot Meunier, Seyval blanc.

This vineyard is currently leased to a local winery.

Spring Barn Vineyard
Laughton, Near Lewes, East Sussex, BN8 6AN

T: 01323 811096. F: 01323 811218

Owners: J & M Stenhouse
Winemaker: Wines are made at Sedlescombe Vineyard
Directions: Vineyard not open to the public.
Vineyard Details: 1.09 ha of vines planted in 1986 at 1.55 m × 1.4 m and Double Guyot trained. The level site is 20 m above sea level and has a clay soil.
Grape Varieties: Müller-Thurgau, Ortega, Reichensteiner.
Wine Sales & Vineyard Visits: By appointment.

SOUTH VINEYARD REGION

Vineyards are listed alphabetically by county. The counties are listed in the following order: Wiltshire, Hampshire, Isle of Wight, Dorset. Vineyards in the Channel Islands then follow.

The 'South' region is one of the smaller regions, having 39 vineyards covering 90 hectares. In my 1989 book *The Vineyards of England*, it had 54 vineyards covering 146 hectares. This region contains a wide variety of landscapes and soils. It has been suggested that some of the best sites in the UK for growing vines are to be found in its coastal areas which are free of frost, have greater than average sunshine and heat levels and free-draining soils. For many years the Ministry of Agriculture maintained a small vineyard at Efford, near to the Hampshire coast, and this helped popularise the region with viticulturalists. The most heavily planted areas of the region are to be found along the coasts of Dorset and Hampshire and on the Isle of Wight – areas which have suitable sites and soils and are the most heavily populated or visited. In this region, farm-gate sales to visitors and tourists are important. The Channel Islands, which has history of growing table grapes under glass, has had a commercial vineyard since the early '70s. Although warmer than the UK, with better light levels, it is prone to high rainfall and damaging winds.

Two of the very first commercial vineyards of the twentieth century were planted here: the Salisbury-Jones' established one at Hambledon in Hampshire in the winter of 1951 and the Gore-Brownes at Beaulieu in 1958. Another early vineyard was Cranmore on the Isle of Wight, planted by Nick Poulter and Bob Gibbons in 1967. This enterprise eventually became a major supplier of rooted cuttings to many amateur and small vinegrowers who did not mind taking the risk of planting ungrafted vines. In 1968, Ken Barlow planted vines on a sloping site facing the Channel at Adgestone in the centre of the Isle of Wight and was one of the first really professional growers to take on the challenge of UK viticulture. Barlow's early vintages – the 1975, 1976 and 1978 – did well in the English Wine of the Year competition: runner-up in 1977, a gold medal in 1978 and the coveted Gore-Browne Trophy in 1979. Another Isle of Wight vineyard, Barton Manor run by one-time UKVA Chairman Anthony Goddard, won the Gore-Browne Trophy in 1984. The region was also the scene of one of the most ambitious vineyard enterprises yet seen in the UK at Wellow near Romsey in Hampshire. This 32 ha enterprise, established by local entrepreneur, Andy Vining, with help from Lamberhurst wine-maker, Karl-Heinz Johner, was launched with great panache and flair. Sadly, it foundered only a few years later when Vining's expectations of wine sales never materialised and failures in one of his other businesses led to a collapse of his empire.

The state of the region today – as far as viticulture is concerned – is one where decline appears now to have stopped and several new vineyards have recently been planted. There are seven vineyards over 4 ha, the most successful being La Mare on Jersey and Northbrook Springs and Wickham in Hampshire. There is also a large vineyard on the Isle of Wight at Chapel Farm whose grapes are all used by Chapel Down Wines in Kent. There are plenty of good sites in the region and with the correct varieties, fine wines can be produced.

Key to vineyards

WILTSHIRE
1 Chalkhill
2 Elms Cross
3 Little Ashley
4 Sherston
5 Swiss Cottage
6 Wylye Valley

HAMPSHIRE
1 Beaulieu
2 Bishops Waltham
3 Braishfield Manor Estate
4 Buddlemead
5 Coach House
6 Court Lane
7 Danebury
8 Hale
9 Hamble Valley
10 Jays Farm
11 Marlings
12 Meon Valley
13 Northbrook Springs
14 Priors Dean
15 Setley Ridge
16 Titchfield
17 Waterwynch
18 Webb's Land
19 Westward House
20 Wickham
21 Wooldings

ISLE OF WIGHT
1 Adgestone
2 Chapel Farm
3 Kings Cellar
4 Rosemary
5 Rossiters

DORSET
1 Horton Estate
2 Lytchett Matravers
3 Parhams
4 Purbeck
5 Wake Court

Channel Islands
Château le Catillon, Jersey
La Mare, Jersey

South

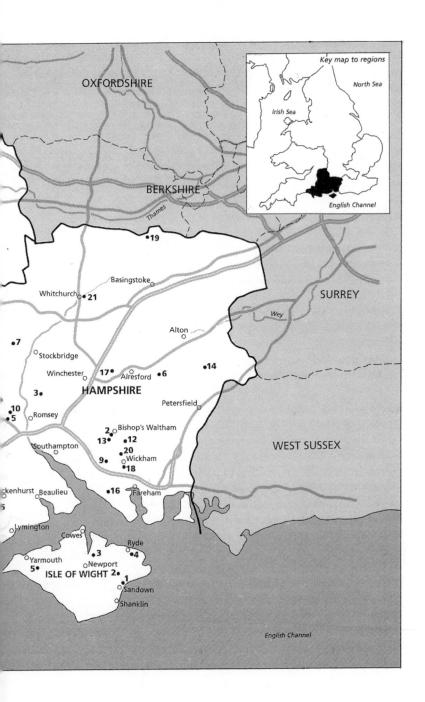

OXFORDSHIRE

BERKSHIRE

Thames

•19

Basingstoke

Whitchurch •21

SURREY

Wey

Alton

•7

Stockbridge

17• Alresford •6

•14

Winchester

HAMPSHIRE

3•

Petersfield

10

5

Romsey

2 Bishop's Waltham

13• •12

WEST SUSSEX

Southampton

20

9• Wickham

•18

kenhurst Beaulieu

•16 Fareham

Lymington

Cowes

Ryde

3 •4

Yarmouth

5• Newport

ISLE OF WIGHT 2• 1

Sandown

Shanklin

English Channel

Key map to regions

North Sea

Irish Sea

English Channel

Chalkhill Vineyard
Vineyard House, Bowerchalke, Salisbury, Wiltshire, SP5 5BE

T: 01722 780089

Owner: Douglas Mann
Directions: Vineyard not open to the public.
Vineyard Details: 1.01 ha of vines planted in 1981 and 1982. Site is between 91 m and 98 m above sea level on a greensand soil. The vines are spur pruned at 4.45 m × 2.59 m and 2.21 m × 1.30 m spacings.
Grape Varieties: Bacchus, Triomphe.

The vineyard lies on the edge of the village of Bowerchalke in the beautiful Chalke Valley and in the 1980s was responsible for producing some fine wines. It also had one of the most striking labels in the UK showing a beautiful light blue butterfly, the Chalk Hill Blue. Today, the vineyard is reduced in size – down from 2.43 ha – and all the grapes are sold to other wineries.

Elms Cross Vineyard
Bradford-on-Avon, Wiltshire, BA15 2AL

T: 01225 866917. F: 01225 866114

Owners: Rowland Dunkley & Gurli Klingenberg-Dunkley
Winemaker: Rowland Dunkley
Directions: Take B3109 Frome road from Bradford-on-Avon. After crossing the old town bridge over the River Avon, proceed for three-quarters of a mile up the hill. Fork right at top of hill signposted Westwood. Vineyard is 300 m on left-hand side.
Vineyard Details: 2 ha of vines planted between 1975 and 1991. The south facing site is 49 m above sea level and the soil is loam and broken limestone. The vines are mainly planted at 3 m × 1.4 m and Double Guyot trained.
Grape Varieties: Auxerrois, Müller-Thurgau, Pinot gris, Pinot noir, Reichensteiner.
Wine Sales: Friday to Monday, 10 am to 5.30 pm.
Vineyard Visits: Guided tours available by appointment. £3.50 per person.

The winery is equipped with stainless tanks, a Vaslin press and Seitz filler. Wines made are mainly blends, still and sparkling.

Little Ashley Vineyard
Little Ashley Farm, Bradford-on-Avon, Wiltshire, BA15 2PW

T: 01225 867616

Owner: Robert Elliott
Winemaker: Wines made at Mumfords Vineyard
Directions: From Bradford-on-Avon take the A363 towards Bath. After 1 mile, opposite the Cumberwell Park Golf Club, take a very narrow lane on the left signposted Ashley. After half a mile you will come to a crossroads with a green in the middle. Farm and vineyard are opposite the green on the right.
Vineyard Details: 0.18 ha of vines planted in 1986 and 1987. The south facing site is between 119 m and 122 m above sea level and the soil is a silt loam topsoil overlying clay. It contains large quantities of big stones.
Grape Varieties: Findling. Madeleine × Angevine 7672. Schönburger.
Wine Sales & Vineyard Visits: By appointment. Case sales only.

Two wines are available; a Schönburger and a Madeleine × Angevine 7672.

ELMS CROSS

MEDIUM DRY

ENGLISH VINEYARDS
QUALITY WINE PSR

ESTATE GROWN & BOTTLED AT
ELMS CROSS VINEYARD, BRADFORD ON AVON
WILTSHIRE, UNITED KINGDOM

10% Vol   75 cl e

Sherston Vineyard
Sherston, Malmesbury, Wiltshire, SN16 0PY

T: 01666 840030. F: 01666 841198

Owners: Tony & Emi Smith
Directions: Vineyard not open to the public.
Vineyard Details: 0.50 of vines planted in the 1970s. Further details not available.
Grape Varieties: Bacchus, Müller-Thurgau, Ortega, Seyval Blanc.

Swiss Cottage Vineyard
Castle Grounds, Devizes, Wiltshire, SN10 1HL

T: 01380 727259. M: 07909 973872
E: chris_and_katy@swiss-cottage.softnet.co.uk

Owner: Christopher Jackson
Directions: Vineyard not open to the public.
Vineyard Details: 0.019 ha (1.9 ares) of vines planted between 1995 and 1997. The site is south facing, 130 m above sea level and the soil is good loam over greensand.
Grape Varieties: Kerner, Müller-Thurgau, Schönburger, Seyval blanc.

This is a small non-commercial vineyard planted within a steep terraced walled garden on the slopes of Devizes Castle. Grapes were grown under glass in the garden in Victorian times and sent to London by train. When the Devizes branch line was closed in the 1960s, the garden was divided into two and a few of the old vines still survive planted against the walls of the neighbouring property. There is a small winery, fruit wines are also made and 'a willing wife' is listed (by Christopher) under 'winery equipment'!

Wylye Valley Vineyard
Crockerton, Warminster, Wiltshire
Address for correspondence:
Mill Farm House, Hill Deverill, Warminster, Wiltshire, BA12 7EF

T: 01985 211337. F: 01985 841066. M: 07768 287064

Owners: Paul & Roger Dale
Winemaker: Paul Dale

WYLYE VALLEY
1997

Watson's Fancy

10% Vol   English Table Wine   75cl e
                    MEDIUM/DRY

Produced and bottled by Wylye Valley Vineyard, Crockerton, Warminster, Wilts, U.K.

Directions: Vineyard is in the village of Crockerton on the A350 Warminster to Poole road, approx. 600 yards from the roundabout on the Warminster bypass (A36).

Vineyard Details: 3.53 ha of vines planted in 1989. The east facing site is between 89 m and 116 m above sea level and has a sandy clay loam soil. The vines are planted at 2.4 m × 2.4 m and are Sylvoz (single curtain) pruned.

Grape Varieties: Kernling, Regner, Seyval blanc.

Wine Sales: January to April, Saturdays only, 10 am to 5.30 pm. May to December, Monday to Saturday, 10 am to 5.30 pm. At all other times by appointment.

Vineyard Visits: As above. Guided tours for groups (15–40 people) available by appointment.

The well-equipped winery has produced some good wines, all named after flies used for fly fishing on the nearby River Wylye: Coachman, Watson's fancy and Teal & Green. The first vintage was in 1993. Recent successes include bronze medals for the 1997 Watson's Fancy, 1997 Coachman and 1998 Coachman in the UKVA's national competition.

Beaulieu Vineyard
John Montagu Building, Brockenhurst, Beaulieu, Hampshire, SO42 7ZN
T: 01590 612345. F: 01590 612624
E: info@beaulieu.co.uk. W: www.beaulieu.co.uk

Owner: Lord Montagu of Beaulieu
Vineyard Manager: S. N. Edmondson
Winemaker: Wines made at Valley Vineyards
Directions: Take B3056 Beaulieu to Lyndhurst. Vineyard lies within the grounds of the National Motor Museum.
Vineyard Details: 0.62 ha of vines planted between 1980 and 1995 on a site 15 m to 20 m above sea level and about 170 m north of the Beaulieu river and 8 miles from the Solent. Soil is south-east facing and is fairly heavy clay loam with some gravel. Vines are all planted on a 3.6 m × 1.8 m GDC system. At present, some 40 per cent of the available vineyard space is fallow, pending replanting.
Grape Varieties: Huxelrebe, Müller-Thurgau, Reichensteiner, Seyval blanc
Wine Sales: Wine is sold at the National Motor Museum shop, open 10 am to 5 pm daily. There is an off-licence for single bottle sales, but wines may not be tasted.
Vineyard Visits: The vineyard is open to the public as part of the national Motor Museum. Guided tours can be arranged by telephoning 01590 612345.

BEAULIEU
DRY WHITE
ENGLISH TABLE WINE
75cl ℮   11% Vol.
Produced from grapes grown at
Beaulieu Vineyards, Hampshire, United Kingdom.
Bottled by The Thames Valley Vineyard, Berkshire.

Beaulieu and its vineyard occupy a special place in the history of viticulture in the United Kingdom. The Cistercian Monks who founded Beaulieu Abbey in 1204, planted a vineyard there, and although King John is reputed to have sent for 'some good French wine' on tasting that offered to him by the Beaulieu monks, the vineyards survived for some years. Some 700 years later, the art of winegrowing was revived by two people who must be counted amongst the pioneers of viticulture in the UK.

In 1956 Lieutenant-Colonel Robert and Mrs Margaret Gore-Browne, who had recently returned to Great Britain from overseas, rented a house adjacent to the Beaulieu Estate called 'The Vineyards'. Despite initial reluctance from the Colonel, but no doubt encouraged by the success of the nearby vineyard at Hambledon (planted by a fellow soldier) they decided to try and establish a vineyard there and in the autumn of 1957 (or perhaps the spring of 1958 – reports differ) planted 4 rows of Müller-Thurgau and Seyval blanc as well as a few Gamay Noir Hâtif des Vosges, Précoce de Malingre and Madeleine Sylvaner, all of which they bought from Brock at Oxted. The vineyard was gradually expanded with more of the same, plus some Wrotham Pinot. By 1960 they had almost 5 acres. Their first vintage, in 1961, was a rosé and was apparently well received. They also experimented with Baco No. 1, Brandt, Pirovano 14, and Cascade (this despite the fact that Mrs Gore-Browne had heard that 'it was prohibited by the Common Market as it is said to have an injurious effect upon the liver' – a common scare story put out by the anti-hybrid growers in France) but by 1967 had decided to eliminate the experimental varieties – no doubt due to poor performance.

Margaret Gore-Browne was evidently a great supporter of viticulture, and in particular Welsh viticulture. In September 1965 she helped Lewis Mathias and George Jones, together with the Development Corporation for Wales, form a 'Welsh Vine Growers Association'. This Association does not seem to have prospered, and at some stage obviously died out. In 1967, she wrote a small book called *Let's plant a vineyard; 6000 vines, 600 or 60 or 6*, published by Mills and Boon (which in itself sounds unlikely given this publisher's current reputation) in which she mentions some vineyards in Wales, one in Glamorganshire which was destroyed by a herd of Welsh mountain goats and another two in Carmarthen and Pembroke where 'healthy vines had mysteriously died due to vibration and drying out of the grafts on the long journey'. In the EVA *Newsletter* of 1970, she is shown as the owner of '1000 plus vines at Lamphey in Pembrokeshire' and '1100 vines at Trimsaran in Carmarthenshire'. Whether any of these vineyards survived to produce wine is not known.

The Gore-Browne's success with 'Beaulieu Abbey', as the wine was known, continued throughout the sixties, with reports of 7000 bottles in 1966, 1800 bottles in 1967 and 8000 bottles in 1968. The wine was made in a small, but well-equipped winery, built in the vineyard at Beaulieu, which is still there and used today as a wine store. The Gore-Brownes continued to run the vineyard until January 1974 when it was given to Margaret's godson, Ralph Montagu. It was then taken over by Montagu Ventures Ltd, and run as part of the National Motor Museum tourist attraction. The Gore-Brownes were involved with the fledgling English Vineyards Association and Margaret donated a magnificent silver bowl, known as the 'Gore-Browne Trophy' in memory of her husband, who died in 1973. This trophy has been awarded annually to the top wine in the national competition since 1974. Margaret Gore-Browne died in 1976.

The Montagu family have been supporters of English Viticulture for many years, and at one time maintained another small vineyard at Blackfield, Southampton, called The King's Rew Vineyard. Belinda, Lady Montagu (Lord Montagu's first wife) was Vice-President of the English Vineyards Association from its founding in 1967 until 1977 and the first English Wine Festival was staged at Beaulieu in September 1974. Lord Montagu became President of the EVA in 1981 on the retirement of Sir Guy Salisbury-Jones.

Over the years, the wines have been made in a number of wineries; Merrydown, Lamberhurst and Lymington. Today they are made at Valley Vineyards.

Bishops Waltham Vineyard
Tangier Lane, Bishops Waltham, Southampton, Hampshire, SO32 1BU

T: 01489 895803. F: 01489 893184
E: jyoules@barclays.net

Owner: John Youles
Winemaker: Wines made at Wickham Vineyards

Directions: Vineyard not open to the public.
Vineyard Details: 1 ha of vines planted in 1982 and 1983 on a gentle south-west facing slope, 27 m above sea level. The vines are planted at 3.35 m × 2.44 m and are GDC trained.
Grape Varieties: Schönburger, Triomphe.
Wine Sales & Vineyard Visits: By appointment.

Bishops Waltham vineyard was established on a bare site by John Youles in 1982. Subsequently, planning permission for a house was applied for, which was granted, and in 1986, having built both a house and adjacent winery, the first crop was harvested. Until recently, the vineyards extended to 4.14 ha and the wines were made on-site. They have now been reduced to 1 ha and the wines are made at nearby Wickham Vineyards.

The first vintage did well in the Wessex Vineyards Association's 1987 Wine of the Year competition, with the 1986 Schönburger winning a Silver Medal and 1986 Würzer a Bronze. The 1986 Schönburger was also declared Wine of the Year in the 1988 Wessex Vineyards Association competition.

Braishfield Manor Estate Vineyard
Pitt Farm, Braishfield, Romsey, Hampshire, SO51 0PS

T: 01794 368321 (Farm Office). F: 01794 368180

Owner: Mr A Dunn
Farm Manager: Nick Wall
Directions: Vineyard not open to the public.
Vineyard Details: 2.47 ha of vines planted between 1980 and 1986 on a 3.66 m × 2.44 m GDC system.
Grape Varieties: Chardonnay, Kerner, Müller-Thurgau, Seyval blanc, Zweigeltrebe.

A small amount of wine is made from this vineyard for home consumption, the balance of the grapes being sold to other wineries.

Buddlemead Vineyard
Buddle Hill, North Gorley, Fordingbridge, Hampshire, SP6 2PF

T: 01425 652318

Owner & Winemaker: Mr Kerry Rogers

Directions: Vineyard not open to the public.
Vineyard Details: 0.08 ha of vines planted between 1985 and 1993. Site is between 35 m and 40 m above sea level and faces west to north-west. The soil is a clay and gravel mixture. The vines are all planted on a 1.5 m × 1.5 m Double Guyot system.
Grape Varieties: Müller-Thurgau, Seyval blanc, Triomphe.

This is a small amateur vineyard with a winery to suit ('just a shed really') and wine is not sold.

Coach House Vineyard

The Coach House, Salisbury Road, West Wellow, Romsey, Hampshire, SO51 6BW

T: 01794 323345. F: 01794 323345

Owners: Roger & Margaret Marchbank
Winemaker: Wines made at Setley Ridge Vineyard
Directions: Vineyard not open to the public.
Vineyard Details: 0.33 ha of vines planted in 1989. The site is 80 m above sea level, south facing and has a sandy soil. All vines are trained on a 3 m × 1.5 m high Double Guyot system.
Grape Varieties: Bacchus, Reichensteiner.

Court Lane Vineyard

Ropley, Alresford, Hampshire, SO24 ODE

T: 01962 773391. F: 01962 773391

Owner & Winemaker: Mr Stephen A Flook
Directions: Take A31 from Alresford towards Alton. After three miles turn east at the Chequers PH into Gascoign Lane. Take first left after 0.8 miles into Court Lane. Vineyard will be found on the right-hand side.
Vineyard Details: 0.51 ha of vines planted between 1978 and 1990. The south west facing site is between 130 m and 135 m above sea level and the soil is a light clay loam overlying chalk containing a high proportion of flints. The vines are all planted at 2 m × 1.2 m and trained on a Double Guyot system.
Grape Varieties: Huxelrebe, Müller-Thurgau, Reichensteiner, Seyval blanc.

Ropley 1996

Medium Dry

English Table Wine

Estate grown and bottled by Court Lane Vineyard
Ropley. Alresford (Hants) UK SO24 0DE

10.5% vol   75 cl ℮

Wine Sales: Open Monday to Saturday, 9 am to 9 pm. Sunday, noon to 5.30 pm. Telephone in advance if possible.
Vineyard Visits: Guided tours available (max. 30 people) at £3 per person which includes tour of the vineyard and winery and a tasting. Includes cheese and biscuits.

This small vineyard has its own well-equipped winery and won a silver medal in the Wessex Vineyards Association's competition for their 1996 Ropley Medium Dry.

Danebury Vineyards
Danebury House, Nether Wallop, Stockbridge, Hampshire, SO20 6JX

T: 01264 781851. F: 01264 782212. M: 07880 725752
E: ann@danebury.com. W: www.danebury.com

Owner: Mr Ernst Piech, Danebury Vineyards Ltd
Winemaker: Wines made at Valley Vineyards
Directions: Telephone for directions.
Vineyard Details: 2.15 ha of vines, planted between 1988 and 1997. The south facing site is approx. 91 m above sea level and the

soil has a high chalk content. The vines are planted on a 2.44 m ×
1.73 m Double Guyot system.
Grape Varieties: Auxerrois, Bacchus, Faberrebe, Madeleine
Angevine, Pinot Blanc, Pinot Gris (Rülander), Schönburger.
Wine Sales: By appointment. Mail order available.
Vineyard Visits: By appointment. Tours and meals available for
groups of up to 20 people.

The wines from this vineyard have started to show well in the
regional competition and their 1994 'Pyrrus' was awarded a
commendation and their 1994 'Cossack Sparkling' a gold medal by
the Wessex Vineyard Association.

Hale Vineyard
Hatchet Close, Hale, Fordingbridge, Hampshire, SP6 2NP

T: 01725 510718. F: 01725 510718

Owners: Roy & Elaine Watts
Winemaker: Roy Watts
Directions: Telephone for directions.
Vineyard Details: 0.25 ha of vines planted between 1990 and 1997.
The south facing site is 110 metres above sea level and has a
shallow New Forest soil. The vines are planted at 1.6 m × 1.3 m
and are Double Guyot trained.
Grape Varieties: Rondo, Schönburger + others.
Wine Sales & Vineyard Visits: By appointment only.

The 1996 Hale Dry, made in the small winery attached to this
vineyard, was awarded a gold medal in the 1997 WVA's annual
competition. Wines are made for family and friends only.

Hamble Valley Vineyard
Wangfield Lane, Curdridge, Southampton, Hampshire,
SO32 2DA

T: 01489 781188

Owner: Roger Flecknor
Winemaker: Wines made at Steeplecourt Vineyard
Directions: Vineyard not open to the public.
Vineyard Details: 0.29 ha of vines planted in 1988 and 1989, all on

Hamble Valley Vineyard

ENGLISH TABLE WINE

10% Vol.
Produced by & Bottled for
R.G. Flecknor, Hamble Valley Vineyard, Wangfield Lane, Curdridge, Southampton, Hampshire UK
75cl e

their own roots. The south west facing site is 23 m above sea level and has a silty clay soil. The vines are all Double Guyot trained and planted at 1.83 m × 1.52 m.
Grape Varieties: Bacchus, Madeleine × Angevine 7672, Müller-Thurgau, Léon Millot, Triomphe, Seyval blanc.
Wine Sales & Vineyard Visits: By appointment only.

Jays Farm Vineyard
Jays Farm, Embley Lane, East Wellow, Hampshire, SO51 6DN

T: 01794 511314. M: 0966 434423

Owners: Jamie & Jane King
Winemaker: Wines made at Camel Valley Vineyard
Directions: Telephone for directions.
Vineyard Details: 1.7 ha of vines planted in 1989 at 2.4 m × 1 m and Double Guyot trained. The south facing site is between 61 m and 70 m above sea level and the soil is a sandy light clay. The vines are Double Guyot trained and planted at 2.4 m × 1 m.
Grape Variety: Seyval blanc.
Wine Sales & Vineyard Visits: By appointment.

Marlings Vineyard
Mead End Road, Sway, Hampshire, SO41 6EE

T: 01590 682256. F: 01590 682256

Owner & Winemaker: John Wright
Directions: From Lyndhurst, take the A337 to Brockenhurst and in town turn right opposite Carey's Manor Hotel onto B3055 towards Sway. Turn right at Meadens Garage to Jubilee Oak, turn right again into Station Road. Leaving station on your left and take left fork in 100 yards into Mead End Road. Marlings is 100 yards on the left just after the 40 mph limit signs.
Vineyard Details: 0.72 ha of vines planted between 1989 and 1995. The south east facing site is between 61 m and 67 m above sea level and the soil is a clay/gravel mix. The vines are planted at 2 m × 1.5 m and are Double Guyot trained.
Grape Varieties: Dornfelder, Léon Millot, Seyval blanc, Reichensteiner, Triomphe.
Wine Sales & Vineyard Visits: By appointment.

Meon Valley Vineyard
Tudor Cottage, Swanmore, Hampshire, SO32 2PZ

T: 01489 890180. T & F: 01489 877435
W: www.hampshirefare.co.uk/meon

Owner & Winemaker: Andrew Nicholas
Directions: From north take A32 south, and turn at south end of Droxford village signed Swanmore. Turn left at the Hunters Inn.
Vineyard Details: 6.48 ha of vines planted between 1977 and 1988, all on a 3 m × 2 m GDC system. The site is between 35 m and 40 m above sea level, on a gentle south facing slope, on the edge of the Meon Valley. The soil is a sandy clay loam.
Grape Varieties: Madeleine × Angevine 7672, Müller-Thurgau, Orion, Schönburger, Seyval blanc, Triomphe.
Wine Sales: Easter until Christmas, weekends only, 1 pm to 4 pm.
Vineyard Visits: By appointment.

This vineyard used to be owned by Chris Hartley, one of the pioneers of winegrowing in this area. His 'Hillgrove' and 'Meonwara' wines were well known (especially the reds) and won several awards. The current owner purchased the property in 1999.

MARLINGS

ENGLISH TABLE WINE
Medium Dry

11% VOL   75cl

ESTATE GROWN   RUSHCROFT ESTATE
MARLINGS VINEYARD   SWAY HAMPSHIRE
PRODUCE OF THE UNITED KINGDOM

Northbrook Springs Vineyard
Beeches Hill, Bishop's Waltham, Southampton, Hampshire,
SO32 1FB

T: 01489 892659. F: 01489 892659

Owner: Brian Cable
Winemaker: Wines made at Wickham Vineyard
Directions: Take the B2177 Fareham to Winchester road and turn right onto the B3035 Corhampton road. Turn left onto the Alresford and Cheriton road and vineyard will be found on the left-hand side.
Vineyard Details: 5.1 ha of vines planted in 1991. The south and south-east facing site is between 41 m and 57 m above sea level and the soil is loam over chalk. The vines are mainly planted at 2.2 m × 1.3 m and single Guyot trained although some are at 2.2 m × 2.6 m and Double Guyot trained.
Grape Varieties: Bacchus, Huxelrebe, Kerner, Reichensteiner, Schönburger.
Wine Sales: Easter to Christmas, Saturdays 11 am to 5 pm, Sundays

NORTHBROOK
Springs

BISHOPS WALTHAM

1 pm to 5 pm. Christmas to Easter, Saturdays 11 am to 4.30 pm. At all other times by appointment.
Vineyard Visits: As above for casual visitors. Guided tours available for groups £2 per person to include talk and tasting by arrangement.

Northbrook Springs vineyards are situated on the warm, free draining slopes of the Hampshire Downs. The wines are made at nearby Wickham Vineyards under the watchful eye of consultant John Worontschak and are all are classified as 'English Vineyards Quality Wine'. Success to date in competitions has been good. The 1993 sparkling wine won a silver medal, the 1995 Oak Barrel Matured and 1996 Aromatic Dry bronze medals and the 1994 Noble Dessert both a gold medal and the President's Trophy in the UKVA's annual competition. This last wine was something of a freak. A late outbreak of *botrytis* affected the grapes and it was assumed that they would be ruined. However, they were already sweet enough for it to turn into 'noble rot' and although only 3,000 half bottles were produced, the quality was excellent. It was one of the best dessert wines ever produced in the UK and won many awards and medals.

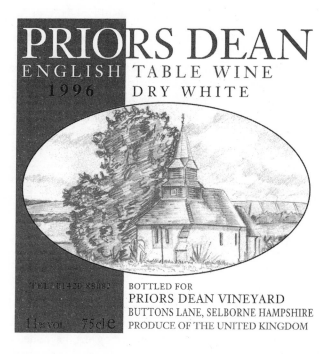

PRIORS DEAN
ENGLISH TABLE WINE
1996 DRY WHITE

TEL. 01420 88082

11% VOL 75cl e

BOTTLED FOR
PRIORS DEAN VINEYARD
BUTTONS LANE, SELBORNE HAMPSHIRE
PRODUCE OF THE UNITED KINGDOM

Priors Dean Vineyard
Alton/Petersfield, Hampshire
Address for correspondence:
Little Kimble, 16 Will Hall Close, Alton, Hampshire, GU34 1QP

T: 01420 88082. F: 01420 88082

Owners: Pamela Morley & Neil Elkins
Winemaker: Wines made at Valley Vineyards
Directions: The vineyard is in an isolated position between Alton and Petersfield. Please telephone for directions.
Vineyard Details: 0.36 ha of vines planted in 1988. The south-east facing site is between 120 m and 150 m above sea level and the soil is a shallow loam over chalk. The vines are planted at 4.2 m × 1.2 m and are GDC trained.
Grape Varieties: Bacchus, Madeleine × Angevine 7672, Seyval blanc.
Wine Sales: By appointment

Vineyard Visits: Small groups by appointment.

The vineyard slopes quite steeply to the south east and has well drained, lean, chalky soil. These factors make it an ideal site. Unusually, the vines are not planted in blocks, but the three varieties are planted in sequence across the vineyard. The aim is to produce high quality grapes, rather than large yields and the vines are pruned with that in mind. The three varieties of grapes go to be made into a single blended wine at Valley Vineyards where John Worontschak oversees production. To date, the results from this small vineyard have been impressive with several good awards and commendations. Their 1997 Medium Dry won a silver medal at the UKVA's annual competition in 1998 and was the WVA's 'Wine of the Year'.

Setley Ridge Vineyards
Lymington Road, Setley, Brockenhurst, Hampshire, SO42 7UF

T: 01590 622246. M: 07977 466793

Owner & Winemaker: Paul Girling
Directions: On A337 Lyndhurst, Brockenhurst, Lymington road, one mile south of Brockenhurst.
Vineyard Details: 1.68 ha of vines (including 0.1 ha under glass) planted between 1982 and 1997. Outdoor vines are planted at 2.2 m × 1.5 m and are mainly single curtain trained. The south south-east facing site is between 15 m and 30 m above sea level and has a sandy loam soil, overlying shingle and gravel.
Grape Varieties: Pinot blanc, Rondo, Schönburger, Seyval blanc, Muscat of Alexandria (under glass)

Setley Ridge Vineyard (formerly known as Holly Bush Vineyards) was bought by the current owner in April 1999. Many changes are planned including converting to organic status so that Soil Association approved wines can be produced. The winery and shop are being totally renovated and will re-open in 2001.

Titchfield Vineyard
Misty Haze, Brownwich Lane, Titchfield, Hampshire, PO14 4NZ

T: 01329 845531

Owner: Colin Baker
Winemaker: Hans Schleifer

Directions: Vineyard not open to the public.
Vineyard Details: 0.89 ha of vines planted between 1991 and 1999. The site is 15 m above sea level and has a gravel soil. The vines are all spaced at 2.5 m × 1 m and Double Guyot pruned.
Grape Varieties: Auxerrois, Bacchus, Dornfelder, Dunkelfelder, Frühburgunder, Madeleine × Angevine 7672, Pinot noir, Regent, Reichensteiner, Rondo, Seyval blanc.

Waterwynch Vineyards
Waterwynch, Itchen Abbas, Winchester, Hampshire, SO21 1AX

T: 01962 779229
E: pkgordon@aol.com

Owner: Kenneth Gordon
Directions: Vineyard not open to the public.
Vineyard Details: 0.04 ha of vines planted in 1998 and trained on a 2.5 m × 1.5 m Sylvoz system. The south facing site is 65 m above sea level and has a flinty loam soil over chalk.
Grape Varieties: Dornfelder, Schönburger, Seyval blanc.

Webb's Land Vineyard
Webb's Land, Off Tanfield Lane, Wickham, Hampshire, PO17 5NS

T: 01329 833633. F: 01329 834800

Owners: Philip & Catherine Peters
Winemaker: Wines made at Valley Vineyards
Vineyard Details: Approximately 3 ha of vines planted in 1993 on both Single Guyot and GDC training.
Grape Varieties: Bacchus, Pinot noir, Reichensteiner, Seyval blanc, Würzer.

Westward House Vineyard
Silchester Road, Little London, Tadley, Hampshire, RG26 5EX

T: 01256 851599

Owner & Winemaker: Bryan Garney
Directions: Vineyard not open to the public.
Vineyard Details: 0.1 ha of vines planted in 1993. The soil is a deep loam over well drained clay and gravel. The vines are planted at 2 m × 2 m and are single curtain trained.

Grape Varieties: Blauer Portugieser Gagarin Blue, Gewürztraminer, Kerner, Madeleine × Angevine 7672, Müller-Thurgau, Pinot blanc, Pinot noir, Siegerrebe, Triomphe, Zweigeltrebe.

Wickham Vineyard
Botley Road, Shedfield, Southampton, Hampshire, SO32 2HL

T: 01329 834042. F: 01329 834907

Owners: Angela Baart & Gordon Channon
Winemaker: John Charnley
Directions: On the north side of the A334, halfway between Botley and Wickham.
Vineyard Details: 7.28 ha of vines planted between 1984 and 1997. The south and south-west facing site is between 50 m and 60 m above sea level and the soil is a clay loam. The vines are GDC trained and planted at 3.7 m × 2.4 m and 2 m.
Grape Varieties: Bacchus, Dornfelder, Faberrebe, Kerner, Pinot noir, Reichensteiner, Rondo, Schönburger, Seyval blanc, Triomphe, Würzer.
Wine Sales: February to December, Monday to Saturday, 10.30 am to 5.30 pm, Sunday, 11.30 am to 4.30 pm.

Vineyard Visits: During above hours. Audio Tours available. Tours, tastings and meals available for groups (15–50 people) by appointment from £3.50. Telephone the Terracotta Restaurant (01329 835454) for details of meals available. There is also a 3 ha Nature Reserve.

Wickham has established a fine reputation for both its wines and its visitor facilities. It was started by John and Caroline Charnley, but in 2000 was sold to its present owners. The winery is housed in a beautifully restored eighteenth-century brick and timber barn and is very well equipped with 80,000 litres of stainless tanks, two 3 tonne Howard pneumatic presses, Pedia-Kreyer chiller, Velo filter and Enos labeller. A GAI semi-automatic bottling line is mounted on a trailer and shared with two other local vineyards. There is also a well-stocked vineyard shop and the Terracotta Restaurant located in new buildings which have been carefully designed to blend in with their surroundings.

A wide range of wines is made including a barrel aged *Fumé* (supplied to the House of Commons), an oaked red from Pinot noir and Triomphe and a bottle fermented sparkling rosé from Pinot noir.

Wooldings Vineyard

Wooldings, Whitchurch, Hampshire, RG28 7QT
T: 01256 895200. F: 01256 895200
E: charles@wooldingsvineyard.co.uk
W: www.wooldingsvineyard.co.uk

Owner & Winemaker: Charles Cunningham
Directions: 1 mile north of Whitchurch just off the A34. Follow the brown tourist signs.
Vineyard Details: 4.93 ha of vines planted between 1989 and 1997. The south-west facing site has a chalky soil and is between 90 m and 120 m above sea level. The vines are planted at 2.05 m × 1.4 m and apart from 150 Triomphe vines on Scott Henry and 1,400 Kernling on Single Curtain, all are Double Guyot trained.
Grape Varieties: Bacchus, Chardonnay, Dornfelder, Faberrebe, Kernling, Madeleine × Angevine 7672, Pinot blanc, Pinot gris, Pinot Meunier, Pinot noir, Regent, Reichensteiner, Schönburger, Seyval blanc, Triomphe.
Wine Sales: May to October, daily, 11 am to 6 pm. November to Christmas, 11 am to 4 pm. At all other times by appointment.

Vineyard Visits: During opening hours as above. Audio tours available at £2.50 per person. Guided tours for groups available by appointment. Vineyard restaurant with home cooked food using fresh local ingredients is also open as above. Group parties and functions are welcomed and have the use of a beautiful 300-year-old barn.

The winery at Wooldings is housed in a converted farm building and has a selection of stainless steel tanks. There is a Willmes pneumatic press, Velo earth filter, plate and membrane filters, a GAI bottler and full sparkling wine line. The reds are fermented above press level and then gravity fed to the press and tanks. Red skins are only lightly pressed and then soaked with white juice (held back under refrigeration) to make a rosé. Grapes for sparkling wine are whole berry pressed (40 per cent extraction). Some wines are also 'barrique' fermented and aged and there is a special 'warm room' for those wines undergoing a malolactic fermentation.

  Wooldings wines have been awarded several 'commendeds' and one bronze medal in recent International Wine Challenge tastings as well as T&CVA 'Wine of the Year' with the 1992 Wooldings Brut and Wessex 'Wine of the Year' with their 1992 Schönburger. Their wines were served by the Queen at a gala dinner in Paris in November 1998 and have been supplied to Government Hospitality and to several British embassies around the world. They have a wide range of wines for sale, white and red, oaked and unoaked, still and sparkling.

Adgestone Vineyard

Upper Road, Sandown, Isle of Wight, PO36 0ES

T: 01983 402503. F: 01983 402503
W: www.english-wine.co.uk

Owners: Alan & Gill Stockman
Winemaker: Alan Stockman
Directions: Turn off A3055 at Brading and follow signs for vineyard.
Vineyards Details: Approx. 3.2 ha of vines planted between 1968 and 1991. The site is south facing, between 45 m and 60 m above sea level, with a predominantly chalky loam soil mixed with flints. This is a naturally well-drained soil and one which makes the vines

really work for a living. The vines are planted on two different systems; 1.83 m × 1.83 m High Cordons and 1.83 m × 1.37 m Pendlebogen.

Grape Varieties: Müller-Thurgau, Reichensteiner, Seyval blanc, Rondo.

Wine Sales: Vineyard open to visitors and for wine sales all year round. Easter–October 10 am to 5.30 pm. November–Easter 10 am–4.30 pm Tuesday–Sunday. On and Off Licence. No charge for tastings.

Vineyard Visits: Open as above. Vineyard and cellar tour £2.50 per person. Light snacks and cream teas served.

Established in 1968, Adgestone Vineyard was one of the first commercial vineyards in the UK. Ken Barlow, who established the vineyards, spent over 20 years in agricultural crop research and, when looking for a site for a vineyard, recognised that the Isle of Wight, with its higher than average temperatures and sunshine

Adgestone

1996
ENGLISH TABLE WINE

Dry Fruity Wine

75cl ℮   Bottled by WD1074 at DTI 1QT, UK.   11% vol

ESTATE GROWN AT ADGESTONE VINEYARD,
SANDOWN, ISLE OF WIGHT

hours, had particular advantages, especially an absence of frost. Despite the warmth of the site, the harvest usually starts quite late owing to its proximity to the sea. The grapes do seem to ripen well and achieve high natural sugars. The current owners, Alan and Gill Stockman, bought the vineyard in 1995.

The winery at Adgestone is partially underground, which is unusual for the UK and what was originally Ken Barlow's wine store (which is partially above the cellars) has now been converted into living accommodation. The winery is equipped with both Vaslin and Howard presses, Romicon lees filter and a twelve head rotary filler; fermentation and storage of wines is mainly in fibreglass tanks, although some wines are barrel fermented. Adgestone has a good reputation for its wines and Ken Barlow won the Gore-Browne Trophy in 1978. Since then, the wines have won numerous awards and medals. Today, the vineyard sells both still and sparkling white wines, as well as a red.

Chapel Farm Vineyard

Lower Adgestone Road, Brading, Isle of Wight
Address for correspondence:
8 Victoria Road, Kensington, London, W8 5RD

T: 0207 9373711. F: 0207 9375945
E: adpilcher@aol.com

Owner: Anthony Pilcher
Directions: Vineyard not open to the public.
Vineyard Details: Approximately 8 ha of vines planted between 1980 and 1999. Site is between 15 m and 45 m above sea level on a gentle south facing slope and the soil is mostly well-drained chalky greensand and plateau gravel. There are some clay areas which are tile drained.
Grape Varieties: Müller-Thurgau, Reichensteiner, Seyval blanc, Rondo.

This vineyard sells all its grapes to Chapel Down Wines Ltd where Anthony Pilcher is Chairman. Plantings of Rondo, Phoenix and Seyval blanc are being planned for 2000. Red hybrids seem to very well on this site and are used to make Chapel Down's Epoch and Epoch Reserve. Phoenix, the new Geilweilerhof white hybrid, ought to do well there also.

The Kings Cellar Vineyard
Wootton, Ryde, Isle of Wight
Address for correspondence:
113 Trafalgar Road, Newport, Isle of Wight, PO30 1QU

T: 01983 825843. F: 01983 884055

Owner: Mr C R Lunn
Directions: Vineyard not open to the public.
Vineyards Details: 1.73 ha of vines planted between 1997 and 2000. The site is south facing with a stone clay and sandy soil. The vines are planted at 2.44 m × 1.83 m and 2.44 m × 1.52 m and at present are trained to a single wire.
Grape Varieties: Chardonnay, Reichensteiner, Rondo, Schönburger, Seyval blanc, Triomphe.

This is a new vineyard, owned by a consortium of growers, and is not yet in production. The first vintage will be in 2001.

Rosemary Vineyard
Smallbrook Lane, Ryde, Isle of Wight, PO33 2UX

T: 01983 811084. F: 01983 812899

Owner: Conrad Gauntlett
Winemaker: Hans Schleifer
Directions: Take Ryde to Brading road, turn right at Westridge Garage and follow brown tourist signs.
Vineyard Details: 11.33 ha of vines planted between 1987 and 1988. The south facing site is between 18 m and 27 m above sea level and has a loam over clay and greensand soil. The vines are planted at various distances and are mainly GDC trained.
Grape Varieties: Bacchus, Madeleine × Angevine 7672, Müller-Thurgau, Orion, Pinot gris, Reichensteiner, Rondo, Schönburger, Seyval blanc, Triomphe.
Wine Sales: Open all year, Monday to Saturday 10 am to 5 pm. Sundays (summer only), 11 am to 4 pm. Shop and café for light meals, teas etc.
Vineyard Visits: Free self-guided tours during opening hours as above. Group tours by appointment from £1.50 per person. Coaches welcome.

ROSEMARY VINEYARD
—— ENGLISH TABLE WINE ——

PRODUCE OF THE U.K   L.R.V. 097 16

75CL e   WHITE   11% VOL

MADELEINE ANGEVINE

ESTATE GROWN & BOTTLED BY ROSEMARY VINEYARD, RYDE, ISLE OF WIGHT UK

Rosemary is the largest vineyard on the Isle of Wight and has in recent years been upgrading its visitor facilities. It has a fully equipped winery with a 2 tonne press, fully automatic bottling line (ex-Harveys of Bristol) and all the other usual equipment. Fermentation in mainly in stainless steel. Hans Schleifer (ex-Denbies) is now winemaker. They make a wide range of English wines – they currently list eight wines including four whites, two reds, a rosé and two sparkling wines – as well as ciders and fruit wines.

Rossiters Vineyard
Rossiters Farmhouse, Wellow, Yarmouth, Isle of Wight, PO41 OTE

T: 01983 761138. F: 01983 760263
E: mail@rossitersvineyard.freeserve.co.uk

Owners: Prof. Rod Thompson & Mrs Camilla Lambert
Winemaker: Rod Thompson

Directions: From Yarmouth take the A3054 towards Newport. Just outside the town, turn right onto the B3401 towards Thorley and Wellow. Vineyard on left-hand side in centre of village.
Vineyard Details: 2.43 ha of vines planted between 1990 and 1998. The south facing site is between 91 m and 101 m above sea level and has a clay soil.
Grape Varieties: Bacchus, Madeleine × Angevine 7672, Orion, Regner, Reichensteiner, Rondo, Schönburger, Seyval blanc.
Wine Sales & Vineyard Visits: By appointment. Case sales only.

At present a blended wine is made in the winery, but once the 1998 plantings come on stream, it is planned that a wider range of wines will be made and visitor facilities improved.

Horton Estate Vineyard
Horton, Wimborne, Dorset, BH21 7JG

T: 01258 840258/480990
E: info@horton-vineyard.com. W: www.horton-vineyard.com

Owners: Brian & Jane Burch
Winemaker: Brian Burch
Directions: From A338/A31 roundabout take C road to Horton via Three Legged Cross. Turn north 50 yds east of Horton village onto stone drive at side of telephone box.
Vineyard Details: 3.63 ha of vines planted between 1985 and 1996. All vines trained to GDC at 4.2 m × 3.5 m or 4.2 m × 2.5 m. The south-west facing site is between 30 m and 40 m above sea level and has a sandy loam soil over chalk.
Grape Varieties: Bacchus, Kerner, Léon Millot, Pinot noir, Reichensteiner, Triomphe.
Wine Sales: March to end December, open every Saturday 10 am to 4 pm. July, August and December, open Sundays 10 am to 4 pm. At all other times by appointment.
Vineyard Visits: Tours for small and large groups available by arrangement.

The winery is in a building purpose designed for natural wine-making and is well equipped with a Willmes UP 1800 press, stainless steel tanks and a GAI monobloc filler/corker. The wines all undergo a malolactic conversion, most are unfined and some are barrel aged. White, red and sparkling wines are made. There is a

ENGLISH QUALITY SPARKLING WINE

HORTON ESTATE VINEYARD

VINTAGE 1994 BRUT

12% vol   ESTATE GROWN AND PRODUCED BY THE TRADITIONAL METHOD
AT HORTON ESTATE, DORSET, BH21 7JG, UNITED KINGDOM   75cl e

wide range of wines available from the vineyard and in local outlets. It is 'management policy' not to enter into wine competitions!

Lytchett Matravers Vineyard
Eaton Cottage, Dolman's Hill, Lytchett Matravers, Poole, Dorset, BH16 6HP

T: 01929 459526

Owner & Winemaker: Andrew McClure
Directions: Vineyard not open to the public.
Vineyard Details: 0.03 ha of vines planted between 1985 and 1991. The west facing site is between 75 m and 80 m above sea level and the soil is a sandy loam. The vines are planted at 1.5 m × 1.34 m and are all Single Guyot trained.
Grape Varieties: Madeleine × Angevine 7672, Reichensteiner.

This is a small amateur vineyard and the wines are made for personal consumption. A specially built extension to the house has been built with a cellar below. Madeleine is the preferred variety as it (almost) always produce a crop, although the Reichensteiner has higher natural sugars.

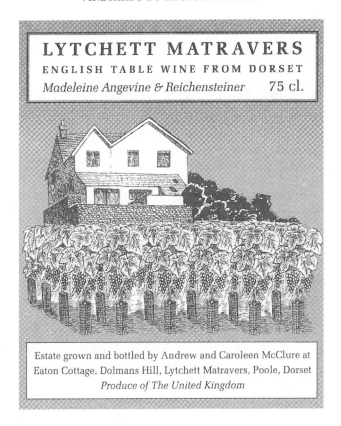

LYTCHETT MATRAVERS
ENGLISH TABLE WINE FROM DORSET
Madeleine Angevine & Reichensteiner   75 cl.

Estate grown and bottled by Andrew and Caroleen McClure at
Eaton Cottage, Dolmans Hill, Lytchett Matravers, Poole, Dorset
Produce of The United Kingdom

Parhams Vineyard
Parhams Farm, Melbury Abbas, Shaftesbury, Dorset, SP7 0DE

T: 01747 853122. F: 01747 853122
E: royphillips@parhamsfarm.freeserve.co.uk

Owner: Roy Phillips
Winemaker: Wines made at Setley Ridge Vineyard
Directions: 1 mile south of Shaftesbury on the C13 Upper
Blandford Road.
Vineyard Details: approx. 0.40 ha of vines planted in 1993 on a
south facing slope whose soil is a loamy greensand over chalk. The
vines are planted at 2.4 m × 1.5 m and are Scott Henry trained.
Grape Variety: Reichensteiner
Wine Sales & Vineyard Visits: By appointment.

Purbeck Vineyard
Knolldown, Valley Road, Harmans Cross, Corfe Castle, Dorset,
BH20 5HU

T: 01929 481525. F: 01929 481535. M: 07976 761766
E: mhthorpe@lineone.net. W: www.purbeckvineyard.co.uk

Owners: Michael & Susan Thorpe
Directions: From Wareham, take the A351 south towards Swanage.
Vineyard is on the right-hand side nearly 2 miles beyond Corfe
Castle on the right-hand side as one enters the village of Harmans
Cross.
Vineyard Details: 0.29 ha of vines planted in 2000. The south
facing site is between 59 m and 69 m above sea level and the soil
is loam over sandstone and clay. The vines are planted at 1.6 m ×
1.2 m.
Grape Varieties: Bacchus, Rondo.

This is a new vineyard in an area reputed to have had one in Roman
times. Further plantings will include Chardonnay and Pinot noir. By
2002 it will extend to 1.2 ha with further expansion possible
thereafter. The south facing site is on the northern end of the belt of
Kimmeridgian Clay that extends under the Channel and emerges in
France as far away as Chablis – where it is the favoured soil in the
finest vineyards. The site is surrounded on three sides by the sea,
some three miles distant in each direction and well protected by
higher hills to the south and north. Michael Thorpe has completed
a vinegrowing course at Plumpton College.

Wake Court Vineyard
Wake Court, Bishops Caundle, Sherborne, Dorset, DT9 5NG

T: 01963 323249
E: enquiries@sherbornecastle.com. W: www.sherbornecastle.com

Owner: Mr John Wingfield Digby, Sherborne Castle Estates
Winemaker: Wines made at Bagborough Vineyard
Directions: Take the A3030 Sherborne to Blandford Forum road. In
the village of Bishops Caundle, 6 miles south-east of Sherborne,
take 2nd turning on the right beyond the White Hart Inn. Go down
Ryalls Lane and at sharp bend enter white gates.
Vineyard Details: 1.27 ha of vines planted in 1982. The south

facing site is 61 m above sea level and the soil is described as 'loam, limestone and clay'. The vines are planted at 3.66 m × 2.44 m and are GDC trained.

Grape Varieties: Bacchus, Léon Millot, Pinot Noir, Regner, Reichensteiner, Schönburger, Seyval blanc.

Wine Sales & Vineyard Visits: By appointment only. The wines can be purchased by the bottle or case from the shop at Sherborne Castle. Telephone 01935 813182 or see their web-site for opening times.

Mr Wingfield Digby writes that his vineyard is 'the perfect example of an English vineyard' and that his Bacchus and Reichensteiner blend has been compared by people in the wine trade to a Sancerre or New Zealand Sauvignon blanc. His Schönburger resembles a 'light Gewürztraminer'. Wake Court are also one of the very few UK vineyards to have experimented with distillation and are now producing brandy to be enjoyed as 'an aperitif or as a perfect after-dinner companion'. They sell a blend of all their varieties under the 'Wake Court Special Reserve' label and in supermarkets under the 'Trinity' label.

Château le Catillon
Le Catillon de Bas, Grouville, Jersey, Channel Islands

T: 01534 852840. F: 01534 856642

Owner: Ralph Mauger
Directions: Vineyard not open to the public.
Vineyard Details: 3.67 ha of vines planted in 1986 and 1987. The south facing site is between 28 m and 46 m above sea level and the soil is a fertile sandy loam. The vines are all trellised on a 3.35 m × 1.52 m GDC system.
Grape Varieties: Huxelrebe, Pinot blanc, Pinot noir, Reichensteiner, Schönburger, Seyval blanc.
Wine Sales & Vineyard Visits: By arrangement.

Château le Catillon's grapes used to be pressed on site and the juice then sent to the Bottle Green Drinks Co. in Gloucestershire where Kit Morris (ex-Three Choirs winemaker) used to make the wine for return to Jersey for sale. For the last few years some grapes have been sold to La Mare Vineyard, the major Jersey vineyard, and used in their wines. From 1999, the vineyard has been leased to La Mare and all Château le Catillon's crop now goes there.

La Mare Vineyards Ltd
St Mary, Jersey, Channel Islands, JE3 3BA

T: 01534 481178. F: 01534 485210. M: 07797 735578
E: lamarewine@aol.com. W: www.lamarejersey.com

Owner: Trevor Owen
Winemaker: Simon Day
Directions: From village of St Mary take C103, La Grande Rue, and follow vineyard signs
Vineyard Details: 6.9 ha of vines planted between 1972 and 1996. The south and south-east facing site is between 50 m and 105 m above sea level and the soil is loam over granite bed rock. The vines are trained on both 1.90 m × 1.40 m Double Guyot and 4 m × 1.4 m GDC systems.
Grape Varieties: Huxelrebe, Phoenix, Pinot blanc, Pinot noir, Reichensteiner, Schönburger, Seyval Blanc, Triomphe.
Wine Sales: April to December, Monday to Saturday 10 am to 5 pm. At all other times by appointment.
Vineyard Visits: April to October, Monday to Saturday 10 am to 5 pm. Lunches and cream teas, children's playground, animals and gardens. Guided tours £3.85 per adult to include three wine tasting,

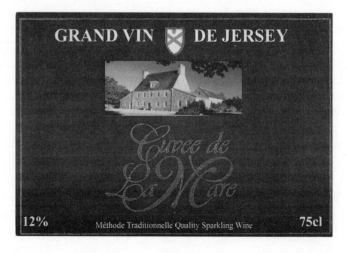

audio-visual show, winery and distillery tour etc. Guided tours and meals for groups by appointment only. Can also arrange conferences for groups from 10–800 people. Full details on website.

La Mare Vineyards were the first commercial vineyards for wine production in Jersey and were planted by Robert and Ann Blayney who had family connections with the wine trade stretching back 150 years. The original planting at La Mare was a trial acre of many recommended varieties, few of which really proved to be successful. Weedkiller spray damage from a neighbouring farm in 1975 killed 1000 vines, but did afford the opportunity to replant with some more suitable varieties. La Mare Vineyards first opened to the public in 1976.

In 1997 the Blayneys sold to the present owner, Trevor Owen. The vineyard, winery, shop tea rooms etc., now run by Andrew Blayney (son of the former owners) are undergoing major changes and exciting developments are planned for its visitor facilities. New vineyards and orchards – for the production of apples suitable for making their apple brandy – have also been planted and the winery is being upgraded.

Since 1998, the winemaker has been Simon Day (ex-Lamberhurst and son of Tom and Brenda Day, late of Three Choirs) and is now getting to grips with the La Mare winery and its wines. The winery is well equipped with a 15 hl Vaslin press and mainly stainless steel tanks. Three wines are currently made; a 'Domaine de La Mare' from Seyval blanc and Phoenix, oak fermented and aged in new Nevers and Alliers barriques with lees stirring and malolactic fermentation; a 'Clos de La Mare' from a blend or Reichensteiner, Huxelrebe and Seyval blanc, a stainless steel fermented white with a small amount of residual sugar; and 'Cuvée de La Mare', a whole bunch pressed, bottle fermented sparkling wine. The wines are nearly all sold on the island and such is the demand that some are on allocation. La Mare has recently taken over Le Catillon Vineyards, the island's other major vineyard and is taking their grapes. This has expanded their annual production threefold to 36,000 bottles and with this increased output they hope to start exporting some to the UK in the near future.

SOUTH WEST VINEYARD REGION

Vineyards are listed alphabetically by county. The counties are listed in the following order: Herefordshire, Worcestershire, Gloucestershire, South Gloucestershire, Bristol, Somerset, Devon, Cornwall, Isles of Scilly. These are then followed by vineyards in the southern half of Wales, followed by vineyards in the Republic of Ireland.

The 'South West' region has 71 vineyards covering 96 hectares. In my 1989 book, *The Vineyards of England*, there were 92 vineyards covering 116 hectares. The region is geographically huge and much of it unsuitable for viticulture. It is either too wet, too elevated or too far away from potential customers. The centres of viticulture in the area (ignoring Ireland for the time being) are along the south coasts of both England and Wales, where temperatures are warmer and spring frosts less of a problem and in the counties facing towards the Bristol Channel and up the Severn Estuary and Severn River valley towards Gloucester and Worcester. Much of this is traditional fruit and hop territory and sites and soils are well suited to vines. The far south of the region, Devon and Cornwall, suffers from high levels of rainfall and exposure to the Atlantic. However, some compensation is provided by the large number of tourists who visit it. Wales has always been popular with wine-growers, perhaps due to the historic vineyards planted there by the Marquis of Bute at the end of the nineteenth century. Margaret Gore-Browne attempted to establish vineyards there in the 1960s.

Viticulture in Ireland is relatively new and vineyards are even fewer and further between than in the UK. Although spring frosts are rarely a problem, the mild, very damp climate tests the patience of most varieties of vine and yields are small. The oldest vineyard in Ireland, Longueville House, survives by selling its wines at the hotel to which the vineyard is attached and although it is a struggle, does manage to produce a crop in most years. A new vineyard, Thomas Walk, is planted with *Amurensis* hybrids and these appear to be more sucessful than disease-prone *viniferas*.

One of the earliest people to express an interest in modern viticulture in the UK was the late Gillian Pearkes who planted a small trial vineyard at Tillworth near Axminster in 1963 when she was only 18. One of the first commercial vineyards in the UK to achieve fame (if not fortune) was at Pilton Manor in Somerset which Nigel Godden planted in 1966. Pilton was a runner-up in the English Wine of the Year competition in 1974 and then won the Gore-Browne Trophy in the next two years – 1975 and 1976 and again in 1994 (under the ownership of Jim Dowling). Other early vineyards include nearby Wootton planted in 1971 and Gore-Browne Trophy winner in 1982 and 1986 and Three Choirs in Gloucestershire, planted in 1974 and today the third largest vineyard in the UK. The presence of Three Choirs, both as a successful enterprise and as a winery that could take in grapes to make wine under contract, has undoubtedly helped swell the numbers planting vineyards in the region.

Many of today's vineyards in the South West are small. Excluding the largest, Three Choirs, the size of the average vineyard is just under 1 hectare, compared to the UK average of 2.40 ha. This small size, coupled with the relatively large distance of many of them from both their neighbours and large centres of population, sometimes puts them at a disadvantage when it comes to encouraging visitors to visit and buy wine. However, vineyards near the major towns and cities or situated in the main coastal tourist areas are succeeding. Some of the vineyards in south Wales, especially those near Cardiff, report a great deal of interest in their wines, an interest that has increased since Wales was granted its own National Assembly and started to champion all things Welsh.

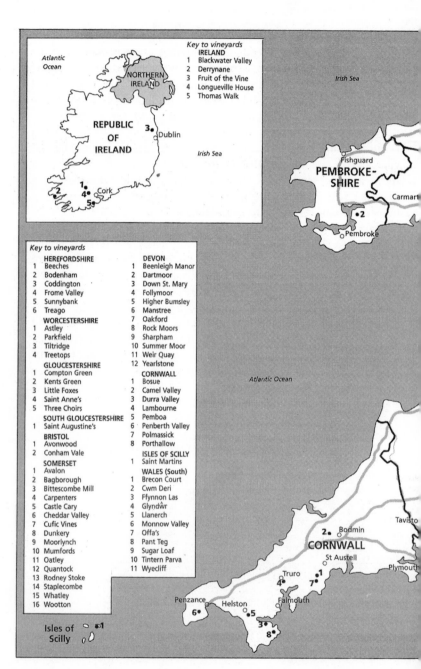

South West and Republic of Ireland

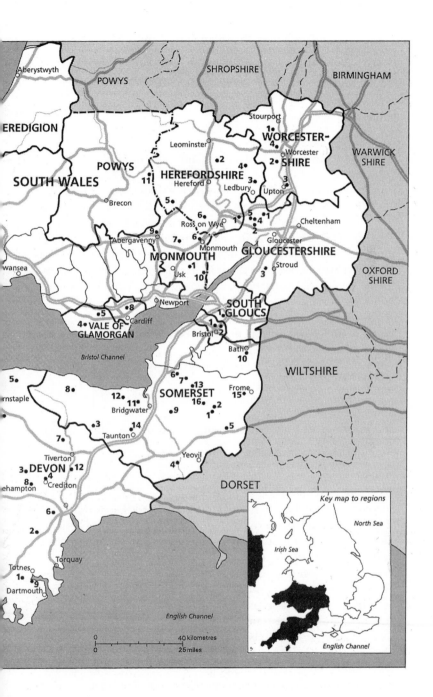

Aberystwyth

POWYS

SHROPSHIRE

BIRMINGHAM

EREDIGION

Stourport

WORCESTER-

1•
4•

•2   Worcester

2• SHIRE

WARWICK
SHIRE

POWYS

Leominster

SOUTH WALES

11• HEREFORDSHIRE
Hereford

4•
3•

3•

Ledbury

Upton

Brecon

5•

6•
Ross on Wye

1•
5•
4•

•1

Cheltenham

Abergavenny

9•
7•   6•

2

Gloucester

Monmouth

GLOUCESTERSHIRE

wansea

MONMOUTH

•1
Usk

3•

Stroud

10•

OXFORD
SHIRE

Newport

SOUTH
GLOUCS

•5
5•   •8
4• VALE OF
GLAMORGAN

Cardiff

1•
Bristol

•2

Bath

10

WILTSHIRE

Bristol Channel

5•

8•

6• 7•
•13

Frome

12•
11•
Bridgwater

SOMERSET
16•

15•

rnstaple

9•

1• •2

•1

7•

•3
14•
Taunton

•5

Tiverton

Yeovil

3• DEVON •12
8•
ehampton   Crediton

4•

DORSET

6•

2•

Torquay

Totnes
1•
9•
Dartmouth

English Channel

40 kilometres

25 miles

Key map to regions

North Sea

Irish Sea

English Channel

Beeches Vineyard

Beeches, Upton Bishop, Ross-on-Wye, Herefordshire, HR9 7UD

T: 01989 780214. F: 01989 780538. M: 0498 625346
E: boyd_john@compuserve.com

Owner: Mrs Ikka Boyd
Winemaker: Wines made at Three Choirs
Directions: From junction 4 of the M50, take the B4221 to Upton
Bishop (2 miles). At the next crossroads (Moody Cow public house
on right) go straight on towards Newent. After 200 m fork left
towards Dymock and Kempley. Vineyard is 200 m on left.
Vineyard Details: 0.12 ha of vines planted in 1991 and 1998. The
south-west facing site is 100 m above sea level and the soil is loam.
The vines are planted on a 2.1 m × 1.2 m Double Guyot system.
Grape Varieties: Madeleine × Angevine 7672, Rondo, Triomphe,
Seyval blanc.
Wine Sales: Open all year by appointment. Telephone 01989
780214. Case sales only as no off-licence. Wines may be tasted in
the Elizabethan vaulted cellar.
Vineyard Visits: Guided tours for individuals by appointment only.
No group tours.

Bodenham English Wines

Broadfield Court Estate, Bodenham, Herefordshire, HR1 3LG

T: 01568 797483. F: 01568 797859. M: 0374 742373

Owner: Keith James
Winemaker: Wines made at Three Choirs
Directions: Take the A49 from Hereford towards Leominster and in
Hope Under Dinmore turn right onto the A417 towards Gloucester.
After approx. 2 miles, turn left at the Murco garage and Broadfield
Court will be found on the right after approx. 1 mile.
Vineyard Details: 3.86 ha of vines planted between 1974 and 1998.
The site is between 105 m and 125 m above sea level, south facing
and mainly a clay loam soil. The vines are all grown on a 2.74 m ×
1.22 m Double Guyot training system.
Grape Varieties: Huxelrebe, Madeleine × Angevine 7672, Müller-
Thurgau, Reichensteiner, Seyval blanc.
Wine Sales: Daily, 10 am to 4 pm.
Vineyard Visits: Tour of the vineyards and gardens, together with a

wine tasting is available for groups of 30–50 people. Lunches, suppers and teas for groups are available from £7 per person to include cost of tour. Telephone Alexandra James for details. Wine Shop and free tasting open every day except Sunday.

Broadfield is mentioned in the Domesday Book of 1085 where Radolphus de Todeni is shown as having been the occupant (although sadly no mention of a vineyard). Vines were first planted in 1971 when 50 Müller-Thurgau and Seyval blanc were planted in the walled garden. These were followed by 500 Reichensteiner in a sloping south-west sloping field adjacent to the garden. Today, the vineyard is one of the largest in the UK and has consistently been able to ripen grapes, even in poor summers. The grapes are sent to Three Choirs for vinification, although in some years, grapes are sold to other wineries.

Coddington Vineyard
Coddington, Nr Ledbury, Herefordshire, HR8 1JJ

T: 01531 640668. F: 01531 640668

Owners & Winemakers: Denis & Ann Savage
Directions: From Ledbury take the B4214 Bromyard Road. Pass under railway bridge and take the next right signposted 'Wellington Heath'. Turn right at T-junction after one and a half miles. Take

next left signposted 'Coddington' and follow signs to Coddington until vineyard sign is seen on the left hand-side. Vineyard is a quarter of a mile down lane on right.

Vineyard Details: 0.96 ha of vines planted between 1985 and 1999. The site is between 73 m and 91 m above sea level, south facing and has a clay loam soil over sandstone. The vines are all trellised on a 2 m × 1.5 m Double Guyot system.

Grape Varieties: Bacchus, Ortega, Kerner, Pinot gris.

Wine Sales: March to December, Thursday to Monday inc. 2 pm to 5 pm. At all other times by appointment.

Vineyard Visits: Self-guided tours during opening hours. Guided tours of vineyards and gardens for groups by arrangement.

This vineyard has a well-equipped small winery with a Velo 1 tonne pneumatic press, Speidel stainless tanks, Velo DE filter and a Velo 'scraped surface' cooling unit for juice concentration. Their wines have been successful in both regional and national competitions; recent awards include a silver medal for their 1996 Kerner Sparkling and the 'Eric Coates Cup' for the best wine from a small winery for their 1997 Bacchus Dry, both in the SWVA competition. They also achieved 'Highly Commended' for their 1996 Bacchus Dry in the UKVA's national competition. Bacchus is their best variety and Kerner is being replaced with Pinot gris.

Frome Valley Vineyard

Paunton Court, Bishops Frome, Herefordshire, WR6 5BJ

T: 01885 490735. F: 01885 490736
E: david@fromewine.co.uk. W: www.fromewine.co.uks

Owners: David & Clare Longman
Winemaker: Wines made at Three Choirs
Directions: Follow brown tourist signs from the A4103 Worcester to Hereford road. From Bishops Frome take the B4214 through the village towards Bromyard. After about 1 mile follow sign to the right 'Paunton Vineyard' which is 1 mile down this lane. Entrance through courtyard.

Vineyard Details: approx. 1 ha of vines planted between 1992 and 1995. The south facing site is between 61 m and 76 m above sea level and the soil is a loamy marl. The vines are all spaced at 2 m × 1.4 m and Double Guyot trained.

FROME VALLEY
Dry White Wine
1995

English Table Wine
BOTTLED FOR
D. M. H. LONGMAN
Paunton Court Vines, Bishops Frome, Worcester.
Produce of the United Kingdom

11% vol.   75cl e

Grape Varieties: Huxelrebe, Madeleine × Angevine 7672, Pinot noir, Reichensteiner, Schönburger, Seyval blanc.
Wine Sales: April to October, Wednesday to Sunday 11 am to 5.30 pm. At all other times by appointment. There is 'an elegant tasting room' – part of an old threshing barn – where visitors may sample the wines
Vineyard Visits: During above hours. There is a 'model vineyard' by the tasting room where different varietals and training systems are displayed. Tours for groups and light refreshments also available by appointment. There are a variety of other attractions in the area to combine with a visit to the vineyard. The vineyard specialises in tours for groups.

This vineyard has won several awards for its wines including a gold medal for their 1996 Schönburger (winner of the Dry White class) and silver medals for their 1997 and 1998 Paunton Medium from the SWVA. Their wines have also been granted Quality Wine status. In 1999, Paunton Court was the first vineyard to win the UKVA's 'Award for Best Presentation' with their Madeleine Angevine 1998.

Sunnybank Vineyard and Vine Nursery
The Old Trout Inn, Dulas, Herefordshire, HR2 0HL

T: 01981 240256
E: vinenursery@hotmail.com

Owner & Winemaker: Brian Edwards
Directions: Vineyard not open to the public.
Vineyard Details: 0.34 ha of vines planted on a south facing site 85 m above sea level. The soil is a medium loam. The vines are planted at 2 m × 1.4 m and double Guyot pruned.
Grape Varieties: Madeleine × Angevine 7672, Seyval blanc, Triomphe + over 100 varieties on experimental basis.
Wine Sales & Vineyard Visits: By appointment.

Brain Edwards has been growing vines since 1974 (at both St Annes Vineyard and Sunnybank) and has one of the largest collections of vines in the UK, many of which are available for sale as rooted cuttings. Wines are made on site in a small winery and are available. Case sales only from the vineyard.

Treago Vineyard
Treago, St Weonards, Hereford, Herefordshire, HR2 8QB

T: 01981 580208. F: 01981 580208

Owner & Winemaker: Sir Richard Mynors, Bt
Directions: St Weonards is on the A466 about half way between Hereford and Monmouth. From St Weonards follow signs to Treago.
Vineyard Details: Approx. 0.3 ha of vines planted within a walled garden. Cabernet Sauvignon and Syrah planted in polythene tunnels. No other details available.
Grape Varieties: Cabernet Sauvignon, Huxelrebe, Madeleine Angevine, Schönburger, Seyval blanc, Syrah, Triomphe.
Wine Sales & Vineyard Visits: By appointment.

Production at this small vineyard is between 500 and 2000 bottles a year and includes a bottle-fermented sparkling wine. The Mynors family have lived at Treago, a fifteenth-century fortified house, for over 500 years and set up the vineyard with help from Martyn Fowke (Three Choirs) and Brian Edwards. There are five holiday cottages within the grounds with access to a heated swimming pool

Seyval/Cabernet Sauvignon 1997
Brut

TREAGO

English Quality Sparkling Wine

Produced and bottled, using the traditional
Champagne method, by Sir Richard Mynors, Bt
on the estate where his family have lived for 500 years

75 cl e   Treago St Weonards Hereford UK   12% vol

and Sir Richard Mynors reports that the vineyard is an 'overgrown hobby' and that most of the wine is sold to visitors staying in the cottages.

Astley Vineyards

Astley, Stourport-on-Severn, Worcestershire, DY13 0RU

T: 01299 822907. F: 01299 822907

Owners: Jonty Daniels & Janet Baldwin
Winemaker: Wines made at Three Choirs
Directions: From Worcester take the A443 (direction Tenbury) then the B4196 (direction Stourport). The vineyard is signposted some 3 miles south of Stourport, between the River Severn and the B4196.
Vineyard Details: 2 ha of vines planted in 1979 and 1980 on a north facing site 55 m above sea level. The soil is sandy loam derived from old red sandstone.
Grape Varieties: Huxelrebe, Kerner, Madeleine × Angevine 7672, Müller-Thurgau.

Wine Sales: The vineyard is open all year round for wine sales. Mondays and Thursday to Saturday 10 am to 5 pm. Sunday noon to 5 pm. Closed Tuesday and Wednesday.
Vineyard Visits: As above. Entry is free and visitors are given an explanatory leaflet and map. Guided tours and meals are not available.

Situated in the Severn Valley, the vineyard was established in an area that has strong historical connections with viticulture. The steep, south-facing slope adjacent to the Norman Church in Astley is known as the Vineyard, and was no doubt connected to the Benedictine Monastery that existed locally until the reign of Henry V.

There is no winery at Astley, but the grapes are taken to the Three Choirs winery, where winemaker Martin Fowke presides. However, Janet and Jonty do not just hand over their grapes and disappear – they like to be part of the winemaking process and make several visits to see how their wines are coming on between pressing and bottling. Over the years, both under the previous owners, Michael and Betty Bache, and the current owners, Astley wines have won numerous awards and medals in both local, national and international competitions. They are twice winners of the President's Trophy in the UKVA's English and Welsh Wine of the Year Competition and in the same competition in 1998, scooped five

awards. Their 1990 Kerner won silver in the International Wine Challenge and their 1994 Madeleine Angevine won gold and the Committee Cup for the best dry white in the South West Vineyards Association's (SWVA) competition. There are nine wines on their retail list including varietals, blends, a late harvest sweet wine as well as their first sparkling wine, a 1996, which won silver at the 1998 SWVA competition. Their 1997 Madeleine Angevine gained a bronze at the 1999 Wine Challenge.

Astley's record of producing sound wines has been very consistent and shows the quality of the site. However, the owners are not resting on their laurels. The original varietal mix is undergoing some changes. Huxelrebe is being phased out and will be replaced by early-ripening Siegerrebe and Müller-Thurgau by Bacchus. Most of their wine is sold locally – one of their good customers being the National Conference Centre at nearby Birmingham. In 1998 they supplied their 'Huxelvaner' (a Huxelrebe/Müller-Thurgau blend) for the G8 summit held there. Taken altogether, Astley must rate as one of the UK's top producers. Well worth a detour!

Parkfield Vineyard

The Orchards, Broadmore Green, Rushwick, Worcestershire, WR2 5TE

T: 01905 420449

Owner & Winemaker: Tony Sharp
Directions: Vineyard not open to the public.
Vineyard Details: 0.12 ha of vines planted in 1991. The south facing site is between 46 m and 55 m above sea level and it has a clay soil. The vines are spaced at 2 m × 1.4 m and 2.5 m × 1.4 m and are Double Guyot trained.
Grape Varieties: Madeleine × Angevine 7672, Reichensteiner.

This is a non-commercial vineyard making both still and sparkling wine for family and friends.

Tiltridge Vineyard

Tiltridge Farm, Upper Hook Road, Upton-upon-Severn, Worcestershire, WR8 0SA

T: 01684 592906. F: 01684 594142
E: elgarwine@aol.com

Owners: Peter & Sandy Barker

Winemaker: Wines made at Three Choirs Vineyard

Directions: Off the A38, take the A4104 towards Ledbury. In Upton-upon-Severn turn down New Street at the HSBC Bank. After half a mile bear left up a bank and the vineyard will be found on the left after another half mile. There are brown tourist signs on most approach roads.

Vineyard Details: 0.51 ha of vines planted between 1988 and 1996. The south-east facing site is at 38 m above sea level and has a soil described as 'mudstones'. The older vines are planted at 2.13 m × 1.4 m and Double Guyot pruned; the 1996 planting is planted at 3.6 m × 3.3 m and GD trained.

Grape Varieties: Huxelrebe, Schönburger, Seyval blanc, Triomphe.

Wine Sales: All year round, Monday to Saturday, 11 am to 5 pm. Sundays, noon to 5 pm. Please telephone in winter months to check opening times.

Vineyard Visits: Tours and simple meals for groups (15 to 40+ people) are available by appointment from £7.50 per person.

Tiltridge Vineyard was once part of a County Council tenanted farm. When the last tenant died, it was in such a poor state that the Council decided to sell and in 1982 the Barkers were able to buy the

ESTABLISHED IN 1988

𝒯ILTRIDGE 𝒱INEYARD

ENGLISH VINEYARDS
QUALITY WINE P.S.R.

75cl

Grown by and bottled for Tiltridge Vineyard, Upton upon Severn, Worcestershire, UK, by WI473.

house, some buildings and land. Having liked the local Three Choirs wines, they thought that they would have a go themselves and in 1988, the first vines were planted. Since the first commercial harvest in 1991, the wines have been made at Three Choirs, although if the planted area is increased beyond its present size, a winery will be considered.

Tiltridge wines – some of which are labelled as 'Elgar' after the composer who lived and worked nearby – have done well in the UKVA's national competition. The 1996 'Elgar' sparkling won a bronze medal, the 1996 'Elgar' medium dry, the 1996 Huxelrebe and the 1996 Schönburger all won highly commended and the last two have also gained Quality Wine status.

Treetops Vineyard

28 Hallow Lane, Lower Broadheath, Worcester, Worcestershire, WR2 6QL

T: 01905 640096

Owner & Winemaker: Dr Dorian Edynbry
Directions: Vineyard not open to the public.
Vineyard Details: 0.03 ha of vines planted in 1994. The south facing site has a sandy loam soil and is 46 m above sea level.
Grape Varieties: Madeleine × Angevine 7672, Müller-Thurgau, Seyval blanc.

This is a small non-commercial vineyard and wine is made (in 'half a garage') for personal consumption.

Compton Green Vineyard

Compton Green, Redmarley, Gloucestershire
Address for correspondence:
Maxstoke, Aston Ingham, Ross on Wye, Herefordshire, HR9 7LS

T: 01989 720465

Owner: Mr Alan Oastler
Winemaker: Wines made at Three Choirs
Directions: Vineyard not open to the public.
Vineyard Details: 1.5 ha of vines planted between 1991 and 1993. The site is between 60 m and 75 m above sea level and the vines are

COMPTON GREEN

11%   **English Table Wine**   75cl

Produced by & bottled for Compton Green Vineyard
Redmarley   Gloucestershire
UK

mainly trellised on a 2.7 m × 1.4 m or 1.8 m Double Guyot system.
Grape Varieties: Madeleine × Angevine 7672, Schönburger, Seyval blanc, Triomphe.
Wine Sales & Vineyard Visits: By appointment.

Kents Green Vineyard
Taynton, Gloucestershire, GL19 3AJ

T: 01452 790212

Owner: Mac Hammond
Winemaker: Wines made at Three Choirs Vineyard
Directions: Telephone for directions.
Vineyard Details: 0.18 ha of vines planted in 1979 on a 2 m × 2 m Double Guyot system. The site is 30 m above sea level, south facing and the soil is a heavy marl.
Grape Variety: Müller-Thurgau.
Wine Sales & Vineyard Visits: By appointment.

Kents Green wines have done well in competitions consistently winning medals in both the national and regional competitions.

Their 1995 Müller-Thurgau and Huxelrebe won a Gold medal and their 1996 a 'Highly Commeded' at the UKVA's 1997 competition. Their wine was the only English Wine chosen by the International Wine and Food Society for their Gala Dinner held in the Lake District in 1991 and hosted by Michael Broadbent MW. Mac Hammond was one time a director at Three Choirs Vineyard.

Little Foxes Vineyard
111 Gloucester Road, Stonehouse, Gloucestershire, GL10 2HB

T: 01453 828930
E: n.h.munro@btinternet.com

Owners: Neil & Helen Munro
Winemaker: Neil Munro
Directions: Vineyard not open to the public.
Vineyard Details: 8.28 sq.m of vines (12 in number) planted between 1994 and 1998. The vines are planted at 0.91 m × 0.75 m and are Double Guyot trained.
Grape Varieties: Chardonnay, Müller-Thurgau, Schönburger, Seyval blanc, Siegerrebe.

The only reference to a Gloucestershire vineyard in the 1086 Domesday Book is to one in 'Stanhus' – today's Stonehouse and it was owned by William De Ow, cousin of William the Conqueror. Stonehouse's proximity to two great Roman towns, Gloucester and Cirencester, make it a likely area for Roman viticulture. Canon Henry Nicholson Ellacombe, a vicar and gardener at Bitton, made a study of English vineyards in the 1890's and wrote of Stonehouse, that 'there could be few warmer spots in the county'. Nearby 'Vinegar Hill' is still marked on maps which might possibly indicate some former viticultural activity in the area! This is the smallest vineyard in this guide and annual production 'in a good year is 70 lbs of grapes which makes 15 bottles'!

Saint Anne's Vineyard
Wain House, Oxenhall, Newent, Gloucestershire, GL18 1RW

T: 01989 720313
w: www.glosibp.co.uk/tt1/areas/forest/vineyard

Owner & Winemaker: David Jenkins

Directions: Take B4215 Gloucester to Newent road. Use B4221 ring road around Newent. Immediately past second Newent turn-off, turn right at Woodyard. Vineyard 2 miles up road.

Vineyard Details: 2.11 ha of vines planted between 1981 and 1996. The south-east and south-west facing sites are between 45 m and 65 m above sea level. The older site is a heavy loam; the newer site is sandy.

Grape Varieties: Madeleine × Angevine 7672, Müller-Thurgau, Seyval blanc, Schönburger, Triomphe + a very wide range of other varieties.

Wine Sales: 1 January to 15 March, weekends only 11 am to 6 pm. 16 March to 15 October, daily 11 am to 6 pm. 16 October to 31 December, Wednesday to Sunday 11 am to 6 pm. At all other times by appointment.

Vineyard Visits: By arrangement. Group tours and light meals available.

St Anne's is a small commercial vineyard that has been producing English wine since 1984. It also makes a wide range of country wines. St Anne's also has a large collection of vines, many of them experimental, and sells vines, both potted and as rooted cuttings in season.

Three Choirs Vineyard
Newent, Gloucestershire, GL18 1LS

T: Office/Winery: 01531 890555
T: Shop/Restaurant: 01531 890223. F: 01531 890877
E: ts@freeserve.co.uk. W: www.threechoirs.com

Owner: Three Choirs Vineyard Ltd
Winemaker: Martin Fowke
Directions: From Newent take the B4215 signposted Dymock and Leominster. After 2 miles turn right into Welsh House lane. Vineyard on right-hand side after 1 mile.

Vineyard Details: 30 ha of vines planted between 1974 and 1999. There are a number of different sites between 24 m and 70 m above sea level and mainly south and south-west facing. The majority of vines are planted at 3.35 m × 3.05 m and GDC trained, although some of the older plantings are 2.74 m × 1.52 m Guyot and 4.27 m × 3.05 m Pergola trained.

Major Grape Varieties: Bacchus, Huxelrebe, Madeleine × Angevine 7672, Müller-Thurgau, Orion, Phoenix, Pinot noir, Regent, Reichensteiner, Schönburger, Seyval blanc, Siegerrebe, Triomphe.
Minor Grape Varieties: Ehrenfelser, Faberrebe, Gamay, Maréchal Foch, Ortega, Pinot blanc, Rondo, Würzer, Zweigeltrebe.
Wine Sales: All year round, daily. Summer 10 am to 5 pm. Winter 11 am to 4 pm. Telephone for Christmas and New Year opening times. Wine also available by mail order. Shop stocks wide range of local gifts, produce etc. 'Madeleine's Café' for light snacks, teas, coffees etc. open 11 am to 4 pm daily.
Restaurant: Tuesday to Sunday, noon to 2.30 pm (last orders). Thursday, Friday and Saturday 7 pm to 9 pm (last orders). Closed on Mondays. Additional evening openings in 2000 – telephone for details. Restaurant also open on other evenings by appointment. Restaurant rated AA two rosettes.
Vineyard Visits: Self-guided tours of vineyards and winery for individuals or groups of up to 20 people available during above opening hours. Guided tours for larger groups by appointment. Exhibition centre and video on winegrowing at Three Choirs. Wide selection of meals available for groups. Eight guest rooms are also available.

THREE CHOIRS

1998
PREMIUM SELECTION
ENGLISH TABLE WINE

PRODUCED AND BOTTLED AT THREE CHOIRS VINEYARDS,
NEWENT, GLOUCESTERSHIRE
75cl e   PRODUCE OF U.K.   10.5% vol

Three Choirs Vineyard was one of the first large commercial vineyards to be planted in the UK and over the last 25 years has established itself as a major force in English wine. It is by far the largest and most important vineyard in the western half of the UK and makes wines under contract for many growers.

Vines were first planted in 1974 by Alan McKechnie on his farm at Newent which was then known as Fairfields Fruit Farm. Tom Day, his farm manager, took a keen interest in the vineyard side of the farm and it is really due to his, and wife Brenda's, endeavours that Three Choirs took shape and became what it is today. (Tom is also father-in-law to current Three Choirs winemaker Martin Fowke and father of Simon Day – ex-Lamberhurst winemaker, now at Jersey's La Mare Vineyard.) In 1984, McKechnie wanted to sell up and Tom persuaded a consortium of local businessmen and vineyard owners to put up some funds and buy it. Under the new ownership, the vineyards expanded and Three Choirs developed in both size and complexity.

To begin with, the winery, shop and offices were housed in the old apple packing buildings which were situated down a rather tortuous lane which coaches could not navigate. However, in 1990 a site which adjoined their land and which fronted on to the main road came up for sale, was purchased and in 1991 a brand new winery – air conditioned, insulated and with a epoxy floor that cost an arm and a leg – was erected. An existing house was converted into offices and a restaurant and a new shop and café were built. Eight well-appointed guest rooms were added in 2000.

As one would expect with a vineyard of this size, the winery is well equipped with two Willmes UP 1800 pneumatic presses, the usual filtration and other winemaking equipment and a fully auto-matic GAI/Enos filling/labelling line. Tanks are a combination of both newer stainless steel and older glass fibre and there is a cold store for the cold stabilisation of their wines as well as for the production and storage of süss-reserve. For the first two vintages, 1976 and 1977, the grapes were sent to Nigel Godden at Pilton Manor, but for the 1976 vintage, a winery was installed and Tom Day took over as winemaker. He was soon joined by Dr Kit Morris (now owner of the Bottle Green Drinks Co.) who remained as winemaker from 1977 until 1988 when the present winemaker, Martin Fowke, succeeded him.

Over the years, Three Choirs have earned themselves a good reputation for their wines and today have a range which is as wide and as good as from any UK winery. They are relatively well distributed. They list whites, both varietal and blended, dry and sweet(er), still and sparkling and a red – although this is usually in short supply. Their best wines tend to be the varietals – Bacchus, Madeleine Angevine, Schönburger, Huxelrebe, Siegerrebe and Phoenix are all on their current list – as well as a 'New Release' which is fermented, clarified and bottled with an almost indecent haste and launched to coincide with Beaujolais Nouveau. This last wine – despite its youth – is usually very drinkable and surprises people with its quality. It would be nice to think that drinking English wine within a few weeks of harvest might catch on in a big way and prove (as it used to be with Beaujolais) a useful way of easing the cash-flow so soon after the expensive harvesting/winemaking period.

Their tally of medals and awards is impressive and over the years have picked up a fair few (although surprisingly never the Gore-Browne Trophy). They won the UKVA's Jack Ward Memorial Salver in 1984 and the President's Trophy in 1995. They have also won a whole host of medals and trophies for vineyards that they make the wine for. In regional competitions, their recent successes include a gold and Best in Competition for the 1997 Bacchus Estate Reserve at the MVA's 1998 competition, a gold and Best Dry Wine for the 1997 Siegerrebe and gold and 'Best in Competition' for their 1997 Late Harvest, both last wines in the SWVA's competition. They also won a bronze at the 'Bourg et Blaye' competition (which is tied in with the huge biennial Vinexpo wine fair) for their British Airways Limited Edition – a wine they supplied for serving in First Class. Many of their wines have achieved Quality and Regional wine status.

Saint Augustine's Vineyard
The Old Parsonage, Aust, South Gloucestershire, BS35 4BG

T: 01454 632236. F: 01454 632236

Owners: Mike & Pat Tayler
Winemaker: Wines made at Three Choirs
Directions: Take M48 towards Chepstow and leave at J1 towards Avonmouth on A403 for 200 yards. Turn right off A403 and

SAINT AUGUSTINE'S VINEYARD

English Table Wine

11% Vol *1996* 75cle

Bottled for Saint' Augustine's Vineyard
Aust', Gloucestershire., United Kingdom
PRODUCE OF THE UNITED KINGDOM

vineyard will be found on the left-hand side in 600 yards. Follow brown tourist signs.

Vineyard Details: 0.40 ha of vines planted between 1987 and 1992. The south west facing site is between 20 m and 25 m above sea level and the soil is a silty loam overlying marl.

Grape Varieties: Kernling, Madeleine × Angevine 7672, Müller-Thurgau, Reichensteiner.

Wine Sales & Vineyard Visits: The vineyard is usually open from May to September on Wednesdays and Saturdays, 2 pm to 5 pm. Tours available by arrangement.

It was at Aust on the banks of the Severn that St Augustine, the first Archbishop of Canterbury, met the Welsh bishops in 603 AD. Whether this confers a special status upon this vineyard in uncertain! The vineyard is landscaped and planted with old French roses. The Taylors are also agents for an exclusive range of French gardening clothes and tools. Their 1996 Madeleine Angevine was awarded a Highly Commended in the 1998 UKVA competition, their 1997 Madeleine Angevine a Very Highly Commended in the

1998 SWVA competition and their 1998 Madeleine Angevine a bronze medal in the 1999 UKVA competition.

Avonwood Vineyard

Sea Walls Road, Sneyd Park, Bristol, BS9 1PH

T: 01179 686613

Owners: Drs John & Norma Minors
Winemaker: Dr John Minors
Vineyard Details: 0.25 ha of vines planted between 1978 and 1992. The site is steeply sloping, south facing and overlooks the Avon Gorge towards the Clifton Suspension Bridge. It is within the boundary of the city of Bristol. The soil is broken limestone. All vines are Guyot trained and planted close together – 1.4 m × 1.4 m and 1.5 m × 1.5m.
Grape Varieties: Müller-Thurgau, Madeleine × Angevine 7672, Pinot noir, Reichensteiner, Schönburger.
Wine Sales and Vineyard Visits: The vineyard is only open by appointment. Tours are available.

Run by two Bristol GPs, Avonwood vineyard occupies a spectacular setting overlooking the Avon Gorge. It is one of the few really steeply sloping vineyards in the UK and gets the benefit of full sunshine. The work in the vineyard and winery is very much a family affair and is described as 'a hobby that got out of control' but also as 'therapy'. Winemaking has been learnt on the job and Dr Minors says that he improves his skills with each vintage. Around 1,500 bottles are produced annually.

Conham Vale Vineyard

Nicholas Lane, White's Hill, Bristol
Address for correspondence:
38 St David's Avenue, Warmley, Bristol, BS30 8DF

T: 01179 670410

Owner & Winemaker: Roger Eynon
Directions: Vineyard not open to the public.
Vineyard Details: 0.06 ha of vines planted between 1986 and 1995 and trained on a 1.22 m × 1.22 m Double Guyot system.
Grape Varieties: Findling, Madeleine × Angevine 7672, Pinot noir, Schönburger, Seyval blanc, Siegerrebe, Triomphe.

Avalon Vineyard

The Drove, East Pennard, Shepton Mallet, Somerset, BA4 6UA

T: 01749 860393
W: www.dorset-info.co.uk/places2visit/avalon_vineyard.htm

Owner: Dr & Mrs H R Howard Tripp
Winemaker: Dr Howard Tripp
Directions: Take A37 five miles south of Shepton Mallet, turn west at crossroad at bottom of Wraxall Hill, opposite Queen's Arms public house. After 1.5 miles look out for vineyard sign on the right-hand side. Vineyard will be found 0.25 miles up a rough track.
Vineyard Details: 0.91 ha planted between 1981 and 1990. The earlier plantings are on a 1.22 m × 1.22 m Guyot system; later plantings on a 3.35 m × 1.68 m Lyre system. The site is between 76 m and 107 m above sea level and is mainly silt, sand and clay loam over clay. The vineyard is organic, only hybrid varieties are grown and chemical sprays are not used.
Grape Varieties: Seyval blanc, Orion.

Wine Sales: Daily, Good Friday to Christmas. 10 am to 3 pm.
Vineyard Visits: Self-guided tours are available for individuals.
Times as above. Tours are available for groups of 10–40 people at
£2 per person which take 1½–2 hours. This includes a tasting of
wines, fruit wines, meads and ciders. A substantial ploughman's
meal is available at £5 per person.

Avalon vineyard is one of the very few organic vineyards in the UK.
It grows only hybrids, Seyval blanc and Orion, a new Geilweilerhof
crossing (Optima × Seyve Villard 12-375) which makes fresh fruity
wines. Winemaking equipment is very traditional and the press used
for the grapes is an old vertical cider press which used straw
'cheeses' to separate layers of fruit pulp to aid juice drainage. Dr
Tripp comments that he finds it 'effective, appropriate and certainly
very organic'. Fermentations are all in stainless. The wines are left
on their gros lees for several months which, although risky, can help
develop more interesting flavours. Apart from making grapes wines,
Avalon also produces a range of fruit wines, ciders and meads. All
wines carry the Soil Association's Organic symbol.

Bagborough Vineyard
Pylle, Shepton Mallet, Somerset, BA4 6SX

T: 01749 831146. F: 01749 830832
E: brooksbank@bagborough.freeserve.co.uk

Owner and Winemaker: Stephen Brooksbank
Directions: Signposted from A37, three miles south of Shepton Mallet.
Vineyard Details: 2.43 ha of vines. The site is 76 m to 84 m above sea level, south facing and mainly clay loam. No other details available.
Grape Varieties: Bacchus, Kerner, Müller-Thurgau, Reichensteiner, Schönburger, Seyval blanc.
Wine Sales and Vineyard Visits: The vineyard is open at 'any reasonable time' – probably best to telephone beforehand. Vineyard and winery tours are not available.

Bagborough winery is well equipped with a Chemo grape trailer, Howard press, Velo earth filter and GAI monobloc filler. All fermentations are in stainless steel. Cider is also made. Steve Brooksbank sells most of his wine at the Glastonbury Festival and at other similar events.

Bittescombe Mill Vineyard
Raddington, Taunton, Somerset, TA4 2QN

T: 01398 361285. F: 01398 361285
E: rb@blackfordantiques.freeserve.co.uk

Owner: Robert Beresford
Directions: Vineyard not open to the public.
Vineyard Details: 3.6 ares of vines (0.036 ha) planted in 1993. The south-east facing site is between 122 m and 152 m above sea level and the soil is described as 'clay/stony'. The vines are planted at 1.6 m × 1.5 m and are Double Guyot pruned.
Grape Varieties: Madeleine × Angevine 7672, Madeleine Sylvaner, Müller-Thurgau.

This is a small private vineyard, high up on the slopes of the Brendon Hills. It is prone to spring and early autumn frosts, but is a sun-trap in the summer.

Carpenters Vineyard

'Carpenters', Higher Street, Norton sub Hamdon, Somerset, TA14 6SN

T: 01935 881255

Owner: Michael Cumberlege
Winemaker: Wines made at Staplecombe
Directions: Vineyard not open to the public.
Vineyard Details: 0.06 ha vines planted in 1996 on a 2.5 × 1.4 Double Guyot system.
Grape Varieties: Madeleine × Angevine 7672, Seyval blanc, Siegerrebe.

This is a small amateur vineyard not open to the public. Wines are not made for sale.

Castle Cary Vineyard

Honeywick Hill, Hadspen, Castle Cary, Somerset, BA7 7LP

T: 01963 351507. F: 01963 351507
E: ccvwine@yahoo.com

Owner: Castle Cary Vineyard and Winery Ltd
Directions: Take A371 Wincanton to Shepton Mallet road. Turn right at Castle Cary and follow vineyard signs.
Vineyard Details: 1.70 ha of vines planted between 1979 and 1988. The site is between 76 m and 96 m above sea level, south facing and has a fine sandy loam soil. The vines are all double guyot trained and planted at 2.13 m × 1.5 m, 1.5 m × 1.5 m and 1.8 m × 1.5 m.
Grape Varieties: Huxelrebe, Madeleine × Angevine 7672, Müller-Thurgau, Regner, Schönburger, Seyval blanc.
Wine Sales and Vineyard Visits: Open all year, 9.30 am to 4.30 pm.

This old established vineyard is situated in a fold in the hills between the historic towns of Bruton and Castle Cary and is on the Cadbury Castle cycle route and Leland walking trail. There is a history of winegrowing in this area with records showing that the nearby Augustinian Priory at Bruton cultivated vines. It has its own small winery complete with two basket presses and a two head Bancroft filler. All wines retail at £7.50 and are sold under the Honeywick Hill and Castle Cary labels.

Cheddar Valley Vineyard
Stoneleys, Hillside, Axbridge, Somerset, BS26 2AN

T: 01934 732280. F: 01934 732280
W: www.welcometo/cvv

Owners: Kay McDonald & Mel Packham
Winemaker: Wines made at Wootton
Directions: Take A371 Axbridge to Wells road. Vineyard on left-hand side, overlooking Cheddar reservoir on Axbridge by-pass.
Vineyard Details: 0.52 ha of vines planted between 1974 and 1986. The south facing site is 26 m above sea level and has a light clay loam soil.
Grape Varieties: Auxerrois, Madeleine × Angevine 7672, Müller-Thurgau, Pinot gris, Reichensteiner, Schönburger.
Wine Sales & Vineyard Visits: The vineyard is open to visitors at different times, depending on the season. Telephone for details. Guided tours and meals are available for groups by appointment.

Cheddar Valley Vineyard occupies a beautiful spot overlooking the Somerset Levels and the Cheddar Reservoir. There is a café where a wide selection of food is served.

Cufic Vines
Tuttors Hill, Cheddar, Somerset, BS27 3JG

T: 01934 839900. F: 01934 839904. M: 0771 809150

Owner: Tony Pinnington
Directions: Vineyard not open to the public.
Vineyard Details: 0.12 ha of vines planted in 1973 and 1974. The site is between 61 m and 76 m above sea level and faces south south-west. The soil is a sandy loam overlying limestone.
Grape Varieties: Huxelrebe, Gewürztraminer, Müller-Thurgau, Reichensteiner, Seyval blanc.

This is a small private vineyard planted on a massive limestone outcrop on the southern slopes of the Mendips. The site, on a 15° slope, is impossible to mechanise. Wine is only sold locally or by word of mouth, although House of Fraser have featured it in their food departments.

Dunkery Vineyard

Ordesa, Wootton Courtenay, Minehead, Somerset, TA24 8RD

T: 01643 841505. F: 01643 841505. M: 07968 094869
E: pritchard@viticulture.co.uk. W: www.exmoor.english-wine.com

Owners: Derek & Val Pritchard
Winemaker: Derek Pritchard
Directions: From the A39 approaching Minehead, take the A396
through the village of Dunster, where you enter the Exmoor
National Park. 2 miles south-west of Dunster, take right-hand
turning signposted Wootton Courtenay one and a half miles.
Vineyard can be seen as you approach the village.
Vineyard Details: 2.89 ha of vines planted between 1984 and 1996.
The site is between 61 m and 110 m above sea level, the older
plantings on a sloping south south-west facing site, the newer
plantings on flatter land. Soil is Devonian red sandstone. The vines
are planted on a variety of systems: 2.5 m × 1.6 m modified Sylvoz,
1.5 m × 1.5 m Mosel Loop, 1.25 m × 1.8 m Double Guyot.

Grape Varieties: Chardonnay, Dornfelder, Dunkelfelder, Kernling, Madeleine × Angevine 7672, Orion, Pinot gris, Pinot noir, Phoenix, Regent, Reichensteiner, Rondo, Schönburger, Senator, plus other trial varieties.

Wine Sales & Vineyard Visits: By appointment.

Dunkery Vineyard is the second largest in Somerset and the only one within the Exmoor National Park. The older 0.4 ha vineyard is on a very well sheltered site and is close planted (1.5 m row width) to capture the maximum heat. All work is done by hand. The newer (1990–1996) vineyard is less sheltered and on relatively flat land, but captures the sunshine all day long. It is trained on a modified Sylvoz system (a combination spur and loose cane system) that is rarely found in the UK.

A new winery, built after a six-year battle to get planning permission (the local authority decided it had to be an industrial building), is now in use. It is partially dug into the hillside and in places has 1.22 m thick retaining walls. It is very well equipped with one 500 litre and one 1800 litre Willmes pneumatic presses – the latter in stainless steel with central filling – a Speidel 180 litre Hydropress, 6 tonne/hr KTM destalker ('the best piece of equipment in the winery'), 6-head KTM filler, two Kiesel mono-pumps, a Seitz Rapid steamer and the remainder of the usual pumps, filters etc. found in most wineries. There are more than 30 tanks, all variable capacity stainless steel, mainly made by Speidel.

A wide range of vines are produced, both varietal and blends. About one third of the production is red – some aged on oak – and their 1990 Pinot noir was awarded one star in a Decanter tasting – way ahead of many better known Burgundies. Wine competitions are not entered into. Sparkling wine is also produced using Pinot noir, Chardonnay and Pinot gris. Since 1984, the Pritchards have imported both vines and winery equipment.

Moorlynch Vineyard
Moorlynch, Bridgwater, Somerset, TA7 9DD

T: 01458 210393. F: 01458 210247. M: 0850 942628
E: moorlynch@aol.com.

Owners: Peter & Anne Farmer
Winemaker: Peter Farmer

Directions: Take A361 Taunton to Glastonbury and follow the road signs at the outskirts of Greinton. From the M5 take the A39 to Glastonbury and look for road signs after 5 miles.

Vineyard Details: 1.5 ha of vines planted between 1981 and 1991. The south facing site is between 66 m and 100 m above sea level and the soil is clay overlying limestone. The vines are planted on two systems; a 2 m × 1.25 m Double Guyot and 3 m × 2 m Bordeaux Lyre.

Grape Varieties: Faberrebe, Huxelrebe, Müller-Thurgau, Schönburger, Seyval blanc, Würzer.

Wine Sales: Easter and May to September, Tuesday to Saturday, 10.30 am to 5 pm, Sunday, noon to 5 pm. During other months, Wednesday to Saturday, 10.30 am to 5 pm. At all times by appointment. In addition to Moorlynch products, the shop stocks a wide range of local goods.

Vineyard Visits: Individuals May to September during hours as above. Adults £3.50 OAPs £2.50. Includes video, winery visit and tasting. The Courtyard Restaurant is open for lunches, teas and light refreshments during above hours. Pre-booked groups from

MOORLYNCH
VINEYARD

Somerset

Estate Grown & Bottled

~ DRY ~

£3.50. Wide range of tours, tastings and meals available, plus special events at Easter, Mothering Sunday, Christmas etc. There are also farm workshops with glass blower, craft potter, photographic studio and music studio.

Vines were first planted at Moorlynch Vineyard in 1981. It is situated on the lower slopes of the Polden Hills with views over Sedgemoor to the Blackdown Hills and was established by Tom Rees, a retired Whitehall civil servant, and his wife, Judith, a specialist dyslexia teacher, after much searching for the ideal farm. With its south facing slopes and its range of eighteenth century stone barns set in a courtyard, it was the perfect site for their venture. At one stage there were 6.5 ha of vines with ten different varieties, some planted under plastic tunnels. The Rees ran it until 1991 (they retired to France and now own a small vineyard) when, shortly before the harvest, Peter (ex-nuclear industry) and Anne Farmer (teacher) purchased it. With little experience of either farming or winemaking, they set to, rolled their sleeves up and learnt the hard way.

Since 1991, the Farmers have rationalised the vineyards – both in terms of number of varieties and area under vines – and concentrated more on the visitor and leisure side of the business. They are helping small local artisans – a potter, glass-blower, photographer and musician – establish their workshops there. They also produce a wide range of special labels for both individuals and companies and can tailor events to suit the occasion.

The converted farm buildings that house the shop, restaurant and photographic and music studios are a delightful collection of eighteenth- and nineteenth-century stone buildings that have unusual continental-style Roman pan-tiled roofs. The winery, which is a newer building and which also houses the glassblower's studio, adjoins them. The winery is very well equipped with mainly stainless steel tanks, a Willmes UP1800 pneumatic press, GAI automatic filler/corker, Sartorious membrane filter and a good range of the usual modern winery equipment. The first vintage was in 1983, and in common with many vineyards just starting out, the wines were made at another local winery. Since 1984, the wines have been made at Moorlynch. A recent venture is that of English brandy production and two 300 litre barrels from the 1997 harvest are currently ageing. More will be produced as and when harvests allow.

Over the years, Moorlynch wines have won many medals and awards. Tom Rees was the SWVA's 1986 Winemaker of the Year, their wines were awarded bronze medals in both the 1985 and 1987 national competition and a silver medal at the SWVA's 1988 competition for the Moorlynch Medium 1986. They also won top prize at the 1987 and 1988 Royal Bath and West Show. More recent accolades include silver for the 1992 Special Reserve Sparkling, golds for both the 1994 Special Reserve Sparkling and Sedgemoor Medium Dry and bronze for the 1997 Polden Hills Medium – all in the SWVA's regional competition. Jancis Robinson praised their 1992 sparkling saying in a *Financial Times* article that it was 'my favourite' – praise from on high indeed!

Mumfords Vineyard
Shockerwick Lane, Bannerdown, Bath, Somerset, BA1 7LQ

T: 01225 858367. F: 01225 852385

Owners: Margaret & Tony Cox
Winemaker: Tony Cox
Directions: Take A4 east of Bath to Batheaston. Turn up Bannerdown Road, signposted to Colerne. After half a mile, turn right into Shockerwick Lane. Vineyard 100 yds on the right-hand side.
Vineyard Details: 1.24 ha of vines planted between 1986 and 1989, mostly on their own roots. The south facing site is 70 m above sea level, has an alkaline brash soil over limestone and the vines are Double Guyot trained at 1.83 m × 1.22 m and 1.52 m.
Grape Varieties: Madeleine × Angevine 7672, Kerner. Reichensteiner, Seyval blanc, Triomphe.
Wine Sales: Open all year, all hours. Telephone in advance.
Vineyard Visits: As above. Groups from 10–30 people welcome by arrangement from mid-June to December. £4 per person including wine tasting.

Mumfords Vineyard is situated in a very attractive setting, overlooking the Avon valley, just two miles from Bath. The winery and wine store are purpose built, equipped with modern German winemaking equipment and the tanks are all stainless steel. Joanna

·MUMFORDS·
VINEYARD

MUMFORDS
ROSÉ
English tablewine

Produced and Bottled at Mumfords Vineyard
Bannerdown. Bath. England.
11%vol   Produce of the United Kingdom   75cl e

Simon (*Sunday Times* wine correspondent) rated their 1990 Kerner highly and said it was 'vibrantly fruity; invigoratingly tangy'. The same wine was also highly rated by *Decanter Magazine*. Their 1993 Madeleine Angevine was awarded silver at the Royal Bath and West Show and their 1997 Medium Dry silver at the West Country Food Awards. The wines are available through Great Western Wines of Wells Road, Bath and their Mumfords medium dry is stocked in both the Bristol and Bath branches of Waitrose.

Oatley Vineyard
Cannington, Bridgwater, Somerset, TA5 2NL

T: 01278 671340. F: 01278 671340
E: wine@oatley.demon.co.uk. W: www.oatley.demon.co.uk

Owner: Iain Awty
Directions: Turn north from A39 1 mile west of Cannington at small crossroads with poplar trees and red post box. Continue for three-quarters of a mile.
Vineyard Details: 1.9 ha of vines planted between 1986 and 1988. The site is between 35 m and 70 m above sea level, south south-east facing and has a red, sandy loam soil. The vines are planted at

ENGLISH TABLE WINE.
1995
OATLEY
SUMMER DRY

75cl e
PRODUCE OF UNITED KINGDOM
BOTTLED FOR OATLEY VINEYARD
CANNINGTON, BRIDGWATER,
SOMERSET, ENGLAND, UK.
11.5% vol

4 m × 1. 5 m and Bordeaux Lyre trained or at 2.4 m × 1.5 m and Double Guyot trained.
Grape Varieties: Kerner, Kernling, Madeleine × Angevine 7672.
Wine Sales & Vineyard Visits: By arrangement. Case sales only.

Oatley's wines (which used to be made by Colin Gillespie at Wootton Vineyards) have an enviable reputation for quality and have won many awards and commendations. For several years they dominated the competition held at the Royal Bath and West Show. Their 1991, 1992 and 1993 vintages achieved Gold or Champion Gold medals. Their 1996 was awarded a Seal of Quality in the International Wine Challenge in 1998.

Quantock Vineyard
The Counting House, Dodington, Bridgwater, Somerset, TA5 1LE

T: 01278 733100. F: 01278 733100. Pager: 01523 775892
E: quantock.vineyards@talk21.com

Owner & Winemaker: Michael Barry
Directions: Vineyard not open to the public.
Vineyard Details: Approx. 0.10 ha of vines planted between 1988

and 1990. The north facing site is approx. 107 m above sea level. The vines are planted at 1.52 m × 0.91 m to 1.52 m and are all 'goblet' pruned.

Grape Varieties: Auxerrois, Gold Riesling, Kerner, Kernling, Madeleine × Angevine 7672, Seyval blanc, Siegerrebe.

A range of wines are made: Dodington Estate from grapes exclusively from the vineyard and Somerset Villages from grapes from other local vineyards. A range of apple wines is also produced under the Quantock label. Wines are sold by the case from the door and customers will be shown the vineyard upon request.

Rodney Stoke Vineyard
Hill Lane, Rodney Stoke, Cheddar, Somerset
Address for correspondence:
1 Berkeley Cresent, Clifton, Bristol, BS8 1HA

Owner: Ivo Reed
Directions: Vineyard not open to the public.
Vineyard Details: 1.43 ha of vines planted between 1986 and 1988. The south facing site is between 90 m and 120 m above sea level and

MENDIP '96

ENGLISH TABLE WINE
DRY
Bottled for Rodney Stoke Vineyard, Cheddar, Somerset, U.K.
75cl ℮   *Head office Stratford-upon-Avon, CV37 0SR*   11% Vol

has a loam soil with varying clay and silt content. The vines are planted at 2 m × 2 m and are all Double Guyot trained.
Grape Varieties: Kernling, Schönburger.

The site, which has great views over the Somerset levels to Glastonbury Tor, the Quantocks and the Severn estuary, is virtually frost free. Kernling is the favoured variety, 'as long as you have the nerve to wait for ever until the acidity drops' says former owner Richard Le Page. The vineyard's wines used to be made at Wootton Vineyard by Colin Gillespie and have done well in competitions and tastings. The 1996 Mendip Dry won bronze in the UKVA's national competition and Highly Commended in the SWVA's regional event. The 1995 was selected for the English Wine promotion in the House of Commons dining room in 1998.

Staplecombe Vineyards
Burlands Farm, Staplegrove, Taunton, Somerset, TA2 6SN

T: 01823 451217. F: 01823 451726

Owners: Martin & Alison Cursham
Winemaker: Martin Cursham
Directions: From A361 Taunton to Minehead road, at Staplegrove

STAPLECOMBE

1997

Troika

MEDIUM

ENGLISH TABLE WINE

MADE AND BOTTLED AT STAPLECOMBE
WINERY, STAPLEGROVE, TAUNTON,
SOMERSET, ENGLAND, TA2 6SN

10.0% vol   75 cl ℮

PRODUCE OF THE UNITED KINGDOM

traffic lights, turn into Manor Road. Pass church on left and then turn into Rectory Road. Follow for half a mile to T-junction, turn left, farm is 100 yds on left.

Vineyard Details: 0.73 ha of vines planted between 1981 and 1997. The south and south-west facing site is between 28 m and 30 m above sea level and the soil is a silty clay loam over deep alluvium. The vines are mainly planted 1.8 m × 1.4 m and 3.6 m × 1.25 m and Double Guyot trained. There are a few 3.6 m × 2.44 m GDC trained Huxelrebe.

Grape Varieties: Dunkelfelder, Huxelrebe, Madeleine × Angevine 7672, Reichensteiner, Rondo, Siegerrebe.

Wine Sales: The wine shop is generally open on summer afternoons, but please telephone in advance.

Vineyard Visits: Self-guided tour when open. Guided tours for groups by appointment.

The winery is in converted farm buildings and is equipped with a Zambelli basket press, fibreglass and stainless steel tanks and a Seitz Fjord filler. The wines have always done well in competitions and recent successes include an SWVA Gold for the 1998 Huxelrebe and an SWVA silver for the 1998 'Rustic' dry red. Recent plantings have been of the red varieties Dunkelfelder and Rondo.

Whatley Vineyard
Whatley, Frome, Somerset, BA11 3LA

T: 01373 836355. F: 01373 836467
E: robwitt@clara.co.uk

Owner: Michael Witt
Winemaker: Wines made at Bagborough Vineyard
Directions: Take A361 from Frome to Shepton Mallet. three miles out of Frome, turn right and follow signs.
Vineyard Details: 0.68 ha of vines planted between 1979 and 1983. The south facing site is between 119 m and 125 m above sea level and the soil is loam over calcareous marl. The vines are planted at 1.98 m × 1.52 m and are Double Guyot trained.
Grape Varieties: Huxelrebe, Madeleine × Angevine 7672, Schönburger, Seyval blanc.
Wine Sales: April to September, Thursday–Sunday, 10 am to 6 pm. At all other times by appointment.

Vineyard Visits: Open during above hours for individuals and small groups. Guided tours, tastings and meals for groups (15–40 people) by arrangement. Farm shop with local produce as well as a formal walled Herb Garden.

The vineyard is undergoing some re-structuring. Varieties such as Müller-Thurgau, Reichensteiner and Gutedal have already been removed and Huxelrebe will be next – poor cropping being blamed. Madeleine Angevine gives the most consistent yields and produces good wine. The 1994 Estate Selection (which is mainly Huxelrebe) won silver in the 1999 Bath and West Show competition.

Wootton Vineyard
North Wootton, Shepton Mallet, Somerset, BA4 4AG

T: 01749 890359

Owners: June & Christian Hills
Directions: Vineyard not open to the public.
Vineyard Details: 0.58 ha of vines planted between 1971 and 1974. The steep south facing site is between 24 m and 37 m above sea level and has a rich red loam soil. The vines are planted at 2 m × 1.5 m and 1.2 m × 1 m and are Double Guyot trained. A small area of M-T is planted at 2.4 m × 2 m and is GDC trained.
Grape Varieties: Müller-Thurgau, Schönburger, Seyval blanc.

Until March 1999, Wootton Vineyard was owned by Colin and Sue Gillespie – two pioneers of the revival of commercial viticulture in the UK and in their day, producers of some of the best English wines. At one time the vineyard extended to over 5 ha. Colin, who retired from the Royal Engineers in the early 1970s, took to viticulture after paying a visit to nearby Pilton Manor, then owned by Nigel Godden. In the week that he retired from the army, he started to plant the first of his vines – 4000 Müller-Thurgau and Seyval blanc.

   Colin mastered the art of winemaking quickly and success in tastings and competitions soon came for Wootton. One of the wines from their first vintage (1973) came top in a blind tasting of English and Continental wines held by the South West Vinegrowers Association at Harveys of Bristol. In 1976, their Schönburger was awarded the Challenge Cup for the best wine from that vintage in the South West Vineyards Association's Competition, and went on to win joint second place at the English Wine of the Year Competition. The 1977 Müller-Thurgau won an EVA gold medal in 1979 and the 1981 Schönburger and 1985 Seyval blanc both won the Gore-Browne Trophy. Colin was also a noted contract wine-maker and made wines for numerous local vineyards. He was a director of the EVA for many years and Chairman between 1981 and 1987. Colin was affectionately known as 'good lunch Gillespie' for his habit of saying, when reporting on a meeting he had attended on behalf of the EVA, 'Well, we had a jolly good lunch . . .'.

The house, winery and vineyard were bought by the Hills in 1999 and they are keeping the vineyard going, although not making wine. The grapes will be sold to a local wine producer. The vineyard has been reduced from its former size of 2.47 ha and is now down to 0.58 ha. It is to be hoped that wine bearing the Wootton label, one of the prettiest of English wine labels, will continue.

Beenleigh Manor Vineyard
Owls Roost, Beenleigh, Harbertonford, Totnes, Devon, TQ9 7EF

T: 01803 732203. F: 01803 732122
E: info@sharpham.com. W: www.sharpham.com

Owner: Mark Sharman
Winemaker: Wines made at Sharpham Vineyard by Mark Sharman.
Directions: Vineyard not open to the public.
Vineyard Details: 0.13 ha of vines planted in the 1970s. All vines are grown on a 1.8 m × 1.44 m Double Guyot system and are in polythene tunnels. The south-east facing site is only 14 m above sea level and the soil is old Devon sandstone loam over shillette.
Grape Varieties: Cabernet Sauvignon, Merlot.
Wine Sales: Wines are available by the bottle from Sharpham Vineyard.
Vineyard Visits: Vineyard not open to the public.

As vineyards in the UK go, Beenleigh Manor must be one of the most unusual. Two red varieties, usually found in much warmer climates, are grown under polythene which, as Mark Sharman says, cuts out both diseases and weeds. The grapes consistently ripen and achieve high sugars. In most years a potential alcohol of at least 12 per cent is achieved as well as good colour. Mark, who is winemaker at Sharpham Vineyard, makes a very traditional red wine, using active cap management, pumping over the wine to extract maximum colour, encouraging a malolactic fermentation and ageing the wine in both French and American oak *barriques*.

The results speak for themselves: President's Trophy in 1992 and the Bernard Theobald Trophy in 1993 with the 1990 Beenleigh Red. Both trophies again in 1997 with the 1995 vintage and the Bernard Theobald Trophy in 1999 with the 1998 vintage. The wine usually has good varietal typicity, a deep colour and takes the oak well. The wines benefit from ageing. Only very small amounts are made (1997 vintage was only 350 bottles, the '98, 560 bottles and the '99 approx. 900) and it must be the most expensive wine in the UK – the 1997 is £19.99 a bottle!

Whether growing them indoors is quite cricket is another matter, although Mark counters this (very mild) criticism by pointing out that 'surely choosing a sheltered, hot site and providing windbreak trees and polythene tunnels to capture more of the sun's heat is far more natural than adding sugar (and in some cases tannin) to unripe grapes grown outdoors?'. Touché Mark and good luck!

Dartmoor Vineyard
Dartmoor View, Mary Street, Bovey Tracey, Devon, TQ13 9HQ

T: 01626 834182. F: 01626 835714

Owner: Justin Knowles

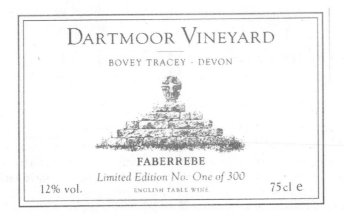

Directions: Telephone for directions.
Vineyard Details: 0.2 ha of vines planted in 1992. The south-west facing site is 27 m above sea level and the vines are planted on a 2 m × 1.66 m Double Guyot system.
Grape Varieties: Faberrebe
Wine Sales & Vineyard Visits: By appointment.

This vineyard is now leased by Plymouth University's Seale Hayne Agricultural College and will be run by students. The 1995 wine did well in both national and regional competitions with a 'Highly Commended' from the UKVA and a silver medal from the SWVA.

Down St Mary Vineyard
The Old Mill, Down St Mary, Nr Crediton, Devon, EX17 6EE

T: 01363 82300

Owners: Simon & Carol Pratt
Winemaker: Simon Pratt
Directions: Take the A377 Crediton to Barnstaple road. After passing through Copplestone, keep following the Barnstaple road and after 1 mile turn left up to Down St Mary. At the village

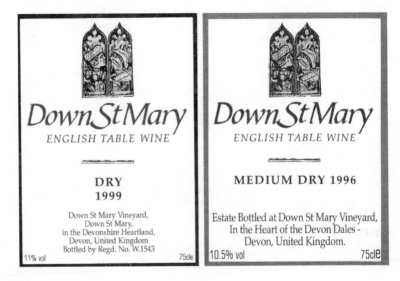

green take the road signposted Zeal Monachorum and the Old Mill is three-quarters of a mile along this lane before the river bridge.

Vineyard Details: 1.52 ha of vines planted in 1986 and 1991. The south facing site is between 43 m and 56 m above sea level and the soil is mainly Devon shale. The vines are mainly planted at 3 m × 1.4 m and trellised using Double Guyot, Scott Henry and GDC training systems. Some of the vines are planted on terraces across the slope.

Grape Varieties: Auxerrois. Huxelrebe. Madeleine × Angevine 7672, Reichensteiner, Siegerrebe, Schönburger.

Wine Sales: 1 April to 31 October and 1 December to 24 December, open Tuesday to Saturday 2 pm to 5.30 pm. At all other times by arrangement.

Vineyard Visits: Group visits by arrangement (15–35 people) £6 per person to include hot and cold canapés and a full tasting of all of their wines including the famous 'Bubbly'.

Down St Mary vineyard prides itself on being able to sell its wines to 'over 100 of the finest gourmet restaurants in this country and also abroad' and eschews all competitive tastings! The site is claimed to be 'one of the hottest places in the UK' and reached '103°F in April 1997'. Further plantings are being considered of two red varieties: Rondo and Pinot noir. The well-equipped winery is in a converted cider mill which was where the Showering family first saw sparkling perry being made which they later developed into Babycham. It is on two floors which allows for the wine to be gravity fed for bottling. Despite a policy of not entering competitions, the vineyard was persuaded to submit wines for the 2000 Bath and West Show and came away with a silver medal for their '99 Dry and a bronze for their '99 medium dry.

Follymoor Vineyard
Follymoor Moorlake, Crediton, Devon, EX17 5EL

T: 01363 772582

Owner: Martin Wreford
Winemaker: Wines made at Bagborough Vineyard
Directions: Vineyard not open to the public.

11% vol   Wreford   75cl ℮

Follymoor
Vineyard

Medium Dry
English Table Wine

of the
Kernling Grape

BOTTLED FOR FOLLYMOOR
VINEYARD, MOORLAKE,
CREDITON,
DEVON, U.K.
FROM GRAPES GROWN
BY MARTIN WREFORD

Vineyard Details: 0.56 ha of vines planted in 1988 on a 2 m ×
1.4 m Double Guyot system. The south facing site is between 75 m
and 78 m above sea level and the soil is a clay loam.
Grape Varieties: Kernling, Reichensteiner.

Vineyard described by its owner as 'an expensive hobby'!

Higher Bumsley Vineyard
Higher Bumsley, Parracombe, Devon, EX31 4PT

T: 01598 763325

Owner: Pamela Smith
Directions: Vineyard not open to the public.
Vineyard Details: 0.02 ha of vines planted in 1989 and trained on
a 1.22 m × 1.22 m Double Guyot system. The south facing site is
213 m above sea level (probably the highest vineyard site in the UK)
and the soil is described as 'thin and very stony'.
Grape Variety: Madeleine × Angevine 7672.

Higher Bumsley Vineyard (surely this should be twinned with
Breaky Bottom Vineyard?) is a domestic vineyard and wine is

made only for home consumption. The vineyard borders a public footpath from the Haddon Valley and the Hunters Inn and affords walkers some interest and surprise as they pass by. Pamela Smith has a long history of involvement in UK viticulture and, together with her husband Roy (first Treasurer of the WDVA), planted the Flexerne vineyard in East Sussex with cuttings obtained from Brock at Oxted in 1963. Her vineyard was well known as it was used by the Agriculture Training Board for its practical sessions on viticulture.

Manstree Vineyard

New Barn Farm, Manstree Road, Shillingford St George, Exeter, Devon, EX2 9QR

T: 01392 832218. F: 01392 832747

Owners: Tim & Simon Boyce
Winemaker: Wines made at Staplecombe
Directions: In Alphington, Exeter take road signposted Shillingford St George. In village fork right in front of Village Hall on to Manstree Road on right.
Vineyard Details: 1.41 ha of vines planted between 1980 and 1990.

MANSTREE

English Table Wine 75cl
"...every man shall sit under his own vine.." Micah 4v4
Made from grape varieties grown at and bottled for
Manstree Vineyard, Shillingford St. George, Exeter, Devon. 01392 832218

Best Served Lightly Chilled

Manstree is the name of the road that passes the Vineyard and also that of the nearby field, indicating that there was once a gallows there for the execution of sheep stealers and other felons.

Today, vines now flourish on the warm Southern slopes of renowned Red Devon Soil, producing fine white wines and grape juices.

The site is between 46 m and 61 m above sea level and the soil is a well drained deep red loam.

Grape Varieties: Bacchus, Madeleine × Angevine 7672, Schönburger. Seyval blanc, Siegerrebe.

Wine Sales: March to December, Tuesdays to Sundays plus Bank Holidays, 10 am to 5 pm.

Vineyard Visits: During opening hours as above. Also 'Open Weekends' in September. Group tours (20–40 people) in July and August by appointment. Vineyard is part of 'Boyces Farm Shop and Nursery' selling hanging baskets, containers and soft fruits, picked or pick-your-own

Manstree wines have done well in competitions. Their 1994 Madeleine Angevine and Bacchus medium dry won a gold and their 1996 Siegerrebe a bronze in the SWVA's competition.

Oakford Vineyard

The Old Rectory, Holme Place, Oakford, Bampton, Devon, EX16 9EW

T: 01398 351486. F: 01398 351486
E: prot@oakford57.fsnet.co.uk

Owner: Peter Rostron
Directions: Take the B3227 Taunton to South Molton road to Oakford. In village turn at the village shop and then left into driveway marked Holme Place.

OAKFORD

11.5%   70 cl

ENGLISH TABLE WINE

Estate grown and bottled by Peter Rostron, The Old Rectory,
Oakford, Tiverton, Devon, EX16 9EW

Vineyard Details: 1.05 ha of vines planted in 1993 and 1997. The south facing site is between 159 m and 183 m above sea level and the soil is a clay loam. The vines are all Double Guyot trained and planted at 1.6 m × 1 m, 1.75 m × 1.4 m and 2.3 m × 1.4 m.
Grape Varieties: Kernling, Orion, Rondo, Siegerrebe + others.
Wine Sales & Vineyard Visits: By appointment. Bed and breakfast available in this charming Victorian rectory.

This vineyard was established in 1993 with an experimental selection of varieties, both *viniferas* and hybrids, whites and reds. In 1997 the vineyard was expanded with Kernling, Orion, Rondo and Siegerrebe and wine will be available from the 1999 harvest. To date, Rondo is preferred because of its excellent wood ripening. The vineyard is partly organic. As one of the highest vineyards in the UK, it will be interesting to see how this selection of varieties fares.

Rock Moors Vineyard
Woodland Head, Yeoford, Crediton, Devon, EX17 5HE

T: 01647 24788

Owners & Winemakers: Desmond & Felicity Carter
Directions: Vineyard not open to the public.
Vineyard Details: 0.24 ha of vines planted between 1982 and 1992. The south facing site is between 98 m and 122 m above sea level and the soil is a base rich clay on culm measures. The vines are planted at 1.83 m × 1.83 m and are Double Guyot pruned.
Grape Varieties: Chardonnay, Léon Millot, Madeleine × Angevine 7672, Triomphe.

This is a small non-commercial vineyard and its wines are not for sale. The site is well sheltered and a 'real sun trap' according to the owners. The wines are made in as natural a way as possible without filtration.

Sharpham Vineyard
Sharpham Estate, Ashprington, Totnes, Devon, TQ9 7UT

T: 01803 732203. F: 01803 732122
E: mark@sharpham.com. W: www.sharpham.com

Owner: Sharpham Partnership Ltd
Winemaker: Mark Sharman

Directions: From Totnes take A381 towards Kingsbridge and Dartmouth. After half a mile take turning on left signposted Ashprington. Continue to village and at the Durant Arms turn left to Sharpham. At the junction turn left down the hill towards winery. Car park at rear.

Vineyard Details: 3.96 ha of vines planted between 1987 and 1993. The south-east facing site is between 30 m and 50 m above sea level and the soil is a silty clay loam. The vines are planted at 2.13 m × 1.52 m, 2 m × 1.4 and 2.2 m × 1.4 m and are all Scott Henry trained.

Grape Varieties: Dornfelder, Huxelrebe, Kernling, Madeleine × Angevine 7672, Phoenix, Reichensteiner.

Wine Sales: March to November, Monday to Saturday, 10.30 am to 5.30 pm. At all other times by appointment.

Vineyard Visits: Self-guided tours during above opening times. Adults £2.50. Group tours (min. 15 people) £4 per person. All tours include a tasting.

SHARPHAM
1996
Dart Valley Reserve

ENGLISH VINEYARDS QUALITY WINE PSR
Dry

BOTTLED BY: SHARPHAM PARTNERSHIP,
TOTNES, SOUTH DEVON, U.K.

11% vol.   PRODUCE OF THE U.K.   75cl.℮

Situated a few miles from Totnes and overlooking the River Dart, Sharpham Vineyard is in a very beautiful part of the country. The Sharpham Estate of 500 ha comprises woodland, pasture and vineyards and has three distinct enterprises: a 50 strong herd of Jersey cows, a creamery making an award winning range of cheeses and the vineyard – also award winning. The partnership that runs Sharpham, founded in 1981, prides itself on managing these enterprises on an environmentally sustainable basis.

The vineyards are managed by Ian A'Court and wines made by Mark Sharman (who owns nearby Beenleigh Manor Vineyard); together they produce wines of real quality and interest. The vineyards are planted with an interesting mix of varieties including Phoenix (the new Geilweilerhof Bacchus × Villard blanc hybrid) and over 1.7 ha of genuine Madeleine × Angevine 7672 (grafted from wood from Robin Don's Elmham Park vineyard – now grubbed up – the vines in which were known to have come from Ray Brock's Oxted vineyard). Mark reckons it is both 'consistent and reliable' and produces 'good flavoured wines on our soil types'. The vineyards are all trellised on the Scott Henry divided curtain system – one of the few vineyards in the UK to adopt this technique.

The winery is well equipped with a UP 1800 Willmes pneumatic press, Seitz plate and membrane filters, KTM kieselguhr filter, stainless steel tanks and KTM six head filler. There are also oak barriques for the fermentation of the Madeleine Angevine which is lees stirred and goes through partial malolactic conversion. Reds, made from Pinot noir and Dornfelder grown at Sharpham and Cabernet Sauvignon and Merlot grown (under polytunnels at Beenleigh) are cold macerated for two to three days, fermented at 30°C and then undergo a short period of oak ageing. Their wines have won a number of awards and medals over the years in both regional and national competitions. Latest crop includes a UKVA bronze for the 1996 Estate Selection, a SWVA silver for the 1996 Dart Valley Reserve, a UKVA bronze and SWVA gold and South West Challenge Cup for the 1996 Barrel Fermented Madeleine Angevine, UKVA highly commended for the 1997 Sharpham Red (100 per cent Dornfelder) SWVA double gold and 'Best in Competition' for the 1995 Sweet Thang (100 per cent botrytis affected Huxelrebe). Taken together, these add up to an impressive tally and underline the quality of the wines being produced here.

(As if this wasn't enough, the estate also makes three stunning cheeses, all unpasteurised, and with really interesting flavours and textures.)

Sharpham Estate has appeared on the BBC's Food and Wine programme and in September 1998 were pleased to welcome Prince Charles who arrived by private launch at the estate's quay and left by helicopter – it's good to see that he supports English food and wine!

Summer Moor Vineyard

Middle Hearson, Swimbridge, Devon
Address for correspondence:
'Fide-et-Amore', 49 South Street, South Molton, Devon, EX36 4AE

T: 01769 574453

Owners: Allan & Julia Petchey
Directions to vineyard: From Barnstaple take the A377 road to Exeter. Just before you leave Bishops Tawton, turn left up a hill opposite a garage. Follow this road for one and three-quarter miles and when it bends sharp right, continue straight on. At next crossroads go straight on (signposted 'Hearson'). Summer Moor is on the left just before the road becomes a track.
Vineyard Details: 1.73 ha of vines planted in 1999 and 2000. The south facing site lies between 75 m and 150 m above sea level. The vines are planted at 2.13 m × 1.52 m and 1.83 m × 1.83 m and are both Double Guyot and Gobelet trained.
Grape Varieties: Chardonnay, Madeleine × Angevine 7672, Rondo, Siegerrebe.
Wine Sales: First vintage not available until 2002.
Vineyard Visits: By appointment.

Weir Quay Vineyard

Cleave Farm, Weir Quay, Bere Alston, Yelverton, Devon, PL20 7BS

T: 01822 840480

Owner & Winemaker: Mrs Lysbeth Gallup
Directions: Vineyard not open to the public.
Vineyard Details: 0.04 ha of vines planted between 1981 and 1986 on a 1.52 × 1.52 Double Guyot system. The west facing site is 6 m above sea level and has a light loam soil.

Grape Varieties: Kernling, Triomphe + miscellaneous.

This is a small hobby vineyard providing wine for the owner and her family. It is on the bank of the river Tamar – at this point half-a-mile wide – which gives good reflected light. Wine and cider are made in the small lean-to winery behind the house. Mrs Gallup laments the fact that there were once five vineyards in this part of the Tamar Valley 'planted hopefully twenty years ago, but grubbed up because of the Customs and Excise penalty on our wines, plus the rules and regulations imposed on us from Europe'.

Yearlstone Vineyard
Bickleigh, Devon, EX16 8RL

T: 01884 855700. F: 01884 855726
E: yearlstone.com@virgin.net

Owners: Roger & Juliet White
Winemaker: Juliet White
Directions: In the village of Bickleigh on the A396 Tiverton to Exeter road. Vineyard overlooks the village. Follow brown tourist signs.
Vineyard Details: 3.04 ha of vines planted between 1976 and 1999. The south and south-west facing site is between 37 m and 76 m above sea level and has a red clay-loam soil over sandstone.
Grape Varieties: Léon Millot, Madeleine × Angevine 7672, Pinot gris, Pinot noir, Reichensteiner, Seyval blanc, Siegerrebe, Triomphe + large varietal collection.
Wine Sales: April to October, Friday to Monday, 11 am to 5 pm. At all other times by appointment.
Vineyard Visits: As above. Guided tours by arrangement.

Yearlstone Vineyard, Devon's oldest, belonged to Gillian Pearkes until her untimely death in 1993. Gillian was one of the best known of the early pioneers in the revival of UK viticulture and was an author and lecturer and made a series of videos on winegrowing and winemaking in England. She was a founder member of the English Vineyards Association and at that time had a small vineyard at Tillworth, near Axminster, which had been planted in 1963 when she was 18. In 1969 the first of her books on viticulture was published. *Growing Grapes in Britain*, published by the *Amateur Winemaker* magazine, helped lay the foundations of many of today's vineyards and was republished throughout the 1970s. Her second book on the subject *Vinegrowing in Britain* was published in 1982 and revised in 1989.

The vineyard was taken over after Gillian's death by Roger White, a journalist and BBC presenter and his wife, Juliet who has a background in interior design. Juliet has completed a course on viticulture and winemaking at Plumpton College. The vineyard has been expanded from one to three hectares and the Whites have planted Seyval blanc and Reichensteiner. Whilst Gillian's preference was for very narrow Double Guyot trained vines, the Whites prefer the wider spaced Scott Henry training and the original vines are being converted. A new viewing area has been built looking over the vineyard and a winery is being constructed.

Recent wines that have done well include the 1997 Estate Selection Dry White and the 1995 Estate Reserve Red, both of which won bronze medals in the SWVA's regional competition. At present, stocks of wine are low. (Yearlstone also claims – as do two other vineyards – to hold the 'National Collection of Outdoor Vines'!)

Bosue Vineyard

Bosue Farm, St Ewe, St Austell, Cornwall, PL26 6EU

T: 01726 843159. F: 01726 72742. M: 07721 689378

Owner: Paul Sibley
Directions: Not open to the public.
Vineyard Details: 0.41 ha of vines planted between 1996 and 1998 on a south facing site, between 30 m and 50 m above sea level on a loam soil. The vines are trellised on both Double Guyot and Scott Henry systems at 2.2 m × 1.4 m. The aim is to concentrate on growing modern hybrid varieties.
Grape Varieties: Dunkelfelder, Orion, Phoenix, Rondo, Schönburger,
Wine Sales: Vineyard not yet in production.

Bosue Vineyard is a new enterprise on a smallholding that produces cut foliage for the flower trade. It is close to the south Cornish coast and only one mile from the Lost Gardens of Heligan. It is hoped in future years to build a winery and open to the public once wines are for sale.

Camel Valley Vineyard

Little Denby Farm, Nanstallon, Bodmin, Cornwall, PL30 5LG

T: 01208 77959. F: 01208 77959
E: boblindo@camelvalley.com. W: www.camelvalley.com

Owners: Bob & Annie Lindo
Winemaker: Bob Lindo
Directions: From Bodmin, take the A389 Wadebridge Road and after 2 miles turn left to Nanstallon. Look for vineyard signs after one and a half miles (before the village).
Vineyard Details: 1.80 ha of vines planted in 1989 and 1990. Vineyard is between 18 m and 55 m above sea level, facing due south over the Camel Valley. The soil is a medium loam over shillet and the vines are planted on a 1.83 × 1.22 m or 1.52 m Double Guyot system.
Grape Varieties: Bacchus, Dornfelder, Reichensteiner, Seyval blanc, Triomphe.
Wine Sales: April to September, Monday, Tuesday, Thursday, Friday, 2 pm to 5 pm, Wednesday, 2 pm to 6 pm.
Vineyard Visits: As above, Monday to Friday. Daily tours at 2.30 pm £3 per person. 'Grand Tour' of winery and vineyards Wednesdays, 5 pm £4 per person. Meals for groups available. Telephone for details.

Camel Valley is Cornwall's largest vineyard and over the past few years the Lindos have won several awards and medals for their

Camel Valley is Cornwall's largest vineyard, situated on the sunny slopes above the River Camel, halfway between the Atlantic and the Channel coasts. Traditional vineyard practices combined with a New World approach to wine making ensure high quality red, white, and sparkling wines.

Camel Valley Vineyard gained a record 5 awards in the 1996 UKVA Wine of the Year Competition. This silver medal wine is fresh, dry and well balanced. Serve chilled with local Cornish sea food. Suitable for vegetarians.

Wine maker

Bob Lindo

413

Cornish wines. They have two wineries; the 'old' one which is now given over to the production of bottle-fermented sparkling wines and the 'new' one (opened by TV chef Rick Stein from nearby Padstow) which is the first one to be built with grant-aid from EU funds. This winery is in a purpose-designed air-conditioned building and is well equipped with stainless tanks and a computer controlled ATI air-bag press. In this family run enterprise, Bob presides over the winery, whilst wife Annie looks after the vineyard, personally pruning each of the 5000 vines.

Their wines have received praise in the past from several noted wine writers; Jancis Robinson said on BBC's 'Today' programme that she was 'very impressed' with the 1995 Red (made from the old hybrid Triomphe which Bob regrets not planting the whole vineyard with) and Tom Stevenson so liked their Camel Valley Brut, that after a tasting 'he and his wife – unusually – drank the whole bottle'. Their sparkling wine bears a back label with the legend of Dr Christopher Merret (or Merrett) the man who, in 1662, presented a paper to the Royal Society on 'how to render wines sparkling'. This predates the claims of the French that Dom Perignon 'invented' the method of making sparkling wines by bottle-fermentation by 30 years! Their Camel Valley Dry Seyval blanc won the President's Trophy in the 1999 UKVA competition and their wines have been used by British Airways to open new terminals in Newquay and Frankfurt, served at the House of Lords and at some fairly high profile Cornish events. They are stocked by Berry Brothers and Rudd at their Heathrow shop, by Safeway and by Rick Stein at his Padstow Seafood Restuarant. Bob Lindo usually sells out of his previous vintage during the summer and says 'visit early in the season to avoid disappointment'. The 1999 harvest came to an impressive 40,000 bottles – all made single-handed – so maybe there will still be some left after Easter?

Durra Valley Vineyard
Trezebel Cottage, Manaccan, Helston, Cornwall, TR12 6JB

T: 01326 231399
E: trezebel@tesco.net

Owner & Winemaker: Trevor Lockwood
Directions: Vineyard not open to the public.
Vineyard Details: 0.04 ha of vines planted in 1993.The site is

between 30 m and 40 m above sea level, south facing, with a mainly shale soil. It is somewhat shaded by the trees that provide shelter from the wind.
Grape Varieties: Madeleine × Angevine 7672, Reichensteiner, Schönburger.

This is a small amateur vineyard with a winery situated in the cellar beneath the cottage. Crops to date have been small and no wine has been made for sale. It is hoped that future larger crops will enable a local market to be supplied. Trevor Lockwood is also well known as a grower of fine garlic and reports that 1999 'was a good year' (for garlic!).

Lambourne Vineyard
Lambourne Farm, Ruan High Lanes, Truro, Cornwall, TR2 5NL

T: 01872 501212. M: 07977 771893

Owner: Graham Sherratt
Directions: Telephone for directions.
Vineyard Details: 0.89 ha of vines planted between 1996 and 1998. The south south-west facing site is between 43 m and 50 m above sea level. The vines are planted on a 2 m × 1.4 m and 1.5 m Scott Henry training system.
Grape Varieties: Bacchus, Dunkelfelder, Orion, Rondo, Schönburger.
Wine Sales & Vineyard Visits: By appointment.

Pemboa Vineyard
Mellangoose Mill, Pemboa, Helston, Cornwall, TR13 0QF

T: 01326 563116
E: lloydjones@clara.net

Owners & Winemakers: Lloyd & Janet Jones
Directions: Off the A394 Truro to Penzance road. Follow the signs to Flambards Theme Park and at the Park entrance bear left. The vineyard is about one and a half miles down the hill.
Vineyard Details: 0.48 of vines planted between 1986 and 1992. The south facing site is approx. 21 m above sea level and has a clay loam soil. The vines are planted at 1.52 m × 1.22 m and 3.05 m × 1.22 m and all Double Guyot trained. Some are in polythene tunnels.

Grape Varieties: Madeleine × Angevine 7672, Kerner, Reichensteiner, Schönburger, Siegerrebe.
Wine Sales: May to September, Thursday to Saturday, 2 pm to 5 pm. At all other times by appointment.
Vineyard Visits: Self-guided tours with tasting in the winery during above hours. Guided tours with a talk on winemaking and a tasting by arrangement. There are also attractive gardens and a duck pond.

This is one of the most southerly vineyards in the UK and is 2 miles outside Helston. The site was deliberately selected by the Joneses for their vineyard because they liked its south facing slopes and buildings suitable to be turned into a winery.

'The winery is housed in a 200-year-old granite corn mill and the mill leat still tumbles past, contributing to a relaxed setting for our wine tastings' Mr Jones writes somewhat idyllically! He uses a hand operated basket press and other small scale equipment and makes a range of varietals which produce five different wines. Some grapes are grown in polythene tunnels to ensure a more consistent crop. Lloyd writes that 'Cornwall enjoys a mild winter with an early bud-burst and our sheltered valley traps any sun and creates a wonderful microclimate'.

ENGLISH TABLE WINE

SAINT PERRAN

MADELEINE ANGEVINE

75cl — 10% vol

Made and bottled at Pemboa Vineyard, Helston, Cornwall UK.

Penberth Valley Vineyard
St Buryan, Penzance, Cornwall, TR19 6HH

T: 01736 810714. F: 01736 810714

Owner & Winemaker: Robin Bryant
Directions: Vineyard not open to the public.
Vineyard Details: 0.45 ha of vines planted between 1979 and 1984. The south facing site has a stony light loam soil, are planted at 1.5 m × 1.2 m and are Double Guyot trained.
Grape Varieties: Chardonnay. Madeleine × Angevine 7672, Pinot noir, Scheurebe, Siegerrebe, Triomphe.
Wine Sales: By appointment only.

The winery is housed in a 250-year-old granite barn and the wine made in glass carboys and oak barrels. A malolactic conversion is induced in the wines. The wines have – at times – been praised in various newspaper and magazine articles. Robin Bryant says that 'the vineyard is commercial when there is a crop'.

PENBERTH VALLEY

MEDIUM DRY RED TABLE WINE

PRODUCT OF UK

75cl 12.0% vol

Produced and Bottled
by R. Bryant Penberth St. Buryan Penzance Cornwall

Polmassick Vineyard

Polmassick, St Ewe, St Austell, Cornwall, PL26 6HA

T: 01726 842239. F: 01726 842239
E: musgrave@polmassick.fsnet.co.uk

Owner & Winemaker: Barbara Musgrave
Directions: From St Austell, follow the Mevagissey road (B3273) as for Heligan Gardens. Pass Heligan, take next right signposted Polmassick and St Ewe and at the bottom of the hill the vineyard is signposted.
Vineyard Details: 0.50 ha of vines planted between 1976 and 1990. The south-west facing site is between 30 m and 50 m above sea level and has a sandy clay loam soil overlying shale. The vines are planted at 1.5 m × 1.2 m and 2.5 m × 1.2 m and are Double Guyot trained.
Grape Varieties: Kernling, Müller-Thurgau, Orion, Ortega, Pinot noir, Seyval blanc.
Wine Sales: Open from the second May Bank holiday to the last Sunday in September, daily, 11 am to 5 pm.
Vineyard Visits: Self-guided tours during opening hours as above. Guided tours by arrangement.

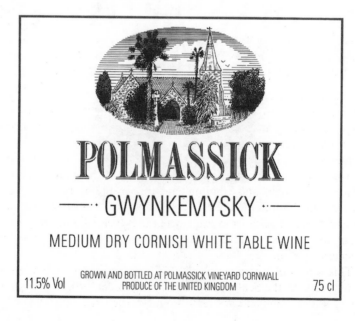

POLMASSICK

—·· GWYNKEMYSKY ··—

MEDIUM DRY CORNISH WHITE TABLE WINE

11.5% Vol — GROWN AND BOTTLED AT POLMASSICK VINEYARD CORNWALL PRODUCE OF THE UNITED KINGDOM — 75 cl

This is a small family run vineyard with its own winery and most of the wine is sold at the gate. There are six wines on their list, including a Pinot noir and a sparkling.

Porthallow Vineyard

Porthallow Road, St Keverne, Helston, Cornwall, TR12 6QH

T: 01326 280050. F: 01326 280050

Owners: Ted & Shelia Jeffries
Winemaker: Bill Roberts
Directions: From Helston take the A3083. After Culdrose take the B3293 to St Keverne and turn left in the village square. Pass the White Hart and turn left again for Porthallow. Take the next turning on the right and then the next turning on the right after that. At the next fork turn left and the vineyard is a quarter of a mile on the right.
Vineyard Details: 0.68 ha of vines planted in 1985. The east facing site is between 30 m and 40 m above sea level and the soil is a fine well-drained stony silt. The vines are planted at 2 m × 1.4 m and single Guyot trained or at 2 m × 2 m and Double Guyot trained.
Grape Varieties: Madeleine × Angevine 7672, Triomphe.
Wine Sales: Easter to October, Monday to Saturday, 11 am to 1 pm and 2 pm to 5 pm.
Vineyard Visits: Self-guided tours during above hours (50p). Guided tours and talks by arrangement. Visitors can see a herb sundial, cider press museum and wildflower beds.

The intention when the Jeffries' established the vineyard was to produce wines from grapes only, but a lack of success with the German varieties that they planted led them to develop wines made from other fruits such as blackberries and elderberries as well as apple wine and cider. Ted Jeffries writes that 'in this maritime climate there are good years and bad years. In the good years the Madeleine is light and fragrant and the Triomphe makes a very pleasant medium bodied red. In the bad years a British Wine made from a blend of juice from our own grapes blended with imported grape juice is also produced.' They also produce a wide range of liqueurs, sloe gin, mead and birch sap wine.

This is possibly the most southerly 'cropping' vineyard in the UK (a new one on the Scilly Isles, yet to produce, is further south and the Channel Islands do not really count as the UK).

Saint Martins
Isles of Scilly
Address for correspondence:
'Greystokes', Beach Road, Heybrook Bay, Plymouth, Devon,
PL9 0BS

T: 01752 862019
E: g.thomas@tinyworld.co.uk

Owners: Graham & Val Thomas
Directions: Vineyard not open to the public.
Vineyard Details: 0.42 ha of vines planted between 1996 and 1999.
The vineyard is at sea level and has a sandy loam soil. The vines are
planted at 1.52 m × 1.83 m and Double Guyot trained.
Grape Varieties: Orion, Findling + others.

This is an experimental vineyard on St Martins, one of the Scilly
Isles, and is believed to be the first attempt at viticulture on these
islands. A vintage is expected in 2001 and a winery and visitor
facilities are planned. Further vines will be planted once the
most suitable varieties for this mild maritime climate have been
identified.

Brecon Court Vineyard
Llansoy, Usk, Raglan, Monmouthshire, Wales, NP5 1DT
Address for correspondence:
Monnow Valley Vineyard, Great Osbaston Farm, Monmouth,
Monmouthshire, Wales, NP25 4DL

T: 01600 716209. F: 01600 772778
W: www.webaware.co.uk/bestofwales/breconco

Owners: Desmond & Barbara McElney
Winemaker: Wines made at Three Choirs
Directions: From the M4 take the sign for South Wales and then the
M48 across the Severn until the Chepstow exit (J22). Go straight
over the first and second roundabouts and at the third, follow sign
for Devauden. At the village green bear left for 1 mile, pass signpost
to Usk and up a slight hill. Turn left signposted Raglan and Llansoy
and follow tourist sign which says Deer Park and Vineyard. Go
down hill, past Star Inn and Brecon Court is 500 yards on the left.
Vineyard Details: 2 ha of vines planted in 1989 and 1992 on a south

facing site between 30 m and 75 m above sea level. The soil is mainly sandstone with clay patches. The vines are almost all on a 2 m × 1.3 m Double Guyot system, except for the Pinot gris which is Single Guyot trained and the Cabernet Sauvignon and Merlot which are under polythene tunnels.

Grape Varieties: Cabernet Sauvignon, Kerner, Merlot, Pinot gris, Schönburger, Seyval blanc, Reichensteiner.

Wine Sales & Vineyard Visits: By appointment only

Brecon Court was originally conceived as a deer farm, but when it was realised that the soil was also suitable for vines, an initial 3000 vines were planted in 1988. The vineyard has now taken over as the main enterprise and deer are only on the farm during the summer calving months. In July 1999, this vineyard was taken over by Monnow Valley Vineyard to whom all inquiries should be addessed.

Cwm Deri Vineyard

Martletwy, Nr Narberth, Pembrokeshire, Wales, SA67 8AP

T: 01834 891274. F: 01834 891274. M: 07971 553897
E: enquiries@cwm-deri.co.uk. W: www.cwm-deri.co.uk

Owner & Winemaker: John Hamilton-Cowburn
Directions: M4/A48 to Carmarthen. A40 westwards from Carmarthen. Take the A4075 south (signposted Pembroke Dock). Shortly after passing Oakwood Park at Cross Hands, turn right towards Martletwy. Follow brown tourist signs to vineyard for 3 miles.
Vineyard Details: 0.74 ha of vines planted in 1990 on a south facing site which is between 15 m and 46 m above sea level. The soil is a clay loam. The vines are trellised at 3.05 m × 1.52 m on a Double Guyot system.
Grape Varieties: Léon Millot, Madeleine × Angevine 7672, Seyval blanc, Triomphe.
Wine Sales: Easter to end of September, Monday to Saturday 11 am to 5 pm. Sunday noon to 5 pm. Winter weekends, Saturday 11 am to 5 pm, Sunday noon to 5 pm. Please telephone at all other times. Winetasting – 'Buy & Try' a tray of tasters.
Vineyard Visits: As above for individuals. Self-guided vineyard walk leaflet available. Teas, coffees and snacks available. Picnic facilities.

CWM DERI
Ddraig Goch
(Red Dragon)
Medium Red Wine

A very special 'limited edition' of Pembrokeshire Red. Made by John the Grape, with our Leon Millot & Triomphe D'Alsace, beautifully blended with other red grapes grown in Pembrokeshire gardens, (including Smugglers Cove). This rare gem is plump with flavour in the well-known Cwm Deri style. Medium, rich in colour with full-bodied bouquet & has a good length on the palate.

Serve at Room Temperature

Once opened this product will keep for 2 - 3 days in a cool place

CWM DERI
Pembrokeshire Country Wine
Ddraig Goch
Medium Red Wine

12% alc   Made in Wales   75cl e

Cwm Deri Vineyard is a family run smallholding, nestling in the beautiful South Pembrokeshire countryside in West Wales. Cwm Deri Vineyard in Welsh is Gwinllan Cwm Deri which literally means "Vineyard in the Valley of the Oaks" and it is on the gentle slope of a lovely Welsh Valley that the vines grow. "John the Grape" owner and wine-maker, creates Estate wines with grapes grown at Cwm Deri, and also a delicious range of Country Wines and Liqueurs with local orchard and hedgerow fruits.

Made and Bottled at
Cwm Deri Vineyard.
Martletwy, Pembrokeshire
Wales. U.K. SA67 8AP
Tel/Fax: 01834 891274
e-mail: john@cwmderi.demon.co.uk

There seems to be plenty to do and see at this vineyard – apart from the vines and the winery – including donkeys and teddy bears. All the wines are made by 'John the Grape' in a purpose-built winery and in addition to grape wines, a wide selection of other fruits, berries and nuts are used to make various products. There is also a well appointed five-berth caravan site (Caravan Club members only). The place seems popular with visitors – 60,000 in 1999.

Ffynnon Las
Lampeter Road, Aberaeron, Ceredigion, Wales, SA46 0ED

T: 01545 570234. F: 01545 570234

Owner and Winemaker: Martin Lewis
Directions: The vineyard is just outside Aberaeron on the A482 Lampeter road.
Vineyard Details: 0.20 ha of vines planted between 1988 and 1991. The east north-east facing site is between 18 m and 24 m above sea level and the soil is a heavy clay loam. The vines are planted at 1.4 m × 1 m and Double Guyot trained.
Grape Varieties: Madeleine × Angevine 7672, Reichensteiner, Schönburger, Seyval blanc.
Wine Sales: Open daily, Easter to end of October, 2 pm to 5 pm. By appointment at all other times.

GWIN GWYN
19 97
CYMRU
FFYNNON LAS
DRY

Made from Estate Grown
Reichensteiner and Madeline
Angevine grapes producing a
delicate fruity fresh crisp finish
Best served slightly chilled.

Produced by & bottled for
Gwinllan Ffynnon Las, Aberaeron,
Ceredigion, U.K.

11% Vol.   75 cl e
PRODUCE OF THE UNITED KINGDOM

Vineyard Tours: For groups by arrangement.

Ffynnon Las produces a range of wines – dry, medium dry, late harvest and a red (from grapes grown away from the vineyard) – as well as a range of fruit wines.

Glyndŵr Vineyard
Glyndŵr House, Llanblethian, Cowbridge, Vale of Glamorgan, Wales, CF71 7JF

T: 02920 220587. F: 01222 456131. M: 07970 165952

Owners: Richard & Robbie Norris
Winemaker: Wines made at Three Choirs
Directions: Take the B4270 from Cowbridge heading south-west towards Llantwit Major. The vineyard is on the left-hand side just after Llanblethian Hill.
Vineyard Details: 1.27 ha of vines planted in 1982, 1983 and 1994. The south-east facing site is between 73 m and 76 m above sea level

and the soil is a light clay over limestone. The 1982/83 plantings are at 1.83 m × 0.91 m and Double Guyot trained; the 1994 plantings at 2.74 m × 0.91 m and GDC trained.

Grape Varieties: Kerner, Léon Millot, Madeleine × Angevine 7672, Regent, Reichensteiner, Seyval blanc, Siegerrebe, Triomphe.

Wine Sales: April to October daily, but it is essential to telephone in advance.

Vineyard Visits: As above. Guided tours by appointment at £5 per person. Ponds and Water Gardens also to be seen.

Glyndŵr Vineyard is now (following the demise of John Bevan's Croffta vineyard) the oldest commercial vineyard in Wales. It is set in rolling countryside only four miles from the sea and benefits from the mild south Wales climate. The area has the second highest average mean temperature in the UK (Penzance being the warmest). It is owned by the Norris brothers who run the Cardiff firm of potato growers and merchants, Edward England and a combination of hard work and good wines have given this vineyard an enviable reputation. They are one of the better known of Welsh vineyards and were featured in an HTV production 'A Case of Wine' which was broadcast on Welsh TV several times.

Many of their wines have won awards including their 1995 'Burgundy style' red which won 'Double Gold' at the SWVA's

annual competition in 1998. Their 1995 bottle fermented sparkling wine was launched by their MP to much acclaim and they state in their price list that 'Owain Glyndŵr would have been pleased to have ridden into battle with this superb wine in his belly'! They had a recent blaze of publicity at the Royal Welsh Winter Fair at Builth Wells where they launched their magnums (1½ litres) of sparkling wine. They have also produced several huge 'Balthazars' which hold the equivalent of 15 bottles. 'These fine monsters are only for the really serious drinkers' says Robbie Norris and can be found in several Cowbridge outlets.

Llanerch Vineyard
Hensol, Pendoylan, Vale of Glamorgan, Wales, CF72 8JU

T: 01443 225877. F: 01443 225546. M: 07974 941157
E: llanerch@cariadwines.demon.co.uk
W: www.llanerch-vineyard.co.uk

Owners: Peter & Diana Andrews
Winemaker: Diana Andrews
Directions: 1 mile south of J34 on M4 and 4 miles north from A48. Follow signs.
Vineyard Details: 2.2 ha of vines planted between 1987 and 1989. The south facing site is between 55 m and 61 m above sea level

75cl.℮ Cariad wines are produced from Welsh grapes, vinified and estate bottled at Llanerch Vineyard, Hensol, Pendoylan, Vale of Glamorgan, Wales, UK CF72 8JU 10.5%

and the soil is a sandy loam over clay. The vines are planted on a 3.35 m × 1.52 m GDC system or a 2.7 m × 1.22 m Bordeaux Lyre system.

Grape Varieties: Bacchus, Huxelrebe, Kernling, Reichensteiner, Seyval blanc, Triomphe.

Wine Sales: March to end December, daily, 10 am to 5 pm. At other times by appointment.

Vineyard Visits: Self-guided tours for individuals during opening hours, £3 per person inc. wine tasting. Refreshments available. Guided tours and meals for groups (min. 25, max. 40 people) from £5 per person by arrangement. Woodland walk and lakes.

When Peter and Diane Andrews, both former pharmacists, bought the dilapidated farmhouse and dairy buildings at Llanerch in 1978, they had to completely restore them before they could be lived in. The property was situated on a lovely south-facing slope and the few vines they successfully grew in their garden gave them the germ of the idea to establish a vineyard as their retirement hobby. Realising that they knew nothing about viticulture, Diana enrolled at Plumpton College in East Sussex to learn more. In the mid-1980s they sold the chain of pharmacies they and a partner had built up and invested some of the proceeds (plus a WDA grant) in the vineyard, winery and farm tourism business that they now run.

The winery, which is in a converted Glamorganshire cow byre, is well equipped with Speidel stainless steel tanks, a 1 tonne Willmes press, harvest trailer, Velo DE filter and semi-automatic filling and bottling equipment. Diana is winemaker and has managed, in a relatively short space of time, to win a reputation for producing good quality accessible wines that both the public and the trade have taken to. Awards have been won in a number of competitions. Their 1996 Blush Sparkling Wine won a silver and the 1996 Rosé and 1996 Medium Dry won bronze, both at the IWSC and their 1996 Dry was Country Landowners Association (CLA) 'Wine of the Year'. The 1996 Blush Sparkling Wine also won a gold medal and was Wine of the Year at the SWVA regional competition. Their 1997 Cariad Celtic Dry won first place in the CLA's dry white class in 1999. Llanerch is the largest Welsh wine producer and all wines sell under the 'Cariad' label. Their wines were used exclusively during the EU summit held in Cardiff in 1998, as well as for banquets held in Cardiff for the Queen and the Emperor of Japan and have been stocked in the House of Commons. Llanerch's Cariad wines are probably the best known of Welsh wines – consumed all over the world wherever Wales or Welshness is being celebrated – and are a tribute to the hard work and enthusiasm of the Andrews'.

At Llanerch, there are also two self-catering cottages and an apartment above an old barn, each of which can sleep six people and all are rated 'Five Dragons' by the Wales Tourist Board and the Andrews' also offer four star bed-and-breakfast in their farmhouse. They won the Schroders Award for the Best Tourism Business in Wales in 1995.

Monnow Valley Vineyard

Great Osbaston Farm, Monmouth, Monmouthshire, Wales, NP25 4DL

T: 01600 716209. F: 01600 772778

Owner: Peter Baker
Winemaker: Wines made at Three Choirs
Directions: Vineyard not open to the public.
Vineyard Details: 1.28 ha of vines planted between 1979 and 1990. The south and south-east facing site is between 20 m and 30 m above sea level and the soil is a clay loam over sandstone.

427

Grape Varieties: Huxelrebe, Madeleine × Angevine 7672, Seyval blanc.
Wine Sales & Vineyard Visits: By appointment.

Monnow Valley Vineyards also lease Brecon Court Vineyard (see entry).

Offa's Vineyard
The Old Rectory, Llanvihangel-Ystern-Llewern, Monmouthshire, Wales, NP25 5HL

T: 01600 780241

Owner: Peter Johnson
Winemaker: Wines made at Three Choirs
Directions: Take B4233 Monmouth – Abergavenny road and turn off at Onen (5 miles west of Monmouth) and follow signs to Llanvihangel and the Old Rectory.
Vineyard Details: 0.60 ha of vines planted between 1989 and 1996. The south facing site is between 60 m and 70 m above sea level and has a clay soil. The vines are all Double Guyot trained and planted

428

at 1.83 m × 1.22 m. 200 Cabernet Sauvignon and Merlot are grown in polythene tunnels.
Grape Varieties: Bacchus, Cabernet Sauvignon, Faberrebe, Kernling, Merlot, Orion, Pinot noir, Regent, Schönburger.
Wine Sales & Vineyard Visits: By appointment.

Offa's Vineyard – which is on the Offa's Dyke walk – sells white, sparkling and red wines (the latter from vines grown in tunnels) and normally there are three white vintages, one red and one sparkling available. Peter Johnson says that 'he is too old to contemplate building a winery!'

Pant Teg Vineyard (Gwinllan Pant Teg)
Ffordd y Graig, Llysfaen, Caerdydd, Wales, CF4 5UF

T: 01222 753834. F: 01222 763284
E: gwinllan@pant-teg.freeserve.co.uk

Owner: Kynric Lewis
Manager: David Gale
Winemaker: Wines made at Three Choirs
Directions: Vineyard not open to the public.

Vineyard Details: 0.708 ha of vines planted in 1986. The south south-east facing site overlooks Bae Caerdydd at between 95 m and 110 m above sea level with Lloger in the far distance. The vines are planted in a red sandstone soil at 3.35 m × 1.52 m and are GDC trained with both canes and spurs.

Grape Varieties: Kerner, Kernling, Madeleine × Angevine 7672, Reichensteiner, Siegerrebe.

Wine Sales & Vineyard Visits: By appointment.

This vineyard makes two wines, Gwin Pefriog, a sparkling wine (made in the 'Môdd Clasurol') from Kerner and Kernling with at least 9 months' lees and Cyfuniad Sych, a blended dry white. The wines have been awarded Welsh Vineyards Quality Wine Status and therefore bear the legend of the mediaeval banqueting halls – *Y Gwin Cain* – which indicates they are of the finest quality.

The owner of this *gwinllan*, Kynric Lewis, is rightly proud of his Welsh (or should that be Cymruish?) roots and says that his 'wines are labelled *yn y Gymraeg* (with translations to the Saesoneg added to placate the regime in Brussels' (or Bruxelles if we really need to placate them). The charming label was designed by Sir Kyffin Williams RA. Mr Lewis also says that his manager, David Gale, does 'all the hard work' and will be 'mightily chuffed' by the mention of the fact.

Sugar Loaf Vineyard

Dummar Farm, Pentre Lane, Abergavenny, Cowent, Monmouthshire, Wales, NP7 7LA

T: 01873 858675. F: 01873 858675
E: rmhofayz@aol.com

Owners: M. & I. B. Hofayz

Winemaker: Wines made at Three Choirs

Directions: One mile from the centre of Abergavenny off the A40 Brecon road.

Vineyard Details: 1.59 ha of vines planted in 1992 and 1994. The south facing site is between 76 m and 96 m above sea level and the soil is a sandy loam. The vines are planted at 3 m × 1 m and are both GDC and Lyre trained.

Grape Varieties: Madeleine × Angevine 7672, Regent, Reichensteiner, Rondo, Seyval blanc, Siegerrebe, Triomphe.

Wine Sales: All year round, daily, from 10 am. Telephone for more details.

This is the only vineyard planted in the Brecon Beacons National Park and is on the south facing slopes of the Sugar Loaf mountain with spectacular views towards the Usk Valley.

Sugar Loaf's wines have won a number of awards including a UKVA bronze for their 1997 Siegerrebe and UKVA Highly Commended for their 1997 Madeleine Angevine and 1997 Reichensteiner. Most of their wines have been awarded 'Welsh Quality Wine' status.

Tintern Parva Vineyard
Parva Farm, Tintern, Near Chepstow, Monmouthshire, Wales, NP16 6SQ

T: 01291 689636

Owners: C & J Dudley
Winemaker: Wines made at Three Choirs
Directions: Take the A466 Monmouth to Chepstow road. Vineyard signposted from the car park of the Wye Valley Hotel in Tintern.
Vineyard Details: 0.80 ha of vines planted between 1979 and 1984. The south-facing site is between 15 m and 40 m above sea level and

has a sandy loam soil. The vines are spaced at 1.6 m × 1.4 m and Double Guyot trained.

Grape Varieties: Bacchus, Müller-Thurgau, Pinot noir, Seyval blanc + collection of 13 other varieties.

Wine Sales: All year round on most days. Summer, 9 am to 7 pm. Winter, 9 am to dusk. Please telephone to avoid a wasted journey.

Vineyard Visits: Self-guided tours during above opening hours – £2 per person. Guided tours for groups available. There is a woodland walk, picnic area and visitor centre which serves teas and light refreshments. There are also a number of well-appointed farm cottages to let.

The vineyard is located in a beautiful and historic area near Tintern Abbey, which has connections going back to the Romans. It is part of a working farm and sheep, cattle and ponies are usually on display.

Wyecliff Vineyard

Wyecliff, Hay-on-Wye, Hereford, HR3 5RS
Address for correspondence:
Andrew Williams, Fforest Mill, Pengenffordd, Talgarth, Powys, LD3 0ER

T: 01874 711081. F: 01874 711552
E: andrewwine@aol.com

Owner: Andrew Gibson-Watt (T: 01497 820317)
Winemaker: Andrew Williams
Directions: Vineyard not open to the public.
Vineyard Details: Approx. 0.66 ha of vines planted between 1985 and 1995. The site is between 91 m and 104 m above sea level and south facing. The vines are planted at 3 m × 2 m and Double Guyot trained.
Grape Varieties: Madeleine × Angevine 7672, Seyval blanc.

The Wyecliff Vineyard, owned by Andrew Gibson-Watt (great-great-great grandson of James Watt of kettle and steam engine fame and now in his mid-70s) has recently been leased to wine journalist Andrew Williams who is now responsible for all vineyard operations. After a bumper 1996 harvest, yields have been patchy and wine is currently not available. The small winery is described as 'basic' and an 'ex-hovel' – but is equipped with GRAF tanks, a small basket press and the usual paraphernalia found in wineries. Fermentations are started on natural yeasts, before being inoculated with a known yeast strain. Despite the English address, the vineyard is in Wales and makes Welsh Wine.

Blackwater Valley Vineyard
Tirraun, Gortnagross, Mallow, County Cork, Republic of Ireland

T: House (+353) 022 21790. Surgery (+353) 022 21508
E: bchrist@eircom.net

Owner & Winemaker: Dr W A Christopher
Directions: From Mallow, take Killarney Road west for 3 miles. Turn right onto Ballycough road and property is first on right.
Vineyard Details: Approx. 2 ha of vines planted between 1985 and 1990. The vineyard is now all trained on a 'modified' GDC system with the vines planted at 3.35 m × 1.52 m. The site is 24 m above sea level and faces south-west.
Grape Varieties: Madeleine × Angevine 7672, Reichensteiner and Seyval blanc

1995

Blackwater Valley

'*The Irish Table Wine*'
REICHENSTEINER
Grown and Bottled at Mallow, Co. Cork
by Dr. Billy Christopher

9.5% Al. by Volume   e 75 cl.

Dr Billy Christopher has the largest commercial vineyard in Ireland and has been producing wine, off and on, since his first vintage in 1989. He reports that 1990 and 1995 were 'good' years with the others cited as 'moderate'. Average production is around 2,500–3,000 bottles, most of which comes from the Reichensteiner, the only variety to fruit and ripen with regularity. The Seyval, although they crop, always have low sugars and are prone to excess acidity. The Madeleine seldom perform well, remaining small and unripe. (I suspect that Dr Christopher may have been supplied with the 'wrong' Madeleine Angevine and that what he has are French table grapes!)

When this guide was first written, most of the vines were planted on a narrow Guyot system, but advancing years and the desire not to bend down so much, have meant that the original vineyards, together with later plantings, have been on a high wire modified GDC system which was suggested by two passing New Zealanders. In 1990, some Schönburger were planted, but these never came to much and were grubbed. My 1989 book *The Vineyards of England* also mentioned that 'the Excise people' had yet to catch up with this winemaking operation. Today, however, they attend with some regularity, sampling the wines and demanding their duty. The wines are sold from the gate and locally and can be found on restaurant lists in the area.

Producing wines in Ireland will never be an easy way to make a living and it is to Dr Christopher's credit that he has remained at it for over 15 years – the economics of producing only 500 or so bottles per acre must make this a labour of love rather than one of profit.

Derrynane Vineyard

Derrynane Beg, Caherdaniel, County Kerry, Republic of Ireland

T: 0667 5344. F: 0669 475344
E: borion@tinet.ie

Owner & Winemaker: Brian Lane
Directions: Vineyard not open to the public.
Vineyard Details: 0.07 ha of vines planted in 1990. The site is approximately 9 m above sea level and faces south south-west. The vines are planted on a 1.5 m × 1.5 m Double Guyot system.
Grape Variety: Bacchus

According to the University of Dublin's Horticulture Department, this is, at 10°+W, Europe's most westerly vineyard. It overlooks and is 400 m from the Atlantic. The wines are made using very traditional techniques.

Fruit of the Vine
Magillstown, Swords, County Dublin, Republic of Ireland

T & F: 01 4934103. M: +353 87 2843879

Owner & Winemaker: David Llewellyn
Directions: Telephone for details.
Vineyard Details: 0.028 ha of vines planted in 2000 on a slightly north facing site, 11 m above sea level. The soil is a medium to heavy textured gravelly clay over limestone. The vines are all Double Guyot trained and spaced at 2.1 m × 1.35 m.
Grape Varieties: Madeleine × Angevine 7672 plus 25 experimental varieties.
Vineyard Visits: The vineyard is not generally open to the public, but visitors with a serious professional interest are welcome.

David Llewellyn has established Ireland's only specialist vine nursery selling vines for both indoor and outdoor cultivation. His own vineyard, small at the moment, will be expanded with suitable varieties as and when they prove themselves. At present only Madeleine × Angevine 7672, Regent and Siegerrebe are recommended by him for outdoor cultivation.

Longueville House Vineyard
Longueville House, Mallow, County Cork, Republic of Ireland

T: 022 47156. F: 022 47459

Owner & Winemaker: Michael O'Callaghan
Directions: Three miles outside Mallow on the Killarney Road. The vineyard is not open to the public.
Vineyard Details: 0.46 ha of vines planted in 1978. The south-west facing site is 61 m above sea level and the soil is loam.
Grape Variety: Reichensteiner.
Wine Sales: The wine is only sold to guests eating in the Longueville House dining room.

Michael O'Callaghan is justly proud of his vineyard and at one time could claim to be 'Ireland's only producing vineyard' and used to say that he 'won every competition for Irish Wine hands down'. He has now been joined by other Irish vignerons, although his wines are still probably the best known, mainly because his hotel is rightly famed for its high standards. Geisenheim's venerated Professor Becker paid at least one visit to Longueville House and encouraged him in his efforts. O'Callaghan had hoped some of the new German hybrids might prove more suitable for the County Cork climate which can have cold Julys, resulting in poor fruit set. He used to grow some Müller-Thurgau, but that has now been grubbed up and only Reichensteiner remains.

The winery is in a converted coach house and the wines are made in stainless steel. A distillation licence has recently been obtained and production of apple brandy is about to start.

Thomas Walk Vineyard
Summercove, Kinsale, County Cork, Republic of Ireland

Owner & Winemaker: Thomas Walk
Directions: Vineyard not open to the public.
Vineyard Details: 0.98 ha of vines planted between 1985 and 1996. The vines are spaced at 1.7 m × 1.2 m and Double Guyot trained.
Grape Varieties: Amurensis hybrids

Thomas Walk – who is a resident of Aschaffenburg in Germany – owns the only vineyard in Ireland to produce commercial quantities of red wine. It is planted with unspecified *vitis Amurensis* varieties which he has been trialling over the last ten years. He makes two types of wine; a fruity red, fermented in stainless steel, which can be drunk chilled and a *barrique*-aged heavier red which repays keeping. The 1996 vintage has just been released. The wine is available at the Blue Haven wine shop in Kinsale and in local restaurants.

CENTRAL VINEYARD REGION

English vineyards are listed alphabetically by county, followed by vineyards in the northern half of Wales. The English counties appear in the following order: Lancashire, Yorkshire, Lincolnshire, Nottinghamshire, Leicestershire, Rutland, Staffordshire, Shropshire, Northamptonshire, Oxfordshire, Buckinghamshire, Bedfordshire, Berkshire, London.

The 'Central' region covers a large number of English counties as well as the north of Wales. It is the smallest region in terms of area under vines – only 49 hectares – and equal to East Anglia in terms of the number of vineyards – 39. However, 53 per cent of the area of vines is within the two most southerly counties – Berkshire and Oxfordshire – with the remainder being spread out from south to north in ever decreasing amounts. Vineyards in the very northern areas are mostly small and widely spread apart. In my 1989 book, *The Vineyards of England*, the region had the same number of vineyards (39) covering 52 hectares.

The region is not one to categorise easily in terms of its sites and soils as it covers so many different landscapes and areas. The southern counties of Berkshire and Oxfordshire have some tradition of fruit growing, but do tend to suffer more from spring frosts than those sites in counties with maritime borders. However, rainfall levels are lower than in many western areas and temperatures are generally higher in the summer than in any other region. The proximity of large conurbations is always good for sales and some of the most commercially successful vineyards are here. Vineyards in the northern counties tend to be in well-selected sites where local microclimate plays an important role. Varieties need to be selected with care and both fruiting and ripening are less certain than in southern areas. However, the very novelty of selling a wine produced in what is generally reckoned to be an unusual area may mean that sales are easier and prices higher.

One of the very earliest vineyards to be planted in the UK was at Stragglethorpe Hall near Lincoln in the early 1960s by Major Alan Rook, a Lincoln wine merchant, who wrote a book about his experiences. Another pioneer in the region, who achieved fame and notoriety through the power of his personality and his individual way of putting his ideas over, was the late Bernard Theobald who established Westbury Vineyards near Reading, Berkshire in 1968.

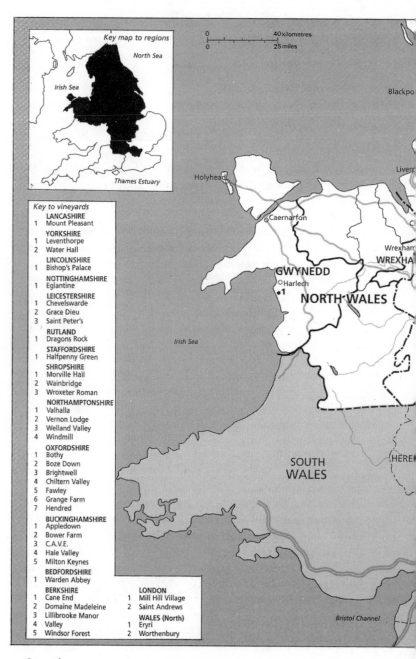

Central

The bearded and monocled Theobald championed the Geneva Double Curtain (GDC) system of growing vines and was fervent in his belief that he could make good red wine in England. Sadly, his vineyard, planted on leased land, was grubbed up after his death. The region's largest vineyard and undoubtedly the most successful (indeed, the most successful in the UK) is Valley Vineyards at Twyford, again near Reading. Valley has won the Gore-Browne Trophy on five separate occasions – 1992, 1993, 1996, 1997 and 1998, plus many other awards and medals. Another commercially successful vineyard is Chiltern Valley in Oxfordshire which won the Gore-Browne Trophy in 1988.

Mount Pleasant Vineyard
Mount Pleasant, Bolton-le-Sands, Carnforth, Lancashire, LA5 8AD

T: 01524 732038. M: 0770 3909485
E: mount.pleasant@onet.co.uk

Owner & Winemaker: Michael Graham
Directions: Vineyard not open to the public.
Vineyard Details: 0.08 ha of vines planted between 1995 and 1998.
The south-east facing site is 91 m above sea level and the soil is an
alkaline loam over sand and gravel. The vines are Double Guyot
trained and planted at 1.4 m × 1.3 m.
Grape Varieties: Gagarin blue, Léon Millot, Madeleine × Angevine
7672, Madeleine Sylvaner No. 3 28/51, Seyval blanc, Triomphe.

This vineyard, situated just north of Morecambe, must be the most
northerly in the UK. At present it is of a trial size within a walled
garden but land is available for expansion if needed. An 1836 stone
barn is being converted into a winery. What can one say but – 'good
luck'!

Leventhorpe Vineyard
Bullerthorpe Lane, Woodlesford, Leeds, West Yorkshire,
LS26 8AF

T: 0113 2667892 or 0113 2889088. F: 0113 2667892
E: janet@leventhorpevineyard.freeserve.co.uk

Owners: George & Janet Bowden
Winemaker: George Bowden
Directions: Take A642 Wakefield to Garforth road. Cross River
Aire, turn immediately left and vineyard will be found about
200 yds along road, behind Leventhorpe Cottages. From M62/M1.
Follow M1 North/East Leeds to Wetherby and A1. Exit J46
signposted A6210 East Leeds. At next roundabout – Sainsbury's
petrol station – turn left onto Bullerthorpe Lane. Follow road, after
Gamblethorpe Farm turn right – signposted Newsam Green. Turn
first left by Lodge Gatehouse. Winery at the end of the road on the
left.
Vineyard Details: 2.21 ha of vines planted between 1986 and 1990.
The site is between 18 m and 26 m above sea level, south facing and
the soil is sandy loam overlying sand and broken sandstone. The

vines are planted on a 2 m × 1.5 m or 2 m Double Guyot system or a 4 m × 1.5 m Lenz Moser system. Most vines are ungrafted.

Grape Varieties: Madeleine × Angevine 7672, Madeleine × Sylvaner No. 3 28/51, Seyval blanc, Triomphe. Also wide range of experimental varieties.

Wine Sales: Weekends 11 am to 5 pm. Open weekdays, but telephone first. 0113 2889088 or 0113 2667892

Vineyard Visits: During opening hours. Group visits by appointment from June to September on a weekday, evening or weekend. £3 per person inc. free tasting.

At latitude 53° 49', Leventhorpe is probably the most northerly commercial vineyard in the United Kingdom and one of the very few that lies within a city boundary. It has a well-drained hungry soil that is free-draining and warms quickly. The sheltered south-facing slope leads down to the River Aire which helps protect against spring frosts. It has its own well-equipped winery and wines are given a long fermentation to preserve nose and delicacy. Their

442

1996 Madeleine Angevine was commended and the 1996 Madeleine Angevine Special Reserve awarded a bronze in the MVA regional competition.

Water Hall Vineyard

Water Hall, Huddersfield Road, Mirfield, West Yorkshire
Address for correspondence:
Mr G F Werner, 14 Vernon Road, Heckmondwike, West Yorkshire, WF16 9LU

T: 01924 405543. F: 01924 492671

Owner: Keith Simpson
Winemaker: Gerhard Werner
Directions: Vineyard not open to the public.
Vineyard Details: 0.06 ha of vines planted between 1985 and 1990 on a 2 m × 1.4 m Double Guyot system. The south facing site is situated between 27 m and 30 m above sea level.
Grape Varieties: Madeleine × Angevine 7672, Madeleine Sylvaner, Müller-Thurgau, Reichensteiner, Schönburger, Seyval blanc, Siegerrebe, Triomphe + experimental varieties.

Bishop's Palace Vineyard

Old Bishop's Palace, Lincoln
Address for correspondence:
Lincoln City Council, Tourism Department, City Hall, Beaumont Fee, Lincoln, LN1 1DH

T: 01522 873503

Owner: Dean and Chapter of Lincoln Cathedral
Directions: The vineyard is located to the south of the Bishop's Palace in the centre of Lincoln.
Vineyard Details: Approx. 0.09 ha of vines, planted in 1972, on a 1.83 m × 1.22 m Double Guyot system. The site is south facing and the soil is a shallow loam over limestone.
Grape Varieties: Madeleine Sylvaner, Müller-Thurgau, Ortega, Portugieser.
Wine Sales: Wine from this vineyard is not available for sale.
Vineyard Visits: The vineyard is within the English Heritage's Old Bishop's Palace site and can be visited upon request.

This small vineyard, situated within the grounds of Lincoln Cathedral, was planted in 1972 with vines donated by Lincoln's twin city, Neustadt an der Weinstrasse, in Germany's Rheinpfalz. It was at one time in the Guiness Book of Records as the world's most northerly vineyard – a record that it cannot retain now that Finland and Norway have vineyards!

For many years the vineyard was looked after by Lincoln Council, but recent cutbacks have forced them to relinquish this task and the vineyard's future is uncertain. The Council is, however, keen that it should be maintained, especially as Neustadt's *Oberburgmeister* takes a keen personal interest in it. The most recent vintages have been produced by Robin Don who for many years had a vineyard and winery at Elmham Park, Norfolk and the wine is shared equally between the Bishop and the Mayor of Lincoln.

Eglantine Vineyard

Ash Lane, Costock, Loughborough, Nottinghamshire, LE12 6UX

T: 01509 852386. F: 01509 852386

Owner & Winemaker: Tony Skuriat
Directions: Take A60 from Loughborough towards Nottingham. Turn west into Ash Lane which is one mile north of Costock.
Vineyard Details: 1.3 ha of vines planted between 1980 and 1999 on 2.25 m by 1.5 Double Guyot system. The site is 75 m to 83 m above sea level, south south-east facing and the soil is glacial drift over calcareous clay over discontinuous carboniferous limestone.
Grape Varieties: Bacchus, Madeleine × Angevine 7672, Madeleine Sylvaner, Reichensteiner, Seyval blanc.
Wine Sales: Open most days, but telephone to check.
Vineyard Visits: The vineyard is open to visitors only by appointment. Guided tours for groups (10–35 people) can be arranged. £3 per person to include a free tasting.

Antoni (Tony) Skuriat was head of science at a Nottingham school, but has now retired to turn his hobby into his livelihood. His interest in viticulture was kindled when he and his wife moved into a house with a dilapidated greenhouse contained a cutting from the famous Black Hamburg vine at Hampton Court. They harvested 20 lbs of grapes from this vine and became interested. After trials

Eglantine

ENGLISH TABLE WINE

AURORA BOREALIS
RESERVE

10% VOL *Estate produced and bottled by A. M. and V. Skuriat from grapes grown at Eglantine Vineyard, Ash Lane, Costock, Nottinghamshire* 75cl

with different varieties of vine in the garden, they found a site and planted a vineyard.

The winery is well equipped for the size of the vineyard and a range of wines – blends and varietals – is made. Their 1990 Madeleine Sylvaner Sweet was awarded a silver medal in the 1997 MVA competition. Cherry wine – a silver medal winner in the 1996 IWSC – is also produced.

Tony maintains a large collection of different vine varieties imported from around the world. He is currently seeking National Collection status. Despite its Leicester postcode, the vineyard is in Nottinghamshire.

Chevelswarde Vineyard
Chevel House, The Belt, South Kilworth, Lutterworth, Leicestershire, LE17 6DX

T: 01858 575309
E: john@chevel.freeserve.co.uk. w: www.chevel.freeserve.co.uk

Owners: John and Ruth Daltry
Winemaker: Wines made at Sedlescombe Organic Vineyard
Directions: Farm shop is a quarter of a mile down unmade lane (The Belt) which runs south-east off the road between South and North Kilworth, about a quarter of a mile from South Kilworth.
Vineyard Details: 0.238 ha of vines planted between 1973 and 2000 on a south-east facing slope at an average of 130 m above sea level. The soil is a sandy clay loam over gravel. The vines are all spur pruned, spaced at either 3.66 m × 2.44 m GDC trained or 1.83 m × 2.44 m and Scott Henry trained. All vines are on their own roots.
Grape Varieties: Madeleine × Angevine 7672, Müller-Thurgau.
Wine Sales: Farm shop open daily, 9 am to 6 pm for wines and organic produce.
Vineyard Visits: By appointment only.

Chevelswarde Vineyard is the oldest organic vineyard in the UK and has been Soil Association (SA) approved since 1975. The Daltrys also grow organic vegetables and fruit and in recent years, these have taken precedence over the vineyard. However, they have been 'struggling to improve the management for the past few years' and although the vineyard is still 'not as they would like it' it is improving. Their wines all carry the SA Organic symbol and are made into wine by Roy Cook at the UK's largest organic wine producer, Sedlescombe Organic Vineyard. Chevelswarde's 1994 and 1997 wines were both awarded Commended in the MVA competition.

Grace Dieu Vineyard

Grace Dieu Road, Whitwick, Coalville, Leicestershire
Address for correspondence:
134 Ashburton Road, Hugglescote, Coalville, Leicestershire, LE67 2HD

T: 01530 839686. M: 07768 477742

Owner: Andrew Redfern
Winemaker: Wines made at Three Choirs
Directions: Telephone for directions.
Vineyard Details: 0.22 ha of vines planted in 1982 and 1983. The south-west facing site is between 137 m and 143 m above sea level and the soil is a clay loam with Charnwood granite. The vines are planted at 1.22 m × 1.22 m and Single Guyot trained.

Grape Varieties: Dornfelder, Madeleine × Angevine 7672, Siegerrebe.
Wine Sales: By appointment. Case sales only.
Vineyard Visits: Small groups by arrangement.

Saint Peter's Vineyard
Leire, Leicestershire
Address for correspondence:
The Willows, Frolesworth Road, Leire, Leicestershire, LE17 5HJ

T: 0800 679003. F: 01455 202227
E: tony.ad.brookes@bt.com

Owner: Tony Brookes
Directions: Vineyard not open to the public.
Vineyard Details: 0.25 ha of vines planted in 1995. The site is 91 m above sea level, flat and has a sandy loam soil. The vines are planted on a 3 m × 1.4 m GDC system.
Grape Varieties: Madeleine × Angevine 7672, Phoenix, Pinot gris, Pinot noir + 40 experimental varieties.
Wine Sales & Vineyard Visits: By arrangement.

This is an amateur vineyard and does not produce wine for sale. Tony Brookes is experimenting with both varieties and techniques in producing high quality grapes, coupled with running a low labour input vineyard. Before planting, a bulldozer was use to recreate a ridge and furrow system with 0.91 m banks upon which the vines were planted. From the first harvest the wine has achieved Commended status in the MVA's annual competition and the aim is always to produce the best possible quality wine.

Dragons Rock Vineyard
Ryhall, Rutland
Address for correspondence:
7 Manor Close, Ryhall, Stamford, Lincolnshire, PE9 4JB

T: 01780 755453

Owner & Winemaker: Mr John Walker
Directions: Vineyard not open to the public.

Vineyard Details: Approx. 0.2 ha of vines, age unknown, planted on a 1 m × 1 m Single Guyot system.
Grape Varieties: Cabernet Franc, Dornfelder, Pinot noir, Siegerrebe.

This vineyard specialises in slightly unusual products (for the UK); sweet white wines made from partially dried grapes, fortified red and white wines and sparkling red wine. John Walker, Chairman of the UKVA Technical Committee, is attempting to get MAFF to clear an experimental winemaking procedure for some of these products so that they may legally be made and sold.

Halfpenny Green Vineyard
Tom Lane, Halfpenny Green, Staffordshire, DY7 5EP

T: 01384 221122. F: 01384 221101. M: 0973 730717

Owner: Martin Vickers
Winemaker: Clive Vickers
Directions: Telephone for directions.
Vineyard Details: 6.20 ha of vines planted between 1983 and 1994. The south and south-west facing site is between 67 m and 70 m above sea level and the soil is a loamy sand. The vines are almost all planted at 2.13 m × 1.37 m and are Double Guyot trained.
Grape Varieties: Chardonnay, Dornfelder, Faberrebe, Findling, Huxelrebe, Kernling, Madeleine × Angevine 7672, Pinot noir, Regner, Reichensteiner, Rondo, Schönburger, Seyval blanc, Triomphe,
Wine Sales: All year round, daily, 10.30 am to 5 pm.
Vineyard Visits: Group visits available by arrangement, £3.50 per person. Also craft centre, coarse fishing lake, tea rooms. Corporate events catered for.

The winery at Halfpenny Green is in a converted seventeenth-century oak barn and incorporates a visitor centre and viewing gallery. It has a 3.5 tonne Willmes pneumatic press, stainless and glass fibre tanks and a semi-automatic bottler. Fermentations can be temperature controlled. Their wines have been awarded bronze medals in the UKVA's national competition and Highly Commended in the MVA regional competition.

Morville Hall Vineyard

Morville Hall, Bridgnorth, Shropshire
Address for correspondence:
The Gate House, Morville Hall, Bridgnorth, Shropshire, WV16 5NB

T: 01746 714357

Owner & Winemaker: Ian Rowe
Directions: Vineyard not open to the public.
Vineyard Details: 0.07 ha of vines planted between 1989 and 1998. The site faces east south-east, is situated between 93 m and 95 m above sea level and the soil is a deep clay loam over boulder clay subsoil. The vines are planted at 2 m × 1.5 m and 2 m × 1 m and are spur pruned.
Grape Varieties: Madeleine × Angevine 7672, Müller-Thurgau, Reichensteiner.
Wine Sales & Vineyard Visits: Serious visitors by appointment. Wine not usually available for sale.

Although small, this vineyard is more than worthy of inclusion in this guide. Ian Rowe is an enthusiastic grower and winemaker who achieves remarkable success in competitions with his wines.

Morville Hall is a Grade I listed mansion owned by the National Trust and the vineyard is planted on land leased from them. The vines are low cordon trained and pruned to short spurs, and there is a high level of canopy management to get full ripeness. The soil is kept bare to improve the micro-climate and reduce the humidity, thus assisting in disease control. Fungicides are used sparingly. Owner and winemaker Ian Rowe considers Madeleine × Angevine 7672 to be the ideal variety for his situation and says that it makes superb wine 'if picked early enough' to capture the acidity. When picked too late, only flabby wines can result.

The winery is in a late-eighteenth-century red brick gazebo with a slate roof which is within the grounds of Morville Hall. Measuring 1.83 m × 1.83 m it must be the smallest winery which makes wine for sale in the country. Equipment befits the size of the operation with a 20 litre oak basket press and fermentations are in glass. The grapes are pressed within minutes of being picked and gently handled throughout the winemaking process. Annual production averages between 300 and 400 bottles a year.

The list of awards and medals won by Morville Hall's wines is a long one and would put many a bigger outfit to shame. In the SWVA's regional competition they have won the Eric Coates Trophy for best wine from a small vineyard no less than five times, the Committee Cup for the best dry white from a small producer twice and the Chairman's Cup for the best non-dry white from a smaller vineyard once. The 1994 Müller-Thurgau Dry and the 1996 Madeleine Angevine Dry were both awarded Mercian Wine of the Year trophy.

Wainbridge Vineyard
Wainbridge House, Clee Saint Margaret, Craven Arms, Shropshire, SY7 9DT

T: 01584 823543. F: 01584 823447
E: mike.hardingham@jet.uk

Owner: Mike Hardingham
Directions: Vineyard not open to the public.
Vineyard Details: 2.20 ha of vines planted between 1996 and 1998. The south-east facing site is between 150 m and 200 m above sea level and the soil is a heavy loam. The vines are planted at 1.5 m ×

1 m and Double Guyot trained (1996 planting) or 3 m × 2 m and GDC trained (1997/98 plantings).
Grape Varieties: Kernling, Madeleine × Angevine 7672, Madeleine Sylvaner, Seyval blanc, Triomphe + others.
Wine Sales: No wine available until 2001 control.

Wroxeter Roman Vineyard
Wroxeter, Shrewsbury, Shropshire, SY5 6PQ

T: 01743 761888. F: 01743 761400

Owners: David & Christine Millington
Winemakers: Martin & David Millington
Directions: Take the A5 Shrewsbury to Telford road and then the B4380 towards Wroxeter. Follow this road past the Roman City ruins and signs for the vineyard will be found on the left as you leave the village.
Vineyard Details: 2.685 ha of vines planted between 1991 and 1997. The site faces south and south-west, is 55 m above sea level and has a light sandy soil. Apart from the 1997 planted Phoenix, which are at 2.2 m × 1.5 m, the vines are planted at 2 m × 1.4 m and Double Guyot trained.

451

Grape Varieties: Dornfelder, Dunkelfelder, Madeleine × Angevine 7672, Phoenix, Regner, Reichensteiner.
Wine Sales: All year round, 11 am to 5.30 pm.
Vineyard Visits: During above hours. Group tours available at any time by appointment. In addition to the vineyard and winery, there is a well-stocked farm shop, a pick-your-own lavender *herbarium*, a scheduled ancient monument (a relic of the Roman City of Uriconium) and a flock of rare breed 'Balwen' sheep. Tours for groups can take place up to 10 pm.

The winery at Wroxeter is housed in a new three-bay Dutch barn and has both stainless and glass fibre tanks, the usual filters and pumps and a filler and semi-automatic corker. The wines continue to improve, winning commended and seal of approval at the IWC and in 1997, a silver medal at the MVA wine competition.

In recent years, the Millingtons have been engaged in a lengthy court battle against the Secretary of State for the Environment who ruled, whilst determining a planning application, that wine could not be considered as an 'agricultural product' for planning purposes and could not be sold without planning permission, even though permission was given for its production.

This decision was successfully challenged in the Court of Appeal who ruled that wine *was* an 'agricultural product' – one judge adding that to say otherwise would be 'an affront to common sense' (something you would have thought John Prescott would have plenty of!) – and its sale from the place of production (taken to mean where it was both grown *and* made) was not therefore subject to planning consent. An appeal by the Secretary of State was dismissed by the House of Lords and therefore the judgement stands.

Valhalla Vineyard
12 Lavender Lane, Horton, Northampton, Northamptonshire, NN7 2AS

T: 01604 870317

Owner & Winemaker: Keith Wilyman
Directions: Take the B526 Northampton to Newport Pagnell road. After about six miles, in the village of Horton and around a right-hand bend with the French Partridge Restaurant on the left after

200 m (stone wall and hedge) turn left into a lane. Valhalla is 200 m dead ahead.

Vineyard Details: 2.35 ares of vines planted in 1990. The site is some 122 m above sea level and the soil is described as 'light'. The vines are planted at 1 m × 1 m and pruned to a permanent cordon.
Grape Varieties: Léon Millot, Madeleine × Angevine 7672, Madeleine Sylvaner, Siegerrebe.

This is a small non-commercial vineyard and wine is made for private consumption. The vineyard is open to visitors by appointment. The winery is described as 'basic'!

Vernon Lodge Vineyard
Tiffield, Towcester, Northamptonshire, NN12 8AB

T: 01327 350077

Owner & Winemaker: Mike Dean
Directions: Vineyard not generally open to the public. Small private visits can be arranged.
Vineyard Details: 0.09 ha of vines planted in 1980. The south-east facing site is 114 m above sea level and the soil is a loam over heavy clay. The vines are planted at 1.52 m × 1.22 m, mainly on a Double Guyot system. A few are trellised on an 'adapted GDC system'.
Grape Varieties: Madeleine × Angevine 7672, Madeleine Sylvaner, Siegerrebe, Triomphe.

This is a private 'hobby' vineyard that relies on village help for harvesting, bottling and pruning. Helpers are rewarded in kind! Mike Dean's vineyard – conveniently situated at the top of his garden – is in the best traditions of small non-commercial vineyards – immaculately maintained with not a weed in sight nor a shoot out of place and able to produce useful crops which are turned into award winning wines. Madeleine Angevine and Siegerrebe are reckoned to be the best varieties – Madeleine for its consistency and Siegerrebe for its 'wonderfully aromatic and flavourful wine'. The wines are made in a well-insulated building – built in 1983 for the first vintage – which houses a small basket press, PVC tanks and a three-head filler together with the usual equipment needed to make wine. Mike tries to ensure a long slow fermentation using cold-tolerant strains of yeast and bottles in the spring following harvest.

His efforts are well worth it as Vernon Lodge wines won Best Non Commercial award in the 1993, 1995 and 1996 T&CVA's competition and a bronze medal in the 1999 MVA competition.

Welland Valley Vineyard
Vine Lodge, Hothorpe Road, Marston Trussell, Market Harborough, Leicestershire, LE16 9TX

T: 01858 434591. M: 07989 091721

Owners: David & Jane Bates
Winemaker: David Bates
Directions to vineyard: From the A508, Northampton to Market Harborough road, turn left in Great Oxenden towards East Farndon. In East Farndon turn left towards Marston Trussel. Vineyard is on right-hand side after approximately half a mile.
Vineyard Details: 0.35 ha of vines planted between 1993 and 1998 on a 2.13 m × 1.22 m Double Guyot system. The south facing site is between 91 m and 107 m above sea level and has a clay and loam soil.

Grape Varieties: Bacchus, Dunkelfelder, Madeleine × Angevine 7672, Pinot noir, Reichensteiner, Rondo, Schönburger, Seyval blanc, Siegerrebe.
Wine Sales & Vineyard Visits: By appointment.

Welland Valley's first wine, the 1997 Trussel Rosé, was judged the best non-white in the MVA's annual competition and the 1998 Siegerrebe took Best in Show in 1999. The wine is being produced on-site in a simple winery with stainless steel tanks, a 90 litre Speidel Hydropress and a three-head filler. Although the address of this vineyard is Leicestershire, it is in fact in Northamptonshire.

Windmill Vineyard
Windmill Hill Farm, Hellidon, Daventry, Northamptonshire, NN11 6HZ

T: 01327 262023

Owners: Doreen Hillier & Thomas Bird
Winemaker: Doreen Hillier
Directions: From the A425 Daventry to Leamington Spa road, turn left just after Staverton towards Hellidon. When you reach the village, stand with your back to the Red Lion PH and you will see the windmill.
Vineyard Details: 0.26 ha of vines planted between 1978 and 1995. The south facing site is between 201 m and 206 m above sea level and the soil is a medium loam over ironstone. The vines are Double Guyot trained.
Grape Varieties: Müller-Thurgau, Madeleine × Angevine 7672, Pinot noir, Seyval blanc, Triomphe.
Wine Sales: Easter to 15 October and December, Wednesday to Sunday, noon to 6 pm. At all other times by appointment.
Vineyard Visits: Individuals and small groups during above times. Larger groups by appointment at any time from £2.50 per person. Also plants, antiques and collectables for sale.

Windmill Vineyard takes its name from the 200-year-old windmill which, until the early years of the twentieth century, was used for grinding corn. It was converted into a residence in 1978. The winery is situated in converted farm buildings and a range of other products, cider from their own orchard and country wines made from local hedgerow fruits, are made. The vineyard, at 206 m, claims to be the highest in England, although in fact Higher Bumsley Vineyard in Devon, at 213 m, just beats them.

Bothy Vineyard
Frilford Heath, Abingdon, Oxfordshire
Address for correspondence:
Amphora, Crays Pond, Reading, Berks, RG8 7QJ

T: 01491 681484. F: 01491 681484. M: 07973 399282
E: roger-fisher@onet.co.uk

Owners: Roger & Dorothea Fisher
Winemaker: Roger Fisher
Directions to vineyard: From A415 Witney to Abingdon road turn north at the garage in Marcham village. Turn left at next crossroads signposted to Tubney. Vineyard is a quarter of a mile on right-hand side.
Vineyard Details: 1.04 ha of vines established in 1978 and 1979. The south facing site is between 80 m and 85 m above sea level and the soil is sandy loam over sand. The vines are, planted on a 2.0 m × 1.3 m Double Guyot system.
Grape Varieties: Albalonga, Findling, Huxelrebe, Optima, Ortega, Perle from Alzey.

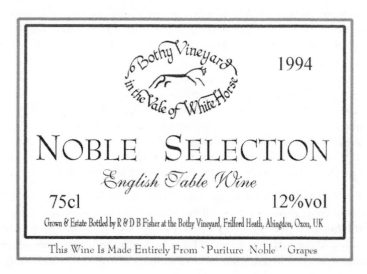

Bothy Vineyard in the Vale of White Horse — 1994

NOBLE SELECTION
English Table Wine
75cl — 12%vol
Grown & Estate Bottled by R & D B Fisher at the Bothy Vineyard, Frilford Heath, Abingdon, Oxon, UK
This Wine Is Made Entirely From 'Puriture Noble' Grapes

Wine Sales: The vineyard is open at weekends and on Tuesdays, Wednesdays and Thursdays from 10 am to 6 pm. The vineyard has an off-licence for single bottle sales and wines may be tasted free-of-charge.

Vineyard Visits: Guided tours, lectures and tastings can be organised for groups of up to 24 people. The charge will vary according to the group's requirements and light refreshments can be arranged. Telephone for details.

Bothy Vineyard was established by Roger and Dorothea Fisher while they were both still working, but since retirement from salaried work, they have taken up the running of the vineyard with considerable enthusiasm. The site was chosen for its suitability for vine growing, and the sandy soil allows for deep rooting and early flowering.

The winery is in an old stone barn, originally the 'bothy' for the garden staff at the adjacent estate. The winery is equipped with both stainless and glass fibre tanks, some with thermostatically controlled cooling/heating coils, a Vaslin press, Seitz filter, four-head filler and the usual sundry other items found in a small winery. Roger's winemaking skills continue to develop and improve and his wines are now consistent medal and award winners in both regional and national competitions. The 1994 and the 1997 Ortega/Optima were both winners of the Overall Best Wine Trophy and the 1996 Ortega was Best Dry White in the Thames and Chilterns Vineyards Association's competition. The 1994 Noble Selection gained Silver in the UKVA's annual competition in 1998.

Boze Down Vineyard
Hardwick Road, Whitchurch-on-Thames, Reading, Oxfordshire, RG8 7QS

T: 0118 9844031. F: 0118 9844426
E: bozedown@compuserve.com
W: http://ourworld.compuserve.com/homepages/bozedown

Owners: Richard & Sandra L Conn
Winemaker: Wines made at Valley Vineyards
Directions: Leave the M4 at junction 12 towards Newbury and at the second roundabout take the A340 to Pangbourne. In Pangbourne, join the A329 at a mini roundabout where you turn

right, then left at the next mini roundabout in 200 yards, passing the George pub' on your left. This is now the B471 which takes you over the Thames via a toll bridge (at a cost of 10p) and through Whitchurch village. At the end of the village at the foot of Whitchurch hill, turn right into Hardwick Road (towards Mapledurham) and the vineyard will be found in half a mile on the left.

Vineyard Details: 2.2 ha of vines planted between 1985 and 1987. The site is between 15 m and 46 m above sea level on south to south-west facing slope and the soil is a thin silty loam over chalk with flints. The vines are mostly trellised on a GDC system at 3.7 m × 1.8 m or 2.5 m.

Grape Varieties: Chardonnay, Dunkelfelder, Maréchal Foch, Müller-Thurgau, Ortega, Pinot blanc, Reichensteiner, Schönburger, Seyval Blanc, Triomphe.

Wine Sales: Open March to December, Saturdays, 11 am to 6 pm, Sundays noon to 5 pm. At all other times by appointment.

Vineyard Visits: Vineyards tours and wine tastings available by prior appointment at £6 per person.

When the first Boze Down vintage (the 1987) was largely consumed by the local badger population, the Conns decided to adopt the beast as their logo and one has appeared on their labels ever since. Initially the vines were trellised on a low wire Guyot system, but they have been forced, by the badgers' appetites for their grapes, to re-trellis the vines on to a high-wire GDC system. The site, overlooking the Thames in an 'area of outstanding natural beauty', is well sheltered and the lean soil structure makes the vines dig deep for nutrients. Over the years, Boze Down has achieved considerable success, especially with barrel aged reds. These are deep in colour, well structured and usually have a distinctive Rioja-like oakiness which marries well with the fruit. The 1995 red was awarded a bronze and the 1996 a silver in the UKVA's annual competition. The wines are made by John Worontschak at Valley Vineyards. Boze Down is also one of the few UK vineyards to have a web-site and it is well worth a visit.

Brightwell Vineyard
Rush Court, Wallingford, Oxfordshire, OX10 8LJ

M: 07771 516376
E: wines@brightvines.freeserve.co.uk

Owners: Bob & Carol Nielsen
Directions: Take the A329 from Wallingford towards Thame. Brightwell Vineyard will be found on the right-hand side before you cross the Thames.
Vineyard Details: 4.27 ha of vines planted between 1987 and 1989. The south facing site is between 55 m and 65 m above sea level. The vines are all trellised on a 3.5 m × 2 m GDC system.
Grape Varieties: Chardonnay, Bacchus, Dornfelder, Huxelrebe, Madeleine × Angevine 7672, Reichensteiner.
Wine Sale & Vineyard Visits: By appointment only. Telephone 07771 516376.

This vineyard was taken over by the current owners in 1999 and wine will be on sale from 2001. The vineyard includes a nature trail and picnic areas along the bank of the Thames.

Chiltern Valley Wines

Old Luxters Vineyard, Hambleden, Henley-on-Thames, Oxfordshire, RG9 6JW

T: 01491 638330. F: 01491 638645
E: enquiries@luxters.co.uk

Owner: David Ealand
Winemaker: Andy Tallent
Directions: Take A4155 Marlow to Henley road. Take turning signposted Hambleden. Continue on this road for two miles beyond Hambleden. Take first left and follow to top of hill. Vineyard on right-hand side.
Vineyard Details: 0.41 ha of vines, all planted in 1982 on a 2 m × 1.8 m GDC system. The site slopes east, is between 183 m and 198 m above sea level and has a clay and chalk soil.
Grape Varieties: Bacchus, Madeleine × Angevine 7672, Reichensteiner.
Wine Sales: Open all year round. Weekdays, 9 am to 5 pm. Weekends, 11 am to 5 pm.
Vineyard Visits: Visitors welcome during opening hours. Group tours (min. 15 people) by arrangement. £8 per person weekdays,

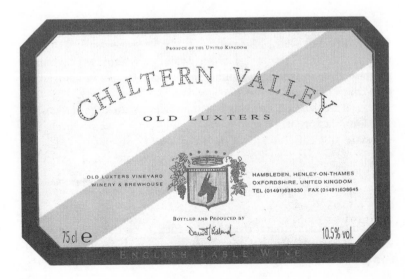

£10 per person weekends. Meals only available for larger groups (40+).

Chiltern Valley have firmly established themselves as one of the major vineyards in the UK, winning many medals and awards for their wines over the years since their first vintage in 1984. Their 1987 Chiltern Valley Dry won the Gore-Browne Trophy and their 1986 Old Luxters Reserve the English Wine of the Year Trophy in the IWSC. Recent triumphs include Best Rosé for their 1994 Rosé and Best Sparkling for their 1996 Sparkling in the T&CVA competition. They specialise in the production of own label wines and ales and have recently produced a special ale for Fortnum and Mason and a range of wines and ales for the World Trade Centre.

The winery at Old Luxters is one of the most modern in the country and has been established in traditional brick and flint buildings, formerly pig sheds and a grain store, and equipped with the latest equipment; a Willmes UP 1800 pneumatic press, stainless steel fermentation and storage tanks and GAI filler. They also have Seguin-Moreau oak barrels for maturation of some of their wines. As their own area of vines is relatively small, much of their output is made from grapes bought from local vineyards. In addition, they also make wines for several vineyards in the area who do not have their own facilities.

Apart from the vineyard and winery, there is also a Real Ale brewery producing bottle cask-conditioned and bottled beers, a beautifully restored seventeenth-century barn which hosts art exhibitions and can be hired for meetings, conferences, dinners etc. Since the early 1990s they have regularly held Dinner and Opera evenings and a restaurant was built in 2000. The area itself is one of outstanding natural beauty and well worth a visit.

Fawley Vineyard
The Old Forge, Fawley Green, Henley-on-Thames, Oxfordshire, RG9 6JA

T: 01491 577998. F: 01491 577477

Owners: Nick & Wendy Sargent
Winemaker: Wines made at Chiltern Valley Vineyards

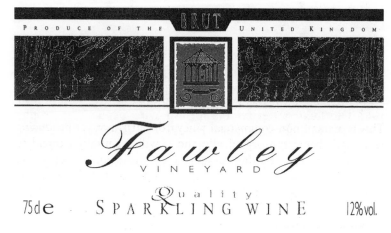

PRODUCE OF THE BRUT UNITED KINGDOM

Fawley

VINEYARD

75d℮ · Quality SPARKLING WINE 12%vol.

PRODUCED BY W1543 U.K. FROM GRAPES GROWN BY FAWLEY VINEYARD
Fawley Vineyard The Old Forge Fawley Green Henley-on-Thames Oxfordshire United Kingdom Tel: (01491) 577998

Directions: From Henley take the A4155 towards Marlow, leaving the river on the right. About 2 miles from Henley, turn left to Fawley (opposite the entrance to Toads Hall Garden Centre). Go to the top of the hill, turn right at the T junction and continue until you reach Fawley Village Hall. The Old Forge is behind the hall.
Vineyard Details: 0.34 ha of vines planted between 1985 and 1995. The south-east facing site is 110 m above sea level and the soil is clay over chalk. The vines are planted on a 2 m × 1.8 m GDC system.
Grape Variety: Bacchus.
Wine Sales & Vineyard Visits: At any time by appointment.

This vineyard, high in the Chilterns, produces both still and sparkling wines. The harvest is gathered in by the proprietor's friends and taken to the winery in a 1930s' lorry.

Grange Farm Vineyard
Grange Farm, Swerford, Oxfordshire, OX7 4AX

T: 01608 730665. F: 01608 730655
E: jonathan@grangefarm3.freeserve.co.uk

Owners & Winemakers: Jonathan Abbott & Jane Brooksmith
Directions: Grange Farm is 5 miles east of Chipping Norton

and 3 miles south of Hook Norton on the edge of the Cotswolds.

Vineyard Details: 2.52 ares (0.0252 ha) of vines planted in 1999. The south facing site is 168 m above sea level and has a loamy soil with Hornton stone shale under 30 cm deep. The vines are planted at 2 m × 1.4 m and are Double Guyot pruned.

Grape Varieties: Auxerrois, Pinot gris, Rondo.

This is a small non-commercial vineyard that is not yet producing wine. It is being run organically and it will eventually expand to approx. 0.75 ha. Further plantings of the same varieties are planned. A winery has been installed in an existing listed stable block and a cider orchard has also been planted.

Hendred Vineyard

Sheephouse Barn, Ludbridge, East Hendred, Oxfordshire, OX12 8HR

T: 01235 833277
E: wine@hendred.co.uk

Owners: Malcolm & Mary MacKinnon
Winemaker: Malcolm MacKinnon

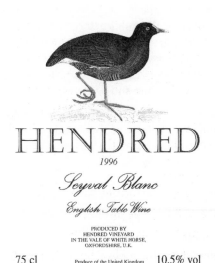

HENDRED

1996

Seyval Blanc

English Table Wine

PRODUCED BY
HENDRED VINEYARD
IN THE VALE OF WHITE HORSE,
OXFORDSHIRE, U.K.

75 cl   Produce of the United Kingdom   10.5% vol

Directions: Telephone for directions.
Vineyard Details: 2 ha of vines planted in 1992 on a 2.5 m × 1.4 m Double Guyot system. The sloping site has a mainly loam soil with some chalk and sand.
Grape Varieties: Madeleine × Angevine 7672, Seyval blanc.
Wine Sales: Weekends 10 am to 5 pm. At other times by arrangement.
Vineyard Visits: Group visits available by arrangement.

The Hendred vineyard goes back to the start of commercial viticulture in the UK and was originally planted in 1972 with Reichensteiner. The grapes were taken to Merrydown to be made into wine and Jack Ward gave the MacKinnons much encouragement. In 1991, they sold their house and the original vineyard site, but retained some land lower down the slope which was planted in 1992. There is a small winery on-site with a Willmes press and all the usual winemaking equipment. Their 1996 Madeleine Angevine was awarded Best Medium Dry White by the T&CVA.

Appledown Vineyard
Aylesbury Road, Monks Risborough, Buckinghamshire, HP27 OJT

T: 01844 274802. F: 01844 274802

Owners: Mr & Mrs Anthony J Clark
Winemaker: Anthony Clark
Directions: Not open to the public.
Vineyard Details: 0.7 ares (45 vines) planted on a 1.5 m × 1 m Pendelbogen system, plus 4 on the house wall. The site is 120 m above sea level on clay over chalk. It is south-east facing.
Grape Varieties: Seyval blanc and Triomphe.

This is a small amateur vineyard and wine is not sold. The vines are grown as organically as possible and made in an 'outside shed'. Equipment consists of a 45 litre basket press, a stainless steel tank and some large glass carboys.

Bower Farm Vineyard
The Vale, Chesham, Buckinghamshire, HP5 3NS

Owner & Winemaker: Shaun Dowling
Directions: Not open to the public.
Vineyard Details: 0.7 ha of vines planted in 1994 and 1996. The site

is between 90 m and 122 m above sea level, south-east facing and the soil is chalky. The vines are a 2 m × 2 m Double Guyot system and a 3.5 m × 2 m spur pruned cordon system. The site is prone to frost.
Grape Varieties: Bacchus, Findling, Schönburger, Seyval blanc.

C.A.V.E.
The Allotments, Botolph Claydon, Buckinghamshire
Address for correspondence:
22 Melbourne House, 50 Kensington Place, London, W8 7PW

T: 0171 7275595. F: 0171 7924455
E: john@jfomarketing.freeserve.co.uk

Chairman: John Olivier
Winemakers: Members of the co-operative
Directions: Vineyard is at the Allotments, Botolph Claydon, Buckinghamshire.
Vineyard Details: 2.97 ares (0.0297 ha) of vines planted in 1997. The site is 107 m above sea level and has a predominantly clay soil. The vines are planted at 1 m × 1.5 m and Double Guyot trained.
Grape Varieties: Rondo, Seyval blanc.
Wine Sales: Wine is for co-operative member's use only.
Vineyard Visits: By appointment only. Telephone 07802 151925.

This is a (very) small amateur vineyard of only 297 sq.m. It is run by the Claydon Association of Vineyard Eccentrics (C.A.V.E.) who manage it on a co-operative basis. The first year of full production was 2000.

Hale Valley Vineyard
Boddington East, Hale Lane, Wendover, Buckinghamshire, HP22 6NQ

T: 01296 623730. F: 01296 623730
E: chap@halevalley.demon.co.uk

Owners: Antony & Carol Chapman
Winemaker: Wines made at Chiltern Valley Vineyards
Directions: From the clock tower in the centre of Wendover take the A4011 and in 25 yards turn right into Hale Road. Take the first left into Hale Lane and the vineyard will be found in 700 yards on the right-hand side.

HALE VALLEY
ENGLISH TABLE WINE

DRY
11% vol   1996   75cl ℮

BOTTLED FOR ANTONY & CAROL CHAPMAN, HALE VALLEY VINEYARD
WENDOVER, BUCKINGHAMSHIRE, UK, HP22 6NQ.

Vineyard Details: 0.62 ha of vines planted in 1988. The site is 150 m above sea level and the soil is 225 mm of loamy rubble over pure chalk. The vines are planted at 2.7 m × 1.5 m and trained on a single high curtain.
Grape Varieties: Bacchus, Findling, Kernling.
Wine Sales & Vineyard Visits: By appointment. The vineyard holds several Open Days during the year.

The 1996 Hale Valley Dry was Highly Commended in the UKVA's annual competition and a sparkling wine is in production.

Milton Keynes Vineyard
Woughton-on-the-Green, Milton Keynes, Buckinghamshire
Address for correspondence:
The Spinney, Bradwell Village, Milton Keynes, Buckinghamshire, MK13 9BX

T: 01908 311264. F: 01908 311264. M: 07771 733715

ENGLISH TABLE WINE

11% vol   75 Cle

PRODUCE OF UK

Grown by Rosemary and Tony Stanyer at Milton Keynes Vineyard.
Bottled by D. Ealand, Old Luxters Vineyard and Winery,
Hambleden, Oxon., UK

Owners: Tony & Rosemary Stanyer
Winemaker: Wines made at Chiltern Valley Vineyards
Directions: Off the Newport Road, below the Swan PH in Woughton-on-the-Green, Milton Keynes.
Vineyard Details: 2 ha of vines planted between 1987 and 1992. The west facing site is approximately 68 m above sea level and the soil is Oxford clay. The vines are planted at 1.52 m × 1.3 m and are Double Guyot pruned.
Grape Varieties: Bacchus, Dornfelder, Dunkelfelder, Madeleine × Angevine 7672, Siegerrebe.
Wine Sales: April to September, Wednesday and Sunday only, 1 pm to 4 pm. At all other times by appointment.
Vineyard Visits: As above. Group tours available by appointment.

This vineyard is perhaps unique in the country in that the site was blessed by the Rector of Woughton-on-the-Green before the vines were planted with a blessing taken from the 1552 Prayer Book. The

Stanyers have planted 0.80 ha of traditional Somerset cider apple trees and the produce is sold to the Cambridge Cider Company. They produce white, rosé and red wines under the Woughton Park label.

Warden Abbey Vineyard
Farms Office, Southill Park, Biggleswade, Bedfordshire, SG18 9LJ

T: 01462 811266. F: 01462 812235. M: 07785 266078

Owner: Jane Whitbread
Farms Manager: R Bailey
Winemaker: Wines made at Chiltern Valley Vineyards
Directions: Vineyard not generally open to the public. An open weekend is held at the vineyard in early September and wine sales days in June and December at Southill Park.
Vineyard Details: 2.26 ha of vines planted in 1986 on a 2.15 m × 1.5 m Double Guyot system. The south facing site is 55 m above sea level and has a 'Hanslope' soil.
Grape Varieties: Bacchus, Madeleine × Angevine 7672, Müller-Thurgau, Regner, Reichensteiner.
Wine Sales: By appointment only. Telephone for details of retail stockists.

Warden Abbey vineyard is one of the very few (Beaulieu and Leeds Castle come to mind) that occupy more or less the same site as a

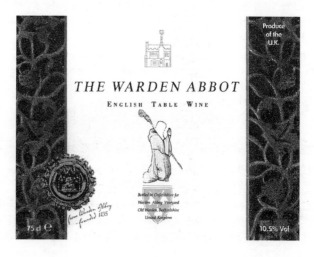

THE WARDEN ABBOT

ENGLISH TABLE WINE

Produce of the U.K.

75 cl ℮

10.5% Vol

medieval counterpart. Monks at the Cistercian abbey of Warden, founded in 1135 by Walter Espec, cleared woodland to plant two vineyards – The Vineyard of four acres and The Great Vineyard of ten acres. The vineyards were maintained until 1538 when, following the dissolution of the monasteries, they were abandoned.

Today, the vineyard produces a range of well-respected wines, white and sparkling, which have won their fair share of awards and prizes. Recent accolades include *Wine Magazine* Seals of Approval for their 1996 Warden Abbot, 1996 Warden Bacchus and 1997 Warden Vineyard Special Cuvée. Their 1996 Warden Vineyard was Country Landowners Association Wine of the Year in 1998 and in 2000 they won the UKVA President's Trophy with their 1998 Warden Vineyard. In 1998 they launched two sparkling wines; Warden Brut and Warden Extra Brut.

Cane End Vineyard

Cane End Farm, Reading, Berkshire, RG4 9HG

T: 0118 9722114. F: 0118 9722114. M: 0850 782546

Owners: Michael Hordern
Winemaker: Wines made at Chiltern Valley

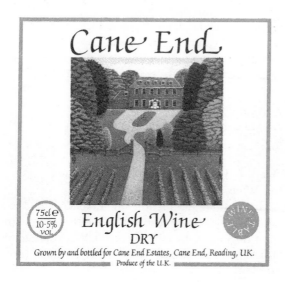

Directions: Take the A4074 Reading to Oxford road and the vineyard will be found on the left-hand side, just after the turning on the right to Henley.

Vineyard Details: 5.53 ha of vines planted between 1982 and 1986 on a south facing slope some 116 m above sea level. The soil is gravel over clay flint. All vines are trellised on a 3 m × 2 m GDC system.

Grape Varieties: Bacchus, Huxelrebe, Madeleine × Angevine 7672, Reichensteiner, Triomphe, Pinot noir.

Wine Sales and Craft Shop: Open all year round, daily, noon to 5 pm.

Cane End produce an interesting range of wines which in the past have achieved success in national competitions. Their current list includes two dry wines, a rosé, a medium dry, sparkling and a sweet dessert wine. Their label is one of the nicest.

Domaine Madeleine Vineyard

2 Littlewick Place, Littlewick Green, Maidenhead, Berkshire, SL6 3RA

T: 01628 822412

Owner: Tormod Madland
Directions: Vineyard not open to the public.
Vineyard Details: 0.65 ha of vines planted between 1988 and 1998 on a 1.8 m × 1.2 m cane pruned system.
Grape Varieties: Auxerrois, Madeleine × Angevine 7672, Pinot gris.
Wine Sales & Vineyard Visits: By appointment only.

Lillibrooke Manor Vineyard

Cox Green, Maidenhead, Berkshire, SL6 3LP

T: 01628 632131. F: 01628 632131

Owners: Mary & David Wheeler
Winemaker: Wines made at Valley Vineyards
Directions: Turn off M4 at junction 8/9. Take A423 to Maidenhead West. After 0.75 miles turn off to White Waltham and Cox Green. At T-junction turn right. In 100 yds turn left at roundabout. After 250 yds turn right into Ockwells Road. After 0.5 miles turn left into Lillibrooke Manor.

Vineyard Details: 0.11 ha of vines planted in 1984 and 1985. The site is between 34 m and 37 m, within a walled garden and the soil is clay. The vines are planted at 3 m × 1.4 m and GDC trained.
Grape Varieties: Bacchus, Ehrenfesler, Müller-Thurgau, Schönburger.
Wine Sales: Easter to Christmas, Monday to Saturday, 10 am to 5 pm, Sundays, noon to 3 pm.
Vineyard Visits: As above. Guided tours and meals for groups available from £5 per person by arrangement. There are two magnificent refurbished Grade II listed barns where functions, weddings, meetings etc. can be held. Windsor Forest vineyard is also owned by the Wheelers.

Much of the wine from this vineyard is used at functions held in one of their two large barns (see above). Their 1990 Ehrenfelser Dry and 1997 Lillibrook Manor Dry were awarded bronze medals by the UKVA and their 1993 Medium Dry won the best wine from a small vineyard in the T&CVA's 1995 competition.

Valley Vineyards
Stanlake Park, Twyford, Reading, Berkshire, RG10 0BN

T: 0118 9340176. F: 0118 9320914
E: vvineyards@aol.com

Owner: Jon Leighton
Winemakers: John Worontschak & Vince Gower
Directions: From Twyford take B3018 road towards Bracknell. Vineyard on left-hand side after three-quarters of a mile.
Vineyard Details: 8.24 ha of vines planted between 1979 and 1997. There are a number of sites, mainly south east-facing or level and between 37 m and 73 m above sea level. The soils vary from sand to loam and clay. The vines are planted on a wide variety of spacings and training systems, the most common being a 3 m–3.5 m × 1.8 m–2.5 m Stanlake Ballerina system which is in effect a short cane/long spur Sylvoz system with a permanent cordon at 1.5 m from the ground with an additional training wire above the cordon. There are also some 1 m × 1. 8 m and 2 m × 1.8 m Double Guyot trained vines in the walled garden. The latest plantings (1997) are 3 m × 3 m Stanlake Ballerina. There are also number of other experimental plots with assorted spacings and training systems.
Major Grape Varieties: Bacchus, Chasselas rosé, Dornfelder,

Ehrenfelser, Kerner, Optima, Ortega, Pinot Meunier, Pinot noir, Regner, Reichensteiner, Scheurebe, Schönburger, Seyval blanc, Siegerrebe, Triomphe, Würzer.

Minor Grape Varieties: Chardonnay, Dunkelfelder, Gewürztraminer, Nobling, Pinot gris, Riesling, Sauvignon blanc, Siegerrebe.

Wine Sales: Winter, Monday to Saturday, 11 am to 4 pm, Sundays, noon to 4 pm. Rest of the year, Monday to Saturday, 11 am to 5 pm, Sundays, noon to 5 pm. Telephone to check if unsure.

Vineyard Visits: Self-guided tours of vineyard only during opening hours. Guided tours of vineyards and winery with wine tastings by arrangement for groups of 25/30 people from £5.95 per person. Meals not available.

Valley Vineyards – which until a few years ago was known as Thames Valley Vineyards – is the home (spiritual if not actual) of two of the most important individuals in the UK winegrowing business: viticuturalist Jon Leighton and winemaker John Worontschak. Together they have forged a reputation for wine quality that is unrivalled and if this was the sole criterion for making one vineyard the best in the UK, then Valley Vineyards would undoubtedly be it.

Jon, part-time Australian and one-time motor racing and rally driver, had his interest in English Wine awakened by a visit to the English Wine Festival held at Charleston Manor in September 1978. As the owner of the Stanlake Estate (although at the time the house and buildings were leased to tenants) he saw the possibility of putting some of his land under vines and in the following year he planted a trial plot of 500 vines and a larger 1 ha acre plot in 1980. He and his then vineyard manager, Patricia White, continued planting and developing the vineyards until by 1988, they extended to over 8 ha and contained one of the largest collections of varieties and trellising and training systems in any UK vineyard. The 'collection' has been developed and refined and the list of varieties is as eclectic as its owner. Who else in the UK grows Chasselas rosé, Gewürztraminer and Scheurebe in quantity? Jon rates Pinot noir – 'the heartbreak' grape as he calls it – for both quality and high retail price, Bacchus and Scheurebe for their wonderful flavours, Ortega, Regner and Siegerrebe for their early ripening, flavoursome grapes and low acid levels, Dornfelder for its excellent early potential and Schönburger and Chasselas rosé for their resistence to *botrytis*, good flavours and in the last variety's case, its suitability for turning into sparkling wine. He proposes to expand his vineyards slowly with Pinot noir, Bacchus, Chasselas rosé, Scheurebe, Siegerrebe and Madeleine Angevine.

Geographically, Stanlake Park is in the heart of the Thames Valley, not far from where Westbury Vineyards used to be, where the bearded, eccentric, Bernard Theobald could often be heard to claim that 'our climate is better than Bordeaux's for growing vines'! Whilst Jon holds back from this claim, he does point out as a matter of fact, that the natural sugar levels of many of the grape varieties grown by him are the highest recorded in the country and that de-acidification seldom has to be carried out. However, this is an area well away from the coast, and spring frosts can be a problem. The house itself dates from the fifteenth century and Charles II is reputed to have stayed there in order to be near Nell Gwynne with whom he had a rendezvous at the local pub – the Dog and Badger! The estate (once part of the Windsor Great Estate) has been in Leighton hands since 1952.

Although born and brought up in England, John spent some 20 years living in Australia and continues to pay regular visits there. Much of his viticulture and winemaking were learnt there and with Antipodean enthusiasm he is not afraid of trying new varieties, new growing systems and new techniques. He spent some time at Riverina College in New South Wales where with viticulturalist Max Loder, he studied the subject. He first questioned the notion, taken then – as now – by many as the gospel truth, that 'competition planting' – where a high density of vines competes for root space, water and nutrients – can actually control and reduce excess vigour. He decided that this was patently not the case (one only has to look at UK vineyards planted at densities as high as 6,000 vines per ha to know that this is not true) and that planting vines in rows between 3 m and 3.5 m wide gave just as much (or as little) vigour control, but offered serious savings on establishment costs (1200 vines/ha) and annual labour and management costs. Whilst yields might not be as high, land costs are relatively low and with the proper pruning system, almost as many annual fruiting buds can still be laid down.

In the mid-1980s, he and Pat White developed the 'Stanlake Bow' which was a Guyot or Pendlebogen system where instead of the replacement arms starting from the middle of the trunk and going out away from the centre, a T-shaped trunk was created with the canes starting from the ends of the T and coming back towards the centre. This made for a clearer area in the centre of the vine which opened it up to light and air and in addition, gave each vine a larger volume of permanent wood in which to store its winter nutrients. This helped promote an early bud-burst and lessened frost damage. This system was tried and for some years worked well, but as the vines got older, the starting point of the annual canes got further and further away from the centre point of the vines until they started to crowd their neighbours and fruiting area was being lost.

Today, many of the vines are trained on another unique system – the 'Stanlake Ballerina'. This is a variant of the Smart-Dyson Ballerina which viticulturalist Richard Smart helped develop and is in effect a mid-height Sylvoz system. This combines the benefits of short cane/long spur pruning – speed, simplicity and the ability to vary bud numbers on an annual basis – with those of having a large body of permanent wood, earlier bud-burst and some protection from spring frost. Added to these are the financial advantages of low density of planting, a lack of summer leaf work and the health benefits of an open growing system.

The vineyard management is of a fairly high standard (but always with an eye on the bank balance) with grass all over and no herbicide strip under the vines, a low nitrogen, high potassium and phosphorous fertiliser regime and a little-and-often pest and disease control programme. Spray materials are switched as often as possible to break the build up of any resistant organisms. This gives a very low disease incidence, leading to clean crops which can be allowed to hang and ripen to maturity. Sheep are often used under the vines to keep the grass down and Schönburger, Reichensteiner and Triomphe are grown as organically as possible.

The winery at Valley Vineyards is housed in a barn built in 1688 to commemorate the Revolution and which was once the head-quarters of the Garth Hunt. It has a fine (listed) clocktower. The modern equipment it contains aims to reduce mechanical damage to the grapes as much as possible. A Demoisy crusher/de-stemmer and 4 tonne pneumatic Europress are at the start of the winemaking process, the tanks are all temperature controlled stainless steel with a Pedia-Kreyer heat exchanger, there is a fully insulated and cooled wine store, fully automatic GAI bottling/labelling line and a sparkling wine disgorging line. Extensive use of French oak *barriques* is made and one third are replaced each year.

Between 1983 – when the first small batches of experimental wine were made – and 1987, the cellar was in the hands of Jon Leighton and an Australian winemaker Andrew Hood; together they made a tentative start on establishing a 'Thames Valley' (as it then was) style. Success came early and in 1988 their Siegerwurzertraminer 1987 won the UKVA's President's Trophy. In 1988, another with Australian connections, namely, John Worontschak, arrived to take over the winery and – as they say in a certain type of cliché-ridden novel – things were never the same again. John arrived at a time when English and Welsh wine was already in a period of change. The old German style of UK-produced wine was, in the light of a rapid decline in sales of this type of wine in general, declining and a new type of English wine was starting to appear. Wines were becoming softer and more approachable, reliance on imported süss-reserve was lessening and winemakers were blending varieties to achieve more consistency. Oak ageing had been in use for several years (Karl-Heinz Johner at Lamberhurst and myself at Tenterden had been making *barrique*-aged wines since 1986) and there were even a few interesting sparkling, sweet and red wines being produced.

To this party, John Worontschak was able to bring his consider-able skills and experience. With the raw materials at his disposal from both Stanlake Park and from the other vineyards where he is either winemaker or consultant, he has, over the last thirteen years, made some impressive wines. They are often gentler and fruitier than other English wines and many have more depth and character. Careful handling, the use of the right enzymes and yeasts, more malolactic fermentations than in most UK wineries, and better control of oxidation and phenolic content have all helped. Judicious blending of varieties to adjust flavours is also seen as a very important part of the winemaking process. John has also produced – or helped produce – some of the best of the sweet wines, red wines and sparkling wines produced in the UK over the last few years. Without wanting to swell his pride any more than would be good for his health, I must acknowledge that he has notched up an impressive and totally unrivalled tally of awards and medals. To list just the major ones says it all.

In the EVA and UKVA national competition, John's wines have won the Gore-Browne Trophy (five times) in 1992 with the 1991 Thames Valley Clocktower Selection Botrytis, in 1993 with the 1991 Valley Vineyards Fumé, in 1996 with the Thames Valley Heritage Brut, in 1997 with the 1995 Valley Vineyards Clocktower Selection Pinot Noir and in 1998 with the Valley Vineyards Heritage Rosé; the President's Trophy (three times) in 1991 with the 1989 Thames Valley Botrytis, in 1995 with the 1994 Northbrook Springs Thames Valley Botrytis and in 1998 with the 1997 Valley Vineyards Clocktower Selection Pinot Noir; the Jack Ward Memorial Salver (four times) in 1990 with the 1989 Thames Valley Sweet Lee, in 1992 with the 1991 Thames Valley Clocktower Selection, in 1997 with the 1996 Hidden Springs Sunset Rosé and in 2000 with the Denbies 1999 Redlands; the Wine Guild of the UK Trophy (five times) in 1993 with the 1991 Valley Vineyards Fumé, in 1996 with both the Thames Valley Heritage Brut and the 1994 Mersea, in 1997 with the 1995 Valley Vineyards Clocktower Selection Pinot Noir and in 1998 with the 1996 Hidden Spring Dark Fields; the Bernard Theobald Trophy (four times) in 1992 with the Valley Vineyards Pinot Noir, in 1995 with the 1993 Hidden Spring Dark Fields, in 1998 with the 1997 Valley Vineyards Clocktower Pinot Noir and in 2000 with the Denbies 1999 Redlands; and the Vintner's Trophy once with the Valley Vineyards Heritage Rosé. In the Country Landowner's Association's English and Welsh Wine Competition the 1995 Regatta won Wine of the Year in 1997, the Ascot Sparkling was Sparkling Wine of the Year in 1998 and Heritage Brut Sparkling Wine of the Year in 1999. Added to this list are UKVA gold, silver and bronze medals, together with awards and commendations in the IWSC, the Wine Challenge and the T&CVA regional competition.

Three separate ranges of wines are usually produced. The Valley Vineyards range consists of the following:

Fumé – a dry white, fermented and aged in French oak for one year.
Regatta – a dry white in a fruitier, spicier style than the Fumé
Stanlake – a crisp, dry white, non-oaked
Hinton Grove – a medium dry aromatic wine mainly made from Schönburger
Ruscombe – a light bodied, smooth red wine
Ascot – a traditional method sparkling wine made in part from Pinot and Chardonnay grapes.

The Heritage range consists of:

Brut – a light bodied traditional method sparkling wine, slightly sweeter than the Ascot
Rosé – a rosé traditional method sparkling wine
Fumé – a dry, white lightly oaked wine.

The Clocktower range consists of:

Pinot Noir – a silky red made in the Burgundian style and aged in French oak
Gamay Brut – a dry, white traditional method sparkling wine
Chardonnay – a dry, smooth white, aged in new French oak
Botrytis – a sweet dessert wine made from *botrytis* infected fruit
Liqkir – a sweet, rich blackcurrant liqueur
Silvkir – a sweet, rich whitecurrant liqueur.

This selection of wines – which run from £4.49 for the Valley Vineyards Stanlake to £16.50 for the Clocktower Pinot Noir – is one of the biggest and most comprehensive available from any UK vineyard.

Historically, viticultural research has always played second fiddle to research into winemaking and the person who made a better wine garnered all the glory, whereas someone who developed a better pruning system was largely forgotten. Whilst Richard Smart and his ilk are helping to change this perception, it is still true that winemakers get most of the glory. The timescale for research into viticulture is of course far greater than it is for winemaking and results take many years, if not decades, to be statistically proven. Most traditional winegrowing countries have relatively ideal growing conditions and actually growing grapes is the least of their worries. However, in the UK growing grapes *is* our problem and in many vineyards the yield and quality of grapes is lamentable. Jon Leighton's work at Valley Vineyards ought to be taken more seriously.

In 1989, in the original text for my earlier book *The Vineyards of England*, two valuable paragraphs were lost during typesetting and in my hurry to finish proofreading (Thames Valley Vineyards, as they were then known, were right at the end of the vineyards section) I missed the fact that these paragraphs had been pruned. In part of the lost paragraphs, I said:

'The ideas and experimentation carried out at The Thames Valley vineyard are a great bonus for the English wine industry and their approach is both scientific and enthusiastic. People with good theories of how or why to grow vines in this country have too often spoilt their chance of being taken seriously by a totally unprofessional approach to both research and statistical proof. Perhaps the Thames Valley Vineyard will take up the cudgel lain down by Barrington Brock when the Viticulture Research Station at Oxted closed in April 1971?'

Twelve years and many grapes on, I still stand by what I then said. The work that Jon has carried out in his vineyard *is* a great bonus to the English and Welsh wine industry. What is more – and what has emerged in those intervening years – is that Jon has not only managed to consistently grow crops of good grapes, but has also had both the foresight and the good fortune to employ a winemaker, John Worontschak, and an assistant winemaker, Vince Gower, who have been given the facilities and encouragement to produce top quality wines. The combination of a dedicated owner/grower and a talented winemaking team have put Valley Vineyards at the top of this industry.

Windsor Forest Vineyard
Drift Road, Ascot, Berkshire
Address for correspondence:
Lillibrooke Manor, Cox Green, Maidenhead, Berkshire, SL6 3LP

T: 01628 632131. F: 01628 632131

Owners: Mary & David Wheeler
Winemaker: Wines made at Valley Vineyards
Directions: Vineyard not open to the public.

Vineyard Details: Approximately 1 ha of vines planted in the early 1980s. The north-west facing site is between 34 m and 38 m above sea level and has a clay soil. The vines are planted at 3 m × 2 m and GDC trained.

Grape Varieties: Ehrenfelser, Madeleine × Angevine 7672, Müller-Thurgau, Ortega, Pinot noir, Reichensteiner, Scheurebe, Schönburger, Seyval blanc, Triomphe.

Wine Sales & Vineyard Visits: See Lillibrooke Manor for details.

This vineyard – which was originally twice its current size and reduced in 1998 – was planted by Charlie Watson under the guidance of the late Bernard Theobald who owned Westbury Vineyard (now grubbed out). The first vintage was in 1992. The vines are random planted (must be fun at picking time!) and owner David Wheeler says that it 'should be grubbed up and re-planted with Triomphe and Pinot noir as they do well here'. Until recently, the only wine under the Windsor Forest label was a still medium dry wine, but a vintage sparkling wine will shortly be released.

Mill Hill Village Vineyard
Lawrence Street Allotments, Mill Hill, London, NW7
Address for correspondence:
68 Millway, Mill Hill, London, NW7 3QY

T: 020 8959 2214. F: 020 8959 4145
E: andy.creighton@free4all.co.uk

Owner & Winemaker: Andrew Creighton
Directions: Vineyard is 1 km from the A1 at Mill Hill Circus.
Vineyard Details: 0.06 ha of vines planted between 1986 and 1993. Vines are either planted at 1.9 m × 1.25 m or 1.7 m × 1.25 m. All are Double Guyot trained. The site faces gently to the south-east and is between 125 m and 135 m above sea level. The soil is a fairly rich loam over London clay.
Grape Varieties: Chardonnay, Huxelrebe, Kerner, Ortega, Pinot noir, Reichensteiner, Schönburger, Seyval blanc, Siegerrebe.
Vineyard Visits: Occasionally open, but only by prior arrangement.

This small non-commercial vineyard is situated on a local authority allotment (one of at least four in the UK) and is overlooked by the usual plots of fruits and vegetables and bordered by a public footpath. Unfortunately, not all the landowners in the vicinity were

PINOT NOIR
1996
12.5%vol   75cl

aware of the vine's susceptibility to weedkillers and their 1997 crop was wiped out by 2,4-D drift which appeared to come from fields over 300–400 metres and three rows of houses away. Their vines were trained on a low wire system, but the predations of the local fox population have forced a re-trellising onto a higher wire (although in my experience a fox can reach up to over 1 m!).

The well-equipped winery is housed in an insulated and partially air conditioned converted garage and the wines are made in a combination of stainless steel tanks, oak barrels, glass carboys and 25 litre plastic drums. After practising on bought-in red Italian and Spanish grapes, Andy Creighton made a good wine out of his first crop of home-grown Pinot noir and his 1996 Mill Hill Pinot noir was awarded Best Non-commercial Wine by the T&CVA in 1998.

Saint Andrews Vineyard
Dors Close Allotments, London, NW9 8DE
Address for correspondence:
5 Lovat Close, London, NW2 7RU

T: 020 8452 0318

Owners: R D & A P Castle and G McMullan
Winemakers: R D & A P Castle
Directions: Vineyard is at Dors Close Allotments, London
NW9 8DE.
Vineyard Details: 0.194 ha of vines planted between 1995 and
1997. The south facing site is between 138 m and 140 m above sea
level and the soil is London Clay. The vines are planted (mainly) at
1.5 m × 1.6 m and Double Guyot trained.
Grape Varieties: Dornfelder, Madeleine × Angevine 7672, Merlot,
Pinot noir, Rondo, Schönburger.
Wine Sales: This is a non-commercial vineyard and wine is not
made for sale.
Vineyard Visits: Tours available by appointment.

The aim of this vineyard, claimed to be 'the largest in London', is to
produce the best red possible using Dornfelder, Rondo and Pinot
noir (which account for almost 90 per cent of it). The wine is made
in a purpose-made timber winery in the garden and well equipped
with suitable equipment. Pectolytic enzymes are used pre-ferment
on the red grapes to aid extraction of flavour and colour and the
wine is aged in French oak.

Eryri Vineyard
Llanbedr, Gwynedd, Wales, LL45 2DZ

T: 01341 241251

Owners: David & Irene Workman
Winemaker: Wines made at Halfpenny Green Vineyard
Directions: Off the A496, two miles south of Harlech. At Llanbedr
follow the road to Shell Island, half a mile from the village.
Vineyard Details: 0.37 ha of vines planted between 1995 and 1998.
The west facing site is between 2 m and 50 m above sea level
and the vines are planted at 1.83 m × 1.83 m and 2.44 m and are
Double Guyot trained.

Grape Varieties: Madeleine × Angevine 7672, Rondo, Phoenix, Sauvignon blanc.
Wine Sales & Vineyard Visits: July to late September. Telephone for details.

Eryri Vineyard is still establishing itself and has limited amounts of wine for sale. They also sell other English and Welsh wines, as well as country wines. A shop, tasting room and winery are planned. The Sauvignon blanc is only for personal consumption.

Worthenbury Wines
The Old Rectory, Worthenbury, Wrexham, Wales, LL13 0AW

T: 01948 770257. M: 07748 547357
E: vineyard@worthenburywines.co.uk
W: www.worthenburywines.com

Owners: Martin & Mary Seed
Winemaker: Wines made at Valley Vineyards

Directions: Worthenbury is a small village, 16 miles south of Chester, situated on the B5069 between Bangor-on-Dee and Malpas. (Bangor is 5 miles from Wrexham on the A525, Malpas is just off the A41, 5 miles from Whitchurch.) The Old Rectory is near the village centre, the first house on Mulsford Lane, and is the large three-storey cream-coloured house with tall chimney stacks.

Vineyard Details: 0.25 ha (cropping area) of vines planted between 1991 and 1999 under polythene growing tunnels. The vines are spaced at 1.84 m × 1.23 m with two rows per tunnel. They are cane pruned in two tiers. The site is level, about 23 m above sea level and the soil is a sandy loam.

Grape Varieties: Chardonnay, Pinot noir, Sauvignon blanc.

Wine Sales & Vineyard Visits: By appointment only.

Worthenbury is one of the more unusual vineyards in the UK. It is fairly far north (latitude 53°) and planted with Chardonnay, Pinot noir and Sauvignon blanc – unusual varieties for the south of the country, let alone well into the northern half. They are, however,

14% VOL · 75CL · e

WORTHENBURY

Chardonnay
Dry White Wine
1997

PRODUCE OF WALES

planted under polythene tunnels – all of which have central heating to protect the vines from early spring frosts – which means that they receive much more heat than were they growing outside. The results to date have been encouraging.

For the first three vintages (1996–98) the grapes were transported several hundred miles to Tenterden in Kent to be made into wine. Since 1999 they have gone to Valley Vineyards in Twyford. The owners, Martin and Mary Seed, take immense pride in their small vineyard and go to great pains to ensure a clean, ripe crop. The wines so far have been mainly white – the Pinot producing its first crop in 1998. The shelter provided by the polytunnels produces very sweet grapes and natural alcohol levels have ranged from 11 per cent to 14 per cent. This is a brave experiment that deserves to succeed!

Appendices

I: UKVA ENGLISH AND WELSH WINE OF THE YEAR COMPETITION

In 1974, the English Vineyards Association (EVA) established the English and Welsh Wine of the Year Competition. Margaret Gore-Browne, a founder member of the EVA, donated a magnificent silver rose bowl in memory of her late husband, Robert, which was to be presented to the best wine in the competition.

Whereas in the early years there was but one class and only one trophy, in later years, as the number of wines entered into the competition grew, so did the awards, medals and trophies. In 1985, the competition was spilt into two sections: A for wines bottled in quantities in excess of 1,500 litres (except for dessert wines which may be entered in section A with 500 litres or more) and B, for wines bottled in quantities of between 100 and 1,499 litres. In 1999 a further class was added (C), for wines bottled in quantities of 10,000 litres or more. Each section is today further subdivided into twelve classes, each class reflecting a different style or vintage of wine. Gold, Silver and Bronze medals are awarded, together with Highly Commended certificates. Until recently, the competition was only open to EVA members, but since the formation of the United Kingdom Vineyards Association (UKVA) in 1996, it has been open to all who make wines from UK grown grapes. The competition rules are reviewed annually and changes are made to reflect the developing nature of English and Welsh wines. Recent changes have seen the introduction of separate classes for sparkling, dessert, oaked, red and rosé wines.

The numbers of wines being entered varies with the vintage and reached a high point in 1991 with 255 entries – a number of wines which the judges found quite daunting in the single day usually allowed for judging. In an attempt to make the judge's task somewhat easier and allow them to concentrate their efforts on fewer wines of better quality, entry fees have been raised and all wines must now conform to the analysis requirements for Quality and/or Regional wine (depending on the wine in question). Growers now tend to enter only their better wines. Since 1982, the awards ceremony has been held on the river terrace at the House of Lords by kind invitation of the UKVA President, Lord Montagu of Beaulieu.

The competition has, over the years, been a tremendous catalyst for the improvement in quality of English and Welsh wines and the prestige and publicity, together with the extra sales that go with winning one of the major prizes, spurs friendly rivalry between growers and winemakers.

The Chairman (or Chairwoman) of the judging panel has, since 1989, been a Master of Wine (MW) although this is not part of the rules, and he or she selects a panel and a venue for the judging. The panel is usually chosen from a wide cross-section of the wine industry, including wine writers, wine merchants and winemakers and they are asked to judge the wines against an international standard; there are no allowances made because these wines are grown in a marginal climate. This ensures that medals gained in this competition are comparable to those awarded in other competitions open to wines from all over the world.

CHAIRMEN OF THE COMPETITION

1974–1980	Michael Broadbent, MW, Christies
1981–1983	Hugh Johnson, winewriter
1984–1985	Kenneth Christie, MW, wine merchant, David Baillie Vintners, Exeter
1986–1988	Christopher Fielden, wine writer
1989–1991	Dr Arabella Woodrow MW, wine merchant
1992–1994	Maggie McNie MW, wine writer
1995–1997	Margaret Harvey, MW, wine merchant, Fine Wines of New Zealand
1998–2000	Rosemary George MW, wine writer
2001–	David Wrigley MW

There are a number of different trophies and awards.

The Gore-Browne Trophy, presented in 1974 by Mrs Margaret Gore-Browne in memory of her husband Robert, is awarded to the best wine in section A or C. The President's Trophy, presented by Lord Montagu of Beaulieu in 1985, is awarded to the best wine in section B.

The Jack Ward Memorial Salver, presented by Mrs Betty Ward in 1987 in memory of her husband who was Chairman of the EVA from 1976 to 1981, is awarded to the best wine of the previous vintage in section A or C. The Wine Guild Trophy presented in 1990 by the Wine Guild of the United Kingdom (Chancellor, Lord Montagu of Beaulieu) is awarded to the best wine of any other vintage in section A or C. Thus the winner of the Gore-

Browne Trophy also wins either the Jack Ward Salver or the Wine Guild Trophy.

The Bernard Theobald Trophy, presented by the Thames and Chilterns Vineyards Association in 1992 in memory of Bernard Theobald, one of the most colourful characters from the modern history of winegrowing in the UK and a great pioneer of English red wines, is awarded to the best red wine in the competition in any section. The Vintner's Trophy for Sparkling Wine, presented by the Worshipful Company of Vintners in 1998, is awarded to the best sparkling wine in section A or C.

The McNie Trophy for Oaked White Wine, presented by Maggie McNie, competition Chairman, 1992–1994, is awarded to the best oaked white wine in the competition. The Dudley Quirk Memorial Trophy, presented by English Wine Producers in memory of founder member Dudley Quirk of Chiddingstone Vineyards, is presented to the best wine in section C. The Award for Best Presentation was presented by the UKVA in 1999 and is given to the wine with the best presented label and bottle.

English Vineyards Association (1974–1994)
United Kingdom Vineyards Association (1995–1999)
Trophy and Gold Medal Winners
(*Note: the name of the winemaker follows the name of the wine*)

1974
Gore-Browne Trophy
   1972 Brede Riesling Sylvaner – Merrydown

1975
Gore-Browne Trophy
   1973 Pilton Manor Riesling Sylvaner – Nigel Godden

1976
Gore-Browne Trophy
   1975 Pilton Manor Riesling Sylvaner – Nigel Godden

1977
Gore-Browne Trophy
   1976 Pulham Magdalen Rivaner – Peter Cook

1978
Gore-Browne Trophy
   1977 Kelsale Müller-Thurgau and Seyval blanc – Peter Cook
Gold Medal
   1976 Adgestone – Ken Barlow
Gold Medal
   1977 Felstar Müller-Thurgau and Siegerrebe – Graham Barrett

1979
Gore-Browne Trophy
  1978 Adgestone – Ken Barlow
Gold Medal
  1977 Wootton Müller-Thurgau – Colin Gillespie

1980
Gore-Browne Trophy
  1979 Pulham Magdalen Rivaner – Peter Cook

1981
Gore-Browne Trophy
  1980 Tenterden Vineyard Spots Farm Seyval blanc – Stephen Skelton

1982
Gore-Browne Trophy
  1981 Wootton Schönburger – Colin Gillespie
Gold Medal
  1980 Adgestone – Ken Barlow

1983
Gore-Browne Trophy
  1982 Lamberhurst Huxelrebe – Karl-Heinz Johner
Gold Medal
  1982 Lamberhurst Schönburger – Karl-Heinz Johner
Gold Medal
  1982 Tenterden Vineyard Spots Farm Medium Dry – Stephen Skelton
Gold Medal
  1982 Tenterden Vineyard Spots Farm Müller-Thurgau Dry –
    Stephen Skelton
Gold Medal
  1982 Tenterden Vineyard Spots Farm Gutenborner Dry –
    Stephen Skelton

1984
Gore-Browne Trophy
  1983 Barton Manor Dry – Anthony Goddard
Gold Medal
  1981 Westbury Müller-Thurgau – Bernard Theobald
Gold Medal
  1982 Westbury Müller-Thurgau and Seyval blanc – Bernard Theobald
Gold Medal
  1983 Abbey Knight Pinot noir Rosé – Patrick Fisher
Gold Medal
  1983 Biddenden Ortega – Richard Barnes

Gold Medal
 1983 Barton Manor Sparkling Rosé – Anthony Goddard

1985
Gore-Browne Trophy
 1984 Lamberhurst Schönburger – Karl-Heinz Johner
President's Trophy
 1984 Avalon Seyval blanc – Colin Gillespie
Gold Medal
 1983 Biddenden Ortega – Richard Barnes
Gold Medal
 1983 Chalkhill Müller-Thurgau – Mark Thompson
Gold Medal
 1983 Wootton Seyval blanc – Colin Gillespie
Gold Medal
 1984 Carr Taylor Reichensteiner – David Carr Taylor
Gold Medal
 1982 Lamberhurst Schönburger – Karl-Heinz Johner

1986
Gore-Browne Trophy
 1985 Wootton Seyval blanc – Colin Gillespie
President's Trophy
 1985 Astley Madeleine Angevine – Kit Morris
Gold Medal
 1984 Three Choirs Seyval blanc and Reichensteiner – Kit Morris

1987
Gore-Browne Trophy
 1986 Biddenden Ortega – Richard Barnes
Jack Ward Memorial Salver
 1984 Three Choirs Medium – Kit Morris
President's Trophy
 1986 Astley Kerner – Kit Morris

1988
Gore-Browne Trophy
 1987 Chiltern Valley Old Luxters – David Ealand
Jack Ward Memorial Salver
 1986 Carr Taylor Reichensteiner – David Carr Taylor
President's Trophy
 1987 Thames Valley Siegerrebe and Gewürztraminer – Jon Leighton
Gold Medal
 Carr Taylor Vintage Sparkling – David Carr Taylor

1989
Gore-Browne Trophy
 1988 Carr Taylor Reichensteiner – David Carr Taylor
Jack Ward Memorial Salver
 Carr Taylor Non-Vintage Sparkling – David Carr Taylor
President's Trophy
 1988 Tenterden Rosé – Stephen Skelton

1990
Gore-Browne Trophy and Wine Guild of the UK Trophy
 1988 Lamberhurst Schönburger Medium Dry – Stephen Skelton
Jack Ward Memorial Salver
 1989 Thames Valley Sweet Lee – John Worontschak
President's Trophy
 1989 Chiltern Valley Noble Bacchus – David Ealand
Gold Medal
 1985 Penshurst Ehrenfelser – David Westphal

1991
Gore-Browne Trophy and Wine Guild of the UK Trophy
 1989 Tenterden Seyval blanc Special Reserve – Stephen Skelton
Jack Ward Memorial Salver
 1990 Chiltern Valley Noble Bacchus – David Ealand
President's Trophy
 1989 Thames Valley Botrytis – John Worontschak

1992
Gore-Browne Trophy and Jack Ward Memorial Salver
 1991 Thames Valley Clock Tower Selection – John Worontschak
Wine Guild of the UK Trophy
 1990 Elham Valley Müller-Thurgau – Peter Warden
President's Trophy
 1990 Sharpham Beenleigh Red – Mark Sharman

1993
Gore-Browne Trophy and Wine Guild of the UK Trophy
 1991 Valley Vineyards Fumé – John Worontschak
Jack Ward Memorial Salver
 1992 Monnow Valley Huxelrebe and Seyval blanc – Martyn Fowke
Bernard Theobald Trophy
 1990 Sharpham Beenleigh Red – Mark Sharman
President's Trophy
 1992 Partridge Bacchus Dry – Winemaker not known
Gold Medal
 1991 Wyken Bacchus – Rob Hemphill

1994
Gore-Browne Trophy and Wine Guild of the UK Trophy
    1992 Pilton Manor Westholme Late Harvest – Jim Dowling
Jack Ward Memorial Salver
    1993 Pilton Manor – Jim Dowling
Bernard Theobald Trophy
    1992 Valley Vineyards Pinot noir – John Worontschak
President's Trophy
    1992 Scott's Hall Bottle Fermented Sparkling Rosé – Stephen Skelton
Gold Medal
    1991 Sandhurst Vineyards Oak Aged Bacchus – Stephen Skelton

1995
Gore-Browne Trophy and Wine Guild of the UK Trophy
    1992 Wyken Bacchus – Rob Hemphill
Jack Ward Memorial Salver
    1994 Pilton Manor Westholme – Jim Dowling
Bernard Theobald Trophy
    1993 Hidden Spring Dark Fields – John Worontschak
President's Trophy
    1994 Northbrook Springs Noble Dessert – John Worontschak

1996
Gore-Browne Trophy
    Thames Valley Heritage Brut – John Worontschak
Jack Ward Memorial Salver
    1995 Nutbourne Sussex Reserve – David Cowderoy
Wine Guild of the UK Trophy (Joint winners)
    Thames Valley Heritage Brut – John Worontschak
    1994 Mersea – John Worontschak
Bernard Theobald Trophy
    1994 Chapel Down Wines Epoch Reserve – David Cowderoy
President's Trophy
    1995 Three Choirs Estate Bacchus Reserve – Martyn Fowke

1997
Gore-Browne Trophy and Wine Guild of the UK Trophy
    1995 Valley Vineyards Clocktower Selection Pinot noir –
        John Worontschak
Jack Ward Memorial Salver
    1996 Hidden Spring Sussex Sunset Rosé – John Worontschak
President's Trophy and Bernard Theobald Trophy
    1995 Beenleigh Red – Mark Sharman
Gold Medal
    1992 Breaky Bottom Seyval blanc – Peter Hall

Gold Medal
  1995 Great Stocks Symphony – Will Davenport
Gold Medal
  1995 Kents Green Müller-Thurgau and Huxelrebe – Martyn Fowke

1998
Gore-Brown Trophy and Vintner's Trophy
  NV Valley Vineyards Heritage Rosé – John Worontschak
Jack Ward Memorial Salver
  1997 Chapel Down Wines Bacchus – David Cowderoy
Wine Guild of the UK Trophy
  1996 Hidden Spring Dark Fields – John Worontschak
President's Trophy and Bernard Theobald Trophy
  1997 Valley Vineyards Clocktower Pinot noir – John Worontschak

1999
Gore-Browne Trophy, Jack Ward Memorial Salver and Dudley Quirk
Memorial Trophy
  1998 Chapel Down Wines Bacchus – David Cowderoy
President's Trophy
  1998 Camel Valley Seyval blanc Dry – Bob Lindo
Wine Guild of the UK Trophy
  1997 Chapel Down Wines Schönburger – David Cowderoy
Bernard Theobald Trophy
  1998 Sharpham Partnership Beenleigh Red – Mark Sharman
Vintner's Trophy
  NV Bearsted Vineyard Brut – John Gibson
McNie Trophy
  NV Chapel Down Wines Downland Oak – David Cowderoy
UKVA Best Presentation Award
  1998 Frome Valley Madeleine Angevine – David Longman (owner)

2000
Gore-Browne Trophy, Wine Guild Trophy and Vintner's Trophy
  1996 RidgeView Estate Cuvée Merret Bloomsbury – Mike Roberts
Jack Ward Memorial Salver and Bernard Theobald Trophy
  1999 Denbies Wine Estate Redlands – John Worontschak
McNie Trophy, Dudley Quirk Memorial Trophy
  NV Chapel Down Wines Downland Oak – David Cowderoy
President's Trophy
  1998 Warden Abbey Vineyard Warden Vineyard – David Ealand
UKVA Best Presentation Award
  1996 Breaky Bottom Vineyard Seyval blanc – Peter Hall (owner)

II: INTERNATIONAL WINE AND SPIRIT COMPETITION TROPHY

The International Wine and Spirit Competition English Wine Trophy

The International Wine and Spirit Competition, based at Ockley in Surrey, runs an annual competition, open to wines from all over the world. Since 1983 there has been a separate section for UK grown wines and the English Wine Trophy is awarded to the best wine in that section. Until 1997 it was sponsored by the *Farmer's Weekly*. Since 1998 it has been sponsored by Perkins Closures Ltd.

1983
Pilton Manor Vineyard – 1982 Pilton Manor Müller-Thurgau

1984
Hambledon Vineyard – 1982 Hambledon

1985
Wickenden Vineyard – 1982 Wickenden 'Green Cap'

1986
Wickenden Vineyard – 1984 Wickenden 'Green Cap'

1987
Chiltern Valley Wines – 1986 Old Luxters Reserve

1988
Bruisyard Wines – 1987 Bruisyard St Peter Müller-Thurgau

1989
Pilton Manor Vineyard – 1982 Pilton Manor Müller-Thurgau

1990
Shawsgate Vineyard – 1986 Shawsgate Müller-Thurgau

1991
Rock Lodge Vineyard – 1989 'Impresario' Sparkling Wine

1992
Throwley Vineyard – 1989 Throwley Chardonnay Sparkling Wine

1993
Carr Taylor Vineyards – 1987 Carr Taylor Vintage Sparkling Wine

1994
Shawsgate Vineyard – 1991 Shawsgate Bacchus

1995
Chapel Down Wines – 1993 Chapel Down Epoch I Red

1996
Denbies Wine Estate – 1995 Denbies Late Harvest Dessert Wine

1997
Nyetimber Vineyard – 1992 Première Cuvée Blanc de Blanc Sparkling Wine

1998
Nyetimber Vineyard – 1993 Classic Cuvée Sparkling Wine

1999
Nyetimber Vineyard – 1993 Première Cuvée Blanc de Blanc Sparkling Wine

2000
RidgeView Estate 1996 – Cuvée Merret Bloomsbury

III: VINEYARD WEBSITES

Adgestone – www.english-wine.co.uk
Avalon – www.dorset-info.co.uk/places2visit/avalon_vineyard.htm
Barnsole – www.barnsole.co.uk
Battle Wine Estate – www.battlewineestate.co.uk
Bearsted – www.bearstedwines.co.uk
Beaulieu – www.beaulieu.co.uk
Beenleigh – www.sharpham.co.uk
Biddenden – www.biddendenvineyards.co.uk
Bookers – www.btinternet.com/~bookersvineyard
Bow in the Cloud – www.bowinthecloud.co.uk
Bozedown – www.ourworld.compuserve.com/homepage/bozedown
Breaky Bottom – www.breakybottom.co.uk
Brecon Court – www.webaware.co.uk/bestofwales/breconco
Camel Valley – www.camelvalley.com
Carr Taylor – www.englishvineyards.co.uk
Carr Taylor – www.carr-taylor.co.uk
Carters – www.englishwines.com
Catawba English Vineyard Site – www.catawba.co.uk/EnglishVineyards
Chapel Down Wines – www.chapeldownwines.co.uk
Cheddar Valley – www.welcome.to/cvv
Chiddingstone – www.winespy.co.uk
Chilford Hall – www.chilfordhall.co.uk
Cwm Deri – www.cwm-deri.co.uk
Danebury – www.danebury.com
Davenport – www.davenportvineyards.co.uk
Denbies – www.denbiesvineyard.co.uk
Dunkery – www.exmoor.english-wine.com
English Wine Centre – www.english-wine.co.uk
English Wine Company – www.englishwinecompany.co.uk
English Wine Producers – www.englishwineproducers.com
English Wine Producers – www.englishwineproducers.co.uk
english-wine.com – www.english-wine.com
englishwine.com – www.englishwine.com
Giffords Hall – www.giffordshall.co.uk
Harbourne – www.harbournevineyard.co.uk
Horton – www.horton-vineyard.com
Leeds Castle – www.leeds-castle.co.uk
Llanerch – www.cariadwines.co.uk
Llanerch – www.llanerch-vineyard.co.uk
Lurgashall – www.lurgashall.co.uk
Meon Valley – www.hampshirefare.co.uk/meon

Mount Ephraim – www.mistral.co.uk/hammerwood/ephraim
New Hall – www.newhallvineyards.fsbusiness.co.uk
Oatley – www.oatley.demon.co.uk
Painshill Park – www.briansys.com/cobham.painshill
Penshurst – www.penshurst.co.uk
Pilton Manor – www.piltonwines.com
Plumpton College – www.plumpton.ac.uk
Purbeck – www.purbeck.ac.uk
Richardson's English Wine Site – www.sol.brunel.ac.uk/~richards/wine
RidgeView Estate www.ridgeview.co.uk – www.ridgeview.co.uk
RidgeView Estate – www.ridgeviewestate.com
Saint Anne's – www.glosibp.co.uk/tt1/areas/forest/vineyard
Sedlescombe Organic – www.tor.co.uk/sedlescombe
Shakespeare – www.welford.co.uk/page5.html
Sharpham – www.sharpham.com
Shawsgate – www.shawsgate.co.uk
Tenterden – www.tenterdenvineyardpark.co.uk
Three Choirs – www.threechoirs.com
UK Wine Site – www.easyweb.easynet.co.uk/~andie
United Kingdom Vineyards Association – www.ukva.org
Viticulture UK – www.viticulture.co.uk
Wooldings – www.wooldingsvineyard.co.uk
Worthenbury – www.worthenburywines.com

IV: ROOTSTOCKS

Information on rootstocks (especially in English) is hard to find and often when it is found, confusing. Lucie T. Morton, who translated Pierre Galet's work on vine varieties (both scion and rootstock), has helped in the preparation of this list. She is currently working on a 500+ page book solely devoted to rootstocks and its publication is awaited with great interest. Lucie comments that: 'the concept of rootstocks changing the vegetative cycle may not be true and may have more to do with French folklore, rather than scientific fact'. Actual distinctions between rootstocks will be influenced by site, soil, moisture, scion variety, age of vine and climate. Vigour indications can only therefore be approximate. This is not a comprehensive list, there are gaps (e.g. Fercal, Binova) and it tends to concentrate more of French varieties. However, it does cover many of those currently in use in the UK.

Please note that not all of those listed here are approved for use in the UK.

Rootstock varieties list prepared with the help of Lucie T. Morton's translation of Pierre Galet's *A Practical Ampelography* (Cornell University 1979) pp. 187–216.

Rootstocks arranged in *general* order of vigour.

Riparia Gloire de Montpelier – Weak rootstock. Lack of vigour favours quality over quantity. Reduces vigour and promotes earlier ripening and winter hardiness.

420A Millardet et de Grasset – Relatively weak rootstock, slightly more vigorous than Riparia Gloire. Hastens maturity. Favoured in N. Italy for quality over more productive 5BB. Some reports indicate that maturity is delayed.

41B Millardet et De Grasset – Short vegetative cycle and exceptionally high resistence to lime. Used in Champagne and Charentes. Mature vines show good fruit set and yields.

101–14 Millardet et de Grasset – More vigorous than Riparia Gloire de M, but less vigorous than 3309C. Said to tolerate 'wet feet' better than 3309C.

333 Ecole de Montpellier – Similar to 41B, but more productive.

1616 Couderc – Fairly weak. Tends to advance maturity. Favours humid soils. Has a reputation of *not* promoting quality, so is less interesting.

161–49 Couderc – Slower in initial development than 420A, in later years it is said to become more vigorous, although there is uncertainty about the truth of this statement! There have also been reports of high failure rates with young vines, possibly due to unhealthy stock.

3306 Couderc – Less vigorous than 3309C and maybe better suited to wet soils.

3309 Couderc – Universal cool climate rootstock. Can be vigorous in fresh, deep soils, but does not like wet feet.

1613 Couderc Moderate vigour. Some nematode resistence, but not to *phylloxera*.

Geisenheim 26 – Having some *vinifera* parentage, is not resistant to *phylloxera*.

Binova – This is an SO4 mutation and good for varieties that suffer from *coulure*. Advances both fruit and wood ripening. Grafts take very well.

Börner – Resistant to attack from *phylloxera* on the roots.

SO4 – Vigorous. Favours fruit set and advances maturity unless over-cropped. Productive in early years but may burn out in later life.

Teleki 5C – Very similar to 5BB. Matures earlier and therefore suitable for northerly regions. Susceptible to Crown Gall.

125 AA – Similar to 5BB in terms of vigour. Not good for varieties liable to *coulure*.

Kober 5BB – Vigorous. Suits humid soils. Not outstanding in cooler regions. Favours quantity over quality.

196–17 – Castel Vigorous. Resistant to drought.

1103 Paulsen – Vigorous. Drought tolerant. For low fertility sites.

99 Richter – Vigorous. Drought tolerant. Not for high fertility sites.

Vialla – Sandy soils only, otherwise low *phylloxera* tolerance.

110 Richter – Relatively vigorous in fertile sites. Drought tolerant. Good for lighter, shallower soils.

44–53 Maleague – Drought tolerant. Moderate Vigour. Picks up Potassium and can cause Magnesium deficiency.

Teleki 8B – Similar to 5BB, although not as good.

AxR1 – Very vigorous and productive. Not 100 per cent *phylloxera* tolerant.

140 Ruggeri – Very vigorous in fertile soils. Drought tolerant, but dies in wet feet. Not recommended.

Dog Ridge – Very vigorous. High pH wines. Not *phylloxera* resistant.

1202 Couderc – Very vigorous. Not *phylloxera* resistant.

Rupestris St George (du Lot) – Very vigorous and tends towards low fruit set. Can delay ripening. Not for humid or fertile soils.

Glossary

━━━━━━━━

Descriptions of individual grape varieties can be found in the separate chapter on the subject.

Acidic – Term used to describe wines that are too high in acid. Grapes contain many different acids, with malic and tartaric being predominant, Grapes picked too early will have excessive levels of malic acid – a harsh sour tasting acid. Grapes picked at optimum ripeness will contain more tartaric acid – a softer tasting acid.

Actual alcohol – The level of alcohol present in the wine or partially fermented juice.

Ampelography – The scientific description of the vine based upon the physical characteristics of all its parts: leaves, flowers, grapes, canes, growth habits, etc.

Are – One hundredth of a hectare or 100 sq.m.

Barewood cuttings – Cuttings without roots.

Barrique – French word for a 225 litre oak barrel used for winemaking.

Bordeaux mixture – Fungicide for combatting Downy Mildew. Made from copper sulphate and slaked lime.

Botrytis – Also called grey mould (or *pourriture gris*). A fungal disease common to vines. When it occurs on sweet grapes at the end of the ripening season, 'noble rot' (or *pourriture noble*') may occur which leads to a concentration of grape sugars and flavours.

Calcium carbonate – Also known as 'precipitated chalk'. Used for removing excess acidity from juice or wine.

Cane pruning – Any system of pruning/training where the fruiting buds are carried on canes rather than on spurs.

Canopy management – Science of managing the growing shoots and leaves of the vine during the summer so that they and the grapes receive the correct amount of heat and light.

Canopy – Term used to describe the growing shoots and leaves of the vine.

Chaptalisation – see Enrichment.

Chlorosis – Condition when vines are starved of iron and cannot photosynthesize properly. Usually found in vines growing in very chalky soils. Can be corrected by the right choice of rootstock.

Cloches – Glass (or sometimes plastic) covers used to protect tender plants growing outside.

Clone – One grape variety may have several – or even many – different clones which although ostensibly identical to the parent variety, will have particular characteristics. Clones have been chosen for attributes such as higher quality, greater yield, better disease resistence etc.

Cold fermentation – A fermentation which is artificially cooled (typically to 10–12°C) so that flavours are retained and alcohol is not lost.

Cold maceration – Technique of soaking de-stemmed and crushed grapes for short period of time (12–36 hours) at low temperatures to extract extra fruit flavours.

Cordons – Term used to describe lengths of spur-bearing permanent vine wood.

Coulure – A physiological condition of the vine caused by cool and/or wet weather before and during flowering, which results in crop loss due to poor pollination – see Flowering.

Cross bred vine variety – Vine variety produced by crossing one variety with another. This is a sexual process and involves taking the pollen from the male parent variety and fertilising the female parent variety. The seeds of the resultant grapes are then planted out and individual seedlings selected for further development.

Customs and Excise – HM Customs and Excise. Government department which (amongst other things) regulates the production of wine under bond in UK wineries.

Cuttings – Lengths of hard wood taken from the vine during dormancy for rooting and/or grafting.

Dessert grapes – see Table grapes.

Double Guyot – A general term to describe cane pruned vines where each vine is trained with two canes one either side of a central trunk. The arms may be flat or arched. Each vine also has a spur to produce wood for the next year.

Downy mildew – Also called *Peronospera*. This is a fungal disease common to vines.

East Anglian Winegrowers Association – Regional vineyard association in the eastern part of England and affiliated to the UKVA.

EAWA – East Anglian Winegrowers Association.

English Vineyards Association Ltd – National vineyard association until 1996. Superseded by the UKVA.

Enrichment – Correct term for what many winemakers still call 'chaptalisation' – the process of adding a sweetening agent to juice in order to raise its level of potential alcohol. In most UK wineries, white granulated sugar is used, although EU regulations permit the use of concentrated grape must and rectified concentrated grape must. Frenchman Comte Jean-Antoine Chaptal de Canteloupe, Minister of the Interior and President of the Academy of Science did not invent the process, but issued orders which regulated it.

EVA – English Vineyards Association Ltd.

Excise duty – Duty levelled on all alcoholic drinks sold in the UK. It is not an import tax and therefore home produced wines are subject to the same levels of duty as foreign wines. Different levels of duty are charged according to alcohol content and type. Sparkling wines pay higher levels of duty than still wines having the same alcohol content.

Flowering – The period in the development of the annual growth of the vine when the flowers open and pollination takes place. If weather conditions are wet and cold, a 'poor flowering' may occur which usually leads to a smaller yield.

Foxy – Term used to describe the flavour found in wines made from some non-*vinifera* varieties, especially *vitis labruscas* such as 'Concord' (found widely in New York vineyards) and other American and American-hybrid varieties.

Fruiting bud – The single bud, carried on the previous year's wood, which is retained to fruit in the coming year.

Geisenheim – Geisenheim is one of world's foremost vine breeding and winemaking colleges. Situated in the heart of Germany's famous Rheingau region, where Riesling dominates, it has spent decades developing improved clones of that variety. It also has a reputation for breeding new crossbreed varieties – Professor Müller developed the variety later to be known as Müller-Thurgau there in 1882 – and under the late Helmut Becker produced several of the varieties grown in the

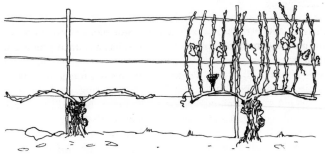

Double Guyot

UK today: Ehrenfelser, Gutenborner, Rondo, Reichensteiner, Schönburger.

Geneva Double Curtain (GDC) – System of pruning/training developed by Professor Nelson Shaulis in 1960s in Cornell University's experimental vineyards at Geneva in New York State's Finger Lakes region. Each vine is high trained on to two parallel fruiting wires with the fruiting wood being carried on spurs. The summer foliage is trained downwards towards the ground. Vines are typically wide spaced with rows at 3.66 m wide with vines at 2.44 m intervals (12 ft × 8 ft) giving a vine density of 1120 vines per ha.

Geneva Double Curtain (GDC)

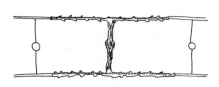

GDC training

Giropallet – Electronically driven and computer controlled device which automatically 'riddles' a bottle of bottle-fermented sparkling wine. 'Riddling' is the process whereby the yeast deposit in the bottle is encouraged to slide down the neck of the bottle so that it can be expelled during the disgorging process. 'Disgorging' is where the plug of yeast left after 'riddling' is expelled by removing the crown cork prior to the cork and wire muzzle being applied.

Gore-Browne Trophy – Trophy, donated by Margaret Gore-Browne, awarded annually to the best wine in the UKVA English and Welsh Wine of the Year Competition.

Grafted vine – Vine consisting of a scion and rootstock grafted together. After rooting and growing in a nursery for a year, grafted vines are ready for planting out in a vineyard.

Grafting – The process of joining scion wood from one variety on to a rootstock. Formerly carried by hand, it is now almost universally done with a grafting machine.

Guyot – General term used to describe any form of cane pruned vine. Named after French horticulturalist, Dr Jules Guyot.

Ha – Hectare or 10,000 sq.m.

Hanging spur training – see Sylvoz.

Hectolitre – 100 litres.

Hl/ha – Hectolitres per hectare. 17 hl/ha = 1 tonne per acre approximately.

Hl – Hectolitre.

HMC&E – HM Customs and Excise. See 'Customs and Excise'.

Hybrid – Variety of vine having some non-*vinifera* species in its ancestry. Also known as 'interspecific cross'.

Interspecific cross – see Hybrid.

Lees – Deposits of yeast left after fermentation. Wines are said to be 'lees aged' (or *sur lie*) when they are allowed to sit in the tank or barrel on top of their lees. This can encourage the malolactic fermentation and impart a distinctive 'yeasty' character to the wine. Bottle-fermented sparkling wines also undergo a period of lees ageing in bottle after the secondary fermentation has finished. Likewise, they also gain a typical 'yeasty' flavour if left long enough.

Lyre or 'U' training – System of pruning/training developed by Dr Alain Carbonneau in Bordeaux in late 1970s. Each vine is trained on to two parallel fruiting wires and the summer shoots are trained vertically into a 'U'. Vines can be cane or spur trained and would typically be planted at similar row widths and vine intervals to GDC.

Lyre or 'U' training

MAFF – see Ministry of Agriculture, Fisheries and Food.

Malic acid – The principal acid contained in apples (the genus *Malus*) and present in high levels in unripe grapes. As grapes ripen the levels of malic acid fall and levels of tartaric acid rise.

Malo-lactic fermentation – Also known as the 'malo-lactic conversion'. The process whereby the harsher tasting malic acid is converted into the less sharp lactic acid. This is usually achieved by inoculating young wine with a lactic acid bacteria (*Leuconostoc eonos*). The bacteria will only work when the wine is low in sulphur dioxide and has a pH of above 3.25 (or thereabouts). It is called a 'fermentation' as the process produces carbon dioxide in small amounts and during the process the wine will have a slight 'prickle' on the tongue. The malo-lactic fermentation is also known as the 'secondary fermentation' although this is a confusing term as this is also the term used to talk about the second fermentation in the *méthode Champenoise* to produce bottle-fermented sparkling wines.

Master of Wine – Member of the prestigious Institute of Masters of Wine.

Mercian Vineyards Association – Regional vineyards association in the northern part of England where vines are grown. Affiliated to the UKVA.

Ministry of Agriculture, Fisheries and Food – Government department which looks after the interests of UK winegrowers.

MVA – see Mercian Vineyards Association.

MW – see Master of Wine.

Natural sugar level – The level of natural sugar at harvest time which gives the level of potential alcohol.

Oechsle – Degrees Oechsle (°OE) are commonly used to express levels of ripeness in UK wineries. The relative density (what used to be known as the specific gravity) of the juice is determined by floating a hydrometer in a cylinder filled with juice and deducting 1000. Therefore if a juice had a relative density of 1060 it would be said to have 60° Oechsle or 60 °OE. From tables one can calculate the amount of sugar present and therefore the level of potential alcohol.

°OE – see Oechsle.

Oidium – Powdery mildew.

Oxidation – Term often used to describe the process by which a wine develops either in cask or in bottle. When oxidation is controlled, it is usually beneficial to the wine. When uncontrolled, it leads to spoilt wine. When 'oxidation' takes place in the bottle, it is not in fact due to the ingress of air into the bottle, but a slow chemical reaction between the different components in the wine.

Oxidised – Term used to describe a wine that has suffered from excess exposure to air. The wine is usually spoilt, turning brown and losing freshness and flavour. When a wine in the bottle becomes 'oxidised' it is not in fact due to the ingress of air into the bottle, but as a result of the slow chemical reaction that occurs in the bottle, referred to above.

Pendlebogen training – A pruning/training system where vines are cane pruned and the canes are bowed in to arches. This is an example of Double Guyot pruning.

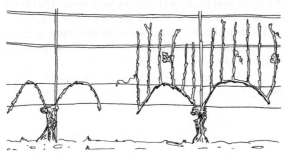

Pendlebogen training

pH – A measure of the active acidity or alkalinity of a solution. The scale runs from 0 to 14 with 7 being neutral. Grape juice and wines (being acidic) are usually between 2.75 and 4 with 3.1–3.4 being optimum. The pH of a juice or wine gives little indication of its total titratable acidity because of the presence of natural buffering agents. However, a knowledge of the pH of a wine is important as a wine with a high pH will require much higher levels of sulphur dioxide to achieve the same level of protection when compared to a wine with a low pH.

Phylloxera vastatrix – Also known as the vine louse. This is an aphid which can exist in various forms on both the leaves and roots of vines. If uncontrolled, will lead to death of vines. If *phylloxera* is present or likely to be present, vines must be grafted on to resistant rootstocks.

Potential alcohol – The level of alcohol which would be in the wine if all sugars present in the juice were fermented.

Pourriture gris – see *Botrytis*.

Pourriture noble – see *Botrytis*.

Powdery mildew – Also called *Oidium tuckerii* or *Uncinula necator*. This is a fungal disease common to vines. First discovered in Europe by a gardener called Tucker in a greenhouse in Margate, Kent in 1847.

Quality wine psr – Quality wine produced in a specified region. The UK's equivalent to *appellation controlée*.

Quality wine scheme – Official scheme for granting quality wine psr status on UK grown wines and open only to those wines made entirely from grapes of the species *Vitis vinifera*. Wines must conform to certain analytical and organoleptical requirements.

QWpsr – Quality wine produced in a specified region. The UK's equivalent to *appellation controlée*.

QWS – see Quality wine scheme.

Rectified concentrated grape must – The produce of grape must after it has been rectified and concentrated. It is a colourless, tasteless and odourless sugar solution used for enriching grape juice prior to fermentation.

Regional wine – The UK's equivalent of *vin de pays*. Regional wine status is open to any UK grown wine which conforms to certain analytical and organoleptical requirements.

Residual sugar – Term used to describe sweetness in a wine. Dry wines will contain from 0 g/l up to about 9 g/l (the legal maximum for wines described as 'dry' on the label). Sweet wines can contain levels in excess of 300 g/l although levels this high are very rare. A medium dry wine would contain around 25 g/l, a medium wine around 45 g/l, a sweet wine between 75 g/l to 150 g/l. The level of tasteable sweetness will to a certain extent depend on the level of acidity. A wine with a high acidity will taste drier than a wine with a low acidity for the same level of residual sugar.

Rooted cuttings – Lengths of hard wood taken from the vine during dormancy that have been planted out in the spring so that roots have developed. Once lifted, these can then be planted out into vineyards.

Rootstocks – Specially developed varieties of vines used only to graft vines on to so that they are resistant to *phylloxera*. Also used to protect vines against viruses and conditions such as chlorosis.

Scion – Term used for the varietal section of a grafted vine.

Scott Henry training – System of pruning/training developed by Mr Scott Henry in Oregon and now used extensively in New Zealand and other cooler regions. Each vine has two layers of fruiting wood, the lower layer being trained downwards, the upper layer upwards. This divided canopy allows each vine to carry a larger number of fruiting buds than a vine with only one layer of fruiting wood. Vines on this system can be either cane or spur pruned and are typically planted at similar spacings to VSP systems.

Seal of Quality – Known as 'the Seal' this was a quality mark which the EVA operated. It was a Certification Trade Mark run under rules approved by the Department of Trade and Industry and was superseded by the Quality Wine Scheme.

SEVA – see South East Vineyards Association.

Single Guyot training

Single Guyot training – A general term to describe cane pruned vines
where each vine is trained with one cane. Each vine also has a spur to
produce fruiting wood for the next year.
Single curtain training – see Sylvoz.
SO_2 – see Sulphur dioxide.
South East Vineyards Association – Regional vineyard association in the
south east of England and affiliated to the UKVA.
South West Vineyards Association – Regional vineyard association in the
south west of England and in Wales and affiliated to the UKVA.
Sport – A 'sport', in horticultural terms, is when a plant shows a variation
(or mutation) from its parent stock – plants that have variegated leaves
are often 'sports' of an original variety. In viticulture, vines where the
grapes are substantially different from the parent plant (sometimes red
grapes are produced on white varieties) would be termed 'sports'.

Scott Henry training

Spur pruning – Any system of pruning/training where the fruiting buds are carried on spurs.

Spurs – Sections of fruiting wood which are carried on old wood and typically have several fruiting buds.

Sterile bottling – Procedure of filling bottles with wine from which all yeasts and bacteria have been excluded. This is most commonly achieved by passing the wine during the bottling process through sheet or membrane filters with a small enough pore size to exclude these contaminants. Many wines are sterile filtered and it should not be thought of as a necessarily detrimental process. However, some dry wines, especially red wines, are routinely bottled with either no or only a minimal filtration and as long as the wines contain no residual sugars, no harm will result. Unfiltered wines that have not undergone a malo-lactic fermentation can be at risk, especially if they have a high pH and/or low levels of SO_2.

Sulphur dioxide – Anti-oxidant and bactericide used in all stages of winemaking. Winemakers will use SO_2 either in the form of potassium or sodium metabisulphite or as an aqueous solution obtained by dissolving SO_2 in water.

Sur lie – see Lees.

Süss-reserve – Sterile grape juice added to wines immediately prior to bottling. Used to add sweetness and fruit character. Also known as sweet reserve.

SWVA – see South West Vineyards Association.

Sylvoz training – A pruning/training system popular in north Italy, but also now found in other areas. Each vine is high trained on to a single fruiting wire with the fruiting wood being carried on spurs. The summer foliage is trained downwards towards the ground. Vines are typically spaced at distances between VSP and GDC systems. Also known as 'single curtain' or 'hanging spur'.

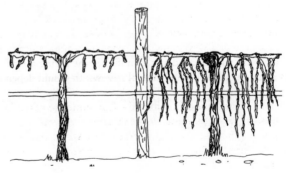

Sylvos training

T&CVA – see Thames and Chilterns Vineyards Association.

Table wines – Lowest level of wine in official hierarchy. Owing to the fact that many of the UK's best wines are made from non-*vinifera* varieties which are excluded from the QWS, the term 'table wine' on a bottle of English and Welsh wine does not necessarily indicate a poor quality wine.

Table grapes – Grapes for the table, i.e. dessert varieties more normally grown under glass in the UK.

Tannin – Substance found in stalks, skins and pips of grapes and present in varying amounts in wine. White wines should contain little, red wines considerably more. When in excess, tannin makes a wine astringent and bitter.

Tartaric acid – The principal acid of ripe grapes (and not found in other fruits) and helpful in both the winemaking and maturation process.

Thames and Chilterns Vineyards Association – Regional vineyard association in the centre of England; affiliated to the UKVA.

Total alcohol – The sum of the actual and potential alcohols present in a wine or juice.

Total titratable acidity – see Total acidity.

Total acidity – Term used to describe the sum of all the acids in grape juice or wine. Although the acids present consist of tartaric, malic and other acids, they are usually (apart from in France) expressed as being all of tartaric acid.

Trelliswork – Term used to describe the posts and wires used for supporting vines.

UKVA – see United Kingdom Vineyards Association Ltd.

United Kingdom Vineyards Association Ltd – National vineyard association.

Vertical shoot positioned training – A general term to describe any pruning/training system where the summer growth is trained upwards vertically. Pairs of catch wires attached to posts are usually used to trap the shoots as they grow. Single Guyot, Double Guyot and Pendlebogen are all examples of VSP systems. Vine spacing would typically be 2 m wide rows with vines spaced at 1.4 m in the row giving a vine density of 3,571 vines per ha although actual row width would depend on machinery widths.

Vine Varieties Classification Committee – Committee required by the EU to oversee the lists of permitted vines in a member state.

Vineyard parcel – A 'parcel' of vines is a separately identifiable area of vines of one variety. Vineyards can have more than one parcel of the same variety.

Vinification – Term used to describe winemaking.

Vintners' Company – Worshipful Company of Vintners. City Livery company with historical links with the wine trade. Owns Vintner's Hall in Upper Thames Street, London.

Viticulture – Cultivation of the species *Vitis*.

Vitis vinifera – Latin name for the European vine – the most common species used for wine production.

Vitis labrusca – One of number of species of the genus *vitis* native to North America and used for making wine, juice and jelly. 'Concord' is the best known *labrusca* variety and grown widely in New York State vineyards and has the typical 'foxy' flavour of these varieties.

VSP – see Vertical shoot positioned.

VVCC – see Vine Varieties Classification Committee.

WDVA – see Weald and Downland Vineyards Association.

Weald and Downland Vineyards Association – Name of SEVA until 1995.

Wessex Vineyards Association – Regional vineyard association in the south of England. Affiliated to the UKVA.

Wine Standards Board – Organisation, funded by MAFF and Vintners' Company, which polices European wine legislation in the UK.

Wood ripening – Term used to describe process of lignification of grape vine canes as they pass from their summer state (green) to their winter or dormant state (brown). Ripe wood is important for the survival of the fruiting buds through the winter.

WSB – see Wine Standards Board.

WVA – see Wessex Vineyards Association.

Bibliography

―――

Barron, A. F. *Vines and Vine Culture*, published by the *Journal of Horticulture*, London, 1883, 1912.

Barry, Sir Edward, *Observations on the Wines of the Ancients*, T. Caddel, London, 1775.

Barty-King, Hugh, *A Tradition of English Wine*, Oxford Illustrated Press, 1977.

A Taste of English Wine, London, Pelham Books/Stephen Greene Press, 1989.

Basserman-Jordan Dr von, *Belgian Vineyards*, London, The Wine and Food Society, No. 86, 1955.

Brock, Ray Barrington, *Report No. 1 – Outdoor Grapes in Cold Climates*, Oxted, Surrey, The Viticultural Research Station, 1949.

Report No. 2 – More Outdoor Grapes, 1950.

'Some Aspects of Viticulture in Southern England', 1951.

Report No. 3 – Progress with Vines and Wines, 1961.

Report No. 4 – Starting a Vineyard, 1964.

Bush, Raymond, *Fruit Growing Outdoors*, London, Faber & Faber, 1935, 1942, 1946.

Castella, François de, *Handbook on Viticulture for Victoria*, Melbourne, Royal Commission on Vegetable Products, Board of Viticulture, 1891.

English Vineyards Association Ltd, Newsletters, Journals and *The Grape Press*, London, EVA Ltd, 1967–96.

Fielden, Christopher, *Is this the Wine you Ordered, Sir?*, London, Christopher Helm, 1989.

Gabler, James M., *Wine into Words – a History and Bibliography of Wine Books in the English Language*, Baltimore, Bacchus Press, 1985.

Galet, Pierre, *A Practical Ampelography – Grapevine Identification*, translated by Lucie T. Morton, London, Cornell University Press, 1979.

Gore-Browne, Margaret, *Let's Plant a Vineyard*, 1967, London, Mills and Boon.

Hamner, Sir Thomas, *The Garden Book of Sir Thomas Hamner 1659*, reprinted by Gerald Howe Ltd, London, 1933.

Hillebrand, Lott and Pfaff, *Taschenbuch der Rebsorten*, 12th edition, Mainz, Germany, Fachverlag Dr Fraund GMBH, 1998.

Hooke, Dr Della, 'A Note on the Evidence for Vineyards and Orchards in Anglo-Saxon England', *The Journal of Wine Research*, Vol. 1, No. 1, London, The Institute of Masters of Wine, 1990, pp. 77–80.

Hughes, W., *The Compleat Vineyard*, London, Will Crook, 1670.

Hyams, Edward, *The Grape Vine in England*, London, John Lane, The Bodley Head, 1949.

From the Waste Land, London, Turnstile Press, 1950.

Grapes Under Cloches, London, Faber & Faber, 1952.

Vineyards in England (editor), London, Faber & Faber, 1953.

The Speaking Garden, London, Longmans, Green and Co, 1957.

Vin – the Wine Country of France, London, George Newnes Ltd, 1959.

Dionysus – A Social History of the Wine Vine, London, Thames and Hudson, 1965.

An Englishman's Garden, London, Thames and Hudson, 1967.

Jackson, David, *Pruning and Training*, Christchurch, New Zealand, Lincoln University Press, 1997.

Jackson D., Schuster D. and Skelton S., *The Production of Grapes and Wine in Cool Climates*, UK edition, Christchurch, New Zealand, Gypsum Press, 1994.

Lee, Roland, *Growing Grapes in the Open*, Birkenhead, Roland Lee Vineyards, 1939.

Loudon J. C., *Encyclopaedia of Gardening*, London, 1834.

Lytle, S. E., *Vines under glass and in the open*, Liverpool, Horticultural Utilities Ltd, *ca.* 1951.

Successful growing of grape vines, ca. 1954.

Ministry of Agriculture, Fisheries and Food, *Outdoor Grape Production*, London, Ministry of Agriculture, Fisheries and Food, 1978.

Grapes for Wine, 1980.

Soils and Manures for Fruit, 1975.

Morton, Lucie T., *Winegrowing in Eastern America*, New York and London, Cornell University Press, 1985.

Ordish, George, *Wine Growing in England*, London, Rupert Hart-Davis, 1953.

The Great Wine Blight, London, J. M. Dent and Sons Ltd, 1972.

Vineyards in England and Wales, London, Faber & Faber, 1977.

The Great Wine Blight, London, Sidgwick & Jackson Ltd, 1986.

Pearkes, Gillian, *Vinegrowing in Britain*, London, J. M. Dent and Sons Ltd, 1982.

Robinson, Jancis, *Vines, Grapes and Wines*, London, Mitchell Beazley, 1986.

Oxford Companion to Wine (editor), Oxford University Press, 1994.

Rook, Alan, *The Diary of an English Vineyard*, London, Wine and Spirit Publication Ltd, 1971.

Rose, John, *The English Vineyard Vindicated*, London, B. Teuke, 1672.

Royal Horticultural Society, *Journals*, Wisley, Surrey, Royal Horticultural Society, 1985, 1898.

Seward, Desmond, *Monks and Wine*, London, Mitchell Beazley, 1979.

Simon, André J., *Bibliotheca Vinaria*, London, The Holland Press Ltd, 1979.

'S.J.' – A Gentleman in his Travels, *The Vineyard*, London, W. Mears, 1727.

Skelton, Stephen P., *The Vineyards of England*, Ashford, Kent, S. P. & L. Skelton, 1989.

Smart, Richard and Robinson, Mike, *Sunlight into Wine – A Handbook for Winegrape Canopy Management*, Adelaide, Winetitles, 1991.

Smith, Joanna, *The New English Vineyard*, London, Sidgwick and Jackson, 1979.

Sneesby, Norman, *A Vineyard in England*, London, Robert Hale Ltd, 1977.

Speechley, William, *A Treatise on the Culture of the Vine*, 1790.

Tod, H. M., *Vine-Growing in England*, London, Chatto & Windus, 1911.

Turner, Ben and Roycroft, Roy, *The Winemaker's Encyclopedia*, London, Faber & Faber, 1980.

United Kingdom Vineyards Association Ltd, Newsletters, journals and *The Grape Press*, London, UKVA Ltd, 1996–99.

Unwin, Dr Tim, 'Saxon and Early Norman Viticulture in England,' *The Journal of Wine Research*, Vol. 1, No. 1, London, The Institute of Masters of Wine, 1990, pp. 61–75.

Wine and the Vine – An Historical Geography of Viticulture and the Wine Trade, London, Routledge, 1991.

Ward H. W., *The Book of the Grape*, London, John Lane, The Bodley Head, 1901.

Ward, Jack, *The Complete Book of Vine Growing in the British Isles*, London, Faber & Faber, 1984.

Wright, Graeme, *Merrydown, Forty Vintage Years*, Horam, East Sussex, Merrydown Wine PLC, 1988.

List of Vineyards

Adgestone Vineyard, Isle of Wight, 350
Appledown Vineyard, Buckinghamshire, 464
Ashburnham Vineyard, East Sussex, 297
Ash Coombe Vineyard, Kent, 246
Astley Vineyards, Worcestershire, 371
Avalon Vineyard, Somerset, 384
Avonwood Vineyard, Bristol, 383

Bagborough Vineyard, Somerset, 386
Bardfield Vineyard, Essex, 211
Barkham Manor Vineyard, East Sussex, 298
Barnsgate Manor Vineyard, East Sussex, 299
Barnsole Vineyard, Kent, 247
Battle Wine Estate, East Sussex, 301
Bayford House, Kent, 249
Bearsted Vineyard, Kent, 249
Beaulieu Vineyard, Hampshire, 333
Beeches Vineyard, Herefordshire, 366
Beenleigh Manor Vineyard, Devon, 400
Bewl Water Vineyard, East Sussex, 303
Biddenden Vineyards, Kent, 251
Bishop's Palace Vineyard, Lincolnshire, 443
Bishops Waltham Vineyard, Hampshire, 336
Bittescombe Mill Vineyard, Somerset, 386
Blackwater Valley Vineyard, County Cork, 433
Bodenham English Wines, Herefordshire, 366
Bodiam Vineyards, East Sussex, 303
Bookers Vineyard, West Sussex, 290
Bosue Vineyard, Cornwall, 412
Bothy Vineyard, Oxfordshire, 456
Bower Farm Vineyard, Buckinghamshire, 464
Boyton Vineyard, Suffolk, 194
Boze Down Vineyard, Oxfordshire, 457
Braishfield Manor Estate Vineyard, Hampshire, 337
Breaky Bottom Vineyard, East Sussex, 304
Brecon Court Vineyard, Monmouthshire, 420
Brickyard Vineyard, East Sussex, 307

Brightwell Vineyard, Oxfordshire, 458
Broxbournebury Vineyard, Hertfordshire, 207
Bruisyard Vineyard, Suffolk, 195
Buddlemead Vineyard, Hampshire, 377
Burwash Weald Vineyard, East Sussex, 307

Camel Valley Vineyard, Cornwall, 413
Cane End Vineyard, Berkshire, 469
Carpenters Vineyard, Somerset, 387
Carr Taylor Vineyards, East Sussex, 308
Carter's Vineyards, Essex, 212
Castle Cary Vineyard, Somerset, 387
Castle Vineyard, Essex, 214
C.A.V.E., Buckinghamshire, 465
Cavendish Manor Vineyard, Suffolk, 197
Chalkhill Vineyard, Wiltshire, 330
Challenden Vineyard, Kent, 253
Chapel Down Wines Ltd, Kent, 254
Chapel Farm Vineyard, Isle of Wight, 352
Château Le Catillon, Channel Islands, 359
Cheddar Valley Vineyard, Somerset, 388
Chevelswarde Vineyard, Leicestershire, 445
Chiddingstone Vineyard, Kent, 258
Chilford Hall Vineyard, Cambridgeshire, 189
Chiltern Valley Wines, Oxfordshire, 460
Chingley Oast Vineyard, East Sussex, 310
Clay Hill Vineyard, Kent, 259
Coach House Vineyard, Hampshire, 338
Coddington Vineyard, Herefordshire, 367
Colne Valley Vineyard, Essex, 214
Compton Green Vineyard, Gloucestershire, 375
Conghurst Vineyard, Kent, 260
Conham Vale Vineyard, Bristol, 384
Court Lane Vineyard, Hampshire, 338
Cufic Vines, Somerset, 388
Cwm Deri Vineyard, Pembrokeshire, 421

Danebury Vineyards, Hampshire, 339
Dartmoor Vineyard, Devon, 401
Davenport Vineyards, East Sussex, 311

LIST OF VINEYARDS

Denbies Wine Estate, Surrey, 233
Derrynane Vineyard, County Kerry, 434
Ditchling Vineyards, East Sussex, 313
Domaine Madeleine Vineyard, Berkshire, 470
Down St Mary Vineyard, Devon, 402
Dragons Rock Vineyard, Lincolnshire, 447
Dunkery Vineyard, Somerset, 389
Durra Valley Vineyard, Cornwall, 414

Eglantine Vineyard, Nottinghamshire, 444
Elham Valley Vineyards, Kent, 260
Elms Cross Vineyard, Wiltshire, 330
Elysian Fields, Cambridgeshire, 190
English Wine Centre, East Sussex, 314
Eryri Vineyard, Gwynedd, 481

Fawley Vineyard, Oxfordshire, 461
Felsted Vineyard, Essex, 215
Ffynnon Las, Ceredigion, 422
Follymoor Vineyard, Devon, 403
Frithsden Vineyard, Hertfordshire, 207
Frome Valley Vineyard, Herefordshire, 368
Fruit of the Vine, County Dublin, 435
Furnace Brook Vineyard, Surrey, 239

Gifford's Hall, Suffolk, 197
Glyndŵr Vineyard, Vale of Glamorgan, 423
Godstone Vineyard, Surrey, 240
Grace Dieu Vineyard, Leicestershire, 446
Grange Farm Vineyard, Oxfordshire, 462
Great Stocks Vineyard, Essex, 218
Greyfriars Vineyard, Surrey, 241

Hackwood Vineyard, East Sussex, 315
Hadlow Down Vineyard, East Sussex, 261
Hale Valley Vineyard, Buckinghamshire, 465
Hale Vineyard, Hampshire, 340
Halfpenny Green Vineyard, Staffordshire, 448
Hamble Valley Vineyard, Hampshire, 340
Harden Vineyard, Kent, 262
Harling Vineyards, Norfolk, 192
Harpenden Garden Fields Vineyard, Hertfordshire, 209
Hazel End Vineyard, Hertfordshire, 209
Helions Vineyard, Suffolk, 199
Hendred Vineyard, Oxfordshire, 463
Hidden Spring Vineyard, East Sussex, 316
Higher Bumsley Vineyard, Devon, 404
High Weald Vineyard, East Sussex, 318
Hintlesham Vineyard, Suffolk, 199
Home Farmhouse Vineyard, Surrey, 241
Horsmonden Vineyards, Kent, 263
Horton Estate Vineyard, Dorset, 355

Ickworth Vineyard, Suffolk, 200

Jays Farm Vineyard, Hampshire, 341

Kempes Hall Vineyard, Kent, 263
Kents Green Vineyard, Gloucestershire, 376
The Kings Cellar Vineyard, Isle of Wight, 353
Knowle Hill Vineyard, Kent, 264

Ladywell Vineyard, Norfolk, 193
La Mare Vineyards Ltd, Channel Islands, 360
Lamberhurst Vineyards, Kent, 264
Lambourne Vineyard, Cornwall, 415
Leeds Castle Vineyard, Kent, 270
Leventhorpe Vineyard, West Yorkshire, 441
Lewins Vineyards, Kent, 272
Lillibrooke Manor Vineyard, Berkshire, 470
Little Ashley Vineyard, Wiltshire, 331
Little Foxes Vineyard, Gloucestershire, 377
Little Knoxbridge Vineyard, Kent, 272
Little Witney Green, Essex, 220
Llanerch Vineyard, Vale of Glamorgan, 425
Longueville House Vineyard, County Cork, 435
Lurgashall Winery, West Sussex, 290
Lydhurst Vineyard, West Sussex, 291
Lytchett Matravers Vineyard, Dorset, 356

Manstree Vineyard, Devon, 405
Marlings Vineyard, Hampshire, 342
Mayshaves Vineyard, Kent, 273
Meldreth Vineyard, Cambridgeshire, 191
Melton Lodge Vineyard, Suffolk, 201
Meon Valley Vineyard, Hampshire, 342
Meopham Valley Vineyard, Kent, 273
Mersea Vineyard, Essex, 220
Mill Hill Village Vineyard, London, 479
Mill Oast Vineyard, East Sussex, 318
Milton Keynes Vineyard, Buckinghamshire, 466
Mimram Valley Vineyard, Hertfordshire, 210
Monnow Valley Vineyard, Monmouthshire, 427
Moorlynch Vineyard, Somerset, 390
Morville Hall Vineyard, Shropshire, 449
Mount Ephraim Vineyard, Kent, 275
Mount Pleasant Vineyard, Lancashire, 441
Mower Vineyards, Essex, 222
Mumfords Vineyard, Somerset, 393

National Vine Collection, Kent, 275
Nevards Vineyard, Essex, 223
New Hall Vineyards, Essex, 224
Northbrook Springs Vineyard, Hampshire, 343
Nutbourne Vineyard, West Sussex, 291
Nyetimber Vineyard, West Sussex, 293

Oakford Vineyard, Devon, 406
Oatley Vineyard, Somerset, 394

Offa's Vineyard, Monmouthshire, 428
Olivers Farm Vineyard, Essex, 227

Painshill Park Vineyard, Surrey, 242
Pant Teg Vineyard, Caerdydd, 429
Parhams Vineyard, Dorset, 357
Parkfield Vineyard, Worcestershire, 373
Pemboa Vineyard, Cornwall, 415
Penshurst Vineyards, Kent, 276
Penberth Valley Vineyard, Cornwall, 417
Plumpton College Vineyard, East Sussex, 319
Polmassick Vineyard, Cornwall, 418
Porthallow Vineyard, Cornwall, 419
Potash Vineyard, Essex, 227
Priors Dean Vineyard, Hampshire, 345
Purbeck Vineyard, Dorset, 358

Quantock Vineyard, Somerset, 395

RidgeView Estate Winery, East Sussex, 320
Rock Lodge Vineyard, West Sussex, 295
Rock Moors Vineyard, Devon, 407
Rodney Stoke Vineyard, Somerset, 396
Rosemary Vineyard, Isle of Wight, 353
Rossiters Vineyard, Isle of Wight, 354
Rowenden Vineyard, Kent, 279

Saint Andrews Vineyard, London, 481
Saint Anne's Vineyard, Gloucestershire, 377
Saint Augustine's Vineyard, Gloucestershire, 381
Saint George's Vineyard, East Sussex, 323
Saint Martins, Isles of Scilly, 420
Saint Peter's Vineyard, Leicestershire, 447
Sandhurst Vineyards, Kent, 279
Scott's Hall, Kent, 280
Sedlescombe Organic Vineyard, East Sussex, 324
Send Vineyard, Surrey, 244
Setley Ridge Vineyards, Hampshire, 346
Sharpham Vineyard, Devon, 407
Shawsgate Vineyard, Suffolk, 202
Shelford Vineyard, Cambridgeshire, 192
Sherston Vineyard, Wiltshire, 332
Spilsted Vineyard, East Sussex, 325
Spring Barn Vineyard, East Sussex, 325
Standen Vineyard, West Sussex, 296
Staplecombe Vineyards, Somerset, 397
Staple St James Winery, Kent, 281
Staverton Vineyard, Suffolk, 204
Stony Hills Vineyard, Essex, 227
Sugar Loaf Vineyard, Monmouthshire, 430
Summer Moor Vineyard, Devon, 410

Sunnybank Vineyard and Vine Nursery, Hereforeshire, 370
Surrenden Vineyard, Kent, 282
Swattenden Ridge Farm Vineyard, Kent, 283
Swiss Cottage Vineyard, Wiltshire, 332

Tenterden Vineyard Park, Kent, 283
Thomas Walk Vineyard, County Cork, 436
Thorncroft Vineyard, Surrey, 246
Three Choirs Vineyard, Gloucestershire, 378
Throwley Vineyard, Kent, 287
Tiltridge Vineyard, Worcestershire, 373
Tintern Parva Vineyard, Monmouthshire, 431
Titchfield Vineyard, Hampshire, 346
Treago Vineyard, Herefordshire, 370
Treetops Vineyard, Worcestershire, 375
Tudor Grange Vineyard, Hertfordshire, 211
Tun Vine Press Company, Kent, 287

Valhalla Vineyard, Northamptonshire, 452
Valley Vineyards, Berkshire, 471
Vernon Lodge Vineyard, Northamptonshire, 453

Wainbridge Vineyard, Shropshire, 450
Wake Court Vineyard, Dorset 358
Warden Abbey Vineyard, Bedfordshire, 468
Water Hall Vineyard, West Yorkshire, 443
Waterwynch Vineyards, Hampshire, 347
Webb's Land Vineyard, Hampshire, 347
Weir Quay Vineyard, Devon, 410
Welland Valley Vineyard, Leicestershire, 454
West Stoke House Vineyard, West Sussex, 296
Westward House Vineyard, Hampshire, 347
Whatley Vineyard, Somerset, 398
Wickham Vineyard, Hampshire, 348
Willow Grange Vineyard, Suffolk, 205
Windmill Vineyard, Northamptonshire, 455
Windsor Forest Vineyard, Berkshire, 478
Wooldings Vineyard, Hampshire, 349
Wootton Park Vineyard, Kent, 289
Wootton Vineyard, Somerset, 399
Worthenbury Wines, Wrexham, 482
Writtle College Vineyard, Essex, 228
Wroxeter Roman Vineyard, Shropshire, 451
Wyecliff Vineyard, Herefordshire, 432
Wyken Vineyards, Suffolk, 206
Wylye Valley Vineyard, Wiltshire, 332

Yearlstone Vineyard, Devon, 411

Index

Note: Grape variety names are in **bold**.

Abbott, Jonathan, 462
Abbs, Jonathan, 287, 288–9
J. H. Abbs and Partners, 287
Abel, Ernst, 112, 266
Abingdon Abbey, 6
Adgestone Vineyard (Isle of Wight), 77, 78, 122, 176, 350–2
Agricultural Central Co-operative Association Ltd, 87
Agricultural Development and Advisory Service (ADAS), 92, 93
Aitov, Ibrahim, 41, 42
Alfred, King, 5
Alicante, 28
Alleweldt, Dr, 148, 161, 166, 168, 173
Alper, Sam, 77, 190
Alper, Simon, 189, 190
Alsace, 150, 169
Alzey Institute for Grapevine Breeding (Rheinland-Pfalz), 38, 39, 156, 158, 161, 168, 177, 181
Ambrose, Basil, 197
Amurensis, 41–2
Anderida label, 72
Andrews, Peter and Diana, 425, 426
Ann, Christopher, 314
Appledown Vineyard (Monks Risborough, Buckinghamshire), 464
Arundel Castle, 17–18
Ascot Citronelle, 33
Ash, Bill, 268, 281
Ash Coombe Vineyard (Canterbury, Kent), 246–7
Ashburnham Vineyard (Battle, E. Sussex), 297
Ashton Manor (Wiltshire), 78
Astley Vineyards (Stourport-on-Severn, Worcestershire), 371–3
Augusta Luise, 70
Augustine, St, 4

Australian wines, 20, 85, 238, 475
Auvernat, 120
Auxerrois, 94, 124, 150
Avalon Vineyard (Shepton Mallet, Somerset), 384–5
Avonwood Vineyard (Sneyd Park, Bristol), 383–4
awards and competitions, 88, 90, 486–94
Awty, Iain, 394

Baart, Angela, 348
Bacchus, 38, 85, 121, 123, 126, 127, 132, 135, 141, 150–1
Baco No. 1, 53, 58, 60, 64, 74
Bagborough Vineyard (Shepton Mallet, Somerset), 386
Baillie-Grohman, T. P., 77
Baker, Colin ,346
Baker, Peter, 427
Baldwin, Janet, 371
Barber, Roger and Jacqui, 220
Bardfield Vineyard (Braintree, Essex), 211–12
Barker, Peter and Sandy, 374
Barkham Manor Vineyard (Uckfield, E. Sussex), 78, 298–9
Barlow, Ken, 77, 254, 351, 352
Barnard, Brian and Gillian, 218
Barnes, Richard and Joyce, 77, 251
Barnsgate Manor Vineyard (Uckfield, E. Sussex), 78, 299–301
Barnsole Vineyard (Canterbury, Kent), 247–9
Barrett, Peter and Sandy, 16
Barrett, Graham and Irene, 77, 87, 89, 216–18
Barron, Archibald, 24–5
Barry, Sir Edward, 16, 19, 120
Barry, Michael, 395
Barty-King, Hugh, 2, 7, 13, 14, 16, 17, 18, 24, 28

Basserman-Jordan, Dr von, 37
Bates, Trevor and Joy, 76
Battle Wine Estate (E. Sussex), 78, 113, 301–3
Baxter, Sheila, 92
Bayford House (Cranbrook, Kent), 249
Bearsted Vineyard (Maidstone, Kent), 249–51
Beaulieu, 121
Beaulieu Vineyard (Hampshire), 49, 74–6, 121, 333–6
Becker, Professor Dr Helmut, 41, 176, 284
Bede, Venerable, 5
Bedfordshire, Warden Abbey Vineyard, 468–9
Beebrock Vineyard, see Oxted Viticultural Research Station (Surrey)
Beech, Fred, 46–7, 111
Beecham's Food and Drink Division Ltd, 47
Beeches Vineyard (Ross-on-Wye, Herefordshire), 366
Beenleigh Manor Vineyard (Totnes, Devon), 400–1
Belgium, 36–7, 118
Bellière, J. N. P., 295
Bellino, 33
Beresford, Robert, 386
Berkshire, Cane End Vineyard, 469–70; Domaine Madeleine Vineyard, 470; Lillibrooke Manor Vineyard, 470–1; Valley Vineyards, 471–8; Windsor Forest Vineyard, 478–9
Berwick, Ian and Eleanor, 78, 195
Bewl Water Vineyard (Wadhurst, E. Sussex), 303
Bianca, 137
Biddenden Vineyards (Ashford, Kent), 73, 77, 113, 251–3
Biddlecombe, Mr and Mrs P, 323
Bird, Thomas, 455
Birk, Professor H., 155, 174, 178
Bishop's Palace Vineyard (Lincoln), 443–4
Bishops Waltham Vineyard (Southampton, Hampshire), 336–7
Bittescombe Mill Vineyard (Taunton, Somerset), 386
Black Campanella, 28
Black Cluster, 120
Black Hamburg, 25, 27, 28, 30, 32, 33, 37
Black Morillon, 120
Blackheath, 13
Blackie, James, 227
Blackwater Valley Vineyard (County Cork, Republic of Ireland), 433–4
Blayney, Robert and Ann, 77, 361
Blue Portuguese, 48
Blunt, Colonel, 13–14
Bodenham English Wines (Herefordshire), 366–7

Bodiam Vineyards (E. Sussex), 303
Boitsfort (Brussels), 36
Bond, Geoffrey, 89
Boogerman, Irene, 209
Bookers Vineyard (Bolney, W. Sussex), 290
Bordeaux, 60, 85
Bosue Vineyard (St Austell, Cornwall), 412
Bothy Vineyard (Abingdon, Oxfordshire), 456–7
botrytis, 44, 54–5, 75, 84, 85, 114, 139
Bowden, George and Janet, 441
Bowden, Graham, 311
Bower Farm Vineyard (Chesham, Buckinghamshire), 464–5
Boyce, Tim and Simon, 405
Boyd, Mrs Ikka, 366
Boyton Vineyard (Sudbury, Suffolk), 194–5
Boze Down Vineyard (Reading, Oxfordshire), 457–8
Braishfield Manor Estate Vineyard (Romsey, Hampshire), 337
Branch, Nicky, 254
Brandt, 23, 30, 44, 53, 64, 74, 120
Braxton, David, 297
Breaky Bottom Vineyard (Lewes, E. Sussex), 78, 304–7
Brecon Court Vineyard (Monmouthshire, Wales), 420–1
Brécot, Henri, 42
Brede Riesling Sylvaner, 72
Brede (Sussex), 76
Breider, Dr H., 167
Brewing Industry Research Foundation, 47
Brickyard Vineyard (Horam, E. Sussex), 307
Bridgwater, Julia, 260
Brightwell Vineyard (Wallingford, Oxfordshire), 458–9
Bristol, Avonwood Vineyard 383–4; Conham Vale Vineyard, 384
The British Viticultural Association, 87
Brock, Ray Barrington, 27, 29, 30–57, 64, 121, 122, 148, 151, 153, 160, 161, 164, 171, 180
Brookes, Tony, 447
Brooksbank, Stephen, 386
Brooksmith, Jane, 462
Brown, Tony, 3
Broxbournebury Vineyard (Hoddesden, Hertfordshire), 207
Bruisyard Vineyard (Saxmundham, Suffolk), 78, 195–7
Bryant, Robin, 417
Buckinghamshire, Appledown Vineyard, 464; Bower Farm Vineyard, 464–5; C.A.V.E. 465; Hale Valley Vineyard, 465–6; Milton Keynes Vineyard, 466–8
Buddlemead Vineyard (Fordingbridge, Hampshire), 337–8
Burch, Brian and Jane, 355

Burgess, William, 20–1
Burglass, Dr Alan, 191
Burwash Weald Vineyard (Etchingham, E. Sussex), 307–8
Bush, Raymond, 29
Bute, Lord, *see* Crichton-Stuart, John Patrick

Cable, Brian, 343
Cambridge Botanic Garden, 120
Cambridgeshire, Chilford Hall Vineyard, 189–90; Elysian Fields, 190–1; Meldreth Vineyard, 191–2; Shelford Vineyard, 192
Camel Valley Vineyard (Bodmin, Cornwall), 341, 413–14
Cammel, Chris, 3
Canary Brand Welsh Wines, 23
Cane End Vineyard (Reading, Berkshire), 469–70
Capbern-Gasqueton, Charles, 258
Capp, Robert, 195
Capper, R. M. O., 77
Carcary, Bill, 68
Cardiff (Wales), 20–1
Cardy, Walter, 77
Carhampton, Earl of, 16
Carlisle, Kenneth and Carla, 206
Carpenters Vineyard (Norton sub Hamdon, Somerset), 387
Carr Taylor, David, 77
Carr Taylor Vineyards (Hastings, E. Sussex), 78, 83, 257, 308–10
Carter, Desmond and Felicity, 407
Carter's Vineyards (Colchester, Essex), 212–14, 218, 227
Cascade, 34, 74, 96, 151–2
Castell Coch (Cardiff), 20–2, 23–4, 30, 53, 120
Castella, François de, 31
Castle Cary Vineyard (Somerset), 387
Castle, R. D. and A. P., 481
Castle Vineyard (Ongar, Essex), 214
Castle Vineyards Ltd, 303
Castlehouse Vineyard (Sussex), 77
Caucasian Research Station, 41
Cava, 133
C.A.V.E. (Botolph Claydon, Buckinghamshire), 465
Cavendish Manor Vineyard (Sudbury, Suffolk), 197
Cecil, Robert, 1st Earl of Salisbury, 13
Central region, described, 437, 440; map of counties/vineyards, 438–9; named vineyards, 441–84
Centre for Viticultural Research (La Mothe–Achard), 42
Chalkhill Vineyard (Salisbury, Wiltshire), 330
Challenden Vineyard (Cranbrook, Kent), 253–4
Chambourcin, 134, 136

Champagne, 83, 113, 138
Channel Islands, Château le Catillon, 359–60; La Mare Vineyards Ltd, 360–1
Channon, Gordon, 348
Channon, Wayne and Debra, 298
Chapel Down Wines Ltd (Tenterden, Kent), 80–1, 83, 113, 220, 239, 254–7, 262, 273, 292, 295
Chapel Farm Vineyard (Isle of Wight), 352
Chapman, Antony and Carol, 465
Chapman, Val, 233
Chardonnay, 17, 68, 83, 120, 123, 132, 138, 139, 152–3
Charnley, John, 348
Chart Sutton (Kent), 6
Chase, J. L. H., 43–4, 52
Chase Protected Cultivation Ltd (Shepperton, Middx), 27, 43–4
Chasselas, 31, 39, 48, 53, 153–4
Chasselas blanc, 37
Chasselas Doré ,28, 33
Chasselas Rosé, 34
Chasselas-de-Bar-sur-Aube, 37
Château le Catillon (Jersey, Channel Islands), 359–60
Cheddar Valley Vineyard (Axbridge, Somerset), 388
Cheshire Vineyards Ltd, 29
Chevelswarde Vineyard (Lutterworth, Leicestershire), 445–6
Chiddingstone Vineyard (Edenbridge, Kent), 78, 113, 258–9
Chilford Hall Vineyard (Linton, Cambridgeshire), 77, 78, 189–90
Chilsdown (Sussex), 78
Chiltern Valley Wines (Henley-on-Thames, Oxfordshire), 460–1
Chingley Oast Vineyard (Wadhurst, E. Sussex), 310–11
Chislet (Kent), 6
Christopher, Dr W. A., 433
Church, Richard, 60–1
cider, 69, 70, 75
Clark, Mr and Mrs Anthony J., 464
Claudius, Emperor, 2
Clay Hill Vineyard (Lamberhurst, Kent), 259–60
Clay, Mr and Mrs Donald, 325
Cleere, Pam, 318
climate, 8–11, 12, 22, 33, 43, 60, 123, 135
cloches, 43–4; Tomato Cloche, 44
Cluster Grape, 119
Coach House Vineyard (Romsey, Hampshire), 338
Codd, Peter, 227
Coddington Vineyard (Ledbury, Herefordshire), 367–8
Cole, Robert and K., 262
Colmar research station (Alsace), 34

Colne Valley Vineyard (Colchester, Essex),
214–15
Columella, 3
Compton Green Vineyard (Redmarley,
Gloucestershire), 375–6
Conghurst Vineyard (Hawkhurst, Kent),
260
Conham Vale Vineyard (White's Hill,
Bristol), 384
Conn, Richard and Sandra L., 457
Constantine, Emperor, 4
Cook, Peter, 78
Cook, Roy, 324
Cooper, Donald W. and T. E., 223
Cooper, Paul, 269
Corkwise Ltd, 75, 117
Cornell University, 35
Cornwall, Bosue Vineyard, 412; Camel
Valley Vineyard, 413–14; Durra Valley
vineyard, 414–15; Lambourne Vineyard,
415; Pemberth Valley Vineyard, 417;
Pemboa Vineyard, 415–16; Polmassick
Vineyard, 418–19; Porthallow Vineyard,
419
Couderc, (nurseryman), 36
Court Lane Vineyard (Alresford,
Hampshire), 338–9
Courtillier musqué ,39
Cowderoy, David (Chapel Down), 113, 254,
295
Cowderoy, Norman (Rock Lodge), 76,
295
Cox, Keith, 210
Cox, Margaret and Tony, 393
Cranmore Vineyards (Isle of Wight), 76,
110–17
Creighton, Andrew, 479
Cremant, 133
Creuss, Professor ,47
Crichton-Stuart, John Patrick, third Marquis
of Bute, 20–2, 24
Crossland-Hinchiffe family, 77
Croxson, William, 241
Cufic Vines (Cheddar, Somerset), 388
Cumberland Lodge (Windsor Park), 25
Cumberledge, Michael, 387
Cunningham, Charles, 349
Curry, David, 99
Cursham, Martin and Alison, 397
Cwm Deri Vineyard (Pembrokeshire, Wales,)
421–2

Dacre, Robert, 28
Dale, Paul and Roger, 332
Daltry, John and Ruth, 446
Danebury Vineyards (Stockbridge,
Hampshire), 339–40
Daniels, Jonty, 371
Danilewicz, John and Adam, 247

Dartmoor Vineyard (Bovey Tracey, Devon),
401–2
Davanzo, Marcello Franco and Sarah-Jane,
215
Davenport Vineyards (Crowborough,
E. Sussex), 113, 218, 263, 311–13
Davenport, Will, 263, 311
Davies, J. O., 280
Dawes, Sandys, 275
Day, Simon, 361
Day, Tom and Brenda, 361
Dean, Mike, 453
Deeley, Peter and June, 240–1
Deeley, Robert, 240–1
Denbies Wine Estate (Dorking, Surrey), 78,
113, 233–9
Denne, Tony, 263
Derrynane Vineyard (County Kerry, Republic
of Ireland), 434–5
dessert wine, 83, 85, 238, 334
Develin, Jill, 296
Devon, Beenleigh Manor Vineyard, 400–1;
Dartmoor Vineyard, 401–2; Down St
Mary Vineyard, 402–3; Follymoor
Vineyard, 403–4; Higher Bumsley
Vineyard, 404–5; Manstree Vineyard,
405–7; Oakford Vineyard, 406–7; Rock
Moors Vineyard, 407; Sharpham Vineyard,
407–10; Summer Moor Vineyard, 410;
Weir Quay Vineyard, 410–11; Yearlstone
Vineyard, 411–12
Diana, 136
Digby, Wingfield, 348–9
Ditchling Vineyards (E. Sussex), 313–14
Domaine Madeleine Vineyard (Maidenhead,
Berkshire), 470
Domitian, Emperor, 2, 4
Don, Robin, 76, 87
Donald, J. R. M., 78
Dornfelder, 84, 114, 138, 154–5
Dorset, Horton Estate Vineyard, 355–6;
Lytchett Matravers Vineyard, 356;
Parhams Vineyard, 357; Purbeck
Vineyard, 348; Wake Court Vineyard,
348–9
Doubleday, Martyn, 3
Dowling, Shaun, 464
Down St Mary Vineyard (Crediton, Devon),
402–3
Downland Dry, 85
Dr Hogg's Muscat, 119
Dragons Rock Vineyard (Stamford,
Lincolnshire), 447–8
Druitt, Michael, 52
Dudley, C and J, 431
Dunkelfelder, 155
Dunkery Vineyard (Minehead, Somerset),
389–90
Dunkley, Rowland, 330

Dunn, A., 337
Dunstan, Abbot of St Mary's Abbey (Glastonbury), 5–6
Durra Valley vineyard (Helston, Cornwall), 414–15
Durrant, Chris, 189
Duruz, Professor, 35, 52
Dusty Miller (Pinot Meunier), 17

Eadwig, King, 5
Early Ripening, 42
Early Violet, 42
East Anglia region, described, 185, 188; map of counties/vineyards, 186–7; named vineyards, 188–228
East Malling Research station, 34
Ebdon, Mark, 242
Edelzwicker, 150
Edgar, King (the Peaceful), 6
Edgerly, Jack, 77
Edwards, Brian, 370
Edwards, Michael and Ruth, 315
Edynbry, Dr Dorian, 375
Efford Experimental Husbandry Station (EHS) (Lymington, Southampton), 92
Eger Vine Breeding Station (Hungary), 137
Eglantine Vineyard (Loughborough, Nottinghamshire), 344–5
Ehrenfelser, 155
Elbling Red, 156
Elbling White, 156
Elham Valley Vineyards (Canterbury, Kent), 260–1
Elias, Owen, 254, 283
Elkins, Neil, 345
Elliott, Robert, 331
Elmham Park (Norfolk), 49, 76
Elms Cross Vineyard (Bradford-on-Avon, Wiltshire), 330
Elwes, Richard, 296
Elysian Fields (Ely, Cambridgeshire), 190–1
Endlandsson, Nils, 35, 59
English Vineyards Association (EVA), xii, 73, 87–91, 94, 95, 97, 98, 102, 121, 123–5, 139, 145, 170, 336, 400, 411, 485–7
English and Welsh Wine Liaison Committee, 93
English Wine Centre (Alfriston, E. Sussex), 314–15
English Wine Producers, 91
English Wines plc, 257
'Epoch Brut', 83
Eryri Vineyard (Gwynedd, Wales), 481–2
Esperione, 120
Essex, Bardfield Vineyard, 211–12; Carter's Vineyard, 212–14; Castle Vineyard, 214; Colne Valley Vineyard, 214–15; Felsted Vineyard, 215–18; Great Stocks Vineyard, 218–20; Little Witney Green, 220; Mersea Vineyard, 220–1; Mower Vineyards, 222–3; Nevards Vineyard, 223–4; New Hall Vineyards, 224–6; Olivers Farm Vineyard, 227; Potash Vineyard, 227; Stony Hills Vineyard, 227–8; Writtle College Vineyard, 228
Etherton, Peter, 307, 318
European Union, 40, 96–102, 115–16, 123–5, 126, 170
Evelyn, John, 14
Eynon, Roger, 384

Faberrebe, 39, 70, 121, 126, 156–7
Farmer, Peter and Anne, 390
Farrar, Bob, 125
Fawley vineyard (Henley–on–Thames, Oxfordshire), 461–2
Fédération Nationale d'Etudes de la Défense des Hybrides et Métis (FENAVINO), 35–6, 67
Felsted Vineyard (Great Dunmow, Essex), 49, 77, 215–18
Fenton, Colin, 52
Ffynnon Las (Ceredigion, Wales), 422–3
Fielden, Christopher, 11
Findling, 157
Finger Lakes Wine Growers Association (New York), 151
Fisher, Roger and Dorothea, 456
Fison, Sir Guy, 52
Flandres, Comte de, 37
Flecknor, Roger, 340
Flexerne (Sussex), 76
Flook, Stephen A., 338
Follymoor Vineyard (Crediton, Devon), 403–4
Ford, Hugh, 193
Forester, E. D., 42–3
Forta, 38
Foss, Chris, 319
Foster's White Seedling, 37
Fowke, Martin, 378
Fowles, Peter and Jill, 205
Frithsden Vineyard (Hemel Hempstead, Hertfordshire), 207–9
Froelich, G. A., 155
Frome Valley Vineyard (Bishop's Frome, Herefordshire), 368–9
Frontiniaq, 119
Fruit of the Vine (County Dublin, Republic of Ireland), 435
fruit wines, 70, 75
Furnace Brook Vineyard (Chipstead, Surrey), 239–40

Gabler, James M., 17
Gagarin Blue, 42
Gaillard Gerrard, 43
Gale, David, 429
Galet, Pierre, 41

Gallup, Lysbeth, 410
Gamay, 21, 23, 31
Gamay Frew [sic], 30
Gamay noir Hâtif des Vosges, 38, 48, 58, 60, 69, 74, 122
Gamay noir, 22, 120, 141
Gamlinglay (Bedfordshire), 77
Garner, Bill, 285
Garner, Jerry, 92
Garney, Barney, 347
Garrett, Lady Jane, 275
Gauntlett, Conrad, 353
Geilweilerhof hybrid, 134
Geilweilerhof Institute for Grapevine Breeding (Pfalz, Germany), 38, 59, 148, 150, 166, 173
Geisenheim Institute for Grapevine Breeding, 41, 136, 157, 163
Geneste, David, 16
Geneva Double Curtain (GDC) training system, 40–1, 107–9, 502
German wine, 85, 112, 113, 120, 136–7, 154
Gewürztraminer, 39, 40, 141
Gibbons, Bob, 76
Gibson, Dr John and Elizabeth, 249
Gibson-Watt, Andrew, 432
Gifford's Hall (Bury St Edmunds, Suffolk), 197–9
Gillespie, Colin and Sue 78, 89, 399
Gilpin, Sawrey, 16
Giraldus Cambrensis, 5
Girling, Paul, 346
Gladwin, Bridget and Peter, 291
Glastonbury, 6
Gloucestershire, Compton Green Vineyard, 375–6; Kents Green Vineyard, 376–7; Little Foxes Vineyard, 377; Saint Anne's Vineyard, 377–8; Saint Augustine's Vineyard, 381–3; Three Choirs Vineyard, 378–81
Glyndŵr Vineyard (Vale of Glamorgan, Wales), 423–5
Godden, Nigel, 8, 76, 111, 380, 399
Godstone Vineyard (Godstone, Surrey), 240–1
Golden Chasselas, 48
Goldsmith, William, 8
Gordon, Kenneth, 347
Gore-Browne, Robert and Margaret, 74–6, 88, 111, 151, 335–6
Gore-Browne Trophy, 181, 188, 207, 238, 254, 256, 326, 336, 352, 363, 440, 476, 486–92
Gower, Vince, 471
Grace Dieu Vineyard (Coalville, Leicestershire), 446–7
Graham, Michael, 441
Graham, R. F. and F. M., 249
Grange Farm Vineyard (Swerford, Oxfordshire), 462–3

Grant, Ian, 77, 264
Graville, Ed, 34
Gray, Mrs D., 262
Great Stocks Vineyard (Ingatestone, Essex), 218–20
greenhouses, 18–19
Greenwood, Bill, 77
Greenwood, C. J., 60
Greenwood, Piers, 224
Gregory, Pope, 4
Grey, Pauline and David, 273
Greyfriards Vineyard (Guildford, Surrey), 241
Grinling, Jasper, 199
Gros Colman (Colmar), 25, 27
Gros Morillon noir, 37
Gurney, Matthew, 260
Gutedal No. 3, 38, 59
Gutenborner, 157–8
Guyot, 107–9

Hach, Mansfield & Co ,23
Hackwood Vineyard (Robertsbridge, E. Sussex), 315–16
Hadlow Down Vineyard (Hadlow Down, E. Sussex), 261
Hale Valley Vineyard (Wendover, Buckinghamshire), 465–6
Hale Vineyard (Fordingbridge, Hampshire), 340
Halfpenny Green Vineyard (Staffordshire), 448
Hall, Peter and Christine, 78, 304
Hamble Valley Vineyard (Southampton, Hampshire), 340–1
Hambledon (Hampshire), 24, 55, 65, 66–8, 109, 121
Hamilton, Charles, 15–16, 120
Hamilton-Cowburn, John, 421
Hammelshoden, 37
Hammond, Mac, 376
Hamner, Sir Thomas, 13–14
Hampshire, Beaulieu Vineyard ,333–6; Bishops Waltham Vineyard, 336–7; Braishfield Manor Estate Vineyard, 337; Buddlemead Vineyard, 337–8; Coach House Vineyard, 338; Court Lane Vineyard, 338–9; Danebury Vineyards, 339–40; Hale Vineyard, 340; Hamble Valley Vineyard, 340–1; Jays Farm Vineyard, 341; Marlings Vineyard, 342; Meon Valley Vineyard, 342; Northbrook Springs Vineyard, 343–4; Priors Dean Vineyard, 345–6; Setley Ridge Vineyards, 346; Tichfield Vineyard, 346; Waterwynch Vineyards, 347; Webb's Land Vineyard, 347; Westward House Vineyard, 347–8; Wickham Vineyard, 348–9; Wooldings Vineyard, 349–50

Harden Vineyard (Tonbridge, Kent), 262
Hardingham, Mike, 450
Harling Vineyards (Norwich, Norfolk), 192–3
Harold, King, 6
Harpenden Garden Fields Vineyard (Hertfordshire), 209
Hartlib, Samuel, 14
Hascombe (Surrey), 77
Hatfield House, 13
Hayward, Lady J., 291
Hazel End Vineyard (Bishop's Stortford, Hertfordshire), 209–10
Heath, Tony, 92
Helions Vineyard (Haverhill, Suffolk), 199
Hemphill, Rob, 202
Hendred Vineyard (Oxfordshire), 463–4
Henry II, 11
Henry VIII, 8
Herefordshire, Beeches Vineyard, 366; Bodenham English Wines, 366–7; Coddington Vineyard, 367–8; Frome Valley Vineyard, 368–9; Sunnybank Vineyard and Vine Nursery, 370; Treago Vineyard, 370–1; Wyecliff Vineyard, 432–3
Herold, August, 159
Hertfordshire, Broxbournebury Vineyard, 207; Frithsden Vineyard, 207–9; Harpenden Garden Fields Vineyard, 209; Hazel End Vineyard, 209–10; Mimram Valley Vineyard, 210–11; Tudor Grange Vineyard, 211
Hidden Spring Vineyard (Heathfield, E. Sussex), 316–18
High Weald Vineyard (Ticehurst, E. Sussex), 73, 318
Higher Bumsley Vineyard (Parracombe, Devon), 404–5
Highwaymans (Bury St Edmunds), 78
Hillebrand, Lott and Pfaff, 136
Hillier, Doreen, 455
Hilliers of Winchester, 30
Hills, June and Christian, 399
Hintlesham Vineyard (Suffolk), 199–200
Hochdorfer, Ludwig, 159
Hofayz, M. and I. B., 430
Home Farmhouse Vineyard (Guildford, Surrey), 241–2
Honess, Tony and Brenda, 261
Hood, Andrew, 475
Hooke, Della, 6
Hopkins, Benjamin Bond, 16
Horam Manor (Sussex), 49, 68–74, 121, 307
Hordern, Edward and Michael, 469
Horsmonden Vineyards (Horsmonden, Kent), 263

Horticultural Trades Association, 55
Horticultural Utilities Ltd (Liverpool), 27, 29, 33
Horton Estate Vineyard (Wimbourne, Dorset), 355–6
Howie, Ian, 69
Hughes, Tom, 253
Hughes, Will, 14, 119
Humphreys, Mr and Mrs Charles, 209
Husfeld, Dr B, 38, 59, 150, 166
Huxelrebe, 39, 84, 85, 123, 127, 131, 135, 158
Hyams, Edward, 1, 29, 30, 36, 44–5, 46, 48, 52, 57–63, 65, 94, 121, 163, 164, 170, 180
hybrids, 29, 36, 38, 43, 54, 96–8, 116, 134, 136–7, 151

Ickworth Vineyard (Bury St Edmunds, Suffolk), 200–1
Industrial and Provident Societies Act, 89
Iona, 43
Ireland, see Republic of Ireland
Isle of Wight, Adgestone Vineyard, 350–2; Chapel Farm Vineyard, 352; The Kings Cellar Vineyard, 353; Rosemary Vineyard, 353–4; Rossiters Vineyard, 354–5
Isles of Scilly, Saint Martin, 419, 420
Issitt, David, 192

Jackson, Allan, 62
Jackson, Christopher, 332
Jacob's Creek, 85
James I and VI, 13
James, Keith, 366
Jays Farm Vineyard (East Wellow, Hampshire), 341
Jeffries, Ted and Sheila, 419
Jeffs, Julian, 137
Jenkins, David, 377
Joannès Seyve, 42
Johannisberg yeast, 44, 45
Johanniter, 136
Johner, Karl-Heinz, 112, 266
Johnson, Keith and Linda, 299
Johnson, Peter, 428
Jones, George, 76, 335
Jones, Lloyd and Jane,t 415
Jordan, Alan, 211
Jordan, F., 28

Kaiser Wilhelm Institut (Berlin), 38
Kanzler, 39, 140
Kelsale (Suffolk), 77
Kemp, John and Jeanie, 197
Kemp, Jonathan, 197
Kempes Hall Vineyard (Ashford, Kent), 263–4

Kent, Ash Coombe Vineyard, 246–7; Barnsole Vineyard, 247–9; Bayford House, 249; Bearsted Vineyard, 249–51; Biddenden Vineyards, 251–3; Challenden Vineyard, 253–4; Chapel Down Wines Ltd, 254–7; Chiddingstone Vineyard, 258–9; Clay Hill Vineyard, 259–60; Conghurst Vineyard, 260; Elham Valley Vineyards, 260–1; Harden Vineyard, 262; Horsmonden Vineyards, 263; Kempes Hall Vineyard, 263–4; Knowle Hill Vineyard, 264; Lamberhurst Vineyards, 264–70; Leeds Castle Vineyard, 270–2; Lewins Vineyards, 272; Little Knoxbridge Vineyard, 272–3; Mayshaves Vineyard, 273; Meopham Valley Vineyard, 273–4; Mount Ephraim Vineyard, 275; National Vine Collection, 275–6; Penshurst Vineyards, 276–9; Sandhurst Vineyards, 279–80; Scott's Hall, 280–1; Staple St James Winery, 281–2; Surrenden Vineyard, 282–3; Swattenden Ridge Farm Vineyard, 283; Tenterden Vineyard Park, 283–7; Throwley Vineyard, 287; Tun Vine Press Company, 287–9; Wootton Park Vineyard, 289–90

Kents Green Vineyard (Taynton, Gloucestershire), 376–7

Kerner, 70, 71, 123, 131, 135, 159

Kernling, 159–60

Kessler, Herr, 34, 52

King, Jamie and Jane, 341

The Kings Cellar Vineyard (Isle of Wight), 353

Klingenberg–Dunkley, Gurli, 330

Knight, W. D. Martin, 207

Knowle Hill Vineyard (Maidstone, Kent), 77, 264

Knowles, Justin, 401

Kraus, Dr, 176

Kuhlmann, Eugene, 182

La Mare Vineyards Ltd (Jersey, Channel Islands), 77, 360–1

Ladywell Vineyard (Hunstanton, Norfolk), 193–4

Lamberhurst Vineyards (Kent), 78, 83, 112, 176, 257, 264–70

Lambert, Camilla, 354

Lambert, Mark, 78

Lambourne Vineyard (Truro, Cornwall), 415

Lamond, Carole, 259

Lamphey Court (Wales), 76

Lancashire, Mount Pleasant Vineyard, 441

Landot, (nurseryman), 36, 58

Lane, Brian, 434

Latchford, Peter and Anne, 207

Le Page, Richard Jocelyn, 396

Lee, Roland, 27–9, 31

Leeds Castle Vineyard (Maidstone, Kent), 6, 7, 270–2

Leggett, Jeremy, 202

Leicestershire, Chevelswarde Vineyard, 445–6; Grace Dieu Vineyard, 446–7; Saint Peter's Vineyard, 447; Welland Valley Vineyard ,454–5

Leighton, Jon, 78, 154, 245, 246, 471, 478

Léon Millot, 37, 54, 96, 116, 160–1

Leventhorpe Vineyard (Leeds, W. Yorkshire), 441–3

Lewins Vineyards (Edenbridge, Kent), 272

Lewis, Kynric, 429

Lewis, Martin, 422

Leyvraz, Mr, 33, 34, 52, 164

Liebfraumilch, 85

Lillibrooke Manor Vineyard (Maidenhead, Berkshire), 470–1

Lincolnshire, Bishop's Palace Vineyard, 443–4; Dragons Rock Vineyard, 447–8

Lindlar, Christopher, 72, 238

Lindo, Bob and Annie, 413

Little Ashley Vineyard (Bradford-on-Avon, Wiltshire), 331

Little Foxes Vineyard (Stonehouse, Gloucestershire), 377

Little Knoxbridge Vineyard (Staplehurst, Kent), 272–3

Little Witney Green (Ongar, Essex), 220

Llanerch Vineyard (Vale of Glamorgan, Wales), 425–7

Llewellyn, David, 435

Lockwood, Trevor, 414

Loftus, Paul, 272

London, Mill Hill Village Vineyard, 479–80; Saint Andrews Vineyard, 481

Long Ashton Research Station (Bristol), 46, 111, 126

Longman, David and Clare, 368

Longueville House Vineyard (County Cork, Republic of Ireland), 435–6

Loudon, J C, 28

Lübeck, 40

Lucas, Paul and Isabel, 246

Luglienca bianca, 39

Lunn, C R, 353

Lurgashall Winery (Petworth, W. Sussex), 241, 290–1

Luxemburg Experimental Vineyard (Remich), 35

Lydhurst Vineyard (Warninglid, W. Sussex), 291

Lytchett Matravers Vineyard (Poole, Dorset), 356

Lytle, S. E., 29, 33

McAlpine, Kenneth, 71–2, 78, 89, 113, 264–9

McClure, Andrew, 356

McDonald, Kay, 388
McElney, Desmond and Barbara, 420
McKechnie, Alan, 78, 380
MacKinnon, Malcolm and Mary, 463
McMillen, Derek, 269
McMullan, G., 481
Macrae, Mary, 78
Macready, Charles, 200
Madeleine Angevine 7672, 33, 38, 39, 40,
    52, 59, 121, 122, 125, 127, 132, 138,
    148–9, 161–3
Madeleine Royale, 34, 48, 69, 140
Madeleine Sylvaner, 38, 49, 52, 54, 122,
    125, 149, 163
Madland, Tormod, 470
malolactic fermentation, 114, 117, 153,
    476
Mann, Douglas, 330
Manresa Lodge (Roehampton), 25
Manstree Vineyard (Exeter, Devon), 405–7
Marchbank, Roger and Margaret, 338
Maréchal Foch, 36, 37, 96
Maréchal Joffre, 122
Mariensteiner, 140
Mariman, Georges, 36, 37
Marlings Vineyard (Sway, Hampshire), 342
Marot, Gerard, 36
Martin, D. C., 51
Martin, Ralph, 209
Massel, Anton, 75, 77, 111, 122
Mathias, Lewis, 76, 335
Mauger, Ralph, 359
Mayshaves Vineyard (Woodchurch, Kent),
    273
Meadows, Ian, 2
Meldreth Vineyard (Cambridgeshire), 191–2
Melton Lodge Vineyard (Melton, Suffolk),
    201–2
Meon Valley Vineyard (Swanmore,
    Hampshire), 342
Meopham Valley Vineyard (Kent), 273–4
Merrydown Wine Company, 69–74, 75, 110,
    111, 122, 126
Mersea Vineyard (Colchester, Essex), 220–1
Merzling, 136
Meslier Précoce, 48
Michael of Amesbury, Abbot of Glastonbury,
    8
Michurin Central Genetic Laboratory, 41
Middleton, C. H., 28
Mill Hill Village Vineyard (London), 479–80
Mill Oast Vineyard (Sedlescombe, E. Sussex),
    318
Miller grape, 120
Miller, Philip, 17, 119
Miller's Burgundy, 120
Millie Blanche (Miel Blanc), 21, 120
Millington, David and Christine, 451
Mills, David, 313

Milton Keynes Vineyard (Buckinghamshire),
    466–8
Mimram Valley Vineyard (Welwyn,
    Hertfordshire), 210–11
Ministry of Agriculture, Fisheries and Food
    (MAFF), 80, 87, 116, 123–6, 139, 170;
    and quality wine scheme, 94–103; and
    vine varieties, 93–4; and wine growing,
    92–3
Minors, John and Norma, 383
Molash Vineyard (Canterbury, Kent), 58–63,
    163
Monnow Valley Vineyard (Monmouthshire,
    Wales), 427–8
Montagu, Lady, of Beaulieu, 87
Montagu, Lord, of Beaulieu, 76, 89, 334,
    336
Montpellier School of Viticulture, 41
Moorlynch Vineyard (Bridgwater, Somerset),
    390–3
Morgan-Grenville, Mr, 52
Morio, Peter, 38, 150, 166
Morio-Muskat, 38
Morley, Pamela, 345
Morris, Ian, 291
Morris, Dr Kit, 359, 380
Morville Hall Vineyard (Bridgnorth,
    Shropshire), 449–50
Moscow Botanical Gardens, 41
Mosey, Graham and Sue, 317
Moss, Stuart and Sandra, 78, 293
Mount Ephraim Vineyard (Faversham, Kent),
    275
Mount Pleasant Vineyard (Carnforth,
    Lancashire), 441
Mower, Bert, 222
Mower Vineyards (Billericay, Essex),
    222–3
Mudd, Mary F., 213
Müller, Dr H., 34, 163–4
Müller-Thurgau, 33, 39, 71, 74, 83, 85, 94,
    117, 121, 122, 123, 127, 131, 132, 134,
    135, 136, 143, 149, 163–6
Mumfords Vineyard (Bath, Somerset), 393–4
Munro, Neil and Helen, 377
Muscadella, 119
Muscadine, 119
Muscadoule, 58
Muscat of Alexandria, 27
Muscat de St Vallier, 58
Muscat (Dr Hogg's), 119
Muscat Hamburg, 33, 42
Muscatel, 30
Musgrave, Barbara, 416
Mynors, Sir Richard, 370

Naeyer, Anthony de, 211
National Farmer's Union (NFU), 93
National Trust, 201

National Vine Collection (Faversham, Kent), 275–6

Nettlestead (Kent), 76

Nevards Vineyard (Colchester, Essex), 223–4

New Hall Vineyards (Chelmsford, Essex), 77, 78, 224–6, 228

New World wine, 113

New Zealand, 42–3, 123, 150, 164, 174

Nicholas, Andrew, 342

Nicholas, J. F. and C. A., 279

Nielsen, Bob and Carol, 459

Nobless, 38

Norfolk, Harling Vineyards, 192–3; Ladywell Vineyard, 193–4

Norfolk, Duke of, 17–18

Norris, Richard and Robbie, 423

North Curry (Somerset), 7

Northamptonshire, Valhalla Vineyard, 452–3; Vernon Lodge Vineyard, 453–4; Windmill Vineyard, 455–6

Northbrook Springs Vineyard (Southampton, Hampshire), 343–4

Northfleet (Kent), 8

Nottinghamshire, Eglantine Vineyard, 344–5

Nutbourne Vineyard (Pulborough, W. Sussex), 291–3

Nyetimber Vineyard (West Chiltington, W. Sussex), 78, 83, 109, 113, 133, 152, 293–5

oak-aged, 83, 84, 114

Oakford Vineyard (Bampton, Devon), 406–7

Oastler, Alan, 375

Oatlands Park (Weybridge, Surrey), 13

Oatley Vineyard (Bridgwater, Somerset), 394–5

Oberlin 595, 36

O'Callaghan, Michael, 435–6

Ockley (Surrey), 77, 122

Odo, Bishop of Bayeux, 7

Oeillade de Conzieu, 58

Österreichischen Rebschulen Teleki, 34

Offa's Vineyard (Monmouthshire, Wales), 428–9

Oglethorpe, James, 15

Oidium tuckerii (powdery mildew), 12, 21, 53–4

Oldaker, Martin, 282

Oliver, John, 465

Olivers Farm Vineyard (Halstead, Essex), 227

Optima, 38, 84, 114, 136, 166

Ordish, George, 30, 63–5, 105

Oregon State College, 35

Orion, 38, 96, 136, 137, 166–7

Ortega, 70, 84, 85, 114, 121, 167–8

Owen, Trevor, 360

Oxfordshire, Bothy Vineyard, 456–7; Boze Down Vineyard, 457–8; Brightwell Vineyard, 458–9; Chiltern Valley Wines, 460–1; Fawley vineyard, 461–2; Grange Farm Vineyard, 462–3; Hendred Vineyard, 463–4

Oxted Viticultural Research Station (Surrey), 30–57, 120, 151, 153, 160, 170, 171

Oxton (Cheshire), 28

Packham, Mel, 388

Paget, Andrew and Ian, 78

Painshill Park Vineyard (Cobham, Surrey), 15–17, 19–20, 120, 242–4

Panborough (Somerset), 6

Pangbourne (Berkshire), 77

Pant Teg Vineyard (Caerdydd, Wales), 429–30

Parhams Vineyard (Shaftesbury, Dorset), 357

Parkfield Vineyard (Rushwick, Worcestershire), 373

Parrish, David, 214, 220

Parsley Grape, 119

Parsons, Reg, 71

Patrick, John, 52

Patrick, Nick, 233

Patterson, John, 68

Patty, Mrs J, 262

Pearkes, Gillian, 76, 162, 411

Pemberth Valley Vineyard (Penzance, Cornwall), 417

Pemboa Vineyard (Helston, Cornwall), 415–16

Pembrey (Wales), 76

Penshurst Vineyards (Tonbridge, Kent), 78, 276–9

Pépinières Teleki SA (Vienna), 34

Pepys, Samuel, 13

Perle, 140

Perle of Alzey, 168

Perle de Czaba, 33–4

perry, 70

Petchley, Allan and Julia, 410

Peters, Philip and Catherine, 347

Petit Morillon noir, 37

Pettigrew, Andrew Jr, 24

Pettigrew, Andrew Snr, 21–4, 66

Phillips, Roy, 357

Phoenix, 38, 96, 136, 137, 168–9

phylloxera, 20, 55, 65, 106, 138

Picard, Sir Henry, 12

Piech, Ernst, 339

Pierce, M., 318

Pilcher, Anthony, 254, 352

Pilton Manor (Somerset), 8, 76, 111, 122

Pinnington, Tony, 388

Pinot, 31, 123, 149

Pinot blanc, 150, 169

Pinot gris, 169–70

Pinot Meunier ('Dusty Miller'), 17, 59, 68, 83, 116, 120, 133, **170**
Pinot noir, 17, 37, 68, 83, 84, 85, 116, 120, 132, 133, 136, 138, **171–3**
Pirovano, 33, 74
Pirovano No. 7 (Primus), 58
Plumpton College Vineyard (Lewes, E. Sussex), 319–20
Pollard, Dr Alfred, 46, 52, 111
Polmassick Vineyard (St Austell, Cornwall), 418–19
Pontac, 43
Porthallow Vineyard (Helston, Cornwall), 419
Portland, Duke of, 18, 120
Portugieser Blau, 34
Potapenko, Yakov, 42
Potash Vineyard (Colchester, Essex), 227
Potter, Tony, 233
Poulter, Nick, 76, 110–17
pourriture gris, 84–5
pourriture noble, 84
Pratt, Rodney and Janet, 290
Pratt, Simon and Carol, 402
Précoce de Malingre, 38, 74
Prichard, Mr and Mrs B. H., 289
Priors Dean Vineyard (Alton, Hampshire), 345–6
Pritchard, Derek and Val, 389
Probus, Emperor, 4
Pulham (Norfolk), 78
Purbeck Vineyard (Corfe Castle, Dorset), 348
Purdey, Richard, 71

Quality Wine, 102, 103, 115–16, 117, 136–7
Quality Wine Produced in a Specified Region (QWpsr), 96, 173
Quality Wine Scheme Committee (QWSC), 96
Quality Wine Scheme (QWS), 88, 96, 97, 100, 143
Quantock Vineyard (Bridgwater, Somerset), 395–6
Queen of Vineyards, 28
Quirk family, 78
Quirk, J. P. and M., 258

Rayleigh (Essex), 7
Ready Mixed Concrete (RMC), 245
red wine, 83, 84, 114, 133–4, 135
Redfern, Andrew, 446
Reece, Gruff, 77
Rees, Tom, 392, 393
Regent, 38, 96, 134, 136, 137, **173**
Regional Wine, 102, 103, 115–16, 117
Regner, 39, 126, **174**
Reichensteiner, 70, 71, 83, 85, 121, 123, 125, 127, 132, 135, 136, 138, **174–5**
Reine Olga, 28

Republic of Ireland, Blackwater Valley Vineyard, 433–4; Derrynane Vineyard, 434–5; Fruit of the Vine, 435; Longueville House Vineyard, 435–6; Thomas Walk Vineyard, 436
RidgeView Estate Winery (West Hassocks, W. Sussex), 83, 113, 133, 152, 320–3
Riesling, 31, 34, 58, 60, 136, 138, **175–6**
Riesling Sylvaner (Müller-Thurgau), 36, 48, 52, 53, 58–9, 64, 69, 149
Riparia Gloire de Montpelier, 106
Rivollier, Mr, 45
Roberts, Derek, 272
Roberts, Mike, 321
Robinson, Jancis, 3, 120, 199, 414
Robinson, Mike, 107
Rochfords (Cheshunt, Hertfordshire), 26
Rock Lodge Vineyard (Haywards Heath, W. Sussex), 76, 254, 255, 295–6
Rock Moors Vineyard (Crediton, Devon), 407
Rodney Stoke Vineyard (Cheddar, Somerset), 396–7
Rogers, Kerry, 337
Roland's Muscatel, 28
Rondo, 41, 84, 96, 114, 116, 136, 137, **176–7**
Rook, Major, 76, 111
rosé, 134
Rose, John, 14, 119
Rosemary Vineyard (Isle of Wight), 353–4
Ross, William, 78
Rossiters Vineyard (Isle of Wight), 354–5
Rostron, Peter, 406
Rowe, Ian, 449
Rowe, Peter, 227
Royal Horticultural Society (RHS), 32, 33, 43, 44, 49, 52, 60
Royal Muscadine, 28, 30, 120

Sackville-West, Vita, 60
Saint Andrews Vineyard (London), 481
Saint Anne's Vineyard (Newent, Gloucestershire), 377–8
Saint Augustine's Vineyard (Aust, S. Gloucestershire), 381–3
Saint George's Vineyard (Heathfield, E. Sussex), 323–4
St James's Palace (London), 13, 14
St Laurent, 41
Saint Margaret's Vineyard (Craven Arms, Shropshire), 450–1
Saint Martin (Isle of Scilly), 420
Saint Peter's Vineyard (Leire, Leicestershire), 447
St Quentins (Wales), 22
Salisbury, Sir Edward, 51
Salisbury-Jones, Sir Guy, 55, 66–8, 74, 75, 87, 89, 111, 180, 336

Sandhurst Vineyards (Cranbrook, Kent),
 279–80
Saperavi Servenyi, 41, 42
Sargent, Nick and Wendy, 461
Sauvignon blanc, 141
Savage, Denis and Ann, 367
Sax, David, 78, 301
Scheu, Georg, 39, 148, 156, 158, 161, 168,
 174, 177, 181, 183
Scheu, Heinz, 40, 161
Scheurebe, 39, 177–8
Schleifer, Hans, 237, 291, 346, 353
Schmidtmann, 35
Schmitt, Karl–Heinz, 112, 266
Schönburger, 71, 125, 127, 131, 136, 138,
 178–9
Schooler, Jerry, 291
Scilly Isles, see Isles of Scilly
Scorer, Tim, 215
Scott's Hall (Ashford, Kent), 280–1
Sedlescombe Organic Vineyard (E. Sussex),
 273, 324–5, 446
Seed, Martin and Mary, 482
Seibel, 33, 36, 42, 49, 54, 58, 60, 121, 136
Seibel (nurseryman), 36
Sekt, 133
Selskabet Til Vinavlens Fremme I Norden
 (Denmark), 35
Senator, 179
Send Vineyard (Ripley, Surrey), 244–6
Septimer, 39
Setley Ridge Vineyards (Brockenhurst,
 Hampshire), 338, 346, 357
Seward, Desmond, 6, 10
Sewell, Ken, 192
Seyval blanc, 53, 54, 58, 64, 74, 83, 121,
 122, 123, 127, 131, 135, 138, 145,
 179–81
Seyve, Bertille Jnr, 179
Seyve, Bertille and Joannès, 36
Seyve-Villard 5/276 (Seyval Blanc), 29, 33,
 36, 48, 58, 60, 67, 136
Sharman, Mark, 400, 407, 409
Sharp, Tony 373
Sharpham Vineyard (Totnes, Devon), 400,
 407–10
Shaulis, Nelson, 40–1
Shawsgate Vineyard (Woodbridge, Suffolk),
 202–4, 215
Sheepshanks, Robin and Lilias, 204
Shelford Vineyard (Cambridge,
 Cambridgeshire), 192
Sherratt, Graham ,415
Sherston Vineyard (Malmesbury, Wiltshire),
 332
Shropshire, Morville Hall Vineyard, 449–50;
 Saint Margaret's Vineyard, 450–1;
 Wroxeter Roman Vineyard, 451–2
Sibley, Paul, 412

Sichel, 53
Siegerrebe, 39, 114, 181–2
Silvaner, see Sylvaner
Simms, Jillian, 200
Simpson, Keith, 443
Sirius, 136
Sitwell, Sir Reresby ,75
Skuriat, Tony, 444
Slater, Sir William, 51
Smart, Richard, 107–8
Smith, Pamela, 76, 404
Smith, Tony and Emi, 332
Somers, David and Carol, 303
Somerset, Avalon Vineyard, 384–5;
 Bagborough Vineyard, 386; Bittescombe
 Mill Vineyard, 386; Carpenters Vineyard,
 387; Castle Cary Vineyard, 387; Cheddar
 Valley Vineyard, 388; Cufic Vines, 388;
 Dunkery Vineyard, 389–90; Moorlych
 Vineyard, 390–3; Mumfords Vineyard,
 393–4; Oatley Vineyard, 394–5; Quantock
 Vineyard, 395–6; Rodney Stoke Vineyard,
 396–7; Staplecombe Vineyards, 397–8;
 Whatley Vineyard, 398–9
South region, described, 326–7; map of
 counties/vineyards, 328–9; named
 vineyards, 330–61
South East region, described, 229, 232; map
 of counties, 230–1; named vineyards,
 233–325
South West region, described, 362–3; map of
 counties/vineyards, 364–5; named
 vineyards, 366–433
Soviet Union, 42
Spain, 137
sparkling wine, 83, 84, 132–3, 135
Spätburgunder, 136
Speechley, William, 18, 19–20, 120
Spilsted Vineyard (Sedlescombe, E. Sussex),
 325
Spring Barn Vineyard (Lewes, E. Sussex),
 325
Staffordshire, Halfpenny Green Vineyard,
 448
Standen Vineyard (East Grinstead,
 W. Sussex), 296
Stanley Park, 85
Stanyer, Tony and Rosemary, 467
Staple St James Winery (Canterbury, Kent),
 281–2
Staplecombe Vineyards (Taunton, Somerset),
 397–8
Stauffer, 136
Staverton Vineyard (Woodbridge, Suffolk),
 204–5
Steen, Anthony, 89
Steeplecourt Vineyard, 340
Stenhouse, J. and M., 325
Stockman, Alan and Gill, 350

Stocks (Worcester), 77
Stony Hills Vineyard (Colchester, Essex), 227–8
Stragglethorpe Hall (Lincoln), 76, 111
Strutt, William, 283
Stuart, Chris, 78
Suetonius, 2
Suffolk, Boyton Vineyard, 194–5; Bruisyard Vineyard, 195–7; Cavendish Manor Vineyard, 197; Gifford's Hall, 197–9; Helions Vineyard, 199; Hintlesham Vineyard, 199–200; Ickworth Vineyard, 200–1; Melton Lodge Vineyard, 201–4; Staverton Vineyard, 204–5; Willow Grange Vineyard, 205–6; Wyken Vineyards, 206–7
Sugar Loaf Vineyard (Monmouthshire, Wales), 430–1
Summer Moor Vineyard (Swimbridge, Devon), 410
Summerland research station (British Columbia), 35
Sunnybank Vineyard and Vine Nursery (Dulas, Herefordshire), 370
Surrenden Vineyard (Ashford, Kent), 282–3
Surrey, Denbies Wine Estate, 233–9; Farmhouse Vineyard, 241–2; Furnace Brook Vineyard, 239–40; Godstone Vineyard, 240–1; Painshill Park Vineyard, 242–4; Send Vineyard, 244–6; Thorncroft Vineyard, 246; Vineyard, 241
Sussex, Ashburnham Vineyard, 297; Barkham Manor Vineyard, 298–9; Barnsgate Manor Vineyard, 299–301; Battle Wine Estate, 301–3; Bewl Water Vineyard, 303; Bodiam Vineyards, 303; Bookers Vineyard, 290; Breaky Bottom Vineyard, 304–7; Brickyard Vineyard, 307; Burwash Weald Vineyard, 307–8; Carr Taylor Vineyards, 308–10; Chingley Oast Vineyard, 310–11; Davenport Vineyards, 311–13; Ditchling Vineyards, 313–14; English Wine Centre, 314–15; Hackwood Vineyard, 315–16; Hadlow Down Vineyard, 261; Hidden Spring Vineyard, 316–18; High Weald Vineyard, 318; Lurgashall Winery, 290–1; Lydhurst Vineyard, 291; Mill Oast Vineyard, 318; Nutbourne Vineyard, 291–3; Nyetimber Vineyard, 293–5; Plumpton College Vineyard, 319–20; RidgeView Estate Winery, 320–3; Rock Lodge Vineyard, 295–6; Saint George's Vineyard, 323–4; Sedlescombe Organic Vineyard, 324–5; Spilsted Vineyard, 325; Standen Vineyard, 296; West Stoke House Vineyard, 296–7
Swanbridge (Wales), 22
Swattenden Ridge Farm Vineyard (Cranbrook, Kent), 283

Swiss Cottage Vineyard (Devizes, Wiltshire), 332
Swiss Federal Vine Testing Station (Caudoz sur Pully), 33
Sylvaner, 134, 136, 149
Sylvaner F2, 38, 59

table grapes, 18, 31, 43, 44, 58, 119
Table Wine, 102, 103, 115–16
Tallent, Andy, 460
Tayler, Mike and Pat, 381
Taylor, Geoff, 117
Teleki, Andor, 29, 34–5
Tenterden Vineyard Park (Kent), 80, 176, 209, 249, 263, 270–2, 283–7
Terseshkova, 42
Teynham (Kent), 8
Thames and Chilterns Vineyards Association, 90
Theobald, Bernard, 77, 245
Thomas Walk Vineyard (County Cork, Republic of Ireland), 436
Thompson, Rod, 354
Thorncroft Vineyard (Leatherhead, Surrey), 246
Thorpe, Mchael and Susan, 348
Three Choirs Vineyard (Newent, Gloucestershire), 78, 79, 100, 113, 134, 366, 371, 376, 378–81, 427, 428, 429, 430, 431, 446
Throwley Vineyard (Faversham, Kent), 287
Tichfield Vineyard (Hampshire), 346
Tiltridge Vineyard (Upton–upon–Severn, Worcestershire), 373–5
Tintern Parva Vineyard (Monmouthshire, Wales), 431–2
Tissier-Ravat, Jean, 36
Tissier-Ravat (Téré Doré), 53, 58
Tod, H. M., 18, 23, 24, 120
Todd, Derek, 285
Tradescant, John, 13
Treago Vineyard (Hereford, Herefordshire), 370–1
Trebbiano, 25
Treetops Vineyard (Worcester, Worcestershire), 375
trellising systems, Double Guyot, 125; Geneva Double Curtain (GDC), 125; Lenz Moser, 125
Triomphe, 37, 40, 96, 116, 182–3
Triomphe d'Alsace, 36
Tripp, Dr and Mrs H. R. Howard, 284
Trzebski, Jan, 254
Tudor Grange Vineyard (Barnet, Hertfordshire), 211
Tun Vine Press Company (Sittingbourne, Kent), 287–9
Tyson-Woodcock, Philip, 76, 87
Tytherley (Wiltshire), 78

INDEX

United Kingdom Vineyards Association
(UKVA), xii, 90–1, 344, 345, 368, 369,
372, 375, 376, 381, 382–3, 397, 409, 414,
431, 457, 468, 471, 475, 476, 485–6
University of California, 35
University of Florida, 35
Unwin, Tim, 1, 5

Valhalla Vineyard (Northampton,
Northamptonshire), 452–3
Valley Vineyards (Reading, Berkshire), 78,
113, 154, 220, 242, 282, 339, 347, 471–8
Vaughan, Colin, 239
Vaughan–Hughes, John, 52
Vernon Lodge Vineyard (Towcester,
Northamptonshire), 453–4
Vickers, Claire, 448
Vickers, Martin, 448
Vilvorde Horticultural School (Brussels),
37
vine varieties, availability of accurate
performance figures, 142–7; classification,
139–42; early vineyards, 118–21; future,
135–9; genetically modified, 139; grapes,
149–84; names, 148–9; natural sugar/
acidity levels, 146–7; revival, 121–7;
yields, 127–35, 143–5
Vine Varieties Classification Committee
(VVCC), 93, 94, 96, 139–41, 139–42
Vineyard Register, 80, 93, 94, 127, 129
vineyard websites, 495–6
vinifera, 29, 38, 115, 136
Vining, Andrew, 78
Vintners' Symposium, 90
Vispré, Xavier, 17, 19
viticulture, commercial, 66–86; Domesday
Surveys, 6–7; establishment, 78–86; expansion, 77–8; from the Middle Ages to the
Great War, 10–26; future prospects, 82–6;
main areas, 25–6; monastic, 7–8; and the
Norman conquest, 6–9; organic, 284–5,
446; planting, 31–2; post–Roman, 4–6;
pre–Roman, 1; revival in, 27–65; Roman,
1–4; rootstocks, 106–7, 497–8; site
selection, 104–6; trellising, training,
pruning, 107–10; and wine descriptors,
98–102
vitus labrusca, 34

Wädenswill Research Station (Switzerland),
34, 44
Wake Court Vineyard (Sherborne, Dorset),
348–9
Wales, Brecon Court Vineyard, 420–1; Cwm
Deri Vineyard, 421–2; Eryri Vineyard,
481–2; Ffynnon Las, 422–3; Glyndwr
Vineyard, 423–5; Llanerch Vineyard,
425–7; Monnow Valley Vineyard, 427–8;
Offa's Vineyard, 428–9; Pant Teg

Vineyard, 429–30; Sugar Loaf Vineyard,
430–1; Tintern Parva Vineyard, 431–2;
Worthenbury Wines, 482–4
Walk, Thomas, 436
Walker, Ernie, 32, 51, 52
Walker, John, 447
Ward, Jack, 68–74, 87, 89, 110, 122, 125,
165, 167, 171, 175, 307
Warden Abbey Vineyard (Biggleswade,
Bedfordshire), 468–9
Water Hall Vineyard (Mirfield,
W. Yorkshire), 443
Waterwynch Vineyards (Winchester,
Hampshire), 347
Watts, Roy and Elaine, 340
Waugh, Harry, 52
Webb's Land Vineyard (Wickham,
Hampshire), 347
Weingut Louis Guntrum, 125
Weinsberg Research Institute (Würtemburg,
Germany), 159
Weir Quay Vineyard (Yelverton, Devon),
410–11
Welbeck, 120
Welland Valley Vineyard (Market
Harborough, Leicestershire), 454–5
Wellow (Romsey, Hampshire), 78
Welsh Office Agricultural Department
(WOAD), 94
Welsh Vine Growers Association, 87
West Stoke House Vineyard (Chichester,
W. Sussex), 296–7
Westbrook Place (Godalming, Surrey), 15
Westbury (Berkshire), 77
Westfield (Hastings, Sussex), 78
Westphal, Bob, 78
Westphal, David, 276
Westward House Vineyard (Tadley,
Hampshire), 347–8
Whatley Vineyard (Frome, Somerset), 398–9
Wheeler, Mary and David, 470, 478
Whitaker, Dr Jonathan, 241
Whitbread, Jane, 46
White, A. E. and G. D., 78, 233
White Frontignon, 33
White, Patricia, 473, 474
White, Roger and Juliet, 411
White Seedling (Foster's), 119
white wine, 83, 114, 137
Wickham Vineyard (Southampton,
Hampshire), 113, 343, 348–9
William I (the Conqueror), 6, 7
William of Malmesbury, 7
Williams, Denis, 52, 53
Williams, Greg, 72, 73
Williams, Roy L. and C. M., 194
Willow Grange Vineyard (Crowfield,
Suffolk), 205–6
Wilson, Duncan, 287

530

Wiltshire, Chalkhill Vineyard, 330; Elms Cross Vineyard, 330; Little Ashley Vineyard, 331; Sherston Vineyard, 332; Swiss Cottage Vineyard, 332; Wylye Valley Vineyard, 332-3
Wilyman, Keith, 452
Windmill Vineyard (Daventry, Northamptonshire), 455-6
Windsor Forest Vineyard (Maidenhead, Berkshire), 478-9
Wine Standards Board (WSB), 88, 93-4, 100, 133, 143
winemaking, 110-17
Wingfield, James, 30
Wisley, 33
Witt, Michael, 398
Wollaston (Nene valley, Northamptonshire), 2-3
Wood, Joanna, 92
Woodall, Guy, 246
Wooldings Vineyard (Whitchurch, Hampshire), 349-50
Wootton Park Vineyard (Canterbury, Kent), 289-90
Wootton Vineyard (Shepton Mallett, Somerset), 78, 89, 388, 399-400
Worcestershire, Astley Vineyards, 371-3; Parkfield Vineyard, 373; Tiltridge Vineyard, 373-5; Treetops Vineyard, 375
Workman, David and Irene, 481
Worontschak, John, 3, 72, 113, 307, 471, 472-6
Worshipful Company of Vintners, 12
Worthenbury Wines (Wrexham, Wales), 482-4

Wreford, Martin, 403
Wright, Graeme, 73
Wright, John, 342
Writtle College Vineyard (Chelmsford, Essex), 228
Wrotham Pinot, 59, 74, 94, 124
Wroxeter Roman Vineyard (Shrewsbury, Shropshire), 451-2
Würzburg Viticultural Institute (Franken, Germany), 167
Würzer, 39, 126, 131, 183-4
Wye College Vineyard (Ashford, Kent), 73, 125, 126, 155, 156, 174
Wyecliff Vineyard (Hay-on-Wye, Hereford), 432-3
Wyken Vineyards (Bury St Edmunds, Suffolk), 206-7
Wylye Valley Vineyard (Warminster, Wiltshire), 332-3

Yalding (Kent), 63-5
Yearlstone Vineyard (Bickleigh, Devon), 49, 411-12
Yearsley, G. G., 41, 42
yeasts, 44, 45, 46-7
yields, 53, 80, 82-3, 95, 97, 107-9, 125, 138, 143-5; of major varieties, 127-34
Yorkshire, Leventhorpe Vineyard, 441-3; Water Hall Vineyard, 443
Youles, John, 336

Zalagyönge, 137
Zimmerman, Dr, 40, 148, 161
Zweigelt, Dr Fritz, 184
Zweigeltrebe, 126, 184